NUMERICAL METHODS FOR ENGINEERS

NUMERICAL METHODS FOR ENGINEERS

(THIRD EDITION)

SANTOSH K GUPTA

Professor
Department of Chemical Engineering
Indian Institute of Technology Kanpur, INDIA

New Academic Science Limited
27 Old Gloucester Street, London, WC1N 3AX, UK
www.newacademicscience.co.uk
e-mail: info@newacademicscience.co.uk

Preface to the Third Edition

I am grateful to all the readers who have accepted this textbook so graciously and have passed on their comments. This computer-set third edition corrects the typos of the first and second editions.

I thank IIT Bombay, Mumbai, for hosting me as a Professor and providing me facilities for revising this book.

I.I.T. Kanpur   SANTOSH K. GUPTA

Preface to the First Edition

This book has been written as a text for either a first course in numerical methods for fourth year (senior) undergraduate students, or for an intermediate level postgraduate course in this area. It can be used by students of all disciplines of engineering, and possibly science. It has evolved through several generations of lecture notes starting from 1985, when I first taught a graduate level course on numerical techniques for chemical engineers at the University of Notre Dame, Notre Dame, IN, USA. A sufficient amount of 'elementary' material is included, *e.g.*, linear algebraic equations, nonlinear algebraic equations involving a single variable, interpolation, differentiation and integration, simple methods of solving ordinary differential equations (Euler, Runge-Kutta, finite difference) and partial differential equations (finite difference). These could easily form the content of a beginning-level, three-unit, one semester course for undergraduate students. The same material could be covered rather rapidly (or assigned for self study) in an intermediate level course for postgraduate students after which one could cover 'advanced' topics, *e.g.*, sets of nonlinear algebraic equations in several variables, stiff ordinary differential equations of the initial-value kind (Gear's method), ordinary differential equations of the boundary-value kind (orthogonal collocation, Galerkin finite element techniques) and partial differential equations (orthogonal collocation, finite element methods). By the end of such a course a student should have developed the capability to understand newer numerical techniques from the current literature.

Perhaps the most important feature of this book is that it has been written as a *text*, never losing sight of the student. It is not intended to be a compendium of all techniques available; nor is it a review of the literature. Concepts which pose difficulties to a student, *e.g.*, stiffness of ordinary differential equations, multiplicity of solutions, chaotic behavior, convergence criteria and error estimates, etc., have been elaborated in detail and illustrated with solved examples. An extensive set of problems has also been included, with hints where necessary. Several of the examples and problems are purely mathematical in nature, so that students from all disciplines of engineering can appreciate them. However, several interesting, real-life examples and problems are discussed from the realm of heat transfer, thermodynamics, fluid mechanics, kinetics, reactor design, etc. These have been included so that the reader develops the confidence of solving research-level problems which are not too elementary. These examples and problems have been so worded that a student who is unfamiliar with the 'physics' of any particular problem can still solve it, looking at the equations purely mathematically. Problems specifically from Chemical Engineering, the author's area of specialization, have been indicated appropriately. A whole array of problems has been included. Some are to give practice, while some require reading of material in journals. Some problems can be solved using a hand-calculator, while some require the student to make computer programs and run them on a mainframe/personal computer (a basic knowledge of computer programming is assumed). There are a few problems which require the use of programs/ subroutines from libraries like NAG, IMSL, MATLAB, etc. Often, the same equations are to be solved by different techniques (cross references are provided) so that a student can observe the advantages and disadvantages of these techniques himself. I strongly believe that full appreciation of this text is possible only when complemented by the solution of several of the problems in each chapter. A teacher's manual outlining solutions to all problems is available from the publisher. This also includes a listing of computer programs (in Fortran) prepared to solve the problems in the textbook. These programs can also be obtained on a CD from the author. The programs are not very user-friendly, but can be used as a good starting point.

It is a pleasure to express my most sincere gratitude to two people who have contributed very significantly to this work. Professor Arvind Varma, Department of Chemical Engineering, University of Notre Dame, Notre Dame, IN, USA (now at Purdne University) has been associated with this work ever since its inception. He has provided detailed suggestions and comments on several chapters. He has also made available his lecture material including several homework problems assigned to his classes. This book owes a lot to him. I had used the book of Professor Bruce A. Finlayson [Nonlinear Analysis in Chemical Engineering, McGraw-Hill, New York, 1980] as a text when I first started teaching numerical methods. If this text bears some striking similarities with his, it is not because of my inadvertant efforts of plagiarising, but because of the profound impact his book has had on my teaching.

I would like to thank Professors Shankar Narasimhan and S. Pushpavanam of the Department of Chemical Engineering, IIT Kanpur (now at IIT Madras), and several groups of graduate students of my ChE 642 class at IIT Kanpur for reading and providing detailed comments on parts or the whole of this book. I take this opportunity to offer my humble obeisance to my Department for providing me such a fertile and exhilarating environment, conducive for both research and bookwriting activities. It is a rare privilege to be part of such a department. I would also like to offer my appreciation to the Department of Chemical Engineering, University of Wisconsin, Madison, WI, USA, for providing me an opportunity to spend part of Summer 1990 there, during which I could finalise some of the chapters of this book. Several of the early ideas for this book were developed at the Department of Chemical Engineering, University of Notre Dame, Notre Dame, IN, USA, when I was a Visiting Professor there (1985–87). The kindness showered on me by everyone in that department is gratefully acknowledged.

I would also like to thank Mr. N.K. Metia and Mr. J.P. Sharma for typing several drafts of this book, Mr. A.K. Ganguli for making the inked drawings and Mr. Hari Ram for cyclostyling the earlier versions of the manuscript. A good fraction of the financial support for the preparation of this manuscript came from Mr. H.S. Gupta, Proprietor, Agrawal Press, Allahabad. This is gratefully acknowledged. Thanks are also due to the Curriculum Development Cell, Quality Improvement Program (MHRD) at IIT Kanpur for partial support for the preparation of this manuscript.

And yet once again, it is such sweet pleasure to thank Shubhra, Aatmeeyata and Akanksha for whispering 'I love you' ever so tenderly in my ears during my seven year long labour pains. I hope this offspring I have given life to, will kindle a light in some.

I.I.T. Kanpur, 1995   SANTOSH K. GUPTA

Contents

Chapter 1

Linear Algebraic Equations

1.1 INTRODUCTION

Several physical operations (most notably, staged operations) can be described in terms of a set of N *coupled, linear algebraic* equations for N unknowns, x_i, $i = 1, 2, ..., N$, having the following form:

$$a_{11}x_1 + a_{12}x_2 + ... + a_{1N}x_N = b_1$$
$$a_{21}x_1 + a_{22}x_2 + ... + a_{2N}x_N = b_2$$

$$a_{N1}x_1 + a_{N2}x_2 + ... + a_{NN}x_N = b_N \qquad ...(1.1)$$

Such equations are also obtained when numerical techniques such as finite difference, orthogonal collocation, finite elements, etc., are applied to sets of ordinary or partial differential equations. Hence, it is important to develop efficient techniques for solving these equations, particularly for large values of N (values of N larger than 100 are not uncommon).

Equation 1.1 can be written more compactly using vector-matrix notation as

$$\mathbf{Ax} = \mathbf{b} \qquad ...(1.2)$$

where

$$\mathbf{A} = \begin{bmatrix} a_{11} & a_{12} & a_{13} & ... & a_{1N} \\ a_{21} & a_{22} & a_{23} & & a_{2N} \\ \cdot & & & & \cdot \\ \cdot & & & & \cdot \\ a_{N1} & a_{N2} & a_{N3} & ... & a_{NN} \end{bmatrix}$$

$$\mathbf{x}^T = \begin{bmatrix} x_1 & x_2 & ... & x_N \end{bmatrix}$$

$$\mathbf{b}^T = \begin{bmatrix} b_1 & b_2 & ... & b_N \end{bmatrix} \qquad ...(1.3)$$

T represents the transpose [1–3], and the (i, j) term (ith row and jth column) in $\mathbf{A}$ is a_{ij}.

The solution of eq. 1.2 can be written using Cramer's rule [1–3] as

$$x_j = |\mathbf{A}_j| / |\mathbf{A}|; \quad j = 1, 2, ..., N \qquad \qquad ...(1.4)$$

where $|\mathbf{A}|$ represents the determinant of matrix $\mathbf{A}$. Matrix $\mathbf{A}_j$ is obtained by replacing the jth column of $\mathbf{A}$ by the column vector, $\mathbf{b}$. Equation 1.2 has a unique solution only if $|\mathbf{A}| \neq 0$ (*i.e.* $\mathbf{A}$ is *non-singular*). If, in addition to this condition, $\mathbf{b} = \mathbf{0}$ (homogeneous equations), then $|\mathbf{A}_j| = 0$ and all the $x_j = 0$ (trivial solution).

Example 1.1: Solve by Cramer's rule:

$$\begin{bmatrix} 1 & 1 \\ 2 & 3 \end{bmatrix} \begin{bmatrix} x_1 \\ x_2 \end{bmatrix} = \begin{bmatrix} 4 \\ 11 \end{bmatrix}$$

$$|\mathbf{A}| = \begin{vmatrix} 1 & 1 \\ 2 & 3 \end{vmatrix} = 1$$

$$|\mathbf{A}_1| = \begin{vmatrix} 4 & 1 \\ 11 & 3 \end{vmatrix} = 1$$

$$|\mathbf{A}_2| = \begin{vmatrix} 1 & 4 \\ 2 & 11 \end{vmatrix} = 3$$

$$\therefore \qquad x_1 = |\mathbf{A}_1| / |\mathbf{A}| = 1$$

$$x_2 = |\mathbf{A}_2| / |\mathbf{A}| = 3$$

$$\mathbf{x}^T = \begin{bmatrix} 1 & 3 \end{bmatrix} \qquad \blacksquare$$

Two possibilities exist if $\mathbf{A}$ is singular, as illustrated by the following example:

Example 1.2: Solve

$$(a) \begin{bmatrix} 2 & 3 \\ 4 & 6 \end{bmatrix} \begin{bmatrix} x_1 \\ x_2 \end{bmatrix} = \begin{bmatrix} 11 \\ 22 \end{bmatrix} \text{ and } (b) \begin{bmatrix} 2 & 3 \\ 4 & 6 \end{bmatrix} \begin{bmatrix} x_1 \\ x_2 \end{bmatrix} = \begin{bmatrix} 11 \\ 20 \end{bmatrix}$$

$\mathbf{A}$ is singular, since $|\mathbf{A}| = 12 - 12 = 0$

(*a*) In this case, it is observed that the two equations are, in fact, identical:

$$2x_1 + 3x_2 = 11$$

This situation, where there are more variables than equations, leads to a set of *infinite solutions*. One can find a value of x_1 corresponding to each value assigned to x_2. Uniqueness is no longer present.

(*b*) In this case the two equations are incompatible:

$$2x_1 + 3x_2 = 11$$

$$2x_1 + 3x_2 = 10$$

and *no solutions* exist. $\qquad \blacksquare$

One can also study the more general case of M linear algebraic equations in N unknowns $\mathbf{x} = [x_1 \ x_2 \ ... \ x_N]^T$:

$$\mathbf{Ax = b} \qquad \qquad ...(1.5)$$

where $\mathbf{b} = [b_1\ b_2\ ...\ b_M]^T$ and $\mathbf{A}$ is an $M \times N$ matrix. An *augmented matrix*, aug $\mathbf{A}$, is formed as given below:

$$\text{aug } \mathbf{A} \equiv [\mathbf{A} \mid \mathbf{b}] = \begin{bmatrix} a_{11} & a_{12} & \cdots & a_{1N} & \mid & b_1 \\ \cdot & & & & \mid \\ \cdot & & & & \mid \\ \cdot & & & & \mid \\ \cdot & & & & \mid \\ \cdot & & & & \mid \\ a_{M1} & a_{M2} & \cdots & a_{MN} & \mid & b_M \end{bmatrix} \qquad ...(1.6)$$

The *rank* (see Appendix 1 – A) [1–3] of $\mathbf{A}$ and aug $\mathbf{A}$ are first determined. The following general results give the conditions under which unique, infinite, or no solutions exist [1]:

(*a*) The necessary and sufficient condition that eq. 1.5 has solutions is that the rank of $\mathbf{A}$ be the same as the rank of aug $\mathbf{A}$ (If this condition is violated the equations are incompatible, and therefore, have no solution).

(*b*) If condition (*a*) is satisfied, and if r is the rank of both $\mathbf{A}$ and aug $\mathbf{A}$, then one can assign arbitrary values to $N - r$ variables, and compute the values of the remaining r variables. A little reflection gives the following table for the number of solutions, when condition (*a*) is satisfied:

$M = N$ $(r \le N)$		$M < N$ $(r \le M)$	$M > N$ $(r \le N)$	
$r = N$	Unique	Infinite	$r = N$	Unique
$r < N$	Infinite		$r < N$	Infinite

(*c*) If $\mathbf{b} = \mathbf{0}$ (homogeneous equations), then *nontrivial* solutions are obtained if and only if the rank of $\mathbf{A}$ is less than N.

Example 1.3: Study examples 1.1 and 1.2 in terms of the general conditions given above.

For example 1.1:

$$\mathbf{A} = \begin{bmatrix} 1 & 1 \\ 2 & 3 \end{bmatrix}, \text{ rank}(\mathbf{A}) = 2$$

$$\text{aug } \mathbf{A} = \begin{bmatrix} 1 & 1 & 4 \\ 2 & 3 & 11 \end{bmatrix}, \text{ rank}(\text{aug } \mathbf{A}) = 2$$

Hence, the equations are compatible (condition (*a*)). Also, $r = N = 2$, and a unique solution exists.

For example 1.2(a):

$$\mathbf{A} = \begin{bmatrix} 2 & 3 \\ 4 & 6 \end{bmatrix}, \text{ rank}(\mathbf{A}) = 1$$

$$\text{aug } \mathbf{A} = \begin{bmatrix} 2 & 3 & 11 \\ 4 & 6 & 22 \end{bmatrix}, \text{ rank}(\text{aug } \mathbf{A}) = 1$$

since all three 2×2 determinants:

$$\begin{vmatrix} 2 & 3 \\ 4 & 6 \end{vmatrix}, \begin{vmatrix} 2 & 11 \\ 4 & 22 \end{vmatrix} \text{ and } \begin{vmatrix} 3 & 11 \\ 6 & 22 \end{vmatrix}$$

are zero. Hence, the equations are compatible. Since $r = 1$ and $N = 2$ $(r < N)$, we have infinite solutions.

For example 1.2(b):

$$\mathbf{A} = \begin{bmatrix} 2 & 3 \\ 4 & 6 \end{bmatrix}, \text{rank}(\mathbf{A}) = 1$$

$$\text{aug}\,\mathbf{A} = \begin{bmatrix} 2 & 3 & 11 \\ 4 & 6 & 20 \end{bmatrix}, \text{ rank}\,(\text{aug}\,\mathbf{A}) = 2$$

since

$$\begin{vmatrix} 2 & 11 \\ 4 & 20 \end{vmatrix} \neq 0$$

Hence condition (*a*) is violated. The equations are, therefore, incompatible, and have *no* solution.
∎

Problems 1.1 and 1.2 consider two examples where there are more equations than unknowns, and the general rules described above can be used to find out the number of solutions possible.

1.2 GAUSS ELIMINATION AND LU DECOMPOSITION

In this and the following sections, methods for solving N linear, simultaneous, algebraic equations in N unknowns are discussed. $\mathbf{A}$ is then an $N \times N$ square matrix. Such systems of equations are quite commonly encountered in Engineering. Cramer's rule, unfortunately, requires excessive calculations. In fact, it can easily be estimated [1, 3, 4] that $(N - 1)$ $(N + 1)$ $(N!)$ + N or approximately $N^2 \times N!$ multiplications and divisions are required to obtain the solution (using determinant expansions in terms of minors [1–3]—see prob. 6.4.4 in Ref. 4). For a value of N equal to 100, this means approximately 10^{162} multiplications and divisions—a prohibitively large number (a third generation computer, e.g. DEC 1090, taking about 5×10^{-6} s per multiplication, would take about 10^{149} years to do these!).

An alternate scheme to solve eq. 1.2 is by using the inverse of $\mathbf{A}$, *i.e.*

$$\mathbf{x} = \mathbf{A}^{-1}\mathbf{b} \qquad \qquad ...(1.7)$$

This, too, is not a suitable method of solution for large N. In fact, the number of operations involved in computing $\mathbf{A}^{-1}$ and then $\mathbf{A}^{-1}\mathbf{b}$ is identical to that using Cramer's rule to obtain $\mathbf{x}$, if $\mathbf{A}^{-1}$ is computed by its definition [1–3], $\mathbf{A}^{-1} = (\text{adj } \mathbf{A})/ |\mathbf{A}|$. Here adj $\mathbf{A}$ is the adjoint of matrix $\mathbf{A}$, with $(\text{adj } \mathbf{A})_{ji} = \mathbf{A}_{ij}$, where $\mathbf{A}_{ij}$ is the cofactor of the element a_{ij} in the original matrix $\mathbf{A}$. However, faster numerical algorithms could be used to obtain $\mathbf{A}^{-1}$. Besides the extensive computational time required to obtain $\mathbf{A}^{-1}$, this method suffers from the additional problem of *sensitivity* (or *ill-conditioning*), *i.e.* small changes in $\mathbf{A}$ (due to round off errors) may lead to large changes in $\mathbf{A}^{-1}$ and hence in $\mathbf{x}$ (see prob. 1.3). Ill-conditioning of $\mathbf{A}$ occurs when $|\mathbf{A}|$ is close to zero.

Several efficient techniques have been developed to obtain solutions of large sets of equations of the type given in eq. 1.2. These can be classified into *direct* (e.g., Gauss elimination, Gauss-Jordan elimination, Cholesky's or Crout's method, etc.) and *indirect* or *iterative* (e.g., Jacobi, Gauss-Seidel and relaxation) methods. Some of these methods are described in this chapter.

Gauss elimination [5] is a relatively simple technique for solving a system of N linear algebraic equations in N unknowns:

$$\mathbf{A}^{(1)}\mathbf{x} \equiv
\begin{bmatrix}
a_{11}^{(1)} & a_{12}^{(1)} & a_{13}^{(1)} & \cdots & a_{1N}^{(1)} \\
a_{21}^{(1)} & a_{22}^{(1)} & a_{23}^{(1)} & \cdots & a_{2N}^{(1)} \\
a_{31}^{(1)} & a_{32}^{(1)} & a_{33}^{(1)} & \cdots & a_{3N}^{(1)} \\
\cdot & \cdot & \cdot & & \cdot \\
\cdot & \cdot & \cdot & & \cdot \\
a_{N1}^{(1)} & a_{N2}^{(1)} & a_{N3}^{(1)} & \cdots & a_{NN}^{(1)}
\end{bmatrix}
\begin{bmatrix} x_1 \\ x_2 \\ x_3 \\ \cdot \\ \cdot \\ x_N \end{bmatrix}
=
\begin{bmatrix} b_1^{(1)} \\ b_2^{(1)} \\ b_3^{(1)} \\ \cdot \\ \cdot \\ b_N^{(1)} \end{bmatrix}
\equiv \mathbf{b}^{(1)} \qquad ...(1.8)$$

The superscripts (1) on the elements of the non-singular $N \times N$ matrix **A** and on **b** indicate that these are the starting (or first iterate) values. A set of simple operations (e.g., multiplying an entire equation by a constant, adding two equations, etc., which do not alter the solutions) are now performed on the N equations of eq. 1.8. The first row of $\mathbf{A}^{(1)}$ and $\mathbf{b}^{(1)}$ (corresponding to the first equation of the set) is multiplied by $-a_{21}^{(1)}/a_{11}^{(1)}$ and added to the second row, to eliminate the (2, 1) term. Similarly, the first row is multiplied by $-a_{31}^{(1)}/a_{11}^{(1)}$ and added to the third row to eliminate the (3, 1) term, etc. This leads to

$$\mathbf{A}^{(2)}\mathbf{x} \equiv
\begin{bmatrix}
a_{11}^{(1)} & a_{12}^{(1)} & a_{13}^{(1)} & \cdots \\
0 & \left[a_{22}^{(1)} - \dfrac{a_{21}^{(1)}}{a_{11}^{(1)}} a_{12}^{(1)} \right] & \left[a_{23}^{(1)} - \dfrac{a_{21}^{(1)}}{a_{11}^{(1)}} a_{13}^{(1)} \right] & \cdots \\
0 & \left[a_{32}^{(1)} - \dfrac{a_{31}^{(1)}}{a_{11}^{(1)}} a_{12}^{(1)} \right] & \left[a_{33}^{(1)} - \dfrac{a_{31}^{(1)}}{a_{11}^{(1)}} a_{13}^{(1)} \right] & \cdots \\
\cdot & \cdot & \cdot & \cdots \\
\cdot & \cdot & \cdot & \cdots \\
0 & \left[a_{N2}^{(1)} - \dfrac{a_{N1}^{(1)}}{a_{11}^{(1)}} a_{12}^{(1)} \right] & \left[a_{N3}^{(1)} - \dfrac{a_{N1}^{(1)}}{a_{11}^{(1)}} a_{13}^{(1)} \right] & \cdots
\end{bmatrix}
\begin{bmatrix} x_1 \\ x_2 \\ x_3 \\ \cdot \\ \cdot \\ x_N \end{bmatrix}
=
\begin{bmatrix} b_1^{(1)} \\ b_2^{(1)} - \dfrac{a_{21}^{(1)}}{a_{11}^{(1)}} b_1^{(1)} \\ b_3^{(1)} - \dfrac{a_{31}^{(1)}}{a_{11}^{(1)}} b_1^{(1)} \\ \cdot \\ \cdot \\ b_N^{(1)} - \dfrac{a_{N1}^{(1)}}{a_{11}^{(1)}} b_1^{(1)} \end{bmatrix}
\equiv \mathbf{b}^{(2)} \quad ...(1.9)$$

It can easily be verified that these operations are described by the following equations:

$$a_{ij}^{(k)} \equiv a_{ij}^{(k-1)} - \frac{a_{i,k-1}^{(k-1)}}{a_{k-1,\,k-1}^{(k-1)}} a_{k-1,\,j}^{(k-1)} \qquad ...(a)$$

$$\qquad\qquad ...(1.10)$$

$$b_i^{(k)} \equiv b_i^{(k-1)} - \frac{a_{i,k-1}^{(k-1)}}{a_{k-1,\,k-1}^{(k-1)}} b_{k-1}^{(k-1)} \qquad ...(b)$$

$$i = 2, 3, ..., N$$
$$j = 2, ..., N$$

with $k = 2$. The unnecessary operations for $j = 1$ need not be performed since it is clear that the end result is zero. We therefore, have

$$\mathbf{A}^{(2)}\mathbf{x} = \begin{bmatrix} a_{11}^{(1)} & a_{12}^{(1)} & a_{13}^{(1)} & .. & a_{1N}^{(1)} \\ 0 & a_{22}^{(2)} & a_{23}^{(2)} & .. & a_{2N}^{(2)} \\ 0 & a_{32}^{(2)} & a_{33}^{(2)} & .. & a_{3N}^{(2)} \\ . & . & . & & . \\ . & . & . & & . \\ . & . & . & & . \\ 0 & a_{N2}^{(2)} & a_{N3}^{(2)} & & a_{NN}^{(2)} \end{bmatrix} \begin{bmatrix} x_1 \\ x_2 \\ x_3 \\ . \\ . \\ . \\ x_N \end{bmatrix} = \begin{bmatrix} b_1^{(1)} \\ b_2^{(2)} \\ b_3^{(2)} \\ . \\ . \\ . \\ b_N^{(2)} \end{bmatrix} \qquad ...(1.11)$$

The next iteration attempts to eliminate the (3, 2), (4, 2), ..., (N, 2) terms from $\mathbf{A}^{(2)}$. This is done by successively multiplying the second row with $-a_{32}^{(2)}/a_{22}^{(2)}, -a_{42}^{(2)}/a_{22}^{(2)}, ...,$ and $-a_{N2}^{(2)}/a_{22}^{(2)}$, and adding it to the 3rd, 4th, ..., Nth rows. This leads to

$$\mathbf{A}^{(3)}\mathbf{x} = \begin{bmatrix} a_{11}^{(1)} & a_{12}^{(1)} & a_{13}^{(1)} & ... \\ 0 & a_{22}^{(2)} & a_{23}^{(2)} & ... \\ 0 & 0 & \left[a_{33}^{(2)} - \dfrac{a_{32}^{(2)}}{a_{22}^{(2)}}a_{23}^{(2)}\right] & ... \\ 0 & 0 & \left[a_{43}^{(2)} - \dfrac{a_{42}^{(2)}}{a_{22}^{(2)}}a_{23}^{(2)}\right] & ... \\ . & . & . & ... \\ . & . & . & ... \\ . & . & . & ... \\ 0 & 0 & \left[a_{N3}^{(2)} - \dfrac{a_{N2}^{(2)}}{a_{22}^{(2)}}a_{23}^{(2)}\right] & ... \end{bmatrix} \begin{bmatrix} x_1 \\ x_2 \\ x_3 \\ x_4 \\ . \\ . \\ . \\ x_N \end{bmatrix} = \begin{bmatrix} b_1^{(1)} \\ b_2^{(2)} \\ b_3^{(2)} - \dfrac{a_{32}^{(2)}}{a_{22}^{(2)}}b_2^{(2)} \\ b_4^{(2)} - \dfrac{a_{42}^{(2)}}{a_{22}^{(2)}}b_2^{(2)} \\ . \\ . \\ . \\ b_N^{(2)} - \dfrac{a_{N2}^{(2)}}{a_{22}^{(2)}}b_2^{(2)} \end{bmatrix} \equiv \mathbf{b}^{(3)} \qquad ...(1.12)$$

It can again be verified that these operations are described by eq. 1.10 using

$$i = 3, 4, ..., N$$
$$j = 3, 4, ..., N$$
$$k = 3 \qquad ...(1.13)$$

This sequence is continued until all the lower triangular elements are eliminated, to give finally

$$\mathbf{A}^{(N)}\mathbf{x} \equiv \mathbf{Ux} \equiv
\begin{bmatrix}
a_{11}^{(1)} & a_{12}^{(1)} & a_{13}^{(1)} & a_{14}^{(1)} & \cdots & a_{1N}^{(1)} \\
0 & a_{22}^{(2)} & a_{23}^{(2)} & a_{24}^{(2)} & \cdots & a_{2N}^{(2)} \\
0 & 0 & a_{33}^{(3)} & a_{34}^{(3)} & \cdots & a_{3N}^{(3)} \\
. & . & . & . & . & . \\
. & . & . & . & . & . \\
. & . & . & . & . & . \\
0 & 0 & 0 & 0 & \cdots & a_{NN}^{(N)}
\end{bmatrix}
\begin{bmatrix} x_1 \\ x_2 \\ x_3 \\ . \\ . \\ . \\ x_N \end{bmatrix}
=
\begin{bmatrix} b_1^{(1)} \\ b_2^{(2)} \\ b_3^{(3)} \\ . \\ . \\ . \\ b_N^{(N)} \end{bmatrix}
\equiv \mathbf{b}^{(N)} \qquad \ldots(1.14)$$

where **U** is the upper triangular matrix $\mathbf{A}^{(N)}$.

The algorithm which can be readily used on a computer is described by eq. 1.10, with the following values of the indices i, j and k (in the sequence given)

$$k = 2, 3, \quad 4, \quad \ldots, N$$
$$i = k, k+1, \quad k+2, \quad \ldots, N \qquad \ldots(1.15)$$
$$j = k, k+1, \quad k+2, \quad \ldots, N$$

It is assumed that $a_{k-1,k-1}^{(k-1)}$ does not become zero at any stage (see Example 1.5 and the discussion thereafter for what is to be done if it is so). It may be added that at each iteration, the computed values of $\mathbf{A}^{(k)}$ can be stored at the same locations as $\mathbf{A}^{(k-1)}$, since the older elements are not used later.

The solution **x** can now be easily obtained by solving eq. 1.14 sequentially, in the reverse direction (backward sweep), since the last equation involves only x_N, the one before this x_N and x_{N-1}, etc. Thus we have

$$x_N = b_N^{(N)} / a_{NN}^{(N)} \qquad \ldots(1.16)$$

and

$$x_i = \left[b_i^{(i)} - \sum_{j=i+1}^{N} a_{ij}^{(i)} x_j \right] / a_{ii}^{(i)}, \quad i = N-1, N-2, \ldots, 1 \qquad \ldots(1.17)$$

Example 1.4: Solve using Gauss elimination with backward sweep

$$\begin{bmatrix} 2 & 1 & 0 \\ 1 & 2 & 1 \\ 0 & 1 & 1 \end{bmatrix} \begin{bmatrix} x_1 \\ x_2 \\ x_3 \end{bmatrix} = \begin{bmatrix} 1 \\ 2 \\ 4 \end{bmatrix}$$

2nd Iterate Values: Multiply 1st row by $-1/2$ and add to 2nd row; no operation is required on third row since $a_{31}^{(1)} = 0$ already:

$$\begin{bmatrix} 2 & 1 & 0 \\ 0 & 3/2 & 1 \\ 0 & 1 & 1 \end{bmatrix} \begin{bmatrix} x_1 \\ x_2 \\ x_3 \end{bmatrix} = \begin{bmatrix} 1 \\ 3/2 \\ 4 \end{bmatrix}$$

3rd Iterate Values: Multiply 2nd row by $-2/3$ and add to third row;

$$\begin{bmatrix} 2 & 1 & 0 \\ 0 & 3/2 & 1 \\ 0 & 0 & 1/3 \end{bmatrix} \begin{bmatrix} x_1 \\ x_2 \\ x_3 \end{bmatrix} = \begin{bmatrix} 1 \\ 3/2 \\ 3 \end{bmatrix}$$

Backward substitution:

$$\frac{1}{3}x_3 = 3 \qquad\qquad \therefore \quad x_3 = 9$$

$$\frac{3}{2}x_2 + x_3 = \frac{3}{2} \qquad\qquad \therefore \quad x_2 = -5$$

$$2x_1 + x_2 = 1 \qquad\qquad \therefore \quad x_1 = 3$$

Hence, $\mathbf{x}^T = [3 \quad -5 \quad 9]$. ■

The total number of operations required in Gauss elimination and backward sweep are given as follows:

$$\text{Multiplications and divisions: } \frac{(N^3 + 3N^2 - N)}{3} \cong N^3/3 \qquad ...(a)$$

$$...(1.18)$$

$$\text{Additions and subtractions: } \frac{(2N^3 + 3N^2 - 5N)}{6} \cong N^3/3 \qquad ...(b)$$

The number of multiplications and divisions (which take relatively more time on a computer than additions and subtractions) is found to be far less than in Cramer's rule and fewer than the number required to compute $\mathbf{A}^{-1}$ (used in $\mathbf{x} = \mathbf{A}^{-1} \mathbf{b}$) using one of the more efficient algorithms. For $N = 100$, Gauss elimination and backward sweep requires only 3.3×10^5 of these operations, as compared to about 10^{160} for Cramer's rule. Even though the number required is lower than for Cramer's rule, it is still very high, and more efficient relaxation methods are, in fact, available, which are preferred for values of N above about twenty five. The number of storage locations required for Gauss elimination is approximately $2N^3 + N$.

The Gauss elimination technique would lead to problems when the diagonal or *pivot* element, $a_{k-1,\,k-1}^{(k-1)}$ (in eq. 1.10), becomes zero, or close to zero at any stage. This could occur even when $\mathbf{A}$ is nonsingular, as described in the following example. In such cases, the order of the equations is changed by exchanging the rows, and the elimination procedure is continued.

Example 1.5: Solve by Gauss elimination and backward sweep $\begin{bmatrix} 1 & -1 & 2 \\ 2 & -2 & 3 \\ 1 & 1 & 1 \end{bmatrix} \mathbf{x} = \begin{bmatrix} -8 \\ -20 \\ -2 \end{bmatrix}$

The second iterate is seen to be $\begin{bmatrix} 1 & -1 & 2 \\ 0 & 0 & -1 \\ 0 & 2 & -1 \end{bmatrix} \mathbf{x} = \begin{bmatrix} -8 \\ -4 \\ 6 \end{bmatrix}$ $\qquad ...(a)$

We cannot proceed further since $a_{22}^{(2)} = 0$. However, we can reorder the set of three equations represented by the matrix equation to circumvent this problem. It is obvious that if we interchange the second and third equations, we can continue Gauss elimination without changing the solution values. Reordering leads to

$$\begin{bmatrix} 1 & -1 & 2 \\ 0 & 2 & -1 \\ 0 & 0 & -1 \end{bmatrix} \begin{bmatrix} x_1 \\ x_2 \\ x_3 \end{bmatrix} = \begin{bmatrix} -8 \\ 6 \\ -4 \end{bmatrix}$$

The third iteration need not be performed since $a_{32}^{(2)} = 0$. In the general case of more equations, one would continue the elimination process after exchanging the rows. The solution is

$$\mathbf{x}^T = \begin{bmatrix} -11 & 5 & 4 \end{bmatrix}$$ ■

The above technique is referred to as maximal *column* pivoting (or partial pivoting). In case it turns out at any stage, that an exchange of rows is not possible (*i.e.* all elements below the pivot are also zero), the procedure stops. This occurs when the set of equations does not have a unique solution.

Instead of interchanging rows as in example 1.5, one could also interchange columns (being careful to redefine **x** so that the equations remain the same). Thus, eq. (*a*) in example 1.5 could be rewritten by exchanging the second and third columns, as

$$\begin{bmatrix} 1 & 2 & -1 \\ 0 & -1 & 0 \\ 0 & -1 & 2 \end{bmatrix} \begin{bmatrix} x_1 \\ x_3 \\ x_2 \end{bmatrix} = \begin{bmatrix} -8 \\ -4 \\ 6 \end{bmatrix} \qquad ...(1.19)$$

It can easily be confirmed that eq. 1.19 is the same as eq. (*a*) of example 1.5. Gauss elimination can now be continued to give

$$\begin{bmatrix} 1 & 2 & -1 \\ 0 & -1 & 0 \\ 0 & 0 & 2 \end{bmatrix} \begin{bmatrix} x_1 \\ x_3 \\ x_2 \end{bmatrix} = \begin{bmatrix} -8 \\ -4 \\ 10 \end{bmatrix} \qquad ...(1.20)$$

giving the same solution as before, $\mathbf{x}^T = \begin{bmatrix} -11 & 5 & 4 \end{bmatrix}$.

Example 1.6 shows that at times, particularly when **A** is non-singular, it helps to interchange rows and/or columns, so that one brings the largest (in the absolute value sense) of the *remaining* elements (below and to the right) in $\mathbf{A}^{(k)}$ to the pivot position. This strategy is known as Gauss elimination using the *maximum pivoting* strategy, [6, 7] and it reduces round-off errors. Several computer libraries have programs which use this technique, e.g., IMSL [6, 8] has LEQT1F, the NAG (Numerical Algorithms Group, Oxford University) library has F01BTF; special packages like LINPAK and ITPACK etc., are also available [6, 9, 10], etc. Since search operations involved in maximum pivoting take somewhat more computer time than additions or subtractions, this increases the computer time. For this reason, maximum pivoting is used only when the larger CPU times required (because of comparisons) can be justified. Partial pivoting, on the other hand, is quite commonly used.

Example 1.6: Solve

$$\begin{bmatrix} 0.000100 & 1.\overline{0} \\ 1.\overline{0} & 1.\overline{0} \end{bmatrix} \begin{bmatrix} x_1 \\ x_2 \end{bmatrix} = \begin{bmatrix} 1.\overline{0} \\ 2.\overline{0} \end{bmatrix}$$

by Gauss elimination and backward sweep, with and without maximum pivoting, using 4 decimal place accuracy.

With pivoting: Since the largest element in $A^{(1)}$ is 1, we can exchange rows to give

$$\begin{bmatrix} 1.0000 & 1.0000 \\ 0.0001 & 1.0000 \end{bmatrix} \begin{bmatrix} x_1 \\ x_2 \end{bmatrix} = \begin{bmatrix} 2.0000 \\ 1.0000 \end{bmatrix}$$

Use Gauss elimination to give

$$\begin{bmatrix} 1.0000 & 1.0000 \\ 0.0000 & 0.9999 \end{bmatrix} \begin{bmatrix} x_1 \\ x_2 \end{bmatrix} = \begin{bmatrix} 2.0000 \\ 0.9998 \end{bmatrix}$$

and so

$$\mathbf{x}^T = [1.0000 \quad 1.0000]$$

More accuracy would lead to $\mathbf{x}^T = [1.0001 \quad 0.9999]$.

Without pivoting: the second iterate is (correct to four decimal places)

$$\begin{bmatrix} 0.0001 & 1.0000 \\ 0.0000 & -9999 \end{bmatrix} \begin{bmatrix} x_1 \\ x_2 \end{bmatrix} = \begin{bmatrix} 1.0000 \\ -9998 \end{bmatrix}$$

giving

$$\mathbf{x}^T = \begin{bmatrix} 0.0000 & 1.0000 \end{bmatrix}$$

which is quite different from the solution with pivoting, and does not satisfy the original equations. Problems with such ill-conditioned A should be solved with single as well as double precision arithmetic on the computer, to ascertain how good the results are. Scaling of equations so that the maximum $|a_{ij}|$ in any row is unity can also be helpful at times. ∎

Example 1.7: Thomas Algorithm [11, 12]

Using Gauss elimination (with normalization of the diagonal elements) and backward sweep, obtain the algorithm required to solve

$$\mathbf{A}^{(1)}\mathbf{x} \equiv \begin{bmatrix} b_1 & c_1 & 0 & 0 & 0 & \cdots & 0 & 0 & 0 \\ a_2 & b_2 & c_2 & 0 & 0 & \cdots & 0 & 0 & 0 \\ 0 & a_3 & b_3 & c_3 & 0 & \cdots & 0 & 0 & 0 \\ \cdot & & & & \cdot & & \cdot & & \cdot \\ \cdot & & & & \cdot & & \cdot & & \cdot \\ 0 & 0 & 0 & 0 & 0 & \cdots & a_{N-1} & b_{N-1} & c_{N-1} \\ 0 & 0 & 0 & 0 & 0 & \cdots & 0 & a_N & b_N \end{bmatrix} \begin{bmatrix} x_1 \\ x_2 \\ x_3 \\ \cdot \\ \cdot \\ x_{N-1} \\ x_N \end{bmatrix} = \begin{bmatrix} d_1 \\ d_2 \\ d_3 \\ \cdot \\ \cdot \\ d_{N-1} \\ d_N \end{bmatrix} \quad \ldots(a)$$

where the tridiagonal matrix $\mathbf{A}^{(1)}$ is known as the Jacobi matrix. This set of equations is quite commonly encountered in staged operations [13] in chemical engineering, and in the solution of ordinary differential equations of the boundary value type by the finite-difference technique (see chapter 6). Bruce et al. [12] attribute this technique to Thomas.

We divide the first row by b_1, the pivot element, and then eliminate a_2 from the second equation. Thus, normalization gives

$$c_1' = c_1/b_1; \quad d_1' = d_1/b_1 \quad \text{(2 divisions)}$$

and then elimination gives

$$
\begin{bmatrix}
1 & c_1' & 0 & 0 & \cdots \\
0 & b_2 - a_2 c_1' & c_2 & 0 & \cdots \\
0 & a_3 & b_3 & c_3 & \cdots \\
\cdot & \cdot & \cdot & & \cdots \\
\cdot & \cdot & \cdot & \cdot & \cdots
\end{bmatrix}
\begin{bmatrix}
x_1 \\ x_2 \\ x_3 \\ \cdot \\ \cdot
\end{bmatrix}
=
\begin{bmatrix}
d_1' \\ d_2 - a_2 d_1' \\ d_3 \\ \cdot \\ \cdot
\end{bmatrix}
$$

There is no need to change the third and lower rows, since their first columns are zero. Also, c_2 remains unaltered. The second row is now normalized, by dividing by $b_2 - a_2 c_1'$, to give

$$c_2' = \frac{c_2}{b_2 - a_2 c_1'}, \quad d_2' = \frac{d_2 - a_2 d_1'}{b_2 - a_2 c_1'}; \qquad \text{(2 multiplications and 2 divisions)}$$

to give

$$
\begin{bmatrix}
1 & c_1' & 0 & 0 & \cdots \\
0 & 1 & c_2' & 0 & \cdots \\
0 & a_3 & b_3 & c_3 & \cdots \\
\cdot & \cdot & \cdot & \cdot & \cdots \\
\cdot & \cdot & \cdot & \cdot & \cdots
\end{bmatrix}
\begin{bmatrix}
x_1 \\ x_2 \\ x_3 \\ \cdot \\ \cdot
\end{bmatrix}
=
\begin{bmatrix}
d_1' \\ d_2' \\ d_3 \\ \cdot \\ \cdot
\end{bmatrix}
$$

Again, a_3 is eliminated using Gauss elimination to give

$$
\begin{bmatrix}
1 & c_1' & 0 & 0 & \cdots \\
0 & 1 & c_2' & 0 & \cdots \\
0 & 0 & b_3 - a_3 c_2' & c_3 & \cdots \\
\cdot & \cdot & \cdot & & \cdots \\
\cdot & \cdot & \cdot & \cdot & \cdots
\end{bmatrix}
\begin{bmatrix}
x_1 \\ x_2 \\ x_3 \\ \cdot \\ \cdot
\end{bmatrix}
=
\begin{bmatrix}
d_1' \\ d_2' \\ d_3 - a_3 d_2' \\ \cdot \\ \cdot
\end{bmatrix}
$$

Division by $b_3 - a_3 c_2'$, for normalization, gives

$$
\begin{bmatrix}
1 & c_1' & 0 & 0 & \cdots \\
0 & 1 & c_2' & 0 & \cdots \\
0 & 0 & 1 & c_3' & \cdots \\
\cdot & \cdot & \cdot & \cdot & \cdots \\
\cdot & \cdot & \cdot & \cdot & \cdots
\end{bmatrix}
\begin{bmatrix}
x_1 \\ x_2 \\ x_3 \\ \cdot \\ \cdot
\end{bmatrix}
=
\begin{bmatrix}
d_1' \\ d_2' \\ d_3' \\ \cdot \\ \cdot
\end{bmatrix}
$$

where

$$c_3' = \frac{c_3}{b_3 - a_3 c_2'}, \quad d_3' = \frac{d_3 - a_3 d_2'}{b_3 - a_3 c_2'} \; ; \qquad \text{(2 multiplications and 2 divisions)}$$

This process is continued until the last row is reached. The algorithm is given by

$$c_1' = c_1/b_1 \; ; \quad d_1' = d_1/b_1$$

$$c_{k+1}' = \frac{c_{k+1}}{b_{k+1} - a_{k+1} c_k'}, \quad d_{k+1}' = \frac{d_{k+1} - a_{k+1} d_k'}{b_{k+1} - a_{k+1} c_k'} \; ; \quad k = 1, 2, 3, ..., N-2$$

$$d_N' = \frac{d_N - a_N d_{N-1}'}{b_N - a_N c_{N-1}'} \qquad \qquad \qquad ...(b)$$

and the total number of multiplications and divisions is $4(N-2) + 5$. This sequence of operations finally leads to

$$\begin{bmatrix} 1 & c_1' & 0 & 0 & \cdots & 0 & 0 & 0 \\ 0 & 1 & c_2' & 0 & \cdots & 0 & 0 & 0 \\ \cdot & \cdot & \cdot & \cdot & & & & \cdot \\ \cdot & \cdot & \cdot & \cdot & \cdot & \cdot & \cdot & \cdot \\ 0 & 0 & 0 & 0 & \cdots & 0 & 1 & c_{N-1}' \\ 0 & 0 & 0 & 0 & \cdots & 0 & 0 & 1 \end{bmatrix} \begin{bmatrix} x_1 \\ x_2 \\ \cdot \\ \cdot \\ x_{N-1} \\ x_N \end{bmatrix} = \begin{bmatrix} d_1' \\ d_2' \\ \cdot \\ \cdot \\ d_{N-1}' \\ d_N' \end{bmatrix}$$

Backward sweep leads to the solution vector:

$$x_N = d_N'$$

$$x_k = d_k' - c_k' x_{k+1} \; ; \quad k = N-1, N-2, ..., 1 \qquad \qquad ...(c)$$

with $(N-1)$ multiplications involved. Thus, the total number of multiplications and divisions is $5N - 8$, which is far smaller than the $N^3/3$ operations (approximately) for the Gauss elimination and backward sweep required for dense matrices. An adaptation of the Thomas algorithm has been developed by Hofeling and Seader [14] for the case where **A** is a matrix having nonzero tridiagonal terms, as well as *some* additional nonzero terms other than these. [Such equations arise in chemical engineering, for example, in the simulation of multicomponent distillation towers (as in crude oil distillation), which are interconnected with side strippers (the reader is referred to Ref. 14 and texts on multicomponent staged operations for more details)]. ∎

In many situations (see Sections 5.7, 6.2, etc.), we need to solve **Ax = b** for several different values of **b** (but with the same **A**). In such cases, it is efficient to do Gauss elimination on **A** only once, and store the elements. A common technique to do this is referred to as *LU Decomposition* (or LU factorization). The upper triangular matrix, **U**, corresponding to the Gauss elimination of **A**, has already been defined in eq. 1.14. A lower triangular matrix, **L**, comprising of the multiplying factors used in Gauss elimination, is defined as

$$
\mathbf{L} \equiv
\begin{bmatrix}
1 & 0 & \cdot & \cdot & 0 \\
a_{21}^{(1)}/a_{11}^{(1)} & 1 & \cdot & \cdot & 0 \\
a_{31}^{(1)}/a_{11}^{(1)} & a_{32}^{(2)}/a_{22}^{(2)} & \cdot & \cdot & 0 \\
\cdot & \cdot & \cdot & \cdot & \cdot \\
\cdot & \cdot & \cdot & \cdot & \cdot \\
\cdot & \cdot & \cdot & \cdot & \cdot \\
a_{N1}^{(1)}/a_{11}^{(1)} & a_{N2}^{(2)}/a_{22}^{(2)} & \cdot & \cdot & 1
\end{bmatrix}
\qquad \dots(1.21)
$$

Note that the negative of the multiplying factors are used in **L**, and that the diagonal elements of **L** are all unity. To ensure efficient storage, the non-diagonal elements of **L** can be stored in the lower triangular locations of **A** itself as they get reduced to zero (as Gauss elimination proceeds). The diagonal locations of **A** as well as its upper triangular locations can store the elements of **U**. It can easily be confirmed (see prob. 1.8) that

$$\mathbf{LU = A} \qquad \dots(1.22)$$

The backward sweep used to compute the solution, **x**, is slightly different in the LU Decomposition technique. The operations on **b** to generate $b_2^{(2)}$, $b_3^{(3)}$, ..., $b_N^{(N)}$, as required in Gauss elimination, are not performed. Instead, one defines a new vector $\mathbf{y}^T \equiv [y_1 \ y_2 ... \ y_N]$ such that

$$\mathbf{L\,y = b} \qquad \dots(a)$$

$$\mathbf{U\,x = y} \qquad \dots(b) \qquad \dots(1.23)$$

It is to be noted that the *original* **b** vector is used in eq. 1.23(*a*). One can easily see that eqs. 1.22 and 1.23 give **L U x = A x = b**, as required. A forward sweep using eq. 1.23(*a*) gives **y**, and these are then used in eq. 1.23(*b*) to compute **x** using a backward sweep.

The LU Decomp + (fore and aft) Sweep, as this technique is sometimes called, is quite efficient. For a single **A** and *M* different values of **b**, the number of multiplications and divisions required is $\dfrac{N^3}{3} - \dfrac{N}{3} + MN^2$, which is slightly lower than that for Gauss elimination and backward sweep.

It should be noted that the above technique needs to be modified slightly [4] when row interchanges are involved during Gauss elimination of **A** (**LU** as defined here, is no longer equal to **A**). However, when **A** is such that

$$|a_{ii}| \ge \sum_{\substack{j=1 \\ j \ne i}}^{N} |a_{ij}|; \quad i = 1, 2, ..., N \qquad \dots(1.24)$$

(such matrices are called *diagonally dominant*, for obvious reasons), row interchanges are not necessary and the method, as described above, works.

One could also obtain *other* upper-lower triangular matrix combinations (see Probs. 1.9, 1.10) than the one described above, and develop algorithms which are better. Cholesky's method for positive semi-definite matrices, and Crout [15] reduction are examples of algorithms which are quite efficient. Finlayson [16] provides a listing of computer programs to solve **Ax = b** using LU Decomp and Sweep. The NAG library [17] contains F01BTF (LU Decomp), F04AAF and F04ARF (Crout), F04ABF (Cholesky) and other programs to solve this set of linear equations using decomposition techniques. The IMSL library, similarly, has several programs [6, 8] including LSLRG, LFTRG, etc. LUELMP (LU Decomp), LUDATF + LUELMF (Crout), LFTDS (Cholesky), etc., while LINPACK [6, 9] has several programs using direct methods [SGEFA (LU Decomp), SPOFA(Cholesky), etc.] to solve $\mathbf{Ax = b}$.

Example 1.8: Solve the following set of equations (see example 1.5) using LU Decomp + Sweep

$$\begin{bmatrix} 1 & -1 & 2 \\ 1 & 1 & 1 \\ 2 & -2 & 3 \end{bmatrix} \begin{bmatrix} x_1 \\ x_2 \\ x_3 \end{bmatrix} = \begin{bmatrix} -8 \\ -2 \\ -20 \end{bmatrix}$$

It is easily seen from example 1.5 that the $\mathbf{L}$ and $\mathbf{U}$ matrices for this case are

$$\mathbf{L} = \begin{bmatrix} 1 & 0 & 0 \\ 1 & 1 & 0 \\ 2 & 0 & 1 \end{bmatrix} \quad \mathbf{U} = \begin{bmatrix} 1 & -1 & 2 \\ 0 & 2 & -1 \\ 0 & 0 & -1 \end{bmatrix}$$

and that $\mathbf{LU = A}$. These two matrices can easily be stored in the locations for $\mathbf{A}$ as

$$\begin{bmatrix} 1 & -1 & 2 \\ 1 & 2 & -1 \\ 2 & 0 & -1 \end{bmatrix}$$

it being kept in mind that the diagonal terms in $\mathbf{L}$, which have not been stored, are all unity. Equation 1.23 (*a*) is, thus

$$\begin{bmatrix} 1 & 0 & 0 \\ 1 & 1 & 0 \\ 2 & 0 & 1 \end{bmatrix} \begin{bmatrix} y_1 \\ y_2 \\ y_3 \end{bmatrix} = \begin{bmatrix} -8 \\ -2 \\ -20 \end{bmatrix}$$

A forward sweep leads to

$$y_1 = -8$$

$$y_2 = -2 - y_1 = 6$$

$$y_3 = -20 - 2y_1 - 0y_2 = -4$$

eq. 1.23 (*b*) is

$$\begin{bmatrix} 1 & -1 & 2 \\ 0 & 2 & -1 \\ 0 & 0 & -1 \end{bmatrix} \begin{bmatrix} x_1 \\ x_2 \\ x_3 \end{bmatrix} = \begin{bmatrix} -8 \\ 6 \\ -4 \end{bmatrix}$$

which gives on backward sweep,

$$x_3 = 4$$

$$x_2 = \frac{6 + x_3}{2} = 5$$

$$x_1 = -8 + x_2 - 2x_3 = -11, \text{ as obtained earlier.} \qquad \blacksquare$$

1.3 GAUSS-JORDAN ELIMINATION

An extension of the Gauss elimination technique is the Gauss-Jordan method. The advantage of this method is that it can be used to give the inverse of the square matrix **A**, which can then be used to solve a whole series of equations, $\mathbf{Ax} = \mathbf{b}_k$, $k = 1, 2, \ldots$, using simple matrix multiplications, $\mathbf{x} = \mathbf{A}^{-1}\mathbf{b}_k$. This method, therefore, provides a good alternative to LU Decomp + Sweep for cases where one has below about twenty sets of $\mathbf{b}_k$. In the process, it also provides $\mathbf{A}^{-1}$, which gives some additional insight into the behavior of the physical system.

The technique differs from Gauss elimination in three ways:

(a) An augmented matrix, aug $\mathbf{A} \equiv [\mathbf{A} \mid \mathbf{b} \mid \mathbf{I}]$, with **I** being a unit diagonal matrix, is first formed.
(b) The diagonal elements are normalized to unity (as in the Thomas algorithm).
(c) Elimination of elements below *as well as above* the pivot element is carried out on aug **A**.

Thus, after the procedure is complete, one obtains a unit diagonal matrix at the location of **A** in the matrix aug **A** (Gauss elimination led to an upper triangular matrix **U** instead). In the location of **b**, the solution vector is obtained, and in the location of **I**, one obtains $\mathbf{A}^{-1}$ after the set of operations has been completed. This is illustrated in the following example.

Example 1.9: Solve (see Example 1.8) by Gauss-Jordan elimination

$$\begin{bmatrix} 1 & -1 & 2 \\ 1 & 1 & 1 \\ 2 & -2 & 3 \end{bmatrix} \begin{bmatrix} x_1 \\ x_2 \\ x_3 \end{bmatrix} = \begin{bmatrix} -8 \\ -2 \\ -20 \end{bmatrix}$$

and also evaluate $\mathbf{A}^{-1}$.

The augmented matrix is first formed:

$$\text{aug } \mathbf{A} = \begin{bmatrix} 1 & -1 & 2 & \mid & -8 & \mid & 1 & 0 & 0 \\ 1 & 1 & 1 & \mid & -2 & \mid & 0 & 1 & 0 \\ 2 & -2 & 3 & \mid & -20 & \mid & 0 & 0 & 1 \end{bmatrix}$$

The a_{21} and a_{31} elements are eliminated (since $a_{11} = 1$, normalization of the first row is not required) by multiplying the first row by -1 and -2 and adding to rows 2 and 3, respectively:

$$\begin{bmatrix} 1 & -1 & 2 & \mid & -8 & \mid & 1 & 0 & 0 \\ 0 & 2 & -1 & \mid & 6 & \mid & -1 & 1 & 0 \\ 0 & 0 & -1 & \mid & -4 & \mid & -2 & 0 & 1 \end{bmatrix}$$

The second row is normalized next

$$\begin{bmatrix} 1 & -1 & 2 & \mid & -8 & \mid & 1 & 0 & 0 \\ 0 & 1 & -1/2 & \mid & 3 & \mid & -1/2 & 1/2 & 0 \\ 0 & 0 & -1 & \mid & -4 & \mid & -2 & 0 & 1 \end{bmatrix}$$

The a_{12} element is now eliminated by multiplying the second row by 1 and adding it to the first row. No operation is required on the third row since its second element is already zero:

$$\begin{bmatrix} 1 & 0 & 3/2 & | & -5 & | & 1/2 & 1/2 & 0 \\ 0 & 1 & -1/2 & | & 3 & | & -1/2 & 1/2 & 0 \\ 0 & 0 & -1 & | & -4 & | & -2 & 0 & 1 \end{bmatrix}$$

The third row is normalized by dividing by -1

$$\begin{bmatrix} 1 & 0 & 3/2 & | & -5 & | & 1/2 & 1/2 & 0 \\ 0 & 1 & -1/2 & | & 3 & | & -1/2 & 1/2 & 0 \\ 0 & 0 & 1 & | & 4 & | & 2 & 0 & -1 \end{bmatrix}$$

The third row is multiplied by $-3/2$ and $1/2$, and added to the first and second rows respectively, to give

$$\begin{bmatrix} 1 & 0 & 0 & | & -11 & | & -5/2 & 1/2 & 3/2 \\ 0 & 1 & 0 & | & 5 & | & 1/2 & 1/2 & -1/2 \\ 0 & 0 & 1 & | & 4 & | & 2 & 0 & -1 \end{bmatrix}$$

The $(i, 4)$; $i = 1, 2, 3$ elements of the above matrix give the solution vector (note that backward substitution is not necessary since in the ith row or equation, only x_i is present). It can easily be verified that $\mathbf{AA}^{-1} = \mathbf{I}$:

$$\begin{bmatrix} 1 & -1 & 2 \\ 1 & 1 & 1 \\ 2 & -2 & 3 \end{bmatrix} \begin{bmatrix} -5/2 & 1/2 & 3/2 \\ 1/2 & 1/2 & -1/2 \\ 2 & 0 & -1 \end{bmatrix} = \begin{bmatrix} 1 & 0 & 0 \\ 0 & 1 & 0 \\ 0 & 0 & 1 \end{bmatrix}$$

∎

The Gauss-Jordan procedure takes approximately twice the CPU time required (without $\mathbf{A}^{-1}$ computation) by the Gauss elimination technique, and so is not preferred when only a single equation $\mathbf{Ax} = \mathbf{b}$ is to be solved. Row interchanges (partial pivoting) may be required in this method as well. These can be performed on aug $\mathbf{A}$ in a manner similar to Gauss elimination. After all the matrix operations on aug $\mathbf{A}$ are completed and one obtains $\mathbf{I}$ in place of $\mathbf{A}$, the $N \times N$ matrix $\mathbf{B}$ obtained in the last N columns of aug $\mathbf{A}$ is taken. [18] This is $\mathbf{A}^{-1}$ (see prob. 1.12).

The algorithm for the Gauss-Jordan technique without pivoting is given by:

$$
\begin{aligned}
& \text{DO} \quad k = 1, 2, ..., N \\
& \quad \text{DO} \quad j = N + M, N + M - 1, N + M - 2, ..., k \\
& \quad\quad a_{kj} \leftarrow a_{kj} / a_{kk} \\
& \quad \text{DO} \quad i = 1, 2, ..., k - 1, k + 1, ..., N \\
& \quad\quad \text{DO} \quad j = N + M, N + M - 1, ..., k \\
& \quad\quad\quad a_{ij} \leftarrow a_{ij} - a_{ik} a_{kj}
\end{aligned}
\qquad \text{...(1.25)}
$$

where $M = N + 1$, and the arrows, $\leftarrow$, indicate equality as used on a computer (*i.e.* compute right hand side, and replace left hand side variable value with this value).

1.4 GAUSS-SEIDEL AND RELAXATION METHODS

The direct methods discussed in the previous two sections are not suitable for solving large problems (*N* more than about 25) which are quite commonly encountered in engineering practice. This is because the round-off errors become excessive (Rice [6] points out that iterative techniques are not necessarily better for ill-conditioned problems than Gauss elimination). Approximate iterative techniques can be used in such cases, particularly if **A** is relatively sparse, as in the solution of partial differential equations using the finite difference technique. Among these, the Gauss-Seidel [19, 20] technique is quite popular. In this method, values for all of the *N* variables [$x_i^{(1)}$; $i = 1, 2, ..., N$] are first assumed (the physics of the problem is frequently used advantageously for this guess). The first equation in **Ax = b** is rearranged as

$$x_1^{(2)} = \frac{\left(b_1 - a_{12}x_2^{(1)} - a_{13}x_3^{(1)} - ... - a_{1N}x_N^{(1)}\right)}{a_{11}} \qquad ...(1.26)$$

to obtain an updated value for x_1. The second equation uses the *most recent values* of **x** in

$$x_2^{(2)} = \frac{\left(b_2 - a_{21}x_1^{(2)} - a_{23}x_3^{(1)} - a_{24}x_4^{(1)} - ... - a_{2N}x_N^{(1)}\right)}{a_{22}} \qquad ...(1.27)$$

to obtain an updated value for x_2. This continues until all *N* equations have been used to compute **x**$^{(2)}$. The algorithm is thus given by

$$x_1^{(k)} = \frac{\left(b_1 - \sum_{j=2}^{N} a_{1j}x_j^{(k-1)}\right)}{a_{11}}$$

$$x_i^{(k)} = \frac{\left(b_i - \sum_{j=1}^{i-1} a_{ij}x_j^{(k)} - \sum_{j=i+1}^{N} a_{ij}x_j^{(k-1)}\right)}{a_{ii}}; \quad \begin{matrix} i = 2, ..., N \\ k = 2, 3, ... \end{matrix} \qquad ...(1.28)$$

The computations are continued until some prescribed error criterion is met, as for example,

$$\text{Error}_i = \left| \frac{x_i^{(k)} - x_i^{(k-1)}}{x_i^{(k)}} \right| \leq \text{TOL}; \text{ for all } i \qquad ...(1.29)$$

The number of multiplications and divisions for a set of *M* iterations is easily seen to be MN^2, and if *M* is less than the order of *N*/3, this technique can be faster than Gauss elimination or LU Decomp + Sweep techniques, where the number of these operations is proportional to $N^3/3$. The iterations in the Gauss-Seidel method can be continued until a desired error criterion is met, and so the problem of excessive round-off errors associated with direct methods is not encountered here (slow convergence could, however, lead to excessive costs.). It can be shown (Section 8.2 of Ref. 4; also see prob. 3.10 in this book) that a *sufficient* (but not necessary [4, 6]) condition to ensure convergence of this technique is that **A** be diagonally dominant, *i.e.* if **A** satisfies eq. 1.24, then convergence is guaranteed (convergence *could* also be achieved if eq. 1.24 is not satisfied, since this is not a necessary condition). One could, therefore, interchange rows and columns of **A** (and **b**) to get it into a diagonally dominant form.

Example 1.10: Solve (see example 1.4)

$$\begin{bmatrix} 2 & 1 & 0 \\ 1 & 2 & 1 \\ 0 & 1 & 1 \end{bmatrix} \begin{bmatrix} x_1 \\ x_2 \\ x_3 \end{bmatrix} = \begin{bmatrix} 1 \\ 2 \\ 4 \end{bmatrix}$$

using the Gauss-Seidel technique. Carry out three iterations, starting with $\mathbf{x}^{(1)} = \begin{bmatrix} 1 & 2 & 1 \end{bmatrix}^T$. Note that eq. 1.24 is satisfied, and so convergence is assured. The appropriate equations and computations are given below:

	$k = 2$	$k = 3$	$k = 4$
$x_1^{(k)} = \dfrac{1 - x_2^{(k-1)}}{2}$	$\dfrac{1-2}{2} = -\dfrac{1}{2}$	$\dfrac{1-\dfrac{3}{4}}{2} = \dfrac{1}{8}$	$\dfrac{27}{32}$
$x_2^{(k)} = \dfrac{2 - x_1^{(k)} - x_3^{(k-1)}}{2}$	$\dfrac{2+\dfrac{1}{2}-1}{2} = \dfrac{3}{4}$	$\dfrac{2-\dfrac{1}{8}-\dfrac{13}{4}}{2} = -\dfrac{11}{16}$	$-1\dfrac{49}{64}$
$x_3^{(k)} = 4 - x_2^{(k)}$	$4 - \dfrac{3}{4} = \dfrac{13}{4}$	$4 + \dfrac{11}{16} = 4\dfrac{11}{16}$	$5\dfrac{49}{64}$

$\mathbf{x}^{(4)} = [0.844 \ -1.766 \ 5.766]^T$, as compared to the exact value $[3 \ -5 \ 9]^T$, which is still quite far off. A computer calculation leads to $\mathbf{x}^{(10)} = [2.616 \ -4.424 \ 8.424]^T$, and $\mathbf{x}^{(20)} = [2.978 \ -4.968 \ 8.968]^T$. ∎

An adaptation of the Gauss-Seidel technique is to use the updated values, $x_i^{(k)}$, *only* in the next iteration, *i.e.*

$$x_i^{(k)} = \dfrac{\left(b_i - \displaystyle\sum_{\substack{j=1 \\ j \neq i}}^{N} a_{ij} x_j^{(k-1)} \right)}{a_{ii}}; \quad \begin{array}{l} i = 1, 2, ..., N \\ k = 2, 3, ... \end{array} \qquad ...(1.30)$$

This is *Jacobi's* [21] *algorithm.* Under certain conditions, the Gauss-Seidel technique is about twice as fast as the Jacobi technique. However, it is not necessary that the Gauss-Seidel method always works better than the Jacobi method (see Section 6.3 of Rice [6] for details).

The convergence of the Gauss-Seidel technique can be speeded up using *successive (or systematic) over-relaxation* (SOR). Using $\mathbf{x}^{(k-1)}$, the *entire* vector, $\mathbf{x}_{GS}^{(k)}$, is first estimated from the Gauss-Seidel algorithm, and *then* $\mathbf{x}^{(k)}$ is calculated using a weighted-average value of $\mathbf{x}^{(k-1)}$ and $\mathbf{x}_{GS}^{(k)}$:

$$x_i^{(k)} = w x_{i,GS}^{(k)} + (1 - w) x_i^{(k-1)}$$

$$= x_i^{(k-1)} + w \left[x_{i,GS}^{(k)} - x_i^{(k-1)} \right] \qquad ...(1.31)$$

Thus, for $w = 1$, one goes from $x_i^{(k-1)}$ to $x_{i,GS}^{(k)}$ in an iteration but with $w > 1$ (over-relaxation), one overshoots and extrapolates a little beyond $x_{i,GS}^{(k)}$ to speed up the computation. $w < 1$ can be tried to obtain convergence in systems which do not converge with the Gauss-Seidel technique. The best value of w to be employed depends on the problem to be solved. *Usually, $1 < w < 2$, but optimal choices for w for specific* problems (*e.g.*, finite difference forms for elliptical partial differential equations) which are regularly solved have been obtained (see, for example, p. 281 of Ref. 16).

The library [10] ITPACK (available from IMSL, Houston) contains several programs using iterative techniques to solve $\mathbf{Ax} = \mathbf{b}$. These programs are, however, quite simple to write. Press et al. [22] also give listings of some programs using popular techniques.

Example 1.11: Repeat Example 1.10 using SOR with $w = 1.5$. Do three iterations and compare with Gauss-Seidel values. Start with $\mathbf{x}^{(1)} = [1 \quad 2 \quad 1]^T$.

	$k = 2$
$x_{1,GS}^{(k)} = \dfrac{1 - x_2^{(k-1)}}{2}$	$-\dfrac{1}{2}$
$x_{2,GS}^{(k)} = \dfrac{2 - x_{1,GS}^{(k)} - x_3^{(k-1)}}{2}$	$\dfrac{3}{4}$
$x_{3,GS}^{(k)} = 4 - x_{2,GS}^{(k)}$	$\dfrac{13}{4}$
$x_1^{(k)} = x_1^{(k-1)} + 1.5\left(x_{1,GS}^{(k)} - x_1^{(k-1)}\right)$	$1 + 1.5\left(-\dfrac{1}{2} - 1\right) = -1.25$
$x_2^{(k)} = x_2^{(k-1)} + 1.5\left(x_{2,GS}^{(k)} - x_2^{(k-1)}\right)$	$2 + 1.5\left(\dfrac{3}{4} - 2\right) = 0.125$
$x_3^{(k)} = x_3^{(k-1)} + 1.5\left(x_{3,GS}^{(k)} - x_3^{(k-1)}\right)$	$1 + 1.5\left(\dfrac{13}{4} - 1\right) = 4.375$

$k = 3$	$k = 4$
$\dfrac{1 - 0.125}{2} = 0.4375$	$\dfrac{1 + 2.171875}{2} = 1.5859375$
$\dfrac{2 - 0.4375 - 4.375}{2} = -1.4062$	$\dfrac{2 - 1.5859375 - 5.921875}{2} = -2.7539062$
$4 + 1.4062 = 5.4062$	$4 + 2.7539062 = 6.7539062$
$-1.25 + 1.5(0.4375 + 1.25)$ $= 1.28125$	$1.28125 + 1.5(1.5859375 - 1.28125)$ $= 1.7383$
$0.125 + 1.5(-1.4062 - 0.125)$ $= -2.171875$	$-2.171875 + 1.5(-2.7539062 + 2.171875)$ $= -3.0449$
$4.375 + 1.5(5.4062 - 4.375)$ $= 5.921875$	$5.921875 + 1.5(6.7539062 - 5.921875)$ $= 7.1699$

The comparison of $\mathbf{x}^T$ with the Gauss-Seidel results is shown below:

Technique/k	2	3	4
G.S. (Example 1.10)	$[-0.5 \ 0.75 \ 3.25]$	$[0.125 \ -0.6875 \ 4.6875]$	$[0.844 \ -1.766 \ 5.766]$
SOR	$[-1.25 \ 0.125 \ 4.375]$	$[1.281 \ -2.172 \ 5.922]$	$[1.783 \ -3.045 \ 7.170]$

Note that the $k = 2$ SOR values, $[-1.25 \ 0.125 \ 4.375]$, are used as $\mathbf{x}^{(2)}$ for obtaining the GS values for $k = 3$ in the SOR technique. The exact values are $[3 \ -5 \ 9]$. The faster convergence of the SOR technique towards the exact solution is observed for all the three variables. Computer calculations with the SOR technique as above give $\mathbf{x}^{(10)} = [2.937 \ -4.887 \ 8.889]^T$ and $\mathbf{x}^{(20)} = [2.999 \ -4.999 \ 8.999]^T$. If one tries $w = 5.0$, unstable results are obtained.

■

APPENDIX 1 – A

Rank of a Matrix [1–3]

From a given matrix, many determinants may be formed (by striking out whole rows and whole columns leaving a *square* array from which a determinant may be found). For example, given the matrix:

$$\begin{bmatrix} a_{11} & a_{12} & a_{13} & a_{14} & a_{15} \\ a_{21} & a_{22} & a_{23} & a_{24} & a_{25} \\ a_{31} & a_{32} & a_{33} & a_{34} & a_{35} \\ a_{41} & a_{42} & a_{43} & a_{44} & a_{45} \end{bmatrix}$$

striking out one column leaves a 4th order determinant, and there are five such 4th order determinants. Striking out two columns and one row leaves a 3rd order determinant and there are forty different such determinants, etc. Many of these determinants may, of course, be zero.

Definition: Suppose in a general $m \times n$ matrix, all determinants formed by striking out whole rows and whole columns of order greater than r are zero, but there exists one determinant of order r which is non-zero; then the matrix is said to have rank r.

For example, in the matrix

$$\begin{bmatrix} 2 & 1 & 3 & 4 \\ -1 & 1 & -2 & -1 \\ 0 & 3 & -1 & 2 \end{bmatrix}$$

all 3rd order determinants are zero, but there is one 2nd order determinant (actually several) which is non-zero. Therefore, this matrix has rank two.

PROBLEMS

1.1 Find out if the following equations are compatible or not using the general rules discussed. If compatible, see if these have multiple or unique solutions. Also solve the equations by elimination to confirm these results:

$$\begin{bmatrix} 2 & 3 \\ 4 & 6 \\ 1 & 1 \end{bmatrix} \begin{bmatrix} x_1 \\ x_2 \end{bmatrix} = \begin{bmatrix} 11 \\ 22 \\ 5 \end{bmatrix}$$

1.2 Repeat prob. 1.1 for

$$\begin{bmatrix} 2 & 3 \\ 4 & 6 \\ 1 & 1 \end{bmatrix} \begin{bmatrix} x_1 \\ x_2 \end{bmatrix} = \begin{bmatrix} 11 \\ 20 \\ 5 \end{bmatrix}$$

1.3 Consider the following equation

$$\begin{bmatrix} 1 & 1 \\ 1 & 1+\varepsilon \end{bmatrix} \begin{bmatrix} x_1 \\ x_2 \end{bmatrix} = \begin{bmatrix} 2 \\ 4 \end{bmatrix}$$

obtain $\mathbf{A}^{-1}$, $|\mathbf{A}|$ and also solve $\mathbf{x}$ using eq. 1.7. Obtain numerical values of $\mathbf{x}$ for $\varepsilon = 0.01, 0.001$ and 0.0001. Thus see how sensitive $\mathbf{x}$ is to changes in ε.

1.4 Solve

$$\begin{bmatrix} 2 & 1 & 0 \\ 1 & 2 & 1 \\ 0 & 1 & 2 \end{bmatrix} \begin{bmatrix} x_1 \\ x_2 \\ x_3 \end{bmatrix} = \begin{bmatrix} 1 \\ 2 \\ 3 \end{bmatrix}$$

using Gauss elimination by hand, and using a program from the computer library available to you. Also evaluate $|\mathbf{A}|$ after reducing it to the upper triangular form [note that Gauss elimination does not alter the value of the determinant; however, each row interchange changes its sign].

1.5 Carefully count the number of multiplications and divisions in Gauss elimination as well as in backward sweep to show that these are:

$$GE: \sum_{i=1}^{N-1} (N-i)(N-i+2)$$

$$BS: 1 + \sum_{i=1}^{N-1} (N-i+1)$$

Thus, deduce eq. 1.18a.

1.6 Solve with and without pivoting (p. 273, Ref. 6)

$$\begin{bmatrix} 0.0003 & 3.0000 \\ 1.0000 & 1.0000 \end{bmatrix} \begin{bmatrix} x_1 \\ x_2 \end{bmatrix} = \begin{bmatrix} 2.0001 \\ 1.0000 \end{bmatrix}$$

The exact solution is $\mathbf{x}^T = [1/3 \quad 2/3]$. Use 4, 5 and 6 decimal place accuracies in the absence of pivoting (use truncation and not round-off).

1.7 Re do prob. 1.6 using

$$\begin{bmatrix} 0.003000 & 59.14 \\ 5.291 & -6.130 \end{bmatrix} \begin{bmatrix} x_1 \\ x_2 \end{bmatrix} = \begin{bmatrix} 59.17 \\ 46.78 \end{bmatrix}$$

The exact solution is $\mathbf{x}^T = [10.000, 1.000]$. Use rounding-off to four digits only.

1.8 Solve prob. 1.4 using LU Decomp + fore and aft Sweep. Check $\mathbf{LU} = \mathbf{A}$.

1.9 Define a different $\mathbf{L}$ and $\mathbf{U}$ than in LU Decomp, as:

$$\mathbf{L} = \begin{bmatrix} l_{11} & 0 & 0 \\ l_{21} & l_{22} & 0 \\ l_{31} & l_{32} & l_{33} \end{bmatrix}; \quad \mathbf{U} = \begin{bmatrix} u_{11} & u_{12} & u_{13} \\ 0 & u_{22} & u_{23} \\ 0 & 0 & u_{33} \end{bmatrix};$$

such that $\mathbf{LU} = \mathbf{A}$, with $\mathbf{A}$ as in prob. 1.4. The 12 elements in $\mathbf{L}$ and $\mathbf{U}$ are related through the 9 equations in $\mathbf{LU} = \mathbf{A}$. Thus, one has the freedom to choose three (N, in general) elements. Choose the diagonal terms as $l_{ii} = 1$ (Doolittle's method). Write equations relating l_{ij} and u_{ij} to the elements of the first row of $\mathbf{A}$. Using the values of u_{1i} so determined, write equations to obtain the first column of $\mathbf{A}$. Proceed (row and then column-wise) to determine $\mathbf{L}$ and $\mathbf{U}$. Compare with the $\mathbf{L}$ and $\mathbf{U}$ matrices of prob. 1.8. The results are more general and Doolittle's technique leads to the same $\mathbf{L}$ and $\mathbf{U}$ as obtained using Gauss elimination. In *Crout's*[15] technique (F04ARF and others in NAG, LUDATF in IMSL, etc.), u_{ii} are defined as unity but the remaining steps are similar to Doolittle's algorithm.

1.10 *Cholesky's Algorithm for Symmetric Positive Definite* $\mathbf{A}$:

Consider the case where $\mathbf{L} = \mathbf{U}^T$ ($\mathbf{U}$ different from that in LU Decomp). Thus obtain $\mathbf{L}$ and $\mathbf{U}$ for $\mathbf{A}$ using

$$\begin{bmatrix} u_{11} & 0 & 0 \\ u_{12} & u_{22} & 0 \\ u_{13} & u_{23} & u_{33} \end{bmatrix} \begin{bmatrix} u_{11} & u_{12} & u_{13} \\ 0 & u_{22} & u_{23} \\ 0 & 0 & u_{33} \end{bmatrix} = \begin{bmatrix} 2 & -1 & 0 \\ -1 & 2 & -1 \\ 0 & -1 & 2 \end{bmatrix} = \mathbf{A}$$

Use the positive values of the square roots. This algorithm involves N square root operations and $(N^3 + 9N^2 + 2N)/6$ multiplications and divisions, and is about twice as fast as the Gauss elimination scheme. The NAG library has several programs (F04ABF, etc., LINPACK has SCHFA, etc.) using this technique.

1.11 Do a LU Decomp and fore and aft Sweep on

$$\begin{bmatrix} 1 & 3 \\ 4 & -1 \end{bmatrix} \begin{bmatrix} x_1 \\ x_2 \end{bmatrix} = \begin{bmatrix} 5 \\ 12 \end{bmatrix}$$

1.12 Solve by Gauss-Jordan technique

$$\begin{bmatrix} 1 & -1 & 2 \\ 2 & -2 & 3 \\ 1 & 1 & 1 \end{bmatrix} \begin{bmatrix} x_1 \\ x_2 \\ x_3 \end{bmatrix} = \begin{bmatrix} -8 \\ -20 \\ -2 \end{bmatrix}$$

Also, simultaneously obtain $\mathbf{A}^{-1}$. Compare with results from example 1.9.

1.13 Solve

$$\begin{bmatrix} 1 & \dfrac{1}{2} & \dfrac{1}{3} \\[2mm] \dfrac{1}{2} & \dfrac{1}{3} & \dfrac{1}{4} \\[2mm] \dfrac{1}{3} & \dfrac{1}{4} & \dfrac{1}{5} \end{bmatrix} \begin{bmatrix} x_1 \\[2mm] x_2 \\[2mm] x_3 \end{bmatrix} = \begin{bmatrix} 1 \\[2mm] 1 \\[2mm] 1 \end{bmatrix}$$

with $a_{ij} = 1/(i+j-1)$ (**A** is then the Hilbert matrix, which is severely ill-conditioned). Solve using the Gauss-Seidel technique with $x^{(1)} = [1 \ 1 \ 1]^T$. Compare with results obtained by hand calculations. Generalize the problem so that $N = 5$ and 15 and use self-made or computer library subprograms to obtain solutions. Discuss your results.

1.14 Solve the equation in example 1.9 by using the Gauss-Seidel and SOR techniques ($w = 1.5$). Note that eq. 1.24 is not satisfied. Use $x^{(1)} = [0 \ 2 \ 2]^T$ and do two iterations only.

1.15 The following equation is obtained after a finite difference technique (see Sec. 6.2) is applied to a particular problem:

$$\begin{bmatrix} \dfrac{3}{2} & \dfrac{-1}{8} & \dfrac{-1}{8} & 0 \\[2mm] \dfrac{-1}{8} & \dfrac{3}{2} & 0 & \dfrac{-1}{8} \\[2mm] \dfrac{-1}{8} & 0 & \dfrac{3}{2} & \dfrac{-1}{8} \\[2mm] 0 & \dfrac{-1}{8} & \dfrac{-1}{8} & \dfrac{3}{2} \end{bmatrix} \begin{bmatrix} x_1 \\[2mm] x_2 \\[2mm] x_3 \\[2mm] x_4 \end{bmatrix} = \begin{bmatrix} 1 \\[2mm] 1 \\[2mm] 1 \\[2mm] 2 \end{bmatrix}$$

If the $k = 1$ choice for x^T are [1 \ 1 \ 1 \ 1], use the SOR technique with $w = 1.5$ to estimate $x^{(2)}$. Make a computer program to obtain the solution.

1.16 Use the Gauss-Jordan technique to obtain A^{-1}, where

$$A = \begin{bmatrix} 2x & 2y \\ 2x & -2y \end{bmatrix}$$

Check your answer by multiplying $A^{-1}A$.

1.17 Make your own computer programs using the Gauss-Seidel and SOR methods, and test it out on examples 1.10 and 1.11. Compare with results given.

1.18 Use your computer programs developed for prob. 1.17 and test it out using single-precision arithmetic on [6]

$$\begin{bmatrix} 0.9143 \times 10^{-4} & 0 & 0 & 0 \\ 0.8762 & 0.7156 \times 10^{-4} & 0 & 0 \\ 0.7943 & 0.8143 & 0.9504 \times 10^{-4} & 0 \\ 0.8017 & 0.6123 & 0.7165 & 0.7123 \times 10^{-4} \end{bmatrix} x = \begin{bmatrix} 0.9143 \times 10^{-4} \\ 0.87627156 \\ 1.60869504 \\ 2.13057123 \end{bmatrix}$$

Use $\mathbf{x}^{(1)} = [0 \quad 0 \quad 0 \quad 1]^T$. The exact solution is $[1 \quad 1 \quad 1 \quad 1]^T$. The lower triangular $\mathbf{A}$ matrix given here is called the Wilkinson matrix, and poses severe computational problems. Use $w = 1.5$.

1.19 Solve using Jacobi's method and $\mathbf{x}^{(1)} = \left[0 \quad \dfrac{1}{2} \quad \dfrac{1}{2} \quad 1\right]^T$, the following equations (see Probs. 3.5 and 6.12)

$$\begin{bmatrix} 1 & 0 & 0 & 0 \\ 1 & -2 & 1 & 0 \\ 0 & 1 & -2 & 1 \\ 0 & 0 & 0 & 1 \end{bmatrix} \begin{bmatrix} x_1 \\ x_2 \\ x_3 \\ x_4 \end{bmatrix} = \begin{bmatrix} 0 \\ 0 \\ 0 \\ 1 \end{bmatrix}$$

Do 5 iterations. The exact solution can be found out easily as $\left[0 \quad \dfrac{1}{3} \quad \dfrac{2}{3} \quad 1\right]^T$.

1.20 Consider the tridiagonal matrix (a) in Example 1.7. Write down the Jacobi algorithm for this case, avoiding unnecessary computations. Calculate the total number of multiplications and divisions required for M iterations, and compare with the value for the *normal* Jacobi algorithm (for non-tridiagonal matrices).

REFERENCES

1. N.R. Amundson, *Mathematical Methods in Chemical Engineering: Matrices and Their Applications*, Prentice Hall, Englewood Cliffs, N.J., 1966.
2. R. Bellman, *Introduction to Matrix Analysis*, 2nd ed., McGraw Hill, New York, 1960. [Refs. 1 and 2 are classic texts on matrices]
3. G.E. Forsythe, in E.F. Beckenbach, ed., *Modern Mathematics for the Engineer*, McGraw Hill, New York, 1956, p. 436.
4. R.L. Burden and J.D. Faires, *Numerical Analysis*, 3rd ed., Prindle, Weber and Schmidt, Boston, 1985.
5. C.F. Gauss, *Theoria Motus corporum coelestium in sectionibus conicus solem ambientium*, Hamburg, 1809; Eng. trans. by C.H. Davis, Boston, 1857, p. 261–262; 266–268.
6. J.R. Rice, *Numerical Methods, Software and Analysis: IMSL Reference Edition*, McGraw Hill, New York, 1983.
   [An excellent discussion of various IMSL routines available]
7. B. Carnahan, H.A. Luther and J.O. Wilkes, *Applied Numerical Methods*, Wiley, New York, 1969.
   [An early classic text for Engineers. Discusses several techniques and gives computer listings as well as detailed results]
8. User's Manual, *IMSL Library Math/Library*, Int. Math. Stat. Lib. Inc., Houston, 1989.
9. J.J Dongarra, J.R. Bunch, C.B. Moler and G.W. Stewart, *LINPACK User's Guide*, SIAM (Soc. Indus. Appl. Math.) Publications, Philadelphia, 1979.
10. L.A. Hageman and D.M. Young, *Applied Iterative Methods*, Academic Press, New York, 1981.
11. L. Lapidus, *Digital Computation for Chemical Engineers*, McGraw Hill, New York, 1962.
    [An excellent discussion of *several* techniques, and a good compilation of early references]
12. G.H. Bruce, D.W. Peaceman, H.H. Rachford and J.D. Rice, *Trans A.I.M.E.*, **198**, 79 (1953).
    [These workers attribute the technique discussed in Example 1.7 to Thomas]

13. E.J. Henley and J.D. Seader, *Equilibrium Stage Separation Operations in Chemical Engineering*, Wiley, New York, 1981, p. 563.

14. B.S. Hofeling and J.D. Seader, *AIChEJ*, **24**, 1131 (1978).

15. P.D. Crout, *Trans. AIEE*, **60**, 1235 (1941).

16. B.A. Finlayson, *Nonlinear Analysis in Chemical Engineering*, McGraw Hill, New York, 1980.

    [An excellent intermediate-level text on numerical methods]

17. T. Hopkins and C. Phillips, *Numerical Methods in Practice Using the NAG Library,* Addison Wesley, Reading, MA, 1988.

18. S.C. Chapra and R.P. Canale, *Numerical Methods for Engineers with PC Applications*, McGraw Hill, New York, 1985.

19. C.F. Gauss, *Abhandlungen zur Methode der Kleinsten Quadrate*: Ger. trans. by A. Börsch and P. Simm, Berlin, 1887; p. 76-77.

20. P.L. Seidel, *Münch. Abh.*, Vol. II, Abt. 3, pp. 81–108 (1874).

21. C.G.J. Jacobi, *J. reine angew Math.*, **13**, 340 (1835).

22. W.H. Press, S.A. Teukolsky, W.T. Vetterling and B.P. Flannery, *Numerical Recipes in Fortran (or C), 2nd ed.,* Cambridge University Press, Cambridge, U.K., 1992.

    [A collection of programs for some popular techniques—not just limited to linear equation solvers. A diskette of programs is also available separately]

Chapter 2

Eigenvalues and Eigenvectors of Matrices

2.1 INTRODUCTION

There are many physical situations, particularly those involving stability analysis of systems whose dynamic behaviour is governed by a system of ordinary differential equations, where a set of homogeneous linear algebraic equations of the following type are encountered:

$$
\begin{aligned}
\left(a_{11} - \lambda\right)x_1 + a_{12}x_2 + a_{13}x_3 + \dots + a_{1N}x_N &= 0 \\
a_{21}x_1 + \left(a_{22} - \lambda\right)x_2 + a_{23}x_3 + \dots + a_{2N}x_N &= 0 \\
&\vdots \\
a_{N1}x_1 + a_{N2}x_2 + a_{N3}x_3 + \dots + \left(a_{NN} - \lambda\right)x_N &= 0
\end{aligned}
$$

...(2.1)

Equation 2.1 can be written in matrix notation as

$$
(\mathbf{A} - \lambda\mathbf{I})\mathbf{x} \equiv \mathbf{B}\mathbf{x} = \mathbf{0}
$$

...(2.2)

where $\mathbf{A}$ and $\mathbf{x}$ are the same as in eq. 1.3, $\mathbf{I}$ is the unit (diagonal) matrix or the idem matrix [2] (example 1.9), and $\mathbf{0}^T$ is the ($1 \times N$) null matrix, [0 0 ... 0]. The constant, λ, could be a parameter of the system. An example where one obtains such equations is in the study of the stability of *lumped parameter* systems (*i.e.,* whose dynamic behaviour is governed by a system of ordinary differential equations), e.g., distillation, absorption, extraction, CSTR sequences, etc., in chemical engineering as discussed in the example below.

Example 2.1: Many systems in engineering can be described by a series of coupled, nonlinear ordinary differential equations (ODEs):

$$
\frac{dx_1}{dt} = f_1\left(x_1, x_2, \dots, x_N\right)
$$

$$\frac{dx_2}{dt} = f_2\left(x_1, x_2, ..., x_N\right)$$

$$\vdots \qquad \qquad \vdots$$

$$\frac{dx_N}{dt} = f_N\left(x_1, x_2, ..., x_N\right) \qquad\qquad ...(a)$$

with initial conditions as follows

$$t = 0: \ x_1 = x_{1o}, x_2 = x_{2o}, ..., x_N = x_{No} \qquad\qquad ...(b)$$

Obtain equations describing how small perturbations around the steady state, decay or increase with time.

In matrix form, eqs. (a) and (b) can be written as

$$\frac{d\mathbf{x}}{dt} = \mathbf{f}(\mathbf{x}); \ \mathbf{x}(t=0) = \mathbf{x}_o$$

where

$$\mathbf{x}^T = \begin{bmatrix} x_1 & x_2 & ... & x_N \end{bmatrix}$$

$$\mathbf{f}^T(\mathbf{x}) \equiv \begin{bmatrix} f_1(\mathbf{x}) & f_2(\mathbf{x}) & ... & f_N(\mathbf{x}) \end{bmatrix}$$

$$\mathbf{x}_o^T \equiv \begin{bmatrix} x_{1o} & x_{2o} & ... & x_{No} \end{bmatrix}$$

The study of the (asymptotic) stability of such a system requires transformation of these equations in terms of deviations from the steady state. The steady state values, x_{is}, of the variables, x_i, corresponding to eq. (a) are given by the solution of the set of nonlinear algebraic equations obtained by putting $d\mathbf{x}/dt = \mathbf{0}$:

$$f_1\left(\mathbf{x}_s\right) = 0$$

$$f_2\left(\mathbf{x}_s\right) = 0$$

$$\vdots \qquad \vdots$$

$$f_N\left(\mathbf{x}_s\right) = 0$$

or

$$\mathbf{f}\left(\mathbf{x}_s\right) = \mathbf{0} \qquad\qquad ...(c)$$

where $\mathbf{x}_s^T = [x_{1s} \ x_{2s} \ ... \ x_{Ns}]$. Equation (c) may have a unique solution (a set of values, $x_{1s}, x_{2s}, ..., x_{Ns}$), or may have multiple solutions (which can be obtained using methods discussed in Chapter 3). Defining deviation variables, ζ_i, as

$$\zeta_i(t) \equiv x_i(t) - x_{is}; \ \ i = 1, 2, ..., N$$

we get

$$\frac{d\zeta_i}{dt} = \frac{dx_i}{dt} - \frac{dx_{is}}{dt} = f_i\left(x_{1s} + \zeta_1, x_{2s} + \zeta_2, ..., x_{Ns} + \zeta_N\right), \qquad i = 1, 2,..., N$$

since $dx_{is}/dt = 0$, and $x_i = x_{is} + \zeta_i$. Use of the multivariable Taylor series expansion about $\mathbf{x}_s$ gives:

$$f_i\left(x_{1s} + \zeta_1, x_{2s} + \zeta_2, ..., x_{Ns} + \zeta_N\right) = f_i\left(x_{1s}, x_{2s}, ..., x_{Ns}\right)$$

$$+\left.\frac{\partial f_i}{\partial x_1}\right|_{\mathbf{x}_s} \zeta_1 + \left.\frac{\partial f_i}{\partial x_2}\right|_{\mathbf{x}_s} \zeta_2 + ... + \left.\frac{\partial f_i}{\partial x_N}\right|_{\mathbf{x}_s} \zeta_N + \text{higher order terms}; \qquad i = 1, 2,..., N$$

which, along with eq. (c) leads to

$$\frac{d\zeta_i}{dt} = \sum_{j=1}^{N} \left.\frac{\partial f_i}{\partial x_j}\right|_{\mathbf{x}_s} \zeta_j; \quad i = 1, 2, ..., N$$

These linearized equations (note that $\left.\partial f_i/\partial x_j\right|_{\mathbf{x}_s}$ are constants since the partial derivatives are evaluated at the steady state values, $\mathbf{x}_s$) can be written in matrix form as

$$\frac{d\underline{\zeta}}{dt} = \mathbf{A}\underline{\zeta}; \ \underline{\zeta}(t = 0) = \underline{\zeta}_0 \qquad\qquad ...(d)$$

where $\mathbf{A}$ is the matrix of Jacobian elements (called Jacobian matrix for brevity)

$$\mathbf{A} \equiv \begin{bmatrix} \dfrac{\partial f_1}{\partial x_1} & \dfrac{\partial f_1}{\partial x_2} & \cdots & \dfrac{\partial f_1}{\partial x_N} \\[1em] \cdot & \cdot & & \cdot \\ \cdot & \cdot & & \cdot \\ \cdot & \cdot & & \cdot \\[1em] \dfrac{\partial f_N}{\partial x_1} & \dfrac{\partial f_N}{\partial x_2} & \cdots & \dfrac{\partial f_N}{\partial x_N} \end{bmatrix}_{\mathbf{x}_s}$$

Equation (d) describes system behaviour correctly only for small values of $\underline{\zeta}$ (small deviations from the steady state), since higher order terms in the Taylor series expansion have been neglected. Thus, integration of eq. (d) with appropriate initial values of the deviations, $\underline{\zeta}$, will give an idea of how the system responds to perturbations around the steady state.

The linear ODEs in eq. (d) can easily be solved [1–3]. The following solution can be assumed

$$\zeta_i = z_i e^{\lambda t}; \ i = 1, 2, ..., N \qquad\qquad ...(2.3)$$

where λ is a constant to be obtained by substituting eq. 2.3 into eq. (d). This leads to

$$z_i \lambda e^{\lambda t} = a_{i1} z_1 e^{\lambda t} + a_{i2} z_2 e^{\lambda t} + ... + a_{iN} z_N e^{\lambda t}; \ i = 1, 2, ..., N$$

or

$$\sum_{j=1}^{N} a_{ij} z_j = \lambda z_i$$

This is written in vector-matrix form as

$$\mathbf{Az} = \lambda\mathbf{Iz} \qquad \qquad \ldots(f)$$

or

$$(\mathbf{A} - \lambda\mathbf{I})\mathbf{z} \equiv \mathbf{Bz} = \mathbf{0} \qquad \qquad \ldots(2.4)$$

where $\mathbf{z}^T = [z_1 \ z_2 \ \ldots \ z_N]$. Equation 2.4 is of the same form as eq. 2.2. ∎

Equation 2.4 represents a set of N linear algebraic equations which are homogeneous. This means that the rank of $\mathbf{B}$ is the same as the rank of aug $\mathbf{B}$, and so solutions are guaranteed (see condition a in Sec. 1.1). If the rank, r, of $\mathbf{B}$ is equal to N, a unique solution exists for eq. 2.2. It is easy to see that under this situation, the solution is trivial, *i.e.* $z_i = 0$; $i = 1, 2, \ldots, N$, and is of little interest. The more interesting result is when $r < N$ (one can then assign arbitrary values to $N - r$ variables, and compute the remaining r variables; see Sec. 1.1). Thus, nontrivial solutions of eq. 2.4 exist when $r < N$, which implies that the determinant of $\mathbf{B}$ must be zero:

$$|\mathbf{B}| = |\mathbf{A} - \lambda\mathbf{I}| = 0 \qquad \qquad \ldots(2.5)$$

or

$$\begin{vmatrix} a_{11} - \lambda & a_{12} & a_{13} & \ldots & a_{1N} \\ a_{21} & a_{22} - \lambda & a_{23} & \ldots & a_{2N} \\ \cdot & & & & \cdot \\ \cdot & & & & \cdot \\ a_{N1} & a_{N2} & a_{N3} & & a_{NN} - \lambda \end{vmatrix} = 0 \qquad \qquad \ldots(2.6)$$

The determinant in eq. 2.6 can be expanded (using expansions in terms of minors, and induction) to give an Nth degree polynomial in λ

$$P_N(\lambda) = (-1)^N \left[\lambda^N - \alpha_1 \lambda^{N-1} + \alpha_2 \lambda^{N-2} - \ldots + (-1)^N \alpha_N \right] = 0 \qquad \ldots(2.7)$$

where the constant coefficients, α_i, depend on a_{ij} (see example 2.2. In fact, α_i is the sum of the ith order principal minors of $\mathbf{A}$) [1]. The exact relations between α_i and the elements of $\mathbf{A}$ are not required for our discussion. The polynomial in eq. 2.7 is known as the *characteristic polynomial* of $\mathbf{A}$. Equation 2.7 has N roots (not necessarily distinct), and these values of λ_i, $i = 1, 2, \ldots, N$ are known as characteristic values or *eigenvalues* of $\mathbf{A}$. The λ_i satisfying eq. 2.7 may be complex, since an algebraic equation with real coefficients may have roots in complex conjugate pairs, or may be complex if the coefficients themselves are complex (when some a_{ij} are complex). Thus, it is found that nontrivial solutions for eq. 2.4 exist only when λ is equal to any of the N eigenvalues. One can easily obtain the solution vectors, $\mathbf{z}_i$, corresponding to each of the eigenvalues λ_i (noting that $\mathbf{z}_i$ are not uniquely determined, as discussed below). These solutions, $\mathbf{z}_i$, are known as *eigenvectors* of $\mathbf{A}$, and satisfy

$$\mathbf{Az}_i = \lambda_i \mathbf{z}_i; \quad i = 1, 2, \ldots, N \qquad \qquad \ldots(2.8)$$

The eigenvalues of $\mathbf{A}$, therefore, give an idea of how perturbations around a steady state die out (or increase) with time for a system described in example 2.1. Equation 2.3 clearly shows that the perturbations will die out if *all* λ_i are such that their real parts are negative. If so, the steady state is said to be *asymptotically stable*. If any λ_i has a positive real part, the corresponding ζ_i will continue to increase with time, and the system will move farther away from the original steady state (*unstable*). The analysis itself breaks down when ζ_i becomes large. It is easy to see from eq. 2.3 that the λ_is can be interpreted as the reciprocal of the various (relaxation) time constants associated with the system.

Equations having the same form as eq. 2.4 arise very frequently in all engineering disciplines. Examples include the vibration of systems of springs connecting masses, resolution of stress and strains acting at any point in mechanically loaded elements (Mohr circles), etc. [4]

There are some important properties associated with matrices and their eigenvalues and eigenvectors. They are being stated here without proof (for which one is referred to some excellent texts [1–3]):

(a) if λ is an eigenvalue of $\mathbf{A}$ (for $\mathbf{Ax} = \lambda\,\mathbf{x}$), then it is also an eigenvalue of $\mathbf{A}^T$. Also, $1/\lambda$ is an eigenvalue of $\mathbf{A}^{-1}$.

(b) the eigenvectors, $\mathbf{x}_i$, associated with *distinct* eigenvalues, λ_i, of *any* matrix $\mathbf{A}$, are linearly independent (*i.e.*, $\mathbf{x}_i$ cannot be written as a linear combination of $\mathbf{x}_j$). If all N eigenvalues are distinct, the entire set of N $\mathbf{x}_i$ are linearly independent. Any *real symmetric* $\mathbf{A}$ has N linearly independent eigenvectors, even if the eigenvalues are not distinct.

(c) the eigenvalues of a *real symmetric* matrix $\mathbf{A}$ are all real though not necessarily distinct (one can also get real λs for some non symmetric $\mathbf{A}$). The set of N linearly independent eigenvectors for a *real symmetric* $\mathbf{A}$ can be made to form an *orthogonal set* of N vectors using the Gram-Schmidt procedure (two vectors $\mathbf{x}_i$ and $\mathbf{x}_j$ are said to be *orthogonal* if $\mathbf{x}_i^T \mathbf{x}_j = 0$. If, in addition, $\mathbf{x}_i^T \mathbf{x}_i$ and $\mathbf{x}_j^T \mathbf{x}_j$ are unity, then these two vectors are said to be *orthonormal*. This can easily be generalized for a set of N vectors).

(d) the *spectral radius,* $\rho(\mathbf{A})$, of a matrix $\mathbf{A}$ is defined by

$$\rho(\mathbf{A}) = \max_i |\lambda_i| \qquad \ldots(2.9)$$

Example 2.2: Obtain the characteristic polynomial and the eigenvalues of the unsymmetric, real matrix (using expansion in terms of minors)

$$\mathbf{A} = \begin{bmatrix} 0 & 2 & 3 \\ -10 & -1 & 2 \\ -2 & 4 & 7 \end{bmatrix}$$

Also, obtain the eigenvectors, using Gauss elimination to solve the equations. Use $x_3 = 1$ as an *additional* condition (since the rank of $\mathbf{B}$, $r = N-1$) to obtain the eigenvectors. Check if the eigenvectors are orthogonal.

The characteristic polynomial is

$$P_N(\lambda) = \begin{vmatrix} 0-\lambda & 2 & 3 \\ -10 & -1-\lambda & 2 \\ -2 & 4 & 7-\lambda \end{vmatrix} = (-\lambda)\begin{vmatrix} -1-\lambda & 2 \\ 4 & 7-\lambda \end{vmatrix} - 2\begin{vmatrix} -10 & 2 \\ -2 & 7-\lambda \end{vmatrix} + 3\begin{vmatrix} -10 & -1-\lambda \\ -2 & 4 \end{vmatrix}$$

$$= (-\lambda)\left[-(1+\lambda)(7-\lambda)-8\right] - 2\left[-70+10\lambda+4\right] + 3\left[-40+2(-1-\lambda)\right]$$

$$= -\lambda\left[\lambda^2 - 6\lambda - 15\right] - 20\lambda + 132 - 126 - 6\lambda$$

$$= -\left[\lambda^3 - 6\lambda^2 + 11\lambda - 6\right] \quad \text{(thus, } \alpha_1 = 6, \ \alpha_2 = 11, \ \alpha_3 = 6\text{)}$$

$$= -(\lambda-1)(\lambda-2)(\lambda-3).$$

Hence, $\lambda_1 = 1$, $\lambda_2 = 2$, $\lambda_3 = 3$ are the three eigenvalues. Note that the eigenvalues are real, even though $\mathbf{A}$ is unsymmetric. The spectral radius of $\mathbf{A}$ is 3.

Eigenvectors for $\lambda_1 = 1$

$$(A - \lambda_1 I)x = 0$$

or

$$\begin{bmatrix} -1 & 2 & 3 \\ -10 & -2 & 2 \\ -2 & 4 & 6 \end{bmatrix} \begin{bmatrix} x_1 \\ x_2 \\ x_3 \end{bmatrix} = \begin{bmatrix} 0 \\ 0 \\ 0 \end{bmatrix}$$

Note that

$$|B| = \begin{vmatrix} -1 & 2 & 3 \\ -10 & -2 & 2 \\ -2 & 4 & 6 \end{vmatrix} = 0$$

since the third row is twice the first row. However, $\begin{vmatrix} -1 & 2 \\ -10 & -2 \end{vmatrix} \neq 0$. So the rank, r, of B is 2, and

there is one variable which can be chosen arbitrarily (see Sec. 1.1).
    Gauss elimination leads to

$$\begin{bmatrix} -1 & 2 & 3 \\ 0 & -22 & -28 \\ 0 & 0 & 0 \end{bmatrix} \begin{bmatrix} x_1 \\ x_2 \\ x_3 \end{bmatrix} = \begin{bmatrix} 0 \\ 0 \\ 0 \end{bmatrix}$$

Hence

$$-22x_2 = 28x_3 = 28 \qquad \therefore x_2 = -14/11$$
$$x_1 = 2x_2 + 3x_3 \qquad x_1 = 5/11$$

Thus, for $\lambda_1 = 1$, $x^T = \begin{bmatrix} \dfrac{5}{11} & -\dfrac{14}{11} & 1 \end{bmatrix} (\equiv x_1^T)$

    If, instead of $x_3 = 1$, we had used a normalization condition (*i.e.* $x_1^2 + x_2^2 + x_3^2 = 1$), we would have

obtained $x_1^T = \begin{bmatrix} \dfrac{5}{3\sqrt{38}} & -\dfrac{14}{3\sqrt{38}} & \dfrac{11}{3\sqrt{38}} \end{bmatrix}$.

for $\lambda_2 = 2$

$$\begin{bmatrix} -2 & 2 & 3 \\ -10 & -3 & 2 \\ -2 & 4 & 5 \end{bmatrix} \begin{bmatrix} x_1 \\ x_2 \\ x_3 \end{bmatrix} = \begin{bmatrix} 0 \\ 0 \\ 0 \end{bmatrix}$$

and we obtain $x_2^T = \begin{bmatrix} \dfrac{1}{2} & -1 & 1 \end{bmatrix}$

for $\lambda_3 = 3$

$$\begin{bmatrix} -3 & 2 & 3 \\ -10 & -4 & 2 \\ -2 & 4 & 4 \end{bmatrix} \begin{bmatrix} x_1 \\ x_2 \\ x_3 \end{bmatrix} = \begin{bmatrix} 0 \\ 0 \\ 0 \end{bmatrix}$$

which leads to $\qquad x_3^T = \begin{bmatrix} \dfrac{1}{2} & -\dfrac{3}{4} & 1 \end{bmatrix}$

Checking the orthogonality of x_j:

$$x_2^T x_3 = \begin{bmatrix} \dfrac{1}{2} & -1 & 1 \end{bmatrix} \begin{bmatrix} 1/2 \\ -3/4 \\ 1 \end{bmatrix} = 2 \neq 0;$$

$$x_1^T x_3 = \begin{bmatrix} \dfrac{5}{11} & -\dfrac{14}{11} & 1 \end{bmatrix} \begin{bmatrix} 1/2 \\ -3/4 \\ 1 \end{bmatrix} = \dfrac{24}{11};$$

$$x_1^T x_2 = \begin{bmatrix} \dfrac{5}{11} & -\dfrac{14}{11} & 1 \end{bmatrix} \begin{bmatrix} 1/2 \\ -1 \\ 1 \end{bmatrix} = \dfrac{5}{2};$$

Hence, the various eigenvectors are not orthogonal, though they are linearly independent.   ■

2.2 FADDEEV-LEVERRIER'S METHOD

The determination of eigenvalues of a matrix $\mathbf{A}$ using the expansion of $|\mathbf{A} - \lambda\mathbf{I}|$ in terms of minors is very time consuming. More efficient techniques have, therefore, been developed, in view of the importance of calculating eigenvalues in engineering practice. Some of these are discussed in next chapter.

The Faddeev-Leverrier's method (see Ref. 5 for details) has been known for a long time. In this technique the coefficients, α_i, of the characteristic polynomial, $P_N(\lambda)$(eq. 2.7), are generated using multiplication of the $\mathbf{A}$ matrix with itself several times. It uses two properties of matrices:

(a) The trace, tr $\mathbf{A}$, of any matrix $\mathbf{A}$, defined by

$$\text{tr } \mathbf{A} \equiv \sum_{i=1}^{N} a_{ii} \qquad \qquad ...(2.10)$$

is equal to the sum of the eigenvalues of the matrix $\mathbf{A}$, thus

$$\text{tr } \mathbf{A} = \sum_{i=1}^{N} \lambda_i \qquad \qquad ...(2.11)$$

(b) If λ_i, $i = 1, 2, ..., N$ are the eigenvalues of $\mathbf{A}$, then the eigenvalues of $\mathbf{A}^r (\equiv \mathbf{A}\,\mathbf{A}^{r-1}$; so $\mathbf{A}^2 = \mathbf{A}\,\mathbf{A}$, $\mathbf{A}^3 = \mathbf{A}\,\mathbf{A}^2,...)$ are λ_i^r, $r = 1, 2, ...$(see example 2.3 for proof).

Example 2.3: Prove statement (b) above.

Since λ_i are the eigenvalues of $\mathbf{A}$, we have from eq. 2.8

$$\mathbf{A}\mathbf{x}_i = \lambda_i \mathbf{x}_i ; \qquad i = 1, 2, ..., N \qquad \qquad ...(a)$$

Premultiplying both sides of the equation by $\mathbf{A}$, noting that λ_i is a constant, and using this equation again leads to

$$\mathbf{A}^2 \mathbf{x}_i \equiv (\mathbf{A}\mathbf{A})\mathbf{x}_i = \mathbf{A}(\mathbf{A}\mathbf{x}_i) = \mathbf{A}(\lambda_i \mathbf{x}_i) = \lambda_i(\mathbf{A}\mathbf{x}_i) = \lambda_i(\lambda_i \mathbf{x}_i),$$

or
$$\mathbf{A}^2\mathbf{x}_i = \lambda_i^2\mathbf{x}_i \; ; \; i = 1, 2, ..., N$$

Since this equation is of the same form as eq. (*a*) above, this means that the eigenvalues of $\mathbf{A}^2$ are λ_i^2 ; $i = 1, 2, ..., N$. This process can be repeated any number of times, e.g.,

$$\mathbf{A}^3\mathbf{x}_i \equiv \left(\mathbf{A}\mathbf{A}^2\right)\mathbf{x}_i = \mathbf{A}\left(\lambda_i^2\mathbf{x}_i\right) = \lambda_i^2\left(\mathbf{A}\mathbf{x}_i\right) = \lambda_i^2\left(\lambda_i\,\mathbf{x}_i\right) = \lambda_i^3\mathbf{x}_i$$

and, in general,

$$\mathbf{A}^r\mathbf{x}_i = \lambda_i^r\mathbf{x}_i \; ; \; i = 1, 2, ..., N$$

Hence, λ_i^r are the eigenvalues of $\mathbf{A}^r$. Note that $\mathbf{x}_i$ are the eigenvectors of $\mathbf{A}, \mathbf{A}^2, \mathbf{A}^3, ...$ ∎

Since $\lambda_1, \lambda_2, ..., \lambda_N$ are the N roots of eq. 2.7 we can easily write

$$P_N(\lambda) = (-1)^N\left[\lambda^N - \alpha_1\lambda^{N-1} + \alpha_2\lambda^{N-2} - ... + (-1)^N\alpha_N\right]$$

$$= (-1)^N\left[(\lambda - \lambda_1)(\lambda - \lambda_2)...(\lambda - \lambda_N)\right] = 0 \qquad ...(2.12)$$

Upon expanding the right-hand side using long-hand multiplication, the coefficients, α_i can be obtained in terms of the λ_is by comparing corresponding terms. It can easily be seen that

$$(\lambda - \lambda_1)(\lambda - \lambda_2) = \lambda^2 - (\lambda_1 + \lambda_2)\lambda + (\lambda_1\lambda_2)$$

$$(\lambda - \lambda_1)(\lambda - \lambda_2)(\lambda - \lambda_3) = \lambda^3 - (\lambda_1 + \lambda_2 + \lambda_3)\lambda^2 + (\lambda_1\lambda_2 + \lambda_1\lambda_3 + \lambda_2\lambda_3)\lambda - (\lambda_1\lambda_2\lambda_3)$$

$$(\lambda - \lambda_1)(\lambda - \lambda_2)(\lambda - \lambda_3)(\lambda - \lambda_4) = \lambda^4 - (\lambda_1 + \lambda_2 + \lambda_3 + \lambda_4)\lambda^3 + (\lambda_1\lambda_2 + \lambda_1\lambda_3 + \lambda_1\lambda_4$$

$$+ \lambda_2\lambda_3 + \lambda_2\lambda_4 + \lambda_3\lambda_4)\lambda^2 - (\lambda_1\lambda_2\lambda_3 + \lambda_1\lambda_2\lambda_4$$

$$+ \lambda_1\lambda_3\lambda_4 + \lambda_2\lambda_3\lambda_4)\lambda + (\lambda_1\lambda_2\lambda_3\lambda_4) \qquad ...(2.13)$$

etc. Thus, the coefficient of λ^N is unity, that of $-\lambda^{N-1}$ is the sum of all λ_i (taken one at a time), that of λ^{N-2} is the sum of the (distinct) products of λ_i taken two at a time, etc. One can, thus, write,

$$\alpha_1 = \sum_{i=1}^{N}\lambda_i$$

$$\alpha_2 = \lambda_1\lambda_2 + \lambda_1\lambda_3 + ... + \lambda_1\lambda_N + \lambda_2\lambda_3 + \lambda_2\lambda_4 + ... + \lambda_2\lambda_N + ... + \lambda_{N-1}\lambda_N$$

$$\alpha_3 = \lambda_1\lambda_2\lambda_3 + \lambda_1\lambda_2\lambda_4 + ... + \lambda_{N-2}\lambda_{N-1}\lambda_N$$

.

.

.
$$\qquad ...(2.14)$$

We can now define p_i; $i = 1, 2, ..., N$, as the traces of matrices $\mathbf{A}, \mathbf{A}^2,..., \mathbf{A}^N$ and use eq. 2.11 to give

$$p_1 \equiv \operatorname{tr}\mathbf{A} = \sum_{i=1}^{N}\lambda_i$$

$$p_2 \equiv \operatorname{tr}\mathbf{A}^2 = \sum_{i=1}^{N}\lambda_i^2$$

$$\cdot$$
$$\cdot$$
$$\cdot$$

$$p_N \equiv \operatorname{tr} \mathbf{A}^N = \sum_{i=1}^{N} \lambda_i^N \qquad \ldots(2.15)$$

These traces can easily be obtained on the computer with $N-1$ matrix multiplications of $\mathbf{A}$ ($\mathbf{AA}$, $\mathbf{AA}^2$, ..., $\mathbf{AA}^{N-1}$). Equations 2.14 and 2.15 can be combined to obtain $\alpha_1, \alpha_2, ..., \alpha_N$ as follows:

$$\alpha_1 = p_1 \qquad \ldots(a)$$

$$\alpha_1 p_1 = (\lambda_1 + \lambda_2 + ... + \lambda_N)(\lambda_1 + \lambda_2 + ... + \lambda_N)$$

$$= \lambda_1^2 + \lambda_2^2 + ... + \lambda_N^2 + 2(\lambda_1\lambda_2 + \lambda_1\lambda_3 + ... + \lambda_{N-1}\lambda_N)$$

$$= p_2 + 2\alpha_2 \qquad \ldots(b)$$

$$3\alpha_3 = \alpha_2 p_1 - \alpha_1 p_2 + p_3 \qquad \ldots(c) \quad \ldots(2.16)$$

etc. In general, one can show that

$$i\alpha_i = \alpha_{i-1}p_1 - \alpha_{i-2}p_2 + ... + (-1)^{i-1} p_i; \quad i = 1, 2, ..., N \qquad \ldots(2.17)$$

Equation 2.17 gives all the coefficients, α_i, in the characteristic polynomial, $P_N(\lambda)$, which can then be solved using methods discussed in next chapter, in order to obtain the N eigenvalues.

Example 2.4: Obtain the characteristic polynomial of the matrix (see example 2.2)

$$\mathbf{A} = \begin{bmatrix} 0 & 2 & 3 \\ -10 & -1 & 2 \\ -2 & 4 & 7 \end{bmatrix}$$

using the Faddeev-Leverrier method.

$$p_1 = \operatorname{tr} \mathbf{A} = 0 - 1 + 7 = 6$$

$$\mathbf{A}^2 = \begin{bmatrix} 0 & 2 & 3 \\ -10 & -1 & 2 \\ -2 & 4 & 7 \end{bmatrix}\begin{bmatrix} 0 & 2 & 3 \\ -10 & -1 & 2 \\ -2 & 4 & 7 \end{bmatrix} = \begin{bmatrix} -26 & 10 & 25 \\ 6 & -11 & -18 \\ -54 & 20 & 51 \end{bmatrix}$$

Thus, $$p_2 = \operatorname{tr} \mathbf{A}^2 = -26 - 11 + 51 = 14$$

$$\mathbf{A}^3 = \begin{bmatrix} 0 & 2 & 3 \\ -10 & -1 & 2 \\ -2 & 4 & 7 \end{bmatrix}\begin{bmatrix} -26 & 10 & 25 \\ 6 & -11 & -18 \\ -54 & 20 & 51 \end{bmatrix} = \begin{bmatrix} -150 & 38 & 117 \\ 146 & -49 & -130 \\ -302 & 76 & 235 \end{bmatrix}$$

$$p_3 = \operatorname{tr} \mathbf{A}^3 = -150 - 49 + 235 = 36$$

Now using eq. 2.16:

$$\alpha_1 = p_1 = 6$$

$$\alpha_2 = \frac{\alpha_1 p_1 - p_2}{2} = \frac{36 - 14}{2} = 11$$

$$\alpha_3 = \frac{p_3 + \alpha_2 p_1 - \alpha_1 p_2}{3} = \frac{36 + 66 - 84}{3} = 6$$

Hence, $P_3(\lambda) = -[\lambda^3 - 6\lambda^2 + 11\lambda - 6]$

which is the same as in example 2.2. ■

The polynomial method of Faddeev and Leverrier is quite popular for obtaining eigenvalues of moderate-sized matrices (typically for $N < 10$). The determination of the eigenvectors is, however, a bit cumbersome and is given [6–8] in prob. 2.5, along with a method of obtaining the inverse, $\mathbf{A}^{-1}$. It can easily be shown that the number of multiplications and divisions required to obtain all the coefficients, $\alpha_1, \alpha_2, ..., \alpha_N$, in the characteristic polynomial is proportional to N^4 for large N (see Problem 2.6).

2.3 POWER METHOD

The Faddeev-Leverrier technique is quite inefficient for matrices with N larger than about ten. In such cases, iterative techniques are recommended. The power method [4, 6, 8] is quite popular, particularly if one is interested in obtaining the largest (in magnitude) eigenvalue. An added advantage is that this method gives the eigenvectors of the matrix simultaneously. The technique is described here for an $N \times N$ matrix **A,** whose eigenvalues are real and distinct (the method can be used otherwise too, see later). The eigenvalues are assumed to be numbered such that

$$|\lambda_1| > |\lambda_2| > ... > |\lambda_N| \qquad ...(2.18)$$

so that λ_1 is the dominant eigenvalue.

The procedure for obtaining $|\lambda_1|$ is quite simple. We can start with an arbitrary $N \times 1$ vector $\mathbf{v}^{(1)}$ (usually taken as $[1\ 0\ 0\ ...0]^T$ or $[1\ 1\ 1\ ...1]^T$). The following series of iterations are performed

$$\mathbf{v}^{(k)} = \frac{\mathbf{A}\mathbf{v}^{(k-1)}}{\left\|\mathbf{A}\mathbf{v}^{(k-1)}\right\|}; \quad k = 2, 3, ... \qquad ...(2.19)$$

where $\mathbf{A}\mathbf{v}^{(k-1)}$ is a column vector and $\|\ \mathbf{x}\ \|$ is the L_2 or Euclidean norm of a vector $\mathbf{x}$, defined as $\left(\mathbf{x}^T\mathbf{x}\right)^{1/2} \left[= \left(\sum_{i=1}^{N} x_i^2\right)^{1/2}\right.$, the 'length' of the vector $\mathbf{x}$]. In eq. 2.19, the denominator is used to normalize vector $\mathbf{v}^{(k)}$ so that $\|\ \mathbf{v}^{(k)}\ \| = 1$. It is shown in example 2.5 that

$$\underset{k \to \infty}{\text{Lim}}\left\|\mathbf{A}\mathbf{v}^{(k-1)}\right\| = |\lambda_1| \qquad ...(a)$$

and

$$\underset{k \to \infty}{\text{Lim}}\ \mathbf{v}^{(k)} = \mathbf{x}_1 \qquad ...(b) \qquad ...(2.20)$$

where $\mathbf{x}_1$ is the normalized eigenvector of **A** corresponding to λ_1. The convergence to the eigenvalue and eigenvector was first shown by von Mises.

Example 2.5: Deduce eq. 2.20

It has been noted in Sec. 2.1 that any N × N matrix **A** having N distinct eigenvalues (or any real symmetric matrix), has N linearly independent N-dimensional eigenvectors $\mathbf{u}_1, \mathbf{u}_2, \ldots, \mathbf{u}_N$. Also, it can be shown [1] that any arbitrary N-dimensional vector such as $\mathbf{v}^{(1)}$, can be written *uniquely* in terms of a linear combination of these eigenvectors; thus

$$\mathbf{v}^{(1)} = C_1\mathbf{u}_1 + C_2\mathbf{u}_2 + \ldots + C_N\mathbf{u}_N \qquad \ldots(a)$$

where $C_1, C_2, \ldots, C_N$ are constants. Premultiplying eq. (a) by **A** and using $\mathbf{A}\mathbf{u}_i = \lambda_i\mathbf{u}_i$, one obtains

$$\mathbf{A}\mathbf{v}^{(1)} = C_1\mathbf{A}\mathbf{u}_1 + C_2\mathbf{A}\mathbf{u}_2 + \ldots + C_N\mathbf{A}\mathbf{u}_N$$

$$= C_1\lambda_1\mathbf{u}_1 + C_2\lambda_2\mathbf{u}_2 + \ldots + C_N\lambda_N\mathbf{u}_N$$

and so

$$\mathbf{v}^{(2)} = \frac{\mathbf{A}\mathbf{v}^{(1)}}{\left\|\mathbf{A}\mathbf{v}^{(1)}\right\|} = \beta_2\left[C_1\lambda_1\mathbf{u}_1 + C_2\lambda_2\mathbf{u}_2 + \ldots + C_N\lambda_N\mathbf{u}_N\right] \qquad \ldots(b)$$

where $\beta_2\left(= 1/\left\|\mathbf{A}\mathbf{v}^{(1)}\right\|\right)$ is the normalization factor.

Premultiplying eq. (b) by **A** gives

$$\mathbf{A}\mathbf{v}^{(2)} = \beta_2\left[C_1\lambda_1\left(\mathbf{A}\mathbf{u}_1\right) + C_2\lambda_2\left(\mathbf{A}\mathbf{u}_2\right) + \ldots + C_N\lambda_N\left(\mathbf{A}\mathbf{u}_N\right)\right]$$

$$= \beta_2\left[C_1\lambda_1^2\mathbf{u}_1 + C_2\lambda_2^2\mathbf{u}_2 + \ldots + C_N\lambda_N^2\mathbf{u}_N\right]$$

and

$$\mathbf{v}^{(3)} = \frac{\mathbf{A}\mathbf{v}^{(2)}}{\left\|\mathbf{A}\mathbf{v}^{(2)}\right\|} = \beta_3\left[C_1\lambda_1^2\mathbf{u}_1 + C_2\lambda_2^2\mathbf{u}_2 + \ldots + C_N\lambda_N^2\mathbf{u}_N\right]$$

where β_3 is the new normalization factor. The sequence of operations in eq. 2.19 thus leads to

$$\mathbf{v}^{(k)} = \beta_k\left[C_1\lambda_1^{k-1}\mathbf{u}_1 + C_2\lambda_2^{k-1}\mathbf{u}_2 + \ldots + C_N\lambda_N^{k-1}\mathbf{u}_N\right].$$

If $|\lambda_1| > |\lambda_2| > \ldots > |\lambda_N|$, the first term in this equation dominates, and so, as k increases, one obtains

$$\lim_{k\to\infty} \mathbf{v}^{(k)} = \beta_k C_1\lambda_1^{k-1}\mathbf{u}_1 = \mathbf{u}_1 / \left\|\mathbf{u}_1\right\| = \mathbf{x}_1,$$

where the second equality follows from the fact that $\mathbf{v}^{(k)}$ is a normalized vector. Thus, we observe that the sequence of operations in eq. 2.19 gives the eigenvector corresponding to the dominant eigenvalue λ_1. Also from eq. 2.19,

$$\mathbf{A}\mathbf{v}^{(k-1)} = \left\|\mathbf{A}\mathbf{v}^{(k-1)}\right\|\mathbf{v}^{(k)}$$

As $k \to \infty$, this gives

$$\mathbf{A}\mathbf{x}_1 = \left\|\mathbf{A}\mathbf{x}_1\right\|\mathbf{x}_1$$

which is of the form $\mathbf{A}\mathbf{x}_1 = \lambda_1\mathbf{x}_1$. Hence, eq. 2.20($a$) is proved. ∎

If the dominant eigenvalue, λ_1, has a multiplicity of m, one can still obtain N linearly independent [1, 4] eigenvectors of **A** (provided **A** is a real symmetric matrix). One, thus, gets

$$\underset{k \to \infty}{\text{Lim}}\, \mathbf{v}^{(k)} = \beta_k \left[C_1 \lambda_1^{k-1} \mathbf{u}_1 + C_2 \lambda_1^{k-1} \mathbf{u}_2 + \ldots + C_m \lambda_1^{k-1} \mathbf{u}_m \right] \qquad \ldots (2.21)$$

and eq. 2.20 is still valid, provided one interprets $\mathbf{x}_1$ as one of the family of m eigenvectors associated with λ_1. The other $m-1$ eigenvectors can be obtained by starting with different $\mathbf{v}^{(1)}$.

Example 2.6: Obtain the dominant eigenvalue and the corresponding eigenvectors of the following matrix **A,** using the power method (see example 2.2)

$$\mathbf{A} = \begin{bmatrix} 0 & 2 & 3 \\ -10 & -1 & 2 \\ -2 & 4 & 7 \end{bmatrix}$$

Also obtain the correct sign of λ_1.

Starting with $\mathbf{v}^{(1)} = [1\ 0\ 0]^T$, we obtain

$$\mathbf{v}^{(2)} = \frac{\begin{bmatrix} 0 & 2 & 3 \\ -10 & -1 & 2 \\ -2 & 4 & 7 \end{bmatrix} \begin{bmatrix} 1 \\ 0 \\ 0 \end{bmatrix}}{\left\| \mathbf{A}\mathbf{v}^{(1)} \right\|} = \frac{\begin{bmatrix} 0 \\ -10 \\ -2 \end{bmatrix}}{\sqrt{100+4}} = \begin{bmatrix} 0 \\ -0.9806 \\ -0.1961 \end{bmatrix}$$

Estimates $(k=2): \left| \lambda_1 \right| = \left\| \mathbf{A}\mathbf{v}^{(1)} \right\| = 10.198$

$$\mathbf{x}_1 = \begin{bmatrix} 0 \\ -0.9806 \\ -0.1961 \end{bmatrix}$$

$$\mathbf{v}^{(3)} = \frac{\begin{bmatrix} 0 & 2 & 3 \\ -10 & -1 & 2 \\ -2 & 4 & 7 \end{bmatrix} \begin{bmatrix} 0 \\ -0.9806 \\ -0.1961 \end{bmatrix}}{\left\| \mathbf{A}\mathbf{v}^{(2)} \right\|} = \frac{\begin{bmatrix} -2.5495 \\ 0.5884 \\ -5.2951 \end{bmatrix}}{\sqrt{(2.5495)^2 + (0.5884)^2 + (5.2951)^2}}$$

$$= \begin{bmatrix} -0.4317 \\ 0.0996 \\ -0.8965 \end{bmatrix}$$

Estimates $(k=3): \left| \lambda_1 \right| = \left\| \mathbf{A}\mathbf{v}^{(2)} \right\| = 5.9063$

$$\mathbf{x}_1 = \begin{bmatrix} -0.4317 \\ 0.0996 \\ -0.8965 \end{bmatrix}$$

This can be continued more times. It is found (using a computer program) that the results go as follows:

k	5	10	20	actual (Example 2.2)
$\|\lambda_1\|$	4.262	3.089	3.0014	3
$[\mathbf{x}_1]$	$\begin{bmatrix} -0.3921 \\ 0.4789 \\ -0.7854 \end{bmatrix}$	$\begin{bmatrix} -0.3734 \\ 0.5503 \\ -0.7468 \end{bmatrix}$	$\begin{bmatrix} -0.3714 \\ 0.55698 \\ -0.7428 \end{bmatrix}$	$\begin{bmatrix} 0.3714 \\ -0.5571 \\ 0.7428 \end{bmatrix}$

Note that since an eigenvector, **x,** is calculated from $\mathbf{A}\mathbf{x} = \lambda\mathbf{x}$, where λ is the corresponding eigenvalue, it is obtained only upto an arbitrary constant multiplicative factor. In other words, if **x** is an eigenvector, then $c\mathbf{x}$, where c is a constant, is also an eigenvector.

The correct sign of λ_1 can be obtained by checking if $(\mathbf{A} - \lambda\mathbf{I})\, \mathbf{x}_1 = \mathbf{0}$.

If $\lambda_1 = +3$, we get

$$\begin{bmatrix} -3 & 2 & 3 \\ -10 & -4 & 2 \\ -2 & 4 & 4 \end{bmatrix} \begin{bmatrix} 0.3714 \\ -0.5571 \\ 0.7428 \end{bmatrix} = \begin{bmatrix} 0 \\ 0 \\ 0 \end{bmatrix}$$

If $\lambda_1 = -3$, we get

$$\begin{bmatrix} 3 & 2 & 3 \\ -10 & 2 & 2 \\ -2 & 4 & 10 \end{bmatrix} \begin{bmatrix} 0.3714 \\ -0.5571 \\ 0.7428 \end{bmatrix} = \begin{bmatrix} 2.2284 \\ -3.3426 \\ 4.4568 \end{bmatrix}$$

Hence $\lambda_1 = +3$ is the correct dominant eigenvalue. ∎

In some situations, one is interested in obtaining the smallest eigenvalue (in magnitude) of a matrix. For example, in the study of systems of ordinary differential equations for N variables, the 'stiffness' is defined [9] in terms of the ratio of the largest and smallest eigenvalues of a Jacobian matrix associated with the equations (see Chapter 5). The power method can be used to obtain $|\lambda_i|_{min}$ of matrix **A** by first obtaining $\mathbf{A}^{-1}$ (Gauss-Jordan), and then computing the largest eigenvalue of the latter. Since the eigenvalues of $\mathbf{A}^{-1}$ are the reciprocal [1–4] of those of **A**, this gives the eigenvalue with the smallest magnitude.

The power method can be extended by using Hotelling's [10] deflation (or sweeping) techniques, in order to obtain the other eigenvalues and eigenvectors of **A**, *provided that* **A** *is symmetric*. The original matrix, **A**, is redefined as $\mathbf{A}_1$, and its largest eigenvalue, λ_1, and the corresponding eigenvector, $\mathbf{x}_1$, are obtained using the power method. A new $N \times N$ matrix $\mathbf{A}_2$ is then defined as

$$\mathbf{A}_2 = \mathbf{A}_1 - \lambda_1\mathbf{x}_1\mathbf{x}_1^T \qquad \ldots(2.22)$$

It can be shown (see example 2.7) that the matrix $\mathbf{A}_2$ has eigenvalues $0, \lambda_2, \lambda_3, \ldots, \lambda_N$ and corresponding eigenvectors $\mathbf{x}_1, \mathbf{x}_2, \ldots, \mathbf{x}_N$ where $\lambda_1, \lambda_2, \ldots, \lambda_N$ (with $|\lambda_1| > |\lambda_2| > \ldots > |\lambda_N|$ as before) are the eigenvalues of $\mathbf{A}_1$ and $\mathbf{x}_1, \mathbf{x}_2, \ldots, \mathbf{x}_N$ are the associated (normalized) eigenvectors.

Example 2.7: Show that $\mathbf{A}_2$ has eigenvalues $0, \lambda_2, \lambda_3, \ldots, \lambda_N$ and corresponding eigenvectors $\mathbf{x}_1, \mathbf{x}_2, \ldots, \mathbf{x}_N$, as defined above.

$$\mathbf{A}_2 = \mathbf{A}_1 - \lambda_1\mathbf{x}_1\mathbf{x}_1^T \qquad \ldots(a)$$

Postmultiply eq. (*a*) by $\mathbf{x}_1$ to get

$$\mathbf{A}_2\mathbf{x}_1 = \mathbf{A}_1\mathbf{x}_1 - \lambda_1\mathbf{x}_1\left(\mathbf{x}_1^T\mathbf{x}_1\right) = \mathbf{A}_1\mathbf{x}_1 - \lambda_1\mathbf{x}_1$$

since $\mathbf{x}_1^T\mathbf{x}_1 = 1$ (by normalization). Since λ_1 is an eigenvalue of $\mathbf{A}_1$, and $\mathbf{x}_1$ is the associated eigenvector, we have $\mathbf{A}_1\mathbf{x}_1 = \lambda_1\,\mathbf{x}_1$. Hence

$$\mathbf{A}_2\mathbf{x}_1 = 0 = 0\mathbf{x}_1$$

Comparing this with eq. 2.8, we can see that 0 is an eigenvalue of $\mathbf{A}_2$, and the corresponding eigenvector is $\mathbf{x}_1$.

Postmultiplying eq. (*a*) by $\mathbf{x}_i$; $i \neq 1$, gives

$$\mathbf{A}_2\mathbf{x}_i = \mathbf{A}_1\mathbf{x}_i - \lambda_1\mathbf{x}_1\mathbf{x}_1^T\mathbf{x}_i\,; \ \ i \neq 1$$

If $\mathbf{A}_1 (\equiv \mathbf{A})$ is symmetric, its eigenvectors are orthogonal, *i.e.*, $\mathbf{x}_i^T\mathbf{x}_j = 0$ if $i \neq j$ (see Sec. 2.1). Thus,

$$\mathbf{A}_2\mathbf{x}_i = \mathbf{A}_1\mathbf{x}_i = \lambda_i\mathbf{x}_i\,; \ \ i \neq 1 \qquad\qquad \ldots(b)$$

where the second equality follows from the fact that λ_i is an eigenvalue of $\mathbf{A}_1$, with $\mathbf{x}_i$ as the associated eigenvector. Comparing eq. (*b*) with eq. 2.8 we observe that λ_i is also an eigenvalue of $\mathbf{A}_2$, and $\mathbf{x}_i$ is the associated eigenvector. Thus, $\mathbf{A}_2$ has the properties noted above. ∎

The eigenvalue of $\mathbf{A}_2$ with the largest magnitude is λ_2. The power method can now be used on $\mathbf{A}_2$ to compute λ_2 and $\mathbf{x}_2$. This procedure can be repeated. It can easily be shown that if

$$\mathbf{A}_{i+1} \equiv \mathbf{A}_i - \lambda_i\mathbf{x}_i\mathbf{x}_i^T\,; \ \ i = 1, 2, \ldots, N-1 \qquad\qquad \ldots(2.23)$$

then $\mathbf{A}_{i+1}$ has eigenvalues 0, 0, ..., 0, λ_{i+1}, λ_{i+2}, ..., λ_N and corresponding eigenvectors $\mathbf{x}_1$, $\mathbf{x}_2$, ..., $\mathbf{x}_i$, $\mathbf{x}_{i+1}$, $\mathbf{x}_{i+2}$, ..., $\mathbf{x}_N$, where the λ_j are the eigenvalues of $\mathbf{A}_1$ (or $\mathbf{A}$), and the $\mathbf{x}_j$ are the normalized eigenvectors of $\mathbf{A}_1$. The power technique alongwith the deflation method, can thus be used, in principle, to obtain *all* the eigenvalues and eigenvectors of a symmetric matrix $\mathbf{A}$.

Example 2.8: For the symmetric matrix

$$\mathbf{A} = \begin{bmatrix} 2 & 4 \\ 4 & 7 \end{bmatrix}$$

the eigenvalue with the largest magnitude is $+9.217$, and the corresponding normalized eigenvector is $[0.4847\ \ 0.8747]^T$. Carry out Hotelling's deflation to obtain $\mathbf{A}_2$. Obtain the two eigenvalues of $\mathbf{A}_2$ by solving its characteristic equation, $|\,\mathbf{A}_2 - \lambda\mathbf{I}\,| = 0$

$$\mathbf{A}_2 = \mathbf{A}_1 - \lambda_1\mathbf{x}_1\mathbf{x}_1^T$$

$$\mathbf{A}_2 = \begin{bmatrix} 2 & 4 \\ 4 & 7 \end{bmatrix} - 9.217\begin{bmatrix} 0.4847 \\ 0.8747 \end{bmatrix}\begin{bmatrix} 0.4847 & 0.8747 \end{bmatrix}$$

$$= \begin{bmatrix} 2 & 4 \\ 4 & 7 \end{bmatrix} - 9.217\begin{bmatrix} 0.2349 & 0.4240 \\ 0.4240 & 0.7651 \end{bmatrix}$$

$$= \begin{bmatrix} 2 & 4 \\ 4 & 7 \end{bmatrix} - \begin{bmatrix} 2.1651 & 3.9080 \\ 3.9080 & 7.0519 \end{bmatrix}$$

or
$$\mathbf{A}_2 = \begin{bmatrix} -0.1651 & 0.0920 \\ 0.0920 & -0.0519 \end{bmatrix}$$

To obtain the eigenvalues of $\mathbf{A}_2$:

$$\begin{vmatrix} -0.1651 - \lambda & 0.0920 \\ 0.0920 & -0.0519 - \lambda \end{vmatrix} = 0$$

or
$$(0.1651 + \lambda)(0.0519 + \lambda) - 0.0920^2 = 0$$

or
$$\lambda^2 + 0.217\lambda + 0.008587 - 0.008464 = 0$$

or
$$\lambda^2 + 0.217\lambda + 0.000123 = 0$$

Therefore
$$\lambda = \frac{-0.217 \pm \sqrt{0.047089 - 0.000492}}{2}$$

$$= 0.000568; \ -0.2164$$

Therefore
$$|\lambda_2| = 0.2164$$

which matches with the value of $\lambda_2 = -0.217$ obtained by solving $| \mathbf{A} - \lambda \mathbf{I} | = 0$. ■

This technique can be used to compute all the eigenvalues and eigenvectors of matrices for N below about 10. Also, the iterative power method with deflation can be used for higher values of N, but only when the first few eigenvalues and eigenvectors are required. It turns out that the accuracy of the eigenvalues decreases as one sweeps them in descending order. More powerful techniques are then necessary. One such technique is described next.

2.4 HOUSEHOLDER'S AND GIVENS' METHOD

This is a very popular technique for computing *all* the eigenvalues of a *symmetric* matrix $\mathbf{A}$. The Householder method consists of a set of $(N - 2)$ similarity transformations[*] carried out on the $N \times N$ matrix $\mathbf{A}$, such that a tridiagonal matrix is finally obtained. The eigenvalues of this tridiagonal matrix are the same as those of $\mathbf{A}$. Givens' algorithm then computes the eigenvalues of the tridiagonal matrix.

A Householder transformation on the matrix $\mathbf{A}$ is first illustrated through an example. One can write

$$\mathbf{A}' \equiv \mathbf{B}^{-1} \mathbf{A} \mathbf{B} \qquad \qquad ...(2.24)$$

The transformation matrix $\mathbf{B}$ is defined by

$$\mathbf{B} \equiv \mathbf{I} - 2\mathbf{w}\mathbf{w}^T \qquad \qquad ...(2.25)$$

where $\mathbf{w}$ is an $N \times 1$ normalized matrix containing one zero followed by $N - 1$ elements w_i; $i = 2, 3,...,N$:

$$\mathbf{w} = \begin{bmatrix} 0 & w_2 & w_3 & w_4 & ... & w_N \end{bmatrix}^T \qquad \qquad ...(2.26)$$

The nonzero elements of $\mathbf{w}$ are chosen such that the first row of $\mathbf{A}$ is transformed into a tridiagonal form when eq. 2.24 is used.

---

[*] *Similarity Transformations:* A similarity transformation on an $N \times N$ matrix $\mathbf{A}$ is defined by
$$S = \mathbf{B}^{-1} \mathbf{A} \mathbf{B}$$
where $\mathbf{B}$ is a nonsingular $N \times N$ matrix. It can easily be shown (see Prob. 2.12) that the eigenvalues of $\mathbf{S}$ are the same as those of $\mathbf{A}$. Also, if $\mathbf{x}_i$ is an eigenvector of $\mathbf{A}$ corresponding to the eigenvalue λ_i, then $\mathbf{B}^{-1} \mathbf{x}_i$ is the corresponding eigenvector of $\mathbf{S}$.

Example 2.9: Show that the matrix **B** in eq. 2.25 is symmetric and orthogonal (orthogonality requires $\mathbf{B}^{-1} = \mathbf{B}^T$), and so $\mathbf{B}^{-1} = \mathbf{B}$.

$$\mathbf{B} = \mathbf{I} - 2\mathbf{w}\mathbf{w}^T$$

$$\mathbf{B}^T = \left(\mathbf{I} - 2\mathbf{w}\mathbf{w}^T\right)^T = \mathbf{I}^T - \left(2\mathbf{w}\mathbf{w}^T\right)^T$$

$$= \mathbf{I} - 2\left[\left(\mathbf{w}^T\right)^T \mathbf{w}^T\right] = \mathbf{I} - 2\mathbf{w}\mathbf{w}^T = \mathbf{B}$$

Since $\mathbf{B}^T = \mathbf{B}$, **B** is symmetric.

Now,

$$\mathbf{B}^T\mathbf{B} = \left[\mathbf{I} - 2\mathbf{w}\mathbf{w}^T\right]\left[\mathbf{I} - 2\mathbf{w}\mathbf{w}^T\right]$$

$$= \mathbf{I}\mathbf{I} - 2\mathbf{w}\mathbf{w}^T\mathbf{I} - 2\mathbf{w}\mathbf{w}^T\mathbf{I} + 4\mathbf{w}\left(\mathbf{w}^T\mathbf{w}\right)\mathbf{w}^T$$

$$= \mathbf{I} - 4\mathbf{w}\mathbf{w}^T + 4\mathbf{w}\mathbf{w}^T = \mathbf{I}$$

since $\mathbf{w}^T\mathbf{w} = \sum_{i=1}^{N} w_i^2 = 1$ (normalized).

Since $\mathbf{B}^T\mathbf{B} = \mathbf{I}$, $\mathbf{B}^T = \mathbf{B}^{-1}$ which is the condition for orthogonality of **B** eq. 2.24, thus, reduces to $\mathbf{A}' = \mathbf{B}\,\mathbf{A}\,\mathbf{B}$. ∎

Let us now illustrate how to choose **w** for a 4 × 4 matrix **A**:

$$\mathbf{A} = \begin{bmatrix} a_{11} & a_{12} & a_{13} & a_{14} \\ a_{21} & a_{22} & a_{23} & a_{24} \\ a_{31} & a_{32} & a_{33} & a_{34} \\ a_{41} & a_{42} & a_{43} & a_{44} \end{bmatrix} \qquad \text{...(2.27)}$$

eq. 2.24 alongwith the fact that $\mathbf{B}^{-1} = \mathbf{B}$, leads to

$$\mathbf{A}' = \mathbf{B}\,\mathbf{A}\,\mathbf{B} \qquad \text{...(2.28)}$$

with

$$\mathbf{B} = \mathbf{I} - 2\mathbf{w}\mathbf{w}^T = \begin{bmatrix} 1 & 0 & 0 & 0 \\ 0 & 1 & 0 & 0 \\ 0 & 0 & 1 & 0 \\ 0 & 0 & 0 & 1 \end{bmatrix} - 2\begin{bmatrix} 0 \\ w_2 \\ w_3 \\ w_4 \end{bmatrix}\begin{bmatrix} 0 & w_2 & w_3 & w_4 \end{bmatrix}$$

$$= \begin{bmatrix} 1 & 0 & 0 & 0 \\ 0 & 1 & 0 & 0 \\ 0 & 0 & 1 & 0 \\ 0 & 0 & 0 & 1 \end{bmatrix} - 2\begin{bmatrix} 0 & 0 & 0 & 0 \\ 0 & w_2^2 & w_2 w_3 & w_2 w_4 \\ 0 & w_3 w_2 & w_3^2 & w_3 w_4 \\ 0 & w_4 w_2 & w_4 w_3 & w_4^2 \end{bmatrix}$$

$$= \begin{bmatrix} 1 & 0 & 0 & 0 \\ 0 & 1-2w_2^2 & -2w_2w_3 & -2w_2w_4 \\ 0 & -2w_3w_2 & 1-2w_3^2 & -2w_3w_4 \\ 0 & -2w_4w_2 & -2w_4w_3 & 1-2w_4^2 \end{bmatrix} \qquad \ldots(2.29)$$

AB is easily written as

$$\mathbf{AB} = \begin{bmatrix} a_{11} & a_{12}\left(1-2w_2^2\right)-2a_{13}w_2w_3 & -2a_{12}w_2w_3+a_{13}\left(1-2w_3^2\right) & -2a_{12}w_2w_4-2a_{13}w_3w_4 \\ & -2a_{14}w_4w_2 & -2a_{14}w_3w_4 & +a_{14}\left(1-2w_4^2\right) \\ a_{21} & a_{22}\left(1-2w_2^2\right)-2a_{23}w_2w_3 & -2a_{22}w_2w_3+a_{23}\left(1-2w_3^2\right) & -2a_{22}w_2w_4-2a_{23}w_3w_4 \\ & -2a_{24}w_4w_2 & -2a_{24}w_3w_4 & +a_{24}\left(1-2w_4^2\right) \\ a_{31} & a_{32}\left(1-2w_2^2\right)-2a_{33}w_2w_3 & -2a_{32}w_2w_3+a_{33}\left(1-2w_3^2\right) & -2a_{32}w_2w_4-2a_{33}w_3w_4 \\ & -2a_{34}w_4w_2 & -2a_{34}w_3w_4 & +a_{34}\left(1-2w_4^2\right) \\ a_{41} & a_{42}\left(1-2w_2^2\right)-2a_{43}w_2w_3 & -2a_{42}w_2w_3+a_{43}\left(1-2w_3^2\right) & -2a_{42}w_2w_4-2a_{43}w_3w_4 \\ & -2a_{44}w_4w_2 & -2a_{44}w_3w_4 & +a_{44}\left(1-2w_4^2\right) \end{bmatrix}$$

$$\ldots(2.30)$$

If we define

$$p_i \equiv a_{i2}w_2 + a_{i3}w_3 + a_{i4}w_4 ; \qquad i=1, 2, 3, 4 \qquad \ldots(2.31)$$

we can write **AB** more concisely as

$$\mathbf{AB} = \begin{bmatrix} a_{11} & a_{12}-2p_1w_2 & a_{13}-2p_1w_3 & a_{14}-2p_1w_4 \\ a_{21} & a_{22}-2p_2w_2 & a_{23}-2p_2w_3 & a_{24}-2p_2w_4 \\ a_{31} & a_{32}-2p_3w_2 & a_{33}-2p_3w_3 & a_{34}-2p_3w_4 \\ a_{41} & a_{42}-2p_4w_2 & a_{43}-2p_4w_3 & a_{44}-2p_4w_4 \end{bmatrix} \qquad \ldots(2.32)$$

The product **BAB** can now be written, keeping in mind that **A** is symmetric (and so $a_{ij} = a_{ji}$):

$$\mathbf{A}' = \mathbf{BAB} = \begin{bmatrix} a_{11} & a_{12}-2p_1w_2 & a_{13}-2p_1w_3 & a_{14}-2p_1w_4 \\ a_{12}-2p_1w_2 & \cdots & \cdots & \cdots \\ a_{13}-2p_1w_3 & \cdots & \cdots & \cdots \\ a_{14}-2p_1w_4 & \cdots & \cdots & \cdots \end{bmatrix} \qquad \ldots(2.33)$$

which is symmetric, as expected. The remaining terms can be written easily, but are not required for determining **w** since there are only three unknowns, w_2, w_3 and w_4.

In order for **A**′ to have a tridiagonal form in its first row, we must equate a_{13}' and a_{14}' to zero:

$$a_{13} - 2p_1w_3 = 0 \qquad \ldots(2.34)$$

$$a_{14} - 2p_1w_4 = 0 \qquad \ldots(2.35)$$

Let us now use the property [1] that for an orthogonal transformation of a matrix **A** (e.g., **A′** = **BAB**), the sum of squares of the elements in any row of **A′** is the same as in the corresponding row of **A**. Thus

$$a_{11}'^2 + a_{12}'^2 + a_{13}'^2 + a_{14}'^2 = a_{11}^2 + a_{12}^2 + a_{13}^2 + a_{14}^2 \qquad \qquad ...(2.36)$$

or on using eq. 2.33 for the elements of **A′**

$$a_{11}^2 + \left[a_{12} - 2p_1 w_2\right]^2 + 0 + 0 = a_{11}^2 + a_{12}^2 + a_{13}^2 + a_{14}^2 \qquad ...(2.37)$$

or

$$a_{12} - 2p_1 w_2 = \pm\sqrt{a_{12}^2 + a_{13}^2 + a_{14}^2} \equiv \pm S_1 \qquad \qquad ...(2.38)$$

Eqs. 2.34, 2.35 and 2.38 lead to

$$w_2^2 = \frac{1}{2}\left[1 \mp \frac{a_{12}}{S_1}\right]$$

$$w_3 = \mp \frac{a_{13}}{2S_1 w_2}$$

$$w_4 = \mp \frac{a_{14}}{2S_1 w_2} \qquad \qquad ...(2.39)$$

It can easily be checked that the normalization condition, $w_2^2 + w_3^2 + w_4^2 = 1$, is satisfied.

Higher numerical accuracy is obtained if the + sign is used to compute S_1, and w_2 is taken as the largest value given by

$$w_2^2 = \frac{1}{2}\left[1 + \frac{|a_{12}|}{+S_1}\right] \qquad \qquad ...(2.40)$$

with

$$w_3 = \frac{a_{13}\,\mathrm{sgn}\,(a_{12})}{2S_1 w_2}; \quad w_4 = \frac{a_{14}\,\mathrm{sgn}\,(a_{12})}{2S_1 w_2} \qquad ...(2.41)$$

where sgn (*y*) is the sign of *y*. Note that since **A′** is symmetric, a_{31}' and a_{41}' also become zero.

Example 2.10: Carry out the operation of tridiagonalization of the first row on

$$\mathbf{A} = \begin{bmatrix} 2 & 3 & -1 \\ 3 & 1 & 2 \\ -1 & 2 & -1 \end{bmatrix}$$

Note that since $N = 3$, this will transform **A** to the tridiagonal form completely. In fact, we had deliberately chosen a 4 × 4 **A** matrix in the earlier discussion to keep it more general.

$$S_1 = +\sqrt{a_{12}^2 + a_{13}^2} = \sqrt{9+1} = \sqrt{10} = +3.162$$

$$w_2^2 = \frac{1}{2}\left[1 + \frac{3}{3.162}\right] = 0.974 \quad \text{or} \quad w_2 = 0.987$$

$$w_3 = \frac{-1}{2 \times 3.162 \times 0.987} = -0.160$$

and so,

$$\mathbf{w} = \begin{bmatrix} 0 \\ 0.987 \\ -0.160 \end{bmatrix}$$

Note that $\sum_{i=1}^{3} w_i^2 = 0.9998$.

$\therefore$

$$\mathbf{B} = \begin{bmatrix} 1 & 0 & 0 \\ 0 & -0.948 & 0.316 \\ 0 & 0.316 & 0.949 \end{bmatrix}$$

$$\mathbf{A}' = \mathbf{BAB} = \mathbf{B} \begin{bmatrix} 2 & 3 & -1 \\ 3 & 1 & 2 \\ -1 & 2 & -1 \end{bmatrix} \begin{bmatrix} 1 & 0 & 0 \\ 0 & -0.948 & 0.316 \\ 0 & 0.316 & 0.949 \end{bmatrix}$$

$$= \mathbf{B} \begin{bmatrix} 2 & -3.16 & 0 \\ 3 & -0.316 & 2.214 \\ -1 & -2.212 & -0.317 \end{bmatrix}$$

$$= \begin{bmatrix} 1 & 0 & 0 \\ 0 & -0.948 & 0.316 \\ 0 & 0.316 & 0.949 \end{bmatrix} \begin{bmatrix} 2 & -3.16 & 0 \\ 3 & -0.316 & 2.214 \\ -1 & -2.212 & -0.317 \end{bmatrix}$$

$$= \begin{bmatrix} 2 & -3.16 & 0 \\ -3.16 & -0.399 & -2.199 \\ 0 & -2.199 & 0.399 \end{bmatrix}$$

which is, indeed, in the tridiagonal form. ∎

For the 4×4 matrix $\mathbf{A}$ given in eq. 2.27, the choice of w_2, w_3 and w_4 as given in eqs. 2.40 and 2.41 leads to $a_{13}' = a_{31}' = 0$; $a_{14}' = a_{41}' = 0$. A similar set of operations (with different $\mathbf{w}$ and $\mathbf{B}$) can be carried out on $\mathbf{A}'$ so that its (2, 4) and (4, 2) elements are transformed to zero next, by the use of similarity transforms, without affecting the zeros already obtained in the first row and column. The general algorithm is given below:

$$\mathbf{A}^{(1)} \equiv \mathbf{A} \qquad \qquad ...(a)$$

For $k = 1, 2, ..., N - 2$:

$$\mathbf{A}^{(k+1)} = \mathbf{B}^{(k)} \mathbf{A}^{(k)} \mathbf{B}^{(k)} \qquad \qquad ...(b)$$

$$\mathbf{B}^{(k)} = \mathbf{I} - 2\mathbf{w}^{(k)} {\mathbf{w}^{(k)}}^T \qquad \qquad ...(c)$$

$$\mathbf{w}^{(k)} = \begin{array}{c} 1 \\ 2 \\ \cdot \\ \cdot \\ k-1 \\ k \\ k+1 \\ k+2 \\ \cdot \\ \cdot \\ N \end{array} \left[\begin{array}{c} 0 \\ 0 \\ \cdot \\ \cdot \\ 0 \\ 0 \\ w_{k+1}^{(k)} \\ w_{k+2}^{(k)} \\ \cdot \\ \cdot \\ w_N^{(k)} \end{array} \right] \qquad \ldots(d)$$

$$S^{(k)} = +\left\{ \sum_{i=k+1}^{N} \left[a_{ki}^{(k)} \right]^2 \right\}^{1/2} \qquad \ldots(e)$$

$$\left(w_{k+1}^{(k)} \right)^2 = \frac{1}{2}\left[1 + \frac{\left| a_{k,\,k+1}^{(k)} \right|}{+S^{(k)}} \right] \qquad \ldots(f)$$

$$w_i^{(k)} = \frac{a_{k,\,i}^{(k)} \,\mathrm{sgn}\!\left(a_{k,\,k+1}^{(k)} \right)}{2S^{(k)} w_{k+1}^{(k)}}; \quad i = k+2,\, k+3,\, \ldots,\, N \qquad \ldots(g) \qquad \ldots(2.42)$$

where $a_{ij}^{(k)}$ are the elements of $\mathbf{A}^{(k)}$ and $w_i^{(k)}$ are the elements of $\mathbf{w}^{(k)}$

Example 2.11: Carry out Householder's transformations on the matrix

$$\mathbf{A} = \mathbf{A}^{(1)} = \begin{bmatrix} 4 & -2 & 1 & 2 \\ -2 & 3 & 0 & -2 \\ 1 & 0 & 2 & 1 \\ 2 & -2 & 1 & -1 \end{bmatrix}$$

in order to reduce it to a tridiagonal form.

$\underline{k = 1}$ [Note that the superscript (k) on a_{ij} and w_i will be suppressed for convenience]:

$$S^{(1)} = \sqrt{a_{12}^2 + a_{13}^2 + a_{14}^2} = \sqrt{9} = +3$$

$$w_2^2 = \frac{1}{2}\left[1 + \frac{2}{3} \right] = \frac{5}{6}; \text{ thus, } w_2 = 0.9129$$

$$w_3 = \frac{-1}{2 \times 3 \times 0.9129} = -0.1826$$

$$w_4 = \frac{-2}{2 \times 3 \times 0.9129} = -0.3651$$

therefore

$$\mathbf{w} = \begin{bmatrix} 0 \\ 0.9129 \\ -0.1826 \\ -0.3651 \end{bmatrix}$$

and

$$\mathbf{w}\mathbf{w}^T = \begin{bmatrix} 0 \\ 0.9129 \\ -0.1826 \\ -0.3651 \end{bmatrix} \begin{bmatrix} 0 & 0.9129 & -0.1826 & -0.3651 \end{bmatrix}$$

$$= \begin{bmatrix} 0 & 0 & 0 & 0 \\ 0 & 0.8334 & -0.1667 & -0.3333 \\ 0 & -0.1667 & 0.0333 & 0.0667 \\ 0 & -0.3333 & 0.0667 & 0.1333 \end{bmatrix}$$

$$\mathbf{B}^{(1)} = \mathbf{I} - 2\mathbf{w}\mathbf{w}^T = \begin{bmatrix} 1 & 0 & 0 & 0 \\ 0 & -0.6668 & 0.3334 & 0.6666 \\ 0 & 0.3334 & 0.9334 & -0.1333 \\ 0 & 0.6666 & -0.1333 & 0.7334 \end{bmatrix}$$

$$\mathbf{A}^{(1)}\mathbf{B}^{(1)} = \begin{bmatrix} 4 & 3.0002 & 0.0000 & 0.0000 \\ -2 & -3.3336 & 1.2668 & 0.533 \\ 1 & 1.3334 & 1.7335 & 0.4668 \\ 2 & 1.0004 & 0.3999 & -2.1999 \end{bmatrix}$$

and $\quad \mathbf{A}^{(2)} = \mathbf{B}^{(1)}\mathbf{A}^{(1)}\mathbf{B}^{(1)} = \begin{bmatrix} 4 & 3.0002 & 0.0000 & 0.0000 \\ 3.0002 & 3.3343 & -0.0002 & -1.6662 \\ 0.0000 & -0.0002 & 1.9871 & 0.9067 \\ 0.0000 & -1.6662 & 0.9067 & -1.3203 \end{bmatrix}$

$\underline{k = 2}$ [superscript (2) on w_i and a_{ij} is being suppressed again]:

$$S^{(2)} = \left[(-0.0002)^2 + (-1.6662)^2 \right]^{1/2} = 1.6662$$

$$w_3^2 = \frac{1}{2}\left[1 + \frac{0.0002}{1.6662}\right] \text{ therefore } w_3 = 0.7071$$

$$w_4 = \frac{+1.6662}{2 \times 1.6662 \times 0.7071} = 0.7071$$

$$\mathbf{w} = \begin{bmatrix} 0 \\ 0 \\ 0.7071 \\ 0.7071 \end{bmatrix}$$

$$\therefore \quad \mathbf{ww}^T = \begin{bmatrix} 0 \\ 0 \\ 0.7071 \\ 0.7071 \end{bmatrix} \begin{bmatrix} 0 & 0 & 0.7071 & 0.7071 \end{bmatrix} = \begin{bmatrix} 0 & 0 & 0 & 0 \\ 0 & 0 & 0 & 0 \\ 0 & 0 & 0.5 & 0.5 \\ 0 & 0 & 0.5 & 0.5 \end{bmatrix}$$

$$\therefore \quad \mathbf{B}^{(2)} = \begin{bmatrix} 1 & 0 & 0 & 0 \\ 0 & 1 & 0 & 0 \\ 0 & 0 & 0 & -1 \\ 0 & 0 & -1 & 0 \end{bmatrix}$$

$$\mathbf{A}^{(2)}\mathbf{B}^{(2)} = \begin{bmatrix} 4 & 3.0002 & 0 & 0 \\ 3.0002 & 3.3343 & 1.6662 & +0.0002 \\ 0.0000 & -0.0002 & -0.9067 & -1.9871 \\ 0.0000 & -1.6662 & 1.3203 & -0.9067 \end{bmatrix}$$

and so

$$\mathbf{A}^{(3)} = \mathbf{B}^{(2)}\left(\mathbf{A}^{(2)}\mathbf{B}^{(2)}\right) = \begin{bmatrix} 4.0000 & 3.0002 & 0 & 0 \\ 3.0002 & 3.3343 & 1.6662 & +0.0002 \\ 0.0000 & 1.6662 & -1.3203 & 0.9067 \\ 0.0000 & 0.0002 & 0.9067 & 1.9871 \end{bmatrix}$$

which is in tridiagonal form (with 0.0002 present in $a_{24}^{(3)}$ due to round-off errors.) ∎

The NAG library has F01AJF, F01ABF, F01AAF, etc., using the Householder technique to reduce a matrix into a tridiagonal form. The IMSL library [15] has EVLSF, EVCSF, etc. (these include computation of λ, $\mathbf{x}_i$ also), while the EISPACK library [16] has TRED2. LINPACK has the subroutine SQRDC which uses a slightly different Householder transformation [15].

Many efficient techniques are available which can obtain eigenvalues and eigenvectors of tridiagonal matrices. One of these techniques is the Givens method [2, 11]. In this, one starts with the matrix

$$\mathbf{A} = \begin{bmatrix} a_1 & b_1 & 0 & 0 & \cdot & \cdot & & & & 0 \\ c_1 & a_2 & b_2 & 0 & \cdot & \cdot & & & & 0 \\ 0 & c_2 & a_3 & b_3 & \cdot & \cdot & & & & 0 \\ \cdot & \cdot & \cdot & \cdot & \cdot & \cdot & & & & \cdot \\ \cdot & \cdot & \cdot & \cdot & \cdot & \cdot & & & & \cdot \\ & & & & & 0 & c_{N-2} & a_{N-1} & b_{N-1} \\ & & & & & 0 & 0 & c_{N-1} & a_N \end{bmatrix} \qquad \ldots(2.43)$$

Note that the Householder technique will give a symmetric matrix **A**, but a general tridiagonal matrix is being considered here. Such matrices arise naturally in several situations (e.g., in the context of staged separations processes in chemical engineering: distillation, absorption, extraction, etc. [17]).

The eigenvalues can be obtained by solving $|\mathbf{A} - \lambda \mathbf{I}| = 0$, using a simple recursive relationship. In the equation

$$\begin{vmatrix} a_1 - \lambda & b_1 & 0 & 0 & \cdot \\ c_1 & a_2 - \lambda & b_2 & 0 & \cdot \\ 0 & c_2 & a_3 - \lambda & b_3 & \cdot \\ \cdot & \cdot & \cdot & \cdot \\ \cdot & \cdot & \cdot & \cdot \\ & & & & 0 & c_{j-3} & a_{j-2} - \lambda & b_{j-2} & 0 & 0 & \cdot & \cdot \\ & & & & 0 & 0 & c_{j-2} & a_{j-1} - \lambda & b_{j-1} & 0 & \cdot & \cdot \\ & & & & 0 & 0 & 0 & c_{j-1} & a_j - \lambda & b_j & \cdot & \cdot \\ & & & & \cdot & \cdot & \cdot & \cdot & \cdot & \cdot \\ & & & & \cdot & \cdot & \cdot & \cdot & \cdot & \cdot \end{vmatrix} = 0 \qquad \ldots(2.44)$$

we can observe the following sequence (using expansion of the determinants in terms of the last column):

$$P_{-1}(\lambda) \equiv 0$$

$$P_0(\lambda) \equiv 1$$

$$P_1(\lambda) \equiv |a_1 - \lambda| = (a_1 - \lambda) P_0(\lambda) = (a_1 - \lambda) P_0(\lambda) - b_0 c_0 P_{-1}(\lambda)$$

$$P_2(\lambda) \equiv \begin{vmatrix} a_1 - \lambda & b_1 \\ c_1 & a_2 - \lambda \end{vmatrix} = (a_2 - \lambda)|a_1 - \lambda| - b_1|c_1| = (a_2 - \lambda) P_1(\lambda) - b_1 c_1$$

$$= (a_2 - \lambda) P_1(\lambda) - b_1 c_1 P_0(\lambda)$$

$$P_3(\lambda) \equiv \begin{vmatrix} a_1-\lambda & b_1 & 0 \\ c_1 & a_2-\lambda & b_2 \\ 0 & c_2 & a_3-\lambda \end{vmatrix} = (a_3-\lambda)\begin{vmatrix} a_1-\lambda & b_1 \\ c_1 & a_2-\lambda \end{vmatrix} - b_2 \begin{vmatrix} a_1-\lambda & b_1 \\ 0 & c_2 \end{vmatrix}$$

$$= (a_3-\lambda)P_2(\lambda) - b_2 c_2 (a_1-\lambda)$$

$$= (a_3-\lambda)P_2(\lambda) - b_2 c_2 P_1(\lambda)$$

$$P_j(\lambda) \equiv \begin{vmatrix} a_1-\lambda & b_1 & 0 \\ c_1 & a_2-\lambda & b_2 \\ & & \ddots \\ & & & a_{j-1}-\lambda & b_{j-1} \\ & & & c_{j-1} & a_j-\lambda \end{vmatrix}$$

$$= (a_j-\lambda)\begin{vmatrix} a_1-\lambda & b_1 & 0 \\ c_1 & a_2-\lambda & b_2 \\ & & \ddots \\ & 0 & c_{j-2} & a_{j-1}-\lambda \end{vmatrix} - b_{j-1}\begin{vmatrix} a_1-\lambda & b_1 & 0 \\ c_1 & a_2-\lambda & b_2 \\ & & \ddots \\ & & c_{j-3} & a_{j-2}-\lambda & b_{j-2} \\ & 0 & 0 & c_{j-1} \end{vmatrix}$$

$$= (a_j-\lambda)P_{j-1}(\lambda) - b_{j-1}c_{j-1}\begin{vmatrix} a_1-\lambda & b_1 & 0 \\ c_1 & a_2-\lambda & b_2 \\ & & \ddots \\ & & c_{j-3} & a_{j-2}-\lambda \end{vmatrix} \qquad \dots(2.45)$$

by expansion of the last determinant in terms of minors of the last row or column. Thus, in general

$$P_j(\lambda) = (a_j-\lambda)P_{j-1}(\lambda) - b_{j-1}c_{j-1}P_{j-2}(\lambda); \quad j=1, 2, ..., N \qquad \dots(2.46)$$

Note that a few extra terms have been used in the starting equations to suggest a pattern.

It is evident that $P_N(\lambda)$ is the characteristic polynomial of matrix **A**. The sequence $P_0(\lambda)$, $P_1(\lambda)$, ..., $P_N(\lambda)$ forms a *Sturm* chain. One can obtain the approximate location of the roots of $P_N(\lambda)$ by using a simple technique. If $V(\lambda)$ is defined as the number of sign changes observed in going through the sequence $P_0(\lambda)$, $P_1(\lambda)$, ..., $P_N(\lambda)$ for a given value of λ, then the number of zeros of $P_N(\lambda)$, in the region $a \le \lambda \le b$ is $V(a) - V(b)$, provided a and b are not zeros of $P_N(\lambda)$. The bisection method (see Chapter 3) can then be used along with this rule to converge to the roots of $P_N(\lambda)$, as illustrated in example 2.12.

Example 2.12: Use Givens technique on the tridiagonal matrix generated in example 2.11, to obtain the ranges of integers between which the four roots of the characteristic equation lie.

Let us rewrite **A** as

$$A = \begin{bmatrix} 4.000 & 3.000 & 0 & 0 \\ 3.000 & 3.334 & 1.666 & 0 \\ 0 & 1.666 & -1.32 & 0.907 \\ 0 & 0 & 0.907 & 1.987 \end{bmatrix}$$

The strum sequence is

$$P_0(\lambda) = 1$$

$$P_1(\lambda) = 4 - \lambda$$

$$P_2(\lambda) = (3.334 - \lambda)P_1(\lambda) - 9$$

$$P_3(\lambda) = (-1.32 - \lambda)P_2(\lambda) - 1.666^2 P_1(\lambda) = -(1.32 + \lambda)P_2(\lambda) - 2.776P_1(\lambda)$$

$$P_4(\lambda) = (1.987 - \lambda)P_3(\lambda) - 0.907^2 P_2(\lambda) = (1.987 - \lambda)P_3(\lambda) - 0.823P_2(\lambda)$$

The following Table can now be constructed

λ	P_0	P_1	P_2	P_3	P_4	$V(\lambda)$
−3	+1	7	35.338	39.396	170.077	0
−2	+1	6	23.004	−1.0133	−18.945	1
1	+1	3	−1.998	−3.693	−2.0	1
2	+1	2	−6.332	15.47	5.01	2
3	+1	1	−8.667	34.661	−27.98	3
6	+1	−2	−3.668	32.402	−127.01	3
7	+1	−3	1.989	−8.22	39.57	4

Since $V(-2) - V(-3) = 1$, one root lies between $-3 \leq \lambda_1 \leq -2$. Similarly, the other roots of the characteristic equation $P_4(\lambda) = 0$ are bounded as follows:

$$1 \leq \lambda_2 \leq 2, 2 \leq \lambda_3 \leq 3 \quad \text{and} \quad 6 \leq \lambda_4 \leq 7$$

Further, one could now obtain $V(-2.5)$ as 1, and by comparing it with $V(-3)$ and $V(-2)$, it is concluded that $-3 \leq \lambda_1 \leq -2.5$. This procedure can be continued. The range $-3 \leq \lambda_1 \leq -2.5$ can be further bisected and a new tighter bound for λ_1 can be determined. Continued application of this bisection technique will keep reducing the interval in which λ_1 lies, until a desired accuracy of λ_1 is attained. ∎

The NAG library contains a program named F01QBE which uses Givens method for computing the eigenvalues of a tridiagonal matrix. Once the λs are obtained, the corresponding eigenvectors can easily be obtained by solving

$$(A - \lambda I)x = 0 \qquad \qquad \ldots(2.47)$$

or

$$(a_1 - \lambda)x_1 + b_1 x_2 = 0$$

$$c_1 x_1 + (a_2 - \lambda)x_2 + b_2 x_3 = 0$$

.
.
.

$$c_{j-1}x_{j-1} + \left(a_j - \lambda\right)x_j + b_j x_{j+1} = 0$$

.
.
.

$$c_{N-1}x_{N-1} + \left(a_N - \lambda\right)x_N = 0 \qquad \qquad \ldots(2.48)$$

which leads to

$$x_2 = -\frac{1}{b_1}\left(a_1 - \lambda\right)x_1$$

$$x_3 = -\frac{1}{b_2}\left[\left(a_2 - \lambda\right)x_2 + c_1 x_1\right]$$

.
.
.

$$x_{j+1} = -\frac{1}{b_j}\left[\left(a_j - \lambda\right)x_j + c_{j-1}x_{j-1}\right]$$

.
.
.

$$x_N = -\frac{1}{b_{N-1}}\left[\left(a_{N-1} - \lambda\right)x_{N-1} + c_{N-2}x_{N-2}\right] \qquad \ldots(2.49)$$

An arbitrary value of x_1 can be assumed and $x_2, x_3, \ldots, x_N$ can then be computed sequentially using eq. 2.49. Since $\mathbf{x}_i$ is known upto an arbitrary constant, this will be an eigenvector (the first equation:

$$c_{N-1}x_{N-1} + \left(a_N - \lambda\right)x_N = 0 \qquad \qquad \ldots(2.50)$$

will be satisfied for all choices of x_1 since $|\mathbf{A} - \lambda\mathbf{I}| = 0$).

The eigenvectors of the tridiagonal matrix $\mathbf{A}$ can be easily related to those of the symmetric matrix which led to it using Householder's algorithm.

Another method which gives the eigenvalues of a tridiagonal matrix $\mathbf{A}$ is the QL technique. In this, the matrix $\mathbf{A}^{(1)}$ ($\equiv \mathbf{A}$) is factored as

$$\mathbf{A}^{(1)} = \mathbf{Q}^{(1)}\mathbf{L}^{(1)} \qquad \qquad \ldots(2.51)$$

where $\mathbf{Q}^{(1)}$ is an orthogonal matrix and $\mathbf{L}^{(1)}$ is a lower triangular matrix. The matrix $\mathbf{A}^{(2)}$ is then defined as

$$\mathbf{A}^{(2)} = \mathbf{L}^{(1)}\mathbf{Q}^{(1)} \qquad \qquad \ldots(2.52)$$

and is further factored. The algorithm is thus given by

$$\mathbf{A}^{(i)} = \mathbf{Q}^{(i)}\mathbf{L}^{(i)} \qquad \qquad \ldots(2.53)$$

$$\mathbf{A}^{(i+1)} = \mathbf{L}^{(i)}\mathbf{Q}^{(i)}; \quad i = 1, 2, \ldots$$

where $\mathbf{Q}^{(i)}$ are orthogonal and $\mathbf{L}^{(i)}$ are lower triangular matrices. The eigenvalues of $\mathbf{A}$ remain unchanged by these transformations [14], and as i increases, $\mathbf{A}^{(i+1)}$ tends to a diagonal matrix with the eigenvalues placed on the diagonal. The matrices $\mathbf{L}^{(i)}$ and $\mathbf{Q}^{(i)}$ are themselves obtained as products of some simpler matrices (see p. 476 in Ref. 14, for details).

The Householder-QL method is a relatively stable numerical method, and so it is quite popular for computing the eigenvalues of even large matrices (N upto several hundred). The NAG library has F02AMF which uses this technique, while the IMSL library has EVLSF, EVCSF, etc., which use the QL method. The latter are adaptations of the IMTQL1 routine in EISPACK. [16]

Example 2.13: Use an IMSL or NAG routine to obtain the eigenvalues and eigenvectors of the $N \times N$ matrix [17]:

$$\mathbf{A} = \begin{bmatrix} -2 & 1 & 0 & 0 & \cdot & \cdot & 0 & 0 & 0 \\ 1 & -2 & 1 & 0 & \cdot & \cdot & 0 & 0 & 0 \\ 0 & 1 & -2 & 1 & \cdot & \cdot & 0 & 0 & 0 \\ \cdot & \cdot & \cdot & \cdot & \cdot & \cdot & \cdot & \cdot & \cdot \\ \cdot & \cdot & \cdot & \cdot & \cdot & \cdot & \cdot & \cdot & \cdot \\ 0 & 0 & 0 & 0 & \cdot & \cdot & 0 & 1 & -2 \end{bmatrix}$$

using the QL technique ($N = 5$).

The NAG routine F02ABF is used to give the eigenvalues and eigenvectors (correct to 3 decimal figures) as

i	λ_i	$\mathbf{x}_i^T$				
5	−3.732	[−0.289	0.500	−0.577	0.500	−0.289]
4	−3.000	[−0.500	0.500	0.000	−0.500	0.500]
3	−2.000	[−0.577	0.124×10^{-7}	0.577	-0.898×10^{-8}	−0.577]
2	−1.000	[0.500	0.500	-0.149×10^{-7}	−0.500	−0.500]
1	−0.268	[0.289	0.500	0.577	0.500	0.289]

The values of λ_i are quite close to the analytical value of
$$-4 \sin^2\left[\pi i/(2N + 2)\right]; \quad i = 1, 2, \ldots, N. \qquad \blacksquare$$

PROBLEMS

2.1 Obtain the characteristic polynomial for the matrix of example 1.4. Also obtain $P_N(\lambda)$ using the Faddeev-Leverrier technique and see if the same results are obtained. A solution for the λs will be obtained for $P_N(\lambda) = 0$ in Chp. 3 (prob. 3.1).

2.2 Obtain the eigenvalues and eigenvectors of

$$\mathbf{A} = \begin{bmatrix} 5 & 4 \\ 1 & 2 \end{bmatrix}$$

using expansion by minors. Use $x_2 = 1$ as an additional condition. Check the characteristic polynomial using the Faddeev-Leverrier method. Check if the eigenvectors are orthogonal.

2.3 Obtain the eigenvalues and eigenvectors for the symmetric matrix

$$\begin{bmatrix} 3 & 1 \\ 1 & 3/2 \end{bmatrix}$$

Use $x_2 = 1$ as an additional condition. Check if the eigenvalues are real for this case, and if the eignvectors are orthogonal.

2.4 Consider the $N \times N$ tridiagonal matrix

$$\begin{bmatrix} -2 & 1 & 0 & 0 & \cdot & \cdot & 0 & 0 & 0 \\ 1 & -2 & 1 & 0 & \cdot & \cdot & 0 & 0 & 0 \\ 0 & 1 & -2 & 1 & \cdot & \cdot & 0 & 0 & 0 \\ \cdot & & \cdot & \cdot & & & & & \\ \cdot & & \cdot & \cdot & & & & & \\ 0 & 0 & 0 & 0 & \cdot & \cdot & 0 & 1 & -2 \end{bmatrix}$$

Obtain the characteristic polynomial for this case for $N = 3$, using the Faddeev-Leverrier technique. Check if the following analytically obtained expression satisfies this polynomial

$$\lambda_i = -4\sin^2\left[\frac{\pi i}{2(N+1)}\right]; \quad i = 1, 2, ..., N$$

2.5 An alternate algorithm for obtaining the eigenvalues and eigenvectors of a matrix (Faddeev's [5, 6] method) is to define a series of matrices as follows:

$$\mathbf{B}_1 = \mathbf{A} \qquad ; \qquad \alpha_1 = \text{tr } \mathbf{B}_1$$

$$\mathbf{B}_2 = \mathbf{A}(\mathbf{B}_1 - \alpha_1 \mathbf{I}) \qquad ; \qquad -\alpha_2 = \frac{1}{2}\text{tr}\mathbf{B}_2$$

$$\mathbf{B}_3 = \mathbf{A}(\mathbf{B}_2 + \alpha_2 \mathbf{I}) \qquad ; \qquad \alpha_3 = \frac{1}{3}\text{tr } \mathbf{B}_3$$

$$\cdot$$
$$\cdot$$

$$\mathbf{B}_{N-1} = \mathbf{A}\left[\mathbf{B}_{N-2} + (-1)^{N-2}\alpha_{N-2}\mathbf{I}\right] \qquad ; \qquad (-1)^N \alpha_{N-1} = \left(\frac{1}{N-1}\right)\text{tr } \mathbf{B}_{N-1}$$

$$\mathbf{B}_N = \mathbf{A}\left[\mathbf{B}_{N-1} + (-1)^{N-1}\alpha_{N-1}\mathbf{I}\right] \qquad ; \qquad (-1)^{N+1} \alpha_N = \left(\frac{1}{N}\right)\text{tr } \mathbf{B}_N$$

Using the fact that tr $(\mathbf{P} + \mathbf{Q}) = \text{tr } \mathbf{P} + \text{tr } \mathbf{Q}$, show that this is the same as the algorithm discussed in Sec. 2.2 (try upto α_3). The inverse $\mathbf{A}^{-1}$, is obtained as [4, 7]:

$$\mathbf{A}^{-1} = \frac{(-1)^{N+1}}{\alpha_N}\left[\mathbf{B}_{N-1} + (-1)^{N-1}\alpha_{N-1}\mathbf{I}\right]$$

Use this algorithm to obtain the eigenvalues of the 2×2 **A** matrix given in prob. 2.2. Also obtain $\mathbf{A}^{-1}$ using the above formula and check if $\mathbf{A}\mathbf{A}^{-1} = \mathbf{I}$. In fact, if one defines a series of matrices

$\mathbf{C}_j = \mathbf{B}_j + (-1)^j \alpha_j \mathbf{I}$; $j = 1, 2, ..., N - 1$, and defines a matrix polynomial $\mathbf{C}(\lambda) \equiv \lambda^{N-1}\mathbf{I} - \mathbf{C}_1\lambda^{N-2} + \mathbf{C}_2\lambda^{N-3} - ... + (-1)^{N-1}\mathbf{C}_{N-1}$, then the eigenvector corresponding to an eigenvalue λ_i of $\mathbf{A}$ is given by [7] any non-zero column of $\mathbf{C}(\lambda_i)$.

2.6 Estimate the number of multiplications and divisions required to get all the coefficients in the characteristic polynomial using the Faddeev-Leverrier technique.

2.7 Use the power method to obtain $|\lambda_1|$ and $\mathbf{w}_1$ for

$$\mathbf{A} = \begin{bmatrix} 5 & 4 \\ 1 & 2 \end{bmatrix}$$

Show three iterations starting with $\mathbf{v}^{(1)} = [1\ 0]^T$.

2.8 Show that the power method converges to λ_2, $\mathbf{u}_2$ if the initial choice $\mathbf{v}^{(1)}$ is somehow selected to be orthogonal to $\mathbf{u}_1$. Assume $\mathbf{A}$ to be a real symmetric matrix (for which the $\mathbf{u}_i$ form an orthogonal set) [8]. **Hint:** note that $\mathbf{u}_1^T\mathbf{v}^{(1)} = 0$ leads to $C_1 = 0$.

2.9 Make a general computer program using the power technique with Hotelling's deflation method (as also testing to obtain the correct signs for the λs). Test your program on the tridiagonal matrix $\mathbf{A}(N = 3)$ given in prob. 2.4. Note that the method gives fluctuating signs for the eigenvectors.

2.10 Iterative method for obtaining $\mathbf{A}^{-1}$: If one has an approximate inverse $\mathbf{B}$ of a matrix $\mathbf{A}$, one can write the error $\mathbf{E}$ as

$$\mathbf{E} = \mathbf{AB} - \mathbf{I}$$

Show that this leads to $\mathbf{A}^{-1} = \mathbf{B}(\mathbf{I} + \mathbf{E})^{-1} \cong \mathbf{B}(\mathbf{I} - \mathbf{E} +...)$. Thus show that $\mathbf{A}^{-1} \cong \mathbf{B}(2\mathbf{I} - \mathbf{AB})$. This can be used to generate better iterates for $\mathbf{A}^{-1}$ using $\mathbf{B}^{(k)} = \mathbf{B}^{(k-1)}(2\mathbf{I} - \mathbf{AB}^{(k-1)})$.

2.11 Choleskey's method for obtaining $\mathbf{A}^{-1}$: Reconsider prob. 1.10 where $\mathbf{L} = \mathbf{U}^T$ and so $\mathbf{U}^T\mathbf{U} = \mathbf{A}$. Show that $\mathbf{A}^{-1} = \mathbf{U}^{-1}(\mathbf{U}^T)^{-1}$. Obtain $\mathbf{U}^{-1}$ for the matrix $\mathbf{U}$ of prob. 1.10, using the definition that $u_{ij}^{-1} = adj\ \mathbf{U}/|\mathbf{U}|$ (the transpose of the matrix of cofactors of elements of $\mathbf{U}$ is called the adjoint of $\mathbf{U}$). See how much simpler it is to compute the inverse of an upper triangular matrix by writing $\mathbf{U}^{-1}$ for a 3 × 3 matrix in terms of the elements u_{ij}. Also note that $(\mathbf{U}^T)^{-1} = (\mathbf{U}^{-1})^T$. Hence, obtain $\mathbf{A}^{-1}$ for the matrix in prob. 1.10.

2.12 Using $\mathbf{Ax}_i = \lambda_i\mathbf{x}_i$ alongwith $\mathbf{S} \equiv \mathbf{B}^{-1}\mathbf{AB}$ (similarity transform), show that $\mathbf{S}\mathbf{y}_i = \lambda_i\mathbf{y}_i$ where $\mathbf{y}_i = \mathbf{B}^{-1}\mathbf{x}_i$. Hence, show that the eigenvectors of $\mathbf{A}$ and $\mathbf{S}$ are identical, and find the relationship between the eigenvectors of these two matrices.

2.13 Using Householder's transformations obtain the tridiagonal form of

$$\mathbf{A} = \begin{bmatrix} 1 & 2 & -1 \\ 2 & 1 & 2 \\ -1 & 2 & 1 \end{bmatrix}$$

Also use a computer program using Householder's technique and QL method from a computer library to obtain the eigenvalues (and eigenvectors) of this matrix.

2.14 Using the tridiagonal matrix obtained in prob. 2.13, use Givens technique to obtain the range of consecutive integers between which the three eigenvalues lie. Try $-3 < \lambda < 4$.

2.15 Consider the matrix of prob. 2.3

$$\mathbf{A} = \begin{bmatrix} 3 & 1 \\ 1 & 3/2 \end{bmatrix}$$

Use Givens method to locate the roots. Check against the exact results of prob. 2.3.

REFERENCES

1. F.B. Hildebrand, *Methods of Applied Mathematics,* 2nd ed., Prentice Hall, Englewood Cliffs, N.J., 1965.
2. N.R. Amundson, *Mathematical Methods in Chemical Engineering: Matrices and their Applications,* Prentice Hall, Englewood Cliffs, N.J., 1966.
3. R. Bellman, *Introduction to Matrix Analysis,* 2nd ed., McGraw Hill, New York, 1960.
4. M.L. James, G.M. Smith and J.C. Wolford, *Applied Numerical Methods for Digital Computation,* 3rd ed., Harper and Row, New York, 1985.
5. D.K. Faddeev and V.N. Faddeeva, *Computational Methods of Linear Algebra* (trans. R.C. Williams), W.H. Freeman & Co., San Francisco, 1963.
6. B. Carnahan, H.A. Luther and J.O. Wilkes, *Applied Numerical Methods,* Wiley, New York, 1969.
7. F.R. Gantmacher, *The Theory of Matrices,* Chelsea, New York, 1960.
8. L. Lapidus, *Digital Computation for Chemical Engineers,* McGraw Hill, New York, 1962.
9. B.A. Finlayson, *Nonlinear Analysis in Chemical Engineering,* McGraw Hill, New York, 1980.
10. H. Hotelling, *Ann. Math. Stat.,* **14,** 1(1943).
11. W. Givens, *Nat. Bur. Standards Appl. Math.,* **29,** 117(1953).
12. A.S. Householder, *The Theory of Matrices in Numerical Analysis,* Blaisdell, New York, 1964.
    [a detailed exposition of techniques, an excellent bibliography with historical notes].
13. J. Ortega in *Mathematical Methods for Digital Computers,* Vol. **II,** eds., A. Ralston and H.S. Wilf, Wiley, New York, 1967, p. 94.
14. R.L. Burden and J.D. Faires, *Numerical Analysis,* 3rd ed., Prindle, Weber and Schmidt, Boston, 1985.
15. *Users manual, IMSL Math/Library,* Intl. Math. Stat. Lib., Houston, 1989.
16. B.T. Smith, J.M. Boyle, B.S. Garbow, Y. Ikebe, V.C. Klema and C.B. Moler, *Matrix Eigensystems Routines—EISPACK Guide,* 2nd ed., Springer, New York, 1974.
17. E.J. Henley and J.D. Seader, *Equilibrium Stage Separation Operations in Chemical Engineering,* Wiley, New York, 1981.

Chapter 3

Nonlinear Algebraic Equations

3.1 INTRODUCTION

Many operations in engineering are described by a set of N coupled, nonlinear algebraic equations in N variables, $x_1, x_2, x_3, ..., x_N$:

$$F_1\left(x_1, x_2, ..., x_N\right) \equiv F_1(\mathbf{x}) = 0$$

$$F_2\left(x_1, x_2, ..., x_N\right) \equiv F_2(\mathbf{x}) = 0$$

$$\cdot$$
$$\cdot$$
$$\cdot$$

$$F_N\left(x_1, x_2, ..., x_N\right) \equiv F_N(\mathbf{x}) = 0 \qquad \qquad ...(3.1)$$

eq. 3.1 can be written alternatively as

$$\mathbf{F}(\mathbf{x}) \equiv \begin{bmatrix} F_1(\mathbf{x}) \\ F_2(\mathbf{x}) \\ \cdot \\ \cdot \\ F_N(\mathbf{x}) \end{bmatrix} = \mathbf{0} = \begin{bmatrix} 0 \\ 0 \\ \cdot \\ \cdot \\ 0 \end{bmatrix} \qquad \qquad ...(3.2)$$

Note that equations of this type can possess multiple solutions, *i.e.*, more than one set of $\mathbf{x}$ may satisfy the equation. An example of eq. 3.2 is the Nth degree (nonlinear) characteristic equation (eq. 2.7) in a single variable (*i.e.*, $N = 1$), λ, encountered in the study of systems described by N ordinary differential equations. Other cases where such algebraic equations are encountered in chemical engineering include dew and bubble-point calculations, flash and distillation column computations, estimation of power requirements of compressors using any of the popular equations of state, (multiple) steady states in continuous flow stirred-tank reactors (CSTRs), etc. Some of these examples are described in problems at the end of this chapter. In fact, steady state simulation of chemical plants may require solutions of sets of several thousand coupled nonlinear algebraic equations in as many variables. Sets of nonlinear algebraic equations are also obtained during the solution of ordinary differential equations (boundary as well as initial value types) upon using techniques such as finite-differences, orthogonal collocation, implicit Adams-Moulton, etc. [1] (see Chapters 5 and 6). A good understanding of the methods of solving algebraic equations is, thus, important. Some popular methods are discussed in this chapter, *e.g.*, method of successive substitutions, the Newton-Raphson technique, binary chop, etc. The first of these is simple, both conceptually and numerically. The Newton-Raphson technique usually converges faster, but requires derivatives which can either be obtained analytically or computed numerically, requiring more computational effort. The other techniques are slower, but can be fruitfully combined with the Newton-Raphson technique. The various methods are first developed for a single nonlinear algebraic equation in one variable (*i.e.*, $N = 1$). The techniques are then extended to the more general, multivariable problem. Some additional techniques are described in the problems at the end of the chapter.

It will be observed that several popular methods used to obtain the roots of nonlinear algebraic equations require a starting *estimate* for the roots. An **incremental search** technique can be used to obtain these estimates. For the single variable case, $F(x) = 0$, the function $F(x)$ is evaluated *sequentially* at several points, $x^{(1)}$, $x^{(2)}$, ..., which are located Δx apart, with $x^{(k)} > x^{(k-1)}$; $k = 2, 3, ...$. At any stage, k, the product $F[x^{(k)}]F[x^{(k-1)}]$ is evaluated and the mean value theorem for continuous functions [2] is used. This states that if the product is negative, one must have at least one root of $F(x) = 0$ in the range $x^{(k-1)} \le x \le x^{(k)}$. Either of these two values of x can be used as a starting point for the other numerical techniques to obtain more precise estimates of the root. Multivariable extensions of the search techniques are conceptually similar, but their numerical implementation may be more difficult to achieve.

3.2 SINGLE VARIABLE SUCCESSIVE SUBSTITUTIONS (Fixed-Point Method)

For a single variable problem, the equation to be solved is

$$F(x) = 0 \qquad \qquad ...(3.3)$$

where $F(x)$ is a nonlinear function of the variable, x. An example is

$$F(x) = x - \frac{1}{3}e^x = 0 \qquad \qquad ...(3.4)$$

which has two roots (see fig. 3.1), $x = 0.61906$ (R_1) and $x = 1.512135$ (R_2).

In the method of successive substitutions, we first write $F(x) = 0$ in the following form

$$x = f(x) \qquad \qquad ...(3.5)$$

The recasting of eq. 3.3 into eq. 3.5 can be done in many ways, and there is no uniqueness in this step. Some choices of $f(x)$ are better than others, as will be seen in Example 3.1 discussed later. For example, eq. 3.4 can be easily rewritten as

$$x = \frac{1}{3}e^x \equiv f(x) \qquad \qquad ...(3.6)$$

or, as

$$x = 2x - \frac{1}{3}e^x = f(x) \qquad \qquad ...(a)$$

$$x = \frac{3}{2}x - \frac{1}{6}e^x = f(x) \qquad \qquad ...(b)$$

$$x = \left(1 + \frac{1}{j}\right)x - \left(\frac{1}{3j}\right)e^x = f(x); \quad j = 3, 4, ... \qquad ...(c) \qquad ...(3.7)$$

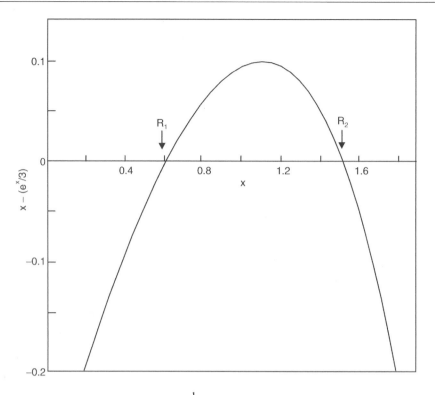

Fig. 3.1 Plot of $F(x) = x - \dfrac{1}{3}e^x$ to show the two roots of $F(x) = 0$

etc. Even though the choices of $f(x)$ are different, all these equations reduce to eq. 3.4 on simplification, and are indistinguishable *analytically*.

In the method of successive substitutions (also referred to as Picard iteration) one assumes a starting (or first iterate) value, $x^{(1)}$, for the variable, x, and uses this in $f(x)$ on the right hand side of eq. 3.6, to get a new (and hopefully, improved) estimate, $x^{(2)}$. Thus,

$$x^{(2)} = f\left[x^{(1)}\right] \qquad \qquad \ldots(3.8)$$

$x^{(2)}$ is now used as the argument of $f(x)$ in eq. 3.6 to yield the next estimate, $x^{(3)}$. The procedure is continued and we have the algorithm as

$$x^{(k+1)} = f\left[x^{(k)}\right]; \; k = 1, 2, \ldots \qquad \qquad \ldots(3.9)$$

The different choices of $f(x)$ in eq. 3.7 obviously give different values for $x^{(k+1)}$ starting from the same $x^{(1)}$, and their convergence characteristics differ. We stop the computation when successive iterates are such that

$$\left|x^{(k+1)} - x^{(k)}\right| \le \varepsilon \qquad \qquad \ldots(a)$$

and/or

$$\left|F\left[x^{(k+1)}\right]\right| \le \varepsilon; \; k = 1, 2, \ldots \qquad \qquad \ldots(b) \qquad \ldots(3.10)$$

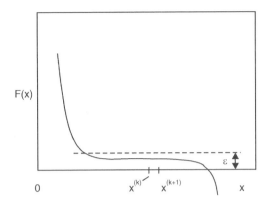

Fig. 3.2 Example of a function $F(x)$ where the convergence criterion, eq. 3.10(*a*) is not recommended. $|x^{(k+1)} - x^{(k)}| < \varepsilon$, yet $x^{(k+1)}$ is far away from the root.

where ε is a desired 'tolerance'. Which of eq. 3.10(*a*) or (*b*) (or both) to be used will depend on the characteristics of the function, $F(x)$. Figure 3.2 shows an example where the use of eq. 3.10(*a*) would not be satisfactory, and eq. 3.10(*b*) is recommended with a very small value of ε.

Example 3.1: Using $x^{(1)} = 1.2500$, obtain the next four iterates of the root of eq. 3.4, using $f(x)$ as given in Eqs. 3.6 and 3.7(*a*). Repeat the calculations using $x^{(1)} = 1.7500$.

The algorithm to be used in the first case is

$$x^{(k+1)} = \frac{1}{3}\exp\left[x^{(k)}\right] \equiv f\left[x^{(k)}\right] \qquad \qquad ...(a)$$

Using $x^{(1)} = 1.2500$,

$$f\left[x^{(1)}\right] = \frac{1}{3}\exp[1.2500] = 1.1634477$$

and so

$$x^{(2)} = f\left[x^{(1)}\right] = 1.1634477$$

This value can be put in $1/3e^x$ to obtain $x^{(3)}$, etc. The following table gives the values obtained, as well as the deviation, $E^{(k)}$, from the root (to which the estimates converge), $x = 0.61906$.

k	$x^{(k)}$	$E^{(k)} \equiv |x^{(k)} - 0.61906|$	$E^{(k+1)}/E^{(k)}$
1	1.25000*	0.6309	–
2	1.16345	0.5444	0.8628
3	1.06698	0.4479	0.8228
4	0.96887	0.3498	0.7809
5	0.87832	0.2593	0.7411
10	0.65272	0.03366	0.6357
20	0.61935	0.0002895	0.6180

* reported to 5 decimal places only

Using $f(x)$ from eq. 3.7(a), we obtain

$$x^{(k+1)} = 2x^{(k)} - \frac{1}{3}\exp\left[x^{(k)}\right]$$

...(b)

The following results are obtained

k	$x^{(k)}$	$E^{(k)} \equiv |x^{(k)} - 1.51213|$
1	1.2500	0.2621
2	1.33655	0.1756
3	1.40447	0.1077
4	1.45115	0.06098
5	1.47963	0.03251
10	1.51115	0.0009892
20	1.51213	7.575×10^{-7}

It is observed that the first choice of $f(x)$ (eq. a) and $x^{(1)}$ leads to convergence to root R_1 (since the successive estimates approach the solution), while the second choice of $f(x)$ (eq. b) and $x^{(1)}$ converges to root R_2. Using a different starting point, $x^{(1)} = 1.7500$, with these two $f(x)$, we obtain

k	$x^{(k)}$ (eq. a)	k	$x^{(k)}$ (eq. b)
1	1.7500	1	1.7500
2	1.91820	2	1.58180
3	2.26957	3	1.54237
4	3.22507	4	1.52619
5	8.38508	5	1.51884
6	1460.4101	20	1.51213

It is observed that for case (a), a different choice of $x^{(1)}$ than earlier, leads to divergence from the roots. However, for case (b), $x^{(1)} = 1.7500$ leads to convergence to root R_2. Convergence is thus observed to depend on the choice of *both* $f(x)$ and the initial estimate, $x^{(1)}$. ∎

Figure 3.3 presents a graphical interpretation of this technique for choice (a) of Example 3.1. $f(x) = \frac{1}{3} e^x$ is plotted, as is the 45° line ($y = x$). The intersection of these two (points R_1 and R_2) gives the roots of $x = f(x)$. Point A represents [$x^{(1)} = 1.2500, 0$]. AB has length $f[x^{(1)}]$. $AB = OE = CD = f[x^{(1)}]$, and since $f[x^{(1)}]$ is equal to $x^{(2)}$ (eq. 3.8), $CD = x^{(2)}$, i.e., point D is on the 45° line. Since $OC = ED = CD$, this means that point C represents [$x^{(2)}, 0$]. Thus, one can go stepwise from point B to points D and then to F, to go from $x^{(1)}$ to $x^{(2)}$. The path followed in the first table in Example 3.1 is illustrated by the graphical path BDFGHIJ..., with points B, F, H, J, ... having x-coordinates as $x^{(1)}$, $x^{(2)}$, $x^{(3)}$, $x^{(4)}$, ..., respectively. It is easy to see graphically that this path converges to the root R_1, $x = 0.61906$, although the improvement in x at any stage becomes more sluggish as the root is approached. It can be observed from fig. 3.3 that we will converge to root R_1 if we start from any point $x^{(1)}$ such that $R_1 < x^{(1)} < R_2$. Similarly, we will again converge to R_1 if $x^{(1)}$ lies to the left of R_1, as from point A'. If, on the other hand, we start from point A'' (or from any point to the right of R_2), we shall move away from the roots. The method of successive substitutions (for this choice of $f[x]$), thus, diverges for $x^{(1)} > R_2 = 1.512144$. In fact, if the slope of $f(x)$ is larger than unity (strictly speaking, if $|df/dx| > 1$) *near a root*, as in this example near R_2, one can never converge to this root. We usually do not make plots of $y = x$ and $f(x)$ in the method of successive substitutions (or else we could get the roots upon plotting these). Instead, we just use eq. 3.9 several times. Yet, a graphical analysis helps in our understanding of the technique and its limitations. Figure 3.3 shows that the first choice of $f(x)$ in the example studied does not yield root R_2, but gives root R_1, provided that $-\infty < x^{(1)} < R_2 = 1.512144$.

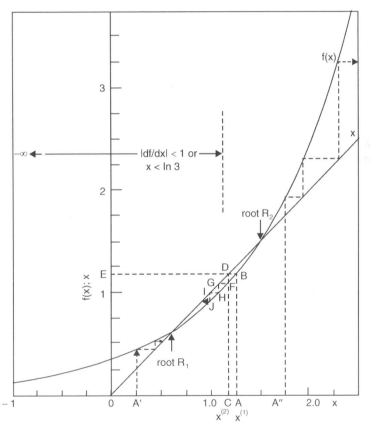

Fig. 3.3 Graphical illustration of path followed by the successive substitutions method, with $f(x) = e^x/3$. The zone described by the condition, eq. 3.16, is also shown.

It is not always easy to find *all* the roots using the method of successive substitutions, but this technique is still quite popular since it is relatively easy to implement. Later, in sec. 3.2, we will see how by coupling this technique with a search method, we can ensure convergence to the roots of $F(x) = 0$.

Figure 3.4 shows how the error, $E^{(k)}$, at the kth stage, varies with the iteration number, k, for the case shown in fig. 3.3 (starting with 1.25). The behaviour is *approximately* described by a straight line of slope -1, on the semilog plot. The following relationship can be written

$$\ln E^{(k)} \cong a_1 k + a_2 \qquad \ldots(a)$$

$$\ln E^{(k+1)} \cong a_1(k+1) + a_2 \qquad \ldots(b) \qquad \ldots(3.11)$$

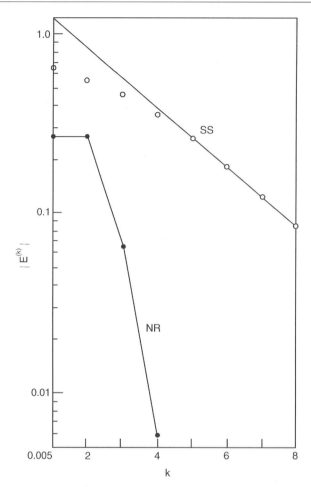

Fig. 3.4 Open circles: Decrease of error, $|E^{(k)}|$, with respect to root R_1, with iteration number for the successive substitutions technique shown in fig. 3.3 (starting from point A). Filled circles: Corresponding error with respect to root R_2, using the Newton-Raphson (NR) technique (see Example 3.5).

Simple algebraic manipulations on these equations give

$$E^{(k+1)} \cong \left(e^{a_1} \right) E^{(k)} = cE^{(k)} \qquad \qquad ...(3.12)$$

i.e., the error reduces by the same *factor* at every iteration. In other words, the same number of iterations is required to increase the accuracy of the results by one significant place, irrespective of how far we are from the root. Techniques which have convergence characteristics given by eq. 3.12, are referred to as *first order* converging methods, or linearly converging methods. It will be seen in sec. 3.3 that the Newton-Raphson technique converges more rapidly than given by eq. 3.12, but it takes more computer time per iteration.

We now study the convergence characteristics of this technique in a more fundamental manner. Let the solution of $x = f(x)$ be $x = \alpha$ [*i.e.*, $\alpha = f(\alpha)$]. We can expand $f[x^{(k)}]$ about $f[\alpha]$ using Taylor's series as:

$$f\left[x^{(k)} \right] = f[\alpha] + \frac{df}{dx}\bigg|_{\alpha + \xi} \left[x^{(k)} - \alpha \right] \qquad \qquad ...(3.13)$$

where the derivative, $\dfrac{df}{dx}$ is evaluated at some (unknown) value of $x = \alpha + \xi$, with $\alpha + \xi$ in $[x^{(k)}, \alpha]$.

Using $x^{(k+1)} = f[x^{(k)}]$ and $\alpha = f[\alpha]$, we obtain

$$x^{(k+1)} - \alpha = \frac{df}{dx}\bigg|_{\alpha+\xi} \left[x^{(k)} - \alpha\right] \qquad \qquad \text{...(3.14)}$$

which relates the deviations of the estimates at the kth and $(k + 1)$th stages. The absolute values can now be taken to give

$$\left|x^{(k+1)} - \alpha\right| = \left|\frac{df}{dx}\bigg|_{\alpha+\xi} \left(x^{(k)} - \alpha\right)\right| = \left|\frac{df}{dx}\right|_{\alpha+\xi} \left|x^{(k)} - \alpha\right| \qquad \text{...(3.15)}$$

which is similar in form to eq. 3.12. It is easy to see from eq. 3.15 that if

$$\left|\frac{df}{dx}\right| < 1 \qquad \qquad \text{...(3.16)}$$

at all values of x between $x^{(k)}$ and α, then $x^{(k+1)}$ will lie closer to the root than $x^{(k)}$. Extending this argument it is observed that the algorithm, eq. 3.9, definitely converges (sufficient condition) to the root, α, if one starts from $x^{(1)}$ and if $\left|\dfrac{df}{dx}\right| < 1$ in the entire domain of x covered by the iterates $x^{(k)}$ [*i.e.*, $\left|\dfrac{df}{dx}\right| < 1$ in $x_{min}^{(k)} \leq x \leq x_{max}^{(k)}$; $k = 1, 2, \dots$ Note from eq. 3.14 that $x^{(k+1)} - \alpha$ could have the opposite sign than $x^{(k)} - \alpha$ and so $x^{(k+1)}$ could lie on the other side of the root than does $x^{(k)}$].

Example 3.2: Study the convergence characteristics of the algorithms used in Example 3.1, with reference to eq. 3.16.

For Example 3.1a:

$$x^{(k+1)} = f[x^{(k)}] = \frac{1}{3}\exp[x^{(k)}]$$

eq. 3.16 leads to the following requirements

$$\left|\frac{1}{3}e^x\right| < 1$$

Since e^x is always positive, this gives

$$e^x < 3 \quad \text{or} \quad x < \ln 3 \ (= 1.099)$$

This is shown in fig. 3.3. Convergence to root R_1 *will* occur if $-\ln 3 < x^{(1)} < \ln 3$, since then, on the *entire* path taken by the algorithm, the required condition is satisfied (Note that if we start at $x^{(1)} < -\ln 3$, the next iterate *could* lie at $x > \ln 3$, where eq. 3.16 is not satisfied). This is a more conservative requirement than the condition $-\infty < x^{(1)} < R_2 = 1.512135$ obtained earlier by inspection of fig. 3.3. Note also that root R_2 does not satisfy the sufficient condition, eq. 3.16, since any path approaching R_2 must pass through the zone where this condition is violated. It was indeed found that the method did not converge to R_2 (Example 3.1).

For Example 3.1b

$$x^{(k+1)} = f\left[x^{(k)}\right] = 2x^{(k)} - \frac{1}{3}\exp\left[x^{(k)}\right]$$

Equation 3.16 gives

$$\left|\frac{df}{dx}\right| = \left|2 - \frac{1}{3}e^x\right| < 1 \text{ for convergence.}$$

Figure 3.5 shows $\left|\dfrac{df}{dx}\right|$ *vs. x*, alongwith the zone, $\left|\dfrac{df}{dx}\right| < 1$, as predicted by this equation. It is observed that this condition is met for $1.0986 < x^{(1)} < 2.1972$, and so convergence is assured to the root R_2 in the range of $1.0986 < x^{(1)} < 1.9256$, with R_2 lying at the mid-point (since all later iterates will be within this range; see Example 3.1). In Example 3.1, this was found to be so with $x^{(1)} = 1.25$ as well as 1.75. ∎

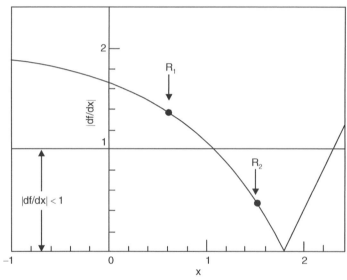

Fig. 3.5 Study of convergence criterion for case *b* of Example 3.1: $f(x) = 2x - \frac{1}{3}e^x$

3.3 MULTIVARIABLE SUCCESSIVE SUBSTITUTIONS

The above technique for the single variable successive substitutions can be easily extended to the more general case involving N variables, $x_1, x_2, ..., x_N$. The ith equation, $F_i(\mathbf{x}) = 0$, in eq. 3.1 can be rearranged (again non uniquely), as

$$x_i = f_i(\mathbf{x}); \ i = 1, 2, ..., N \qquad \qquad ...(3.17)$$

or in matrix form, as

$$\mathbf{x} = \begin{bmatrix} x_1 \\ x_2 \\ . \\ . \\ . \\ x_N \end{bmatrix} = \mathbf{f}(\mathbf{x}) \equiv \begin{bmatrix} f_1(\mathbf{x}) \\ f_2(\mathbf{x}) \\ . \\ . \\ . \\ f_N(\mathbf{x}) \end{bmatrix} \qquad \qquad ...(3.18)$$

The easiest, although not necessarily the best choice of $f_i(\mathbf{x})$ is

$$x_i = f_i(\mathbf{x}) = x_i + F_i(\mathbf{x}); \quad i = 1, 2, ..., N \qquad \qquad ...(3.19)$$

The method of successive substitutions can be written in analogy with eq. 3.9 as

$$x_i^{(k+1)} = f_i\left[\mathbf{x}^{(k)}\right] \equiv f_i\left[x_1^{(k)} \ x_2^{(k)} \ ... \ x_N^{(k)}\right]; \quad i = 1, 2, ..., N \qquad \qquad ...(3.20)$$

One starts with a choice, $\mathbf{x}^{(1)}$, of the N variables in this case and iterates until a convergence criterion *on all x_i* is met:

$$\left| x_i^{(k+1)} - x_i^{(k)} \right| \leq \varepsilon \qquad \qquad ...(a)$$

and/or

$$| F_i[\mathbf{x}^{(k+1)}] | \leq \varepsilon; \ i = 1, 2, ..., N; \ k = 1, 2, ... \qquad ...(b) \qquad ...(3.21)$$

As in the single variable case, depending on the choice of $\mathbf{f}(\mathbf{x})$ or $\mathbf{x}^{(1)}$, convergence to one or more roots of the equations may not occur. Note that this technique has a resemblance to the Jacobi method (eq. 1.30) used for linear equations.

Example 3.3: Solve by the method of successive substitutions

$$F_1(\mathbf{y}) = 4 - 8y_2 + 4y_3 - 2y_2^3 = 0$$

$$F_2(\mathbf{y}) = 1 - 4y_2 + 3y_3 + y_3^2 = 0$$

The exact solution is $\mathbf{y} \equiv [y_2 \ \ y_3]^T = [0.6652 \ \ 0.4776]^T$.

The above equations are obtained when we apply a three-point orthogonal collocation technique to the following nonlinear ordinary differential equation (boundary value type):

$$\frac{d^2y}{dx^2} - 2y^3 = 0; \quad y(0) = 1; \quad \frac{dy}{dx}(x=1) + \left[y(1)\right]^2 = 0$$

(see prob. 6.26). We, thus, see the importance of techniques for solving nonlinear algebraic equations, even in the solution of ordinary differential equations.

A simple choice of $\mathbf{f}(\mathbf{x})$ is given by eq. 3.5:

$$y_2^{(k+1)} = \left(-2y_2^3 - 7y_2 + 4y_3 + 4\right)^{(k)} \equiv f_1\left[\mathbf{y}^{(k)}\right]$$

$$y_3^{(k+1)} = \left(-4y_2 + y_3^2 + 4y_3 + 1\right)^{(k)} \equiv f_2\left[\mathbf{y}^{(k)}\right] \qquad ...(a)$$

Let us start with $\mathbf{y}^{(1)} = [0.5 \ \ 0.5]^T$. The sequence of computation gives

k	$y_2^{(k)}$	$y_3^{(k)}$
1	0.5	0.5
2	2.25	1.25
3	−29.531	−1.438
4	51713.06	115.44

It is observed that the sequence does not converge to the solution.

On the other hand, if the algorithm is written as

$$y_2^{(k+1)} = y_2^{(k)} + \frac{1}{20}\left[4 - 8y_2 + 4y_3 - 2y_2^3\right]^{(k)}$$

$$y_3^{(k+1)} = y_3^{(k)} - \frac{1}{24}\left[1 - 4y_2 + 3y_3 + y_2^3\right]^{(k)}$$

the sequence of iterates starting from $\mathbf{y}^{(1)} = [0.5 \ \ 0.5]^T$ is

k	$y_2^{(k)}$	$y_3^{(k)}$
1	0.5000	0.5000
2	0.5875	0.4688
3	0.6260	0.4573
4	0.6425	0.4540
5	0.6498	0.4541
10	0.6580	0.4619
80	0.6652	0.4776

and convergence is attained, though slowly. ∎

We now extend our earlier analysis of the convergence of this technique to multivariable systems [1]. This will help us in recasting eq. 3.2 in a form which would, hopefully, converge. Let the solution of $\mathbf{x} = \mathbf{f}(\mathbf{x})$ be $\mathbf{x} = [\alpha_1 \ \ \alpha_2 \ \ ... \ \ \alpha_N]^T \equiv \underline{\alpha}$. We can expand $f_i[\mathbf{x}^{(k)}]$ about $f_i[\underline{\alpha}]$ using a multivariable Taylor series (see example 2.1) as follows:

$$f_i\left[\mathbf{x}^{(k)}\right] = f_i[\underline{\alpha}] + \sum_{j=1}^{N}\left[\frac{\partial f_i}{\partial x_j}\right]_{\underline{\alpha}+\underline{\xi}_i^{(k)}}\left[x_j^{(k)} - \alpha_j\right]; \ i = 1, 2, ..., N \qquad ...(3.22)$$

where the partial derivatives are evaluated at some location $\left[\alpha_1 + \xi_{i,1}^{(k)} \ \ \alpha_2 + \xi_{i,2}^{(k)} \ ... \ \alpha_N + \xi_{i,N}^{(k)}\right]^T$ lying between $[\alpha_1 \ \ \alpha_2 \ ... \ \alpha_N]^T$ and $[x_1^{(k)} \ x_2^{(k)} \ ... \ x_N^{(k)}]^T$. Since $f_i\left[\mathbf{x}^{(k)}\right] = x_i^{(k+1)}$, and $f_i(\underline{\alpha}) = \alpha_i$, eq. 3.22 can be rewritten as

$$x_i^{(k+1)} - \alpha_i = \sum_{j=1}^{N}\left[\frac{\partial f_i}{\partial x_j}\right]_{\underline{\alpha}+\underline{\xi}_i^{(k)}}\left[x_j^{(k)} - \alpha_j\right]; \ i = 1, 2, ..., N \qquad ...(3.23)$$

We are interested in the absolute value of the deviation of the numerical estimate from the root, $\left|x_i^{(k+1)} - \alpha_i\right|$. This is given by

$$\left|x_i^{(k+1)} - \alpha_i\right| = \left|\sum_{j=1}^{N}\left[\frac{\partial f_i}{\partial x_j}\right]_{\underline{\alpha}+\underline{\xi}_i^{(k)}}\left[x_j^{(k)} - \alpha_j\right]\right|; \ i = 1, 2, ..., N \qquad ...(3.24)$$

In general, some of the terms in the summation on the right hand side of eq. 3.24 are negative, while some are positive. Thus, the following inequality can be written

$$\left|x_i^{(k+1)} - \alpha_i\right| \leq \sum_{j=1}^{N}\left\{\left|\frac{\partial f_i}{\partial x_j}\right|_{\underline{\alpha}+\underline{\xi}_i^{(k)}}\left|x_j^{(k)} - \alpha_j\right|\right\}; \quad i = 1, 2, ..., N \qquad ...(3.25)$$

in terms of the absolute values of the terms involved. eq. 3.25 can be further written as

$$\underset{i}{\text{Max}}\left|x_i^{(k+1)} - \alpha_i\right| \leq \left[\underset{i}{\text{Max}}\left\{\sum_{j=1}^{N}\left|\frac{\partial f_i}{\partial x_j}\right|_{\underline{\alpha}+\underline{\xi}_i^{(k)}}\right\}\right]\left[\underset{i}{\text{Max}}\left|x_i^{(k)} - \alpha_i\right|\right] \qquad ...(3.26)$$

where the symbol $\underset{i}{\text{Max}}\,\phi_i$ indicates the maximum value of ϕ_i from among all possibilities corresponding to different values of i.

At this stage we do not know the exact location, $\left(\underline{\alpha}+\underline{\xi}^{(k)}\right)$, at which the partial derivatives must be calculated, except that it lies *somewhere* between $\mathbf{x}^{(k)}$ and the unknown root, $\underline{\alpha}$. In several cases, we can estimate the largest values of these derivatives over the *domain of interest*. This can be written as

$$\underset{\mathbf{x}}{\text{Max}}\left[\underset{i}{\text{Max}}\left\{\sum_{j=1}^{N}\left|\frac{\partial f_i}{\partial x_j}\right|\right\}\right] \equiv \mu \qquad ...(3.27)$$

where μ is a constant. We, thus, get from eq. 3.26,

$$\underset{i}{\text{Max}}\left|x_i^{(k+1)} - \alpha_i\right| \leq \mu\,\underset{i}{\text{Max}}\left|x_i^{(k)} - \alpha_i\right| \qquad ...(3.28)$$

so that the maximum error (absolute value), $E^{(k+1)}$, at the $(k+1)$th iteration is related to the value at the previous iteration by

$$E^{(k+1)} \leq \mu E^{(k)} \qquad ...(3.29)$$

which is of the same form as eq. 3.12 for a single variable problem. Table in example 3.1 shows $\dfrac{E^{(k+1)}}{E^{(k)}}$

to be *nearly* constant. The multivariable successive substitutions technique is, therefore, observed to be linearly converging, and the errors decrease (provided $\mu < 1$) as shown in fig. 3.4.

Equation 3.28 can be applied repeatedly, starting with the first iterate, $\mathbf{x}^{(1)}$, to give

$$\underset{i}{\text{Max}}\left|x_i^{(k+1)} - \alpha_i\right| \leq \mu^k\,\underset{i}{\text{Max}}\left|x_i^{(1)} - \alpha_i\right| \qquad ...(3.30)$$

It is obvious that if $\mu < 1$ *over the entire path* [*values of iterates*, $\mathbf{x}^{(k)}$] *followed* from $\mathbf{x}^{(1)}$ to $\underline{\alpha}$, the error will keep decreasing as k increases and the method will converge to the root. For convergence, then

$$\mu \equiv \text{Max}\left\{\sum_{j=1}^{N}\left|\frac{\partial f_i}{\partial x_j}\right|\right\} < 1 \qquad ...(3.31)$$

where the maximization is overall choices of i, as well as over the entire path followed by $\mathbf{x}^{(k)}$. Equation 3.31 is a *sufficient* condition for convergence, *i.e.*, if it is satisfied, then convergence is assured, but if it is violated, then we may or may not have convergence.

Example 3.4: Study the convergence characteristics of the two-variable problem of example 3.3, with reference to eq. 3.31.

Equation 3.31 used on eq. (*a*) of example 3.3 gives

$$\left|\frac{\partial f_1}{\partial y_2}\right| + \left|\frac{\partial f_1}{\partial y_3}\right| = \left|-6y_2^2 - 7\right| + 4$$

and

$$\left|\frac{\partial f_2}{\partial y_2}\right| + \left|\frac{\partial f_2}{\partial y_3}\right| = \left|-4\right| + \left|2y_3 + 4\right|$$

These should be less than unity in the *entire* path between the starting point $[0.5 \quad 0.5]^T$ and the (unknown) root $[0.6652 \quad 0.4776]^T$. At $\mathbf{y}^{(1)}$, the values are

$$\sum_{j=2}^{3} \left|\frac{\partial f_1}{\partial y_j}\right|^{(1)} = 12.5; \quad \sum_{j=2}^{3} \left|\frac{\partial f_2}{\partial y_j}\right|^{(1)} = 9$$

and the sufficient condition is violated immediately at the beginning. The algorithm may or may not converge, and indeed it was found that it did not. When applied to eq. (*b*) of this example, the sufficient condition is violated near the root again, but the algorithm converges. ∎

We can, at times, exploit the sufficient condition to select an appropriate function, $f(x)$, which could lead to convergence. If we write

$$x^{(k+1)} = f[x^{(k)}] = x^{(k)} + \beta F[x^{(k)}] \qquad \qquad \ldots(3.32)$$

we can choose β, a constant, such that the convergence condition is met:

$$\left|\frac{df}{dx}\right| = \left|1 + \frac{\beta dF[x^{(k)}]}{dx}\right| < 1 \qquad \qquad \ldots(3.33)$$

Thus, for the case $F(x) = x - \frac{1}{3}e^x = 0$ studied in example 3.1, we could use

$$x^{(k+1)} = (1+\beta)x^{(k)} - \frac{\beta}{3}\exp[x^{(k)}] \qquad \qquad \ldots(3.34)$$

with β satisfying

$$\left|1 + \beta\left(1 - \frac{1}{3}e^x\right)\right| < 1 \qquad \qquad \ldots(3.35)$$

in the range $x^{(1)} \le x \le 1.512135$ (R_2), so that convergence to root R_2 (for which algorithm *a* in example 3.1 failed) is assured. A choice of $\beta = 2$ makes $\left|1 + 2\left(1 - \frac{1}{3}e^x\right)\right| < 1$ in the range $1.098612 < x < 1.791759$. Any choice of $x^{(1)}$ in the range $1.2325 \le x \le 1.7918$ would give root R_2. Other choices of β could extend the zone of convergence. A computer program may incorporate this technique quite easily—eq. 3.34 may be used with different values of β until a solution is reached. In fact, different starting points, $x^{(1)}$ and β can be used to give all the roots of $F(x) = 0$. This technique is in fact a combination of the method of successive substitutions with a search algorithm (over values of β), and more details on the latter are presented in sec. 3.6. It must be emphasized that some equations may not satisfy the sufficient condition for *any* value of β. For example, in Example 3.3, if one writes $y_3^{(k+1)} = y_3^{(k+1)} + \beta F_2(\mathbf{y})$, the condition is not satisfied *near the root* for any β (though the algorithm converges). It may be worthwhile to try other techniques described later.

3.4 SINGLE VARIABLE NEWTON-RAPHSON TECHNIQUE

A very popular method used for solving sets of nonlinear algebraic equations (eq. 3.2) is the Newton-Raphson [3, 4] (also referred to as the Newton) technique. For the single variable case, we have

$$F(x) = 0 \qquad \qquad \ldots(3.36)$$

As before, $x^{(k)}$ is the estimate of the root, α, at the kth iteration, while $x^{(k+1)}$ is (hopefully) the improved estimate at the next iteration. In order to derive the algorithm, $F[x^{(k+1)}]$ is first expanded about $F[x^{(k)}]$ using the Taylor series:

$$F\left[x^{(k+1)}\right] = F\left[x^{(k)}\right] + \left[\frac{dF}{dx}\right]_{x^{(k)}} \left[x^{(k+1)} - x^{(k)}\right] + \ldots \qquad \ldots(3.37)$$

We equate the left-hand side of this equation to zero, *i.e.*, we choose $x^{(k+1)}$ such that $F[x^{(k+1)}]$ is made zero. This ensures that $x^{(k+1)}$ is at least a better estimate of α than is $x^{(k)}$. If the higher order terms (not written) in eq. 3.37 were exactly zero [*i.e.*, if $F(x)$ were a linear function of x], this choice of $x^{(k+1)}$ would give the root in a single computation, irrespective of the choice of $x^{(1)}$. Equation 3.37 gives

$$F\left[x^{(k)}\right] + \left[\frac{dF}{dx}\right]_{x^{(k)}} \left[x^{k+1} - x^{(k)}\right] = 0 \qquad \ldots(3.38)$$

or

$$x^{(k+1)} = x^{(k)} - \frac{F\left[x^{(k)}\right]}{F'\left[x^{(k)}\right]} \qquad \ldots(3.39)$$

where $F'\left(\equiv \dfrac{dF}{dx}\right)$ is evaluated at $x^{(k)}$. Because of the higher order terms in eq. 3.37 which have been neglected in obtaining eq. 3.39, $x^{(k+1)}$ is not the same as the root, α, but hopefully a better estimate of it than $x^{(k)}$.

Example 3.5: Solve, using the Newton-Raphson technique:

$$F(x) = x - \frac{1}{3}e^x = 0$$

Use $x^{(1)} = 1.2500$, as in example 3.1 (roots $R_1 = 0.61906$; $R_2 = 1.512135$)

The algorithm is

$$x^{(k+1)} = x^{(k)} - \frac{x^{(k)} - \dfrac{1}{3}\exp\left[x^{(k)}\right]}{1 - \dfrac{1}{3}\exp\left[x^{(k)}\right]}$$

The following results are obtained:

k	$x^{(k)}$	$E^{(k)} \equiv \|x^{(k)} - 1.512135\|$	$\dfrac{E^{(k+1)}}{[E^{(k)}]^2}$
1	1.2500	0.2621	–
2	1.779542	0.2674	3.8916
3	1.578487	0.066352	0.9279
4	1.5177845	0.00565004	1.2833
5	1.5121811	0.0000371	1.4575
10	1.5121346	–	–

Note the very rapid convergence to root R_2 (see fig. 3.4) as compared to the successive substitutions technique in example 3.1. Also note that $x^{(k)}$ oscillates about the value R_2 as k increases. ∎

The graphical interpretation of this technique is illustrated in fig. 3.6. Point A represents the starting point $[x^{(1)} = 1.25, 0]$. We go up from point A to the $F(x)$ curve, reaching point B. Thus, $AB = F[x^{(1)}]$. A tangent is drawn at point B, and extended to meet the abscissa at point C. It is easy to see that

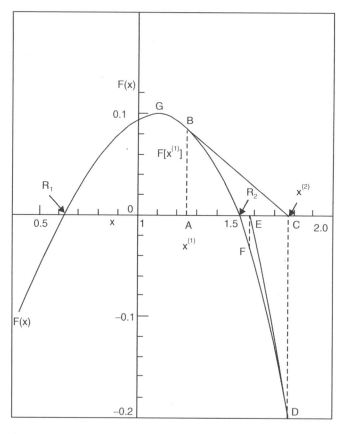

Fig. 3.6 Graphical interpretation of the Newton-Raphson technique applied to

$$F(x) = x - \frac{1}{3}e^x = 0.$$

$$F'\left[x^{(1)}\right] = \text{slope of tangent at } B = -\frac{AB}{AC} \qquad \text{...(3.40)}$$

and so

$$AC = -\frac{AB}{F'\left[x^{(1)}\right]} = -\frac{F\left[x^{(1)}\right]}{F'\left[x^{(1)}\right]} \qquad \text{...(3.41)}$$

Since, from eq. 3.39

$$x^{(2)} = x^{(1)} - \frac{F\left[x^{(1)}\right]}{F'\left[x^{(1)}\right]} \qquad \text{...(3.42)}$$

we have, graphically,

$$x^{(2)} = OA + AC = OC \qquad \text{...(3.43)}$$

where O is the origin of the axes (not shown in fig. 3.6). Thus, point C represents $[x^{(2)}, 0]$. If one goes from any point $[x^{(k)}, 0]$, on the abscissa, to the $F(x)$ curve, and draws a tangent from this point, the point of intersection of the tangent with the abscissa, thus, gives $[x^{(k+1)}, 0]$. The path followed in example 3.5 is ABCDEF... We can see that if we started with, say $x^{(1)} = 0.7$, we would converge to the root R_1 (see prob. 3.11). Also, we can observe that if we had $x^{(k)} = \ln 3 = 1.0986$ at any stage of the calculations, the method would fail since $F'[x^{(k)}] = 0$ at such a point, G (note that $F'[x^{(k)}] = 0$ in eq. 3.39 gives $x^{(k+1)} \to \pm \infty$).

The convergence characteristics for this technique can also be studied. Equation 3.39 can be rewritten by subtracting α from both sides, as

$$\alpha - x^{(k+1)} = \alpha - x^{(k)} + \frac{F\left[x^{(k)}\right]}{F'\left[x^{(k)}\right]} \qquad \text{...(3.44)}$$

where α is the root. Equation 3.44 can be modified to

$$\alpha - x^{(k+1)} = \alpha - x^{(k)} - \frac{F(\alpha) - F\left[x^{(k)}\right]}{F'\left[x^{(k)}\right]} \qquad \text{...(3.45)}$$

since $F(\alpha) = 0$. A three-term Taylor series expansion of $F(\alpha)$ about point $x^{(k)}$ gives

$$F(\alpha) = F\left[x^{(k)}\right] + F'\left[x^{(k)}\right]\left[\alpha - x^{(k)}\right] + F''[\xi]\frac{\left[\alpha - x^{(k)}\right]^2}{2} \qquad \text{...(3.46)}$$

where ξ is some value in the range $x^{(k)} < \xi < \alpha$. This equation can be rearranged to give

$$\frac{F(\alpha) - F\left[x^{(k)}\right]}{F'\left[x^{(k)}\right]} - \left[\alpha - x^{(k)}\right] = \frac{F''(\xi)\left[\alpha - x^{(k)}\right]^2}{2F'\left[x^{(k)}\right]} \qquad \text{...(3.47)}$$

From eqs. 3.45 and 3.47, we get

$$\alpha - x^{(k+1)} = \frac{F''(\xi)}{2F'\left[x^{(k)}\right]}\left[\alpha - x^{(k)}\right]^2 \qquad \text{...(3.48)}$$

or

$$E^{(k+1)} \equiv C\left[\xi, x^{(k)}\right]\left[E^{(k)}\right]^2 \qquad \qquad ...(3.49)$$

Since C can be either positive or negative, we may have oscillatory behaviour about the root, as observed in example 3.5. Equation 3.49 can be rewritten as

$$E^{(k+1)} \leq a\left[E^{(k)}\right]^2 \qquad \qquad ...(3.50)$$

where a is a constant, equal to the maximum value of $|C\left[\xi, x^{(k)}\right]|$ (note that E are absolute values of the deviations). The replacement of the variable value of $\dfrac{-F''(\xi)}{2F'\left[x^{(k)}\right]}$ by a constant, a, makes eq. 3.50 an approximation. Table in example 3.5 shows how this behaviour is (approximately) observed. A convergence characteristic of the type given in eq. 3.50, is called quadratic (or *second-order*) convergence. Equation 3.50 implies that the number of correct significant figures doubles in every iteration [see $E^{(3)}$, $E^{(4)}$ and $E^{(5)}$ in example 3.5]. Thus, convergence is very rapid, but it is achieved at the cost of additional computer time required for the computation of the derivative, $F'\left[x^{(k)}\right]$. If the function, $F(x)$, is not too complicated, one can obtain $\dfrac{dF}{dx}$ analytically and incorporate it in a computer algorithm; however, if $F(x)$ is complicated, then the derivative can be obtained numerically (using algorithms described in Chapter 4). The latter approach, often referred to as the *quasi Newton method*, takes more computer time, since it requires (at least) two function evaluations $\left\{ \text{if } F'\left[x^{(k)}\right] \cong \dfrac{F\left[x^{(k)}+\Delta x\right]-F\left[x^{(k)}\right]}{\Delta x} \right\}$ while

the analytical expression for F' involves only a single function evaluation. Again, as in the method of successive substitutions, we can get stuck in a cycle of repeating values for the Newton-Raphson case.

A major advantage of the Newton-Raphson technique stems from its convergence criterion. If the function, $F(x)$, has a *continuous* derivative in the neighbourhood of a root, α, and if the derivative, $F'(x)$, is *non singular* in the neighbourhood of this root, then it can be shown [6, 7] (see example 3.7 later) that the Newton-Raphson technique converges to α, *provided $x^{(1)}$ is taken sufficiently close to this root*. This means that we can always combine this technique with a simple incremental search technique, as discussed in sec. 3.1, and convergence is assured. We can start from a value provided by this search algorithm and use the Newton-Raphson technique to obtain a more precise estimate of the root. In fact, we can use the incremental search technique (or other search techniques discussed in sec. 3.6), to obtain the approximate locations of *all* the roots of $F(x) = 0$, and then obtain them precisely using several applications of the Newton-Raphson algorithm with different starting points. Example 3.5 and prob. 3.11 show how both the roots of $F(x) = x - \dfrac{1}{3}e^x = 0$ can be obtained from two different starting points.

The only problem that is faced in this method is that we need to know how many roots exist, and the range of x to be scanned in order to identify locations of *all* the roots. Also, we may not know how small Δx should be in our search algorithm, so that only one root lies in an interval. Section 3.8 discusses procedures by which a somewhat better knowledge can be obtained about the number of roots of $F(x) = 0$, where the function, $F(x)$, incorporates a parameter, β. Such problems are frequently encountered in engineering.

3.5 MULTIVARIABLE NEWTON-RAPHSON TECHNIQUE

The extension of the technique discussed in sec. 3.4 to a set of N equations in N variables, $x_1, x_2, ..., x_N$, is straightforward. The ith equation from the set, eq. 3.2, is

$$F_i(\mathbf{x}) = 0; \quad i = 1, 2, ..., N \qquad \qquad ...(3.51)$$

We can write an expression for $F_i[\mathbf{x}^{(k+1)}]$ using a multivariable Taylor series expansion about $\mathbf{x}^{(k)}$ as

$$F_i\left[\mathbf{x}^{(k+1)}\right] = F_i\left[\mathbf{x}^{(k)}\right] + \sum_{j=1}^{N}\left[\frac{\partial F_i}{\partial x_j}\right]_{\mathbf{x}^{(k)}}\left[x_j^{(k+1)} - x_j^{(k)}\right] + ...; \quad i = 1, 2, ..., N \qquad ...(3.52)$$

Once again, the left hand side of this equation is forced to be equal to zero. Upon putting all the N equations together, we obtain

$$-\begin{bmatrix} F_1\left[\mathbf{x}^{(k)}\right] \\ F_2\left[\mathbf{x}^{(k)}\right] \\ \cdot \\ \cdot \\ \cdot \\ F_N\left[\mathbf{x}^{(k)}\right] \end{bmatrix} = \begin{bmatrix} \dfrac{\partial F_1}{\partial x_1} & \dfrac{\partial F_1}{\partial x_2} & \cdot & \cdot & \dfrac{\partial F_1}{\partial x_N} \\ \dfrac{\partial F_2}{\partial x_1} & \cdot & & & \cdot \\ \cdot & & & & \cdot \\ \cdot & & & & \cdot \\ \dfrac{\partial F_N}{\partial x_1} & \dfrac{\partial F_N}{\partial x_2} & \cdot & & \dfrac{\partial F_N}{\partial x_N} \end{bmatrix}_{\mathbf{x}^{(k)}} \begin{bmatrix} x_1^{(k+1)} - x_1^{(k)} \\ x_2^{(k+1)} - x_2^{(k)} \\ \cdot \\ \cdot \\ \cdot \\ x_N^{(k+1)} - x_N^{(k)} \end{bmatrix} \qquad ...(3.53)$$

or

$$-\mathbf{F}\left[\mathbf{x}^{(k)}\right] = \mathbf{A}\left[\mathbf{x}^{(k)}\right]\left[\mathbf{x}^{(k+1)} - \mathbf{x}^{(k)}\right] \qquad \qquad ...(3.54)$$

where $\mathbf{A}[\mathbf{x}^{(k)}]$ is the Jacobian matrix [see example 2.1, eq. (*d*) for nomenclature], evaluated at $\mathbf{x}^{(k)}$ and so it is a matrix of constants. Equation 3.54 can be solved by premultiplying by $\mathbf{A}^{-1}[\mathbf{x}^{(k)}]$ on both sides. This gives

$$\mathbf{x}^{(k+1)} = \mathbf{x}^{(k)} - \left[\mathbf{A}^{(k)}\right]^{-1}\mathbf{F}\left[\mathbf{x}^{(k)}\right] \qquad \qquad ...(3.55)$$

where $\mathbf{A}^{(k)}$ is used for brevity in place of $\mathbf{A}[\mathbf{x}^{(k)}]$. Equation 3.39 is observed to be a special case of the more general eq. 3.55.

Example 3.6: Solve

$$F_1(\mathbf{y}) = 4 - 8y_2 + 4y_3 - 2y_2^3 = 0$$

$$F_2(\mathbf{y}) = 1 - 4y_2 + 3y_3 + y_3^2 = 0$$

using the Newton-Raphson technique, starting with $\mathbf{y}^{(1)} = [y_2^{(1)}\ y_3^{(1)}]^T = [0.5\ 0.5]^T$. Recall that one form of the method of successive substitutions from the same $\mathbf{y}^{(1)}$ did not converge to the root, $[0.6652\ 0.4776]^T$ (example 3.3).

Equation 3.55 leads to

$$\begin{bmatrix} y_2^{(k+1)} \\ y_3^{(k+1)} \end{bmatrix} = \begin{bmatrix} y_2^{(k)} \\ y_3^{(k)} \end{bmatrix} - \begin{bmatrix} -8 - 6y_2^2 & 4 \\ -4 & 3 + 2y_3 \end{bmatrix}_{(k)}^{-1} \begin{bmatrix} 4 - 8y_2 + 4y_3 - 2y_2^3 \\ 1 - 4y_2 + 3y_3 + y_3^2 \end{bmatrix}_{(k)}$$

The inverse can be obtained readily using the definition $\mathbf{A}^{-1} = (\text{Adj } \mathbf{A}) / |\mathbf{A}|$, and we get

$$\begin{bmatrix} y_2 \\ y_3 \end{bmatrix}_{(k+1)} = \begin{bmatrix} y_2 \\ y_3 \end{bmatrix}_{(k)} - \left\{ \frac{1}{4 + 9y_2^2 + 6y_2^2 y_3 + 8y_3} \begin{bmatrix} -\left(\dfrac{3}{2} + y_3\right) & 2 \\ -2 & \left(4 + 3y_2^2\right) \end{bmatrix} \right\}_{(k)} \begin{bmatrix} 4 - 8y_2 + 4y_3 - 2y_2^3 \\ 1 - 4y_2 + 3y_3 + y_3^2 \end{bmatrix}_{(k)}$$

The following results are obtained for $\mathbf{y}^{(2)}$

$$\begin{bmatrix} y_2^{(2)} \\ y_3^{(2)} \end{bmatrix} = \begin{bmatrix} 0.5 \\ 0.5 \end{bmatrix} - \frac{1}{11} \begin{bmatrix} -2 & 2 \\ -2 & 4.75 \end{bmatrix} \begin{bmatrix} 1.75 \\ 0.75 \end{bmatrix} = \begin{bmatrix} 0.68182 \\ 0.49432 \end{bmatrix}$$

The computations can be continued to give the following results

k	$y_2^{(k)}$	$y_3^{(k)}$	$F_1[\mathbf{y}^{(k)}]$	$F_2[\mathbf{y}^{(k)}]$
1	0.5	0.5	1.75	0.75
2	0.68182	0.49432	−0.1112	3.2283×10^{-5}
3	0.6654	0.4779	-1.0928×10^{-3}	2.7110×10^{-4}
4	0.6652	0.4776	-1.7064×10^{-7}	7.7060×10^{-8}
10	0.6652011	0.4775753	0	-8.327×10^{-17}

A very rapid convergence to the root $[0.6652 \ 0.4776]^T$ is observed. The fast approach of $\mathbf{F}(\mathbf{y})$ to zero can also be noted. ∎

The use of the Newton-Raphson algorithm for several variables involves obtaining the inverse of the Jacobian matrix once in every iteration. Even though this can be performed in principle, using a library subroutine, it is time consuming. A variety of techniques [8] can be used to reduce the computational effort. For example, the Jacobian and its inverse can be computed once, and used without updating (*i.e.*, without recomputing it at the new $\mathbf{x}^{(k+1)}$) for several iterations. The rate of convergence may be affected, but savings on the total computational effort may justify this approach. Broyden [9] (also see sec. 3.6 and ref. 10) and Shubert [11], similarly, reduce the computational effort by using procedures to approximate the inverse Jacobian matrix, respectively. These techniques are quite popular in multicomponent distillation column designs [12] in chemical engineering. Alternatively, we can solve the following form of eq. 3.55,

$$\mathbf{A}^{(k)}\mathbf{x}^{(k+1)} = \mathbf{A}^{(k)}\mathbf{x}^{(k)} - \mathbf{F}\left[\mathbf{x}^{(k)}\right] \equiv \mathbf{b} \qquad \qquad …(3.56)$$

This is a *linear* algebraic equation [since $\mathbf{A}^{(k)}$ is a constant at any stage], which can be solved using, for example, the Gauss-Seidel technique (sec. 1.4). Thus, a set of iterations is performed using this equation for $k = 1$ to converge to $\mathbf{x}^{(2)}$, the Jacobian matrix, $\mathbf{A}^{(2)}$, is recalculated using $\mathbf{x}^{(2)}$, the Gauss-Seidel technique is used once again (several iterations required) on eq. 3.56 to obtain $\mathbf{x}^{(3)}$, etc. The computation of the inverse can thus be avoided and as mentioned in chp. 1, it is usually faster to solve the set of linear equations $\mathbf{Ax} = \mathbf{b}$, by the Gauss-Seidel technique, than by inverting the matrix $\mathbf{A}$ and using $\mathbf{x} = \mathbf{A}^{-1}\mathbf{b}$.

Multiple roots can also be obtained by starting from different initial guesses, although it is not easy to explore a multidimensional $\mathbf{x}$ space using an incremental search technique, as it is for a single variable problem. Also, if the partial derivatives required for generating $\mathbf{A}^{(k)}$ in eq. 3.56 are not easily obtained analytically, they can be estimated numerically when required, of course at the cost of greater computational effort.

The convergence criterion [6, 7] for the multivariable Newton-Raphson technique is similar to that for the single variable algorithm. If the functions, F_i (**x**), all have continuous first partial derivatives near a root, $\underline{\alpha}$, and if the Jacobian, |**A**|, is non-singular in the neighbourhood of this root, then the Newton-Raphson iterates will converge to this root if $\mathbf{x}^{(1)}$ is taken sufficiently close to $\underline{\alpha}$ (see example 3.7 below). Hence, if one fails to find a root with this technique, all one needs to do in principle, is to keep trying with different initial guesses, $\mathbf{x}^{(1)}$. The importance of appropriate starting estimates, $\mathbf{x}^{(1)}$, can hardly be overemphasized. Elaborate procedures are sometimes required to obtain good estimates, as for example, in the case of multicomponent, multistage distillation column simulation [12] in chemical engineering, where it is not uncommon to solve 50,000–1,00,000 equations simultaneously. One can also extend the derivation for the single variable case and show that the multivariable Newton-Raphson technique converges quadratically.

Example 3.7: Study the convergence criterion for the multivariable Newton-Raphson technique.

Equation 3.55 can be modified using $\mathbf{F}(\underline{\alpha}) = \mathbf{0}$, as

$$\mathbf{x}^{(k+1)} = \mathbf{x}^{(k)} + \left[\mathbf{A}^{(k)}\right]^{-1}\left\{\mathbf{F}(\underline{\alpha}) - \mathbf{F}\left[\mathbf{x}^{(k)}\right]\right\} \qquad \ldots(a)$$

We can expand $F_i\left[\mathbf{x}^{(k)}\right]$ about $\underline{\alpha}$, using a multivariable Taylor expression, as

$$F_i\left[\mathbf{x}^{(k)}\right] - F_i(\underline{\alpha}) = \sum_{j=1}^{N}\left[\frac{\partial F_i}{\partial x_j}\right]\left(x_j^{(k)} - \alpha_j\right) \qquad \ldots(b)$$

where the partial derivatives on the right hand side are evaluated at $[\alpha_1 + \xi_{i,1}^{(k)}(x_1^{(k)} - \alpha_1)\ \alpha_2 + \xi_{i,2}^{(k)}$ $(x_2^{(k)} - \alpha_2)\ldots\ldots\alpha_N + \xi_{i,N}^{(k)}(x_N^{(k)} - \alpha_N)]$ lying between $\mathbf{x}^{(k)}$ and the root $\underline{\alpha}$. eq. (b) can be written in matrix form as

$$\mathbf{F}\left[\mathbf{x}^{(k)}\right] - \mathbf{F}(\underline{\alpha}) = \mathbf{A}^*\left[\mathbf{x}^{(k)} - \underline{\alpha}\right] \qquad \ldots(c)$$

where $\mathbf{A}^*$ is the Jacobian matrix, with the partial derivatives evaluated at the point described above. Using eq. (c) on the right-hand side of eq. (a), and subtracting $\underline{\alpha}$ from both sides, gives

$$\mathbf{x}^{(k+1)} - \underline{\alpha} = \mathbf{x}^{(k)} - \underline{\alpha} - \left[\mathbf{A}^{(k)}\right]^{-1}\mathbf{A}^*\left(\mathbf{x}^{(k)} - \underline{\alpha}\right)$$

$$= \left[\mathbf{A}^{(k)}\right]^{-1}\left\{\mathbf{A}^{(k)} - \mathbf{A}^*\right\}\left[\mathbf{x}^{(k)} - \underline{\alpha}\right]$$

We can make the terms in $[\mathbf{A}^{(k)}]^{-1}\{\mathbf{A}^{(k)} - \mathbf{A}^*\}$ as small as described by choosing $\mathbf{x}^{(k)}$ close enough to $\underline{\alpha}$ (since $[\mathbf{A}^{(k)}]^{-1}$ is bounded if the Jacobian is nonsingular) and so we get

$$\left|\mathbf{x}^{(k+1)} - \underline{\alpha}\right| \le \left|\mathbf{x}^{(k)} - \underline{\alpha}\right|$$

in the neighbourhood of $\mathbf{x} = \underline{\alpha}$. Thus, the technique converges to the root if our estimate is sufficiently close to it.

The quadratic convergence of the multivariable Newton-Raphson technique can be shown in a manner similar to the 1–variable case. Equation 3.56 can be written for variable x_i, as

$$\sum_{j=1}^{N} A_{ij}^{(k)}\left(\alpha_j - x_j^{(k+1)}\right) = \sum_{j=1}^{N} A_{ij}^{(k)}\left[\alpha_j - x_j^{(k)}\right] - \left\{F_i(\underline{\alpha}) - F_i\left[\mathbf{x}^{(k)}\right]\right\} \qquad \ldots(d)$$

The multivariable Taylor series expression of $F_i(\underline{\alpha})$ about $F_i(\mathbf{x}^{(k)})$ can be written as

$$F_i(\underline{\alpha}) = F_i\left[\mathbf{x}^{(k)}\right] + \sum_{j=1}^{N} A_{ij}^{(k)}\left[\alpha_j - x_j^{(k)}\right] + \frac{1}{2}\left[\underline{\alpha} - \mathbf{x}^{(k)}\right]^T \mathcal{H}_i^{(k)}\left[\underline{\alpha} - \mathbf{x}^{(k)}\right] + \ldots \qquad \ldots(e)$$

where $\mathcal{H}_i^{(k)}$ is the $N \times N$ Hessian matrix with elements

$$\left[\left[\mathcal{H}_i^{(k)}\right]_{pq} = \frac{\partial^2 F_i}{\partial x_p \partial x_q}\right]_{x^{(k)}} \qquad \ldots(f)$$

Equations (d) and (e) can be combined to give

$$\sum_{j=1}^{N} A_{ij}^{(k)}\left[\alpha_j - x_j^{(k+1)}\right] = -\frac{1}{2}\left[\underline{\alpha} - \mathbf{x}^{(k)}\right]^T \mathcal{H}_i^{(k)}\left[\underline{\alpha} - \mathbf{x}^{(k)}\right] + \ldots$$

or

$$\alpha_j - x_j^{(k+1)} = -\frac{1}{2}\sum_{i=1}^{N}\left[\mathbf{A}^{(k)}\right]_{ji}^{-1}\left\{\left[\underline{\alpha} - \mathbf{x}^{(k)}\right]^T \mathcal{H}_i^{(k)}\left[\underline{\alpha} - \mathbf{x}^{(k)}\right]\right\}$$

$$+ \ldots; \quad j = 1, 2, \ldots, N \qquad \ldots(g)$$

Equation 3.48 is a special case of this more general equation.

We now follow an analysis similar to that used for obtaining eq. 3.28. If the maximum absolute value (among all j) of $\left|\alpha_j - x_j^{(k+1)}\right|$ is $E^{(k+1)}$, and the maximum values of $\left|\alpha_j - x_j^{(k)}\right|$, $\left[\mathcal{H}_i^{(k)}\right]_{pq}$ (over all i, p and q) and $\left|\left[\mathbf{A}^{(k)}\right]_{ji}^{-1}\right|$ are $E^{(k)}$ M, R, respectively, then eq. (g) leads to

$$E^{(k+1)} \leq \left(\frac{1}{2}RMN^3\right)\left[E^{(k)}\right]^2 \qquad \ldots(h)$$

The equation predicts second order convergence characteristics of the multivariable Newton-Raphson technique. ∎

Several library subroutines are available [8, 13] which use the Newton-Raphson procedure (coupled with search algorithms, etc.). ZREAL2 (IMSL) used this method, with numerical evaluation of $F'(x)$. ZSCNT and ZSPOW (IMSL) use quasi-Newton techniques (see sec. 3.6) and are quite effective (see example 3.8 later). Hiebert [8, 14] tested eight available library subroutines with about 170 different sets of multivariable nonlinear algebraic equations, and concluded that all the eight subroutines were about equally effective, but most of them were able to solve only about 90 to 100 of these test problems. This gives an idea of how difficult it can be to obtain solutions of nonlinear algebraic equations (see prob. 3.23). It may also be noted that the Newton-Raphson technique can be used when $\mathbf{F}(\mathbf{x})$ is complex. Also, it is better to scale the equations so that all the variables have similar ranges.

3.6 OTHER TECHNIQUES

A multitude of other techniques are available for the solution of sets of nonlinear algebraic equations (eq. 3.2). Many of these are adaptations of the Newton-Raphson algorithm. The *secant method*, for example, replaces the tangent in fig. 3.6 (or the derivative, F', in eq. 3.39) by a secant (or chord). This is illustrated graphically in fig. 3.7. Points A and B corresponding to $x^{(k)}$ and $x^{(k+1)}$, are used to draw a secant, AB, which intercepts the abscissa at point C, which is $x^{(k+2)}$. A secant is then drawn from point B to D, and extended till the abscissa to give $x^{(k+3)}$ etc. One must have two locations, $x^{(1)}$ and $x^{(2)}$, to start off the calculations. The algorithm is given by

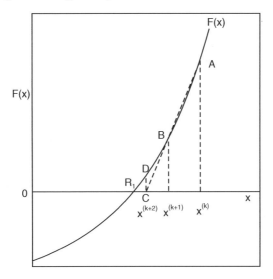

Fig. 3.7 The Secant method for a 1-variable problem.

$$x^{(k+2)} = x^{(k+1)} - \frac{F\left[x^{(k+1)}\right]}{\dfrac{F\left[x^{(k+1)}\right] - F\left[x^{(k)}\right]}{x^{(k+1)} - x^{(k)}}}; \quad k = 1, 2, \ldots \qquad \ldots(3.57)$$

The method is quite similar to the Newton-Raphson technique using a numerical estimate for $F'[x^{(k)}]$, except that the two locations, $x^{(2)}$ and $x^{(1)}$, can be chosen by the user, and can be farther apart than if the derivative is estimated numerically. The multivariable equivalent of eq. 3.57 can be implemented on the computer, but is inconvenient to write down [8]. Expressions for the partial derivatives in $\mathbf{A}^{(k)}$ can be written in a manner similar to what was done for $F'(x)$ in eq. 3.57. The secant method also shows quadratic convergence *as a root is approached.*

Another popular technique which is similar to the secant method is *regula-falsi*, or the method of false positions. In this, two points $[x^{(1)}, 0]$ and $[x^{(2)}, 0]$, are first obtained such that $F[x^{(1)}] \, F[x^{(2)}] < 0$. This may be done by using, for example, an incremental search on the variable, x. It is assumed that there is only one root, α, of $F(x) = 0$, in this region $x^{(1)} \le x \le x^{(2)}$. We now draw a straight line (see fig. 3.8) between points A, $[x^{(1)}, F(x^{(1)})]$ and B, $[x^{(2)}, F(x^{(2)})]$. The next estimate of the root, $x^{(3)}$, is the point of intersection of AB with the abscissa. It is obvious that convergence is assured if the curvature of $F(x)$ does not change in $x^{(1)} \le x \le x^{(2)}$. The algorithm is given by

$$x^{(k+2)} = \frac{x^{(k)} F\left[x^{(k+1)}\right] - x^{(k+1)} F\left[x^{(k)}\right]}{F\left[x^{(k+1)}\right] - F\left[x^{(k)}\right]}$$

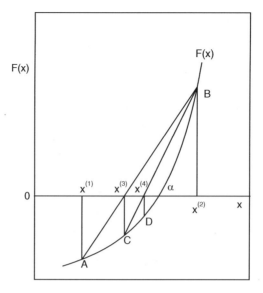

Fig. 3.8 The regula-falsi method.

$$= x^{(k+1)} - \frac{F\left[x^{(k+1)}\right]\left[x^{(k+1)} - x^{(k)}\right]}{F\left[x^{(k+1)}\right] - F\left[x^{(k)}\right]}; \quad k = 1, 2, \ldots \qquad \ldots(3.58)$$

which is the same as that for the method of secants. The difference is that in this method, the two values, $x^{(k+1)}$ and $x^{(k)}$ must lie such that the $F(x)$ are of opposite signs. Thus, we must use:

if $F[x^{(k+2)}]\, F[x^{(k+1)}] < 0$:   continue next iteration as above $\ldots(a)$

if $F[x^{(k+2)}]\, F[x^{(k)}] < 0$:   rename $x^{(k)}$ as $x^{(k+1)}$ and continue next iteration
with $x^{(k+2)}$ and the *new* $x^{(k+1)}$ $\ldots(b)$ $\ldots(3.59)$

In the method of secants, the two latest estimates, $x^{(k)}$ and $x^{(k+1)}$ are used, irrespective of whether $F[x^{(k)}]$ $F[x^{(k+1)}]$ is positive or negative.

The IMSL library contains ZFALSE which uses this technique. In addition, it contains a program ZBRENT which is a combination of [8] the secant and regula-falsi techniques.

A popular technique of solving nonlinear algebraic equations is the Levenberg-Marquardt method [19–21]. In this technique, an objective function, $G(\mathbf{x})$, is first defined:

$$G(\mathbf{x}) = \sum_{i=1}^{N} F_i^2(\mathbf{x}) \qquad \ldots(3.60)$$

The values of $\mathbf{x}$ which minimize $G(\mathbf{x})$ (and make it zero) are the roots of the N equations in eq. 3.2. The Levenberg-Marquardt method uses an adaptation of the Newton's method for seeking the minimum of a function of several variables. The actual function, $G(\mathbf{x})$, is approximated by a quadratic function around $\mathbf{x}^{(k)}$ using a Taylor series:

$$G(\mathbf{x}) \cong G\left[\mathbf{x}^{(k)}\right] + \left[\underline{\nabla} G^{(k)}\right]^T \left[\mathbf{x} - \mathbf{x}^{(k)}\right] + \frac{1}{2}\left[\mathbf{x} - \mathbf{x}^{(k)}\right]^T \mathcal{H}^{(k)}\left[\mathbf{x} - \mathbf{x}^{(k)}\right] \qquad \ldots(3.61)$$

where $\mathcal{H}^{(k)}$ is the Hessian matrix [eq. (*f*), example 3.7] of $G(\mathbf{x})$, evaluated at $\mathbf{x}^{(k)}$. The minimum of this quadratic function is obtained by differentiating G analytically with respect to each of the variables, x_i, and equating the derivatives to zero. This leads to

$$\underline{\nabla} G^{(k)} + \mathcal{H}^{(k)}\left[\mathbf{x} - \mathbf{x}^{(k)}\right] = \mathbf{0}$$

or

$$\mathbf{x}^{(k+1)} = \mathbf{x}^{(k)} - \left[\mathcal{H}^{(k)}\right]^{-1} \underline{\nabla} G^{(k)} \qquad \qquad \dots(3.62)$$

This is Newton's method for the minimization [21] of G $(\mathbf{x})$. Note that if $\mathcal{H}^{(k)}$ is a unit diagonal matrix, we have the steepest descent method. In the Levenberg-Marquardt technique, one uses a modified Hessian matrix $\overline{\mathcal{H}}^{(k)}$, in eq. 3.62:

$$\overline{\mathcal{H}}^{(k)} = \mathcal{H}^{(k)} + \beta^{(k)}\mathbf{I} \qquad \qquad \dots(3.63)$$

where $\beta^{(k)}$ is a large positive constant in the beginning $(k = 1)$. This adaptation makes $\overline{\mathcal{H}}^{(k)}$ positive definite and well conditioned. One starts with a large value, $\beta^{(1)}$, and adapts it along the path towards the optimal [21] in a way that as one approaches the optimum, one switches over from a (near) steepest descent technique to Newton's technique. IMSL has a program NEQNF which uses this method.

The use of the multivariable Newton-Raphson technique (eq. 3.55) often poses numerical problems due to the computation of the inverse of the Jacobian, $[\mathbf{A}^{(k)}]^{-1}$. Several techniques are available to obtain *approximate* values of $[\mathbf{A}^{(k)}]^{-1}$, using values of $\Delta\mathbf{x}^{(k)} \equiv \mathbf{x}^{(k+1)} - \mathbf{x}^{(k)}$ and $\Delta\mathbf{F}^{(k)} \equiv \mathbf{F}[\mathbf{x}^{(k+1)}] - \mathbf{F}[\mathbf{x}^{(k)}]$. Most of these methods start with the approximation $[\mathbf{A}^{(1)}]^{-1} = \mathbf{I}$, and then use eq. 3.55 with a continuous update of $[\mathbf{A}^{(k)}]^{-1}$. The exact equations to be used for the latter are available in ref. 21 (eqs. 6.30–6.33) for several popular techniques [*e.g.*, those of Broyden; Davidon-Fletcher-Powell; and Broyden-Fletcher-Goldfarb-Shanno]. It may be noted that the equations in ref. 21 are applicable to optimization problems, but can be used with eq. 3.55 if $\mathbf{H}^k$ and $\Delta\mathbf{g}^k$ in ref. 21 are replaced by $\mathbf{A}^{(k)}$ and $\Delta\mathbf{F}^{(k)}$, to obtain the roots of $\mathbf{F}$ $(\mathbf{x}) = \mathbf{0}$.

A whole family of search techniques is also available to look for the solution of the 1-variable eq. 3.36. These parallel the techniques used in optimization. The *incremental search technique* has already been described. In this method [as applied to the solution of $F(x) = 0$], a low value of x, say $x^{(1)}$, is taken and values of $F(x)$ are obtained at values of x differing from each other by a constant, Δx. Whenever $F[x^{(k)}]\,F[x^{(k+1)}] < 0$, one stops and uses some other technique to converge to the solution (or solutions) inside this range. The difficulties associated with this method include often not knowing how many roots exist, and the range of x to be explored. Also, it is difficult to extend this method to the multivariable case.

In Bolzano's *bisection method* (also called *binary chop,* or *half-interval* method [15–17]), one computes $F(x)$ at two extreme locations, $x^{(1)}$ and $x^{(2)}$, within which the solution(s) is expected to lie. The points should preferably be chosen such that $F[x^{(1)}]\,F[x^{(2)}]$ is negative, so that at least one root lies between these two locations. The value of $F(x)$ at the mid point, $x^{(3)} = [x^{(1)} + x^{(2)}]/2$, is then computed, and based upon its sign, one must consider only one of the two intervals $x^{(1)} \le x \le x^{(3)}$ {if $F[x^{(1)}]F[x^{(3)}] < 0$} or $x^{(3)} \le x \le x^{(2)}$ {if $F[x^{(3)}]F[x^{(2)}] < 0$}. The half-interval remaining is bisected again in the next iteration, and the relevant interval is retained. This is continued until the interval remaining is small enough and satisfies the requirements of accuracy. The number of function evaluations, NF, required to reduce the interval of uncertainty from $|x^{(2)} - x^{(1)}|$ in the beginning, to a value Δ, can easily be deduced to be

$$NF = 2 + \ln\left\{\left|x^{(2)} - x^{(1)}\right|/\Delta\right\}/\ln 2 \qquad \qquad \dots(3.64)$$

The *golden section* search [21, 22] [as adapted for the solution of $F(x) = 0$] is an improvement over the bisection technique and is faster. Details of these and other techniques useful for multivariable problems can be found in most texts on optimization.

Example 3.8: Solve the following problem [first suggested by Powell [23]]:

$$F_1(\mathbf{x}) \equiv 10^4 x_1 x_2 - 1 = 0$$

$$F_2(\mathbf{x}) \equiv \exp(-x_1) + \exp(-x_2) - 1.0001 = 0$$

starting from $\mathbf{x}^{(1)} = [0 \quad 1]^T$. The solution, $\mathbf{x} = [1.098 \times 10^{-5} \quad 9.106]^T$, is not too easy to obtain. Use an available library program (Buzzi Ferraris and Tronconi [24] study several available computer packages for solving nonlinear algebraic equations and test their performance on a number of difficult equations). Calculate the error defined by

$$\text{Error} \equiv \sum_{i=1}^{N} \left\{ F_i \left[\mathbf{x}^{(k)} \right] \right\}^2$$

The above problem is ill-scaled and has ill-conditioned Jacobian values. A computer program, NEQNF (IMSL), using the Levenberg-Marquardt technique, is used to solve this and the results are given below:

k	$x_1^{(k)}$	$x_2^{(k)}$	Error
1	0.0000	1.0000	1.1353
2	3.4531×10^{-4}	1.0000	6.1526
3	0.0000	1.0003	1.1352
4	9.9999×10^{-5}	2.0000	1.0183
5	-5.8182×10^{-5}	2.5818	6.2665
10	3.5922×10^{-5}	2.7501	4.216×10^{-3}
50	1.5697×10^{-5}	6.3752	3.04×10^{-6}
180	1.09867×10^{-5}	9.1018	5.8×10^{-13}

Note the slow convergence to the root. ∎

Before closing the discussion on the general solution of nonlinear algebraic equations, it must be mentioned that, at times, the number of equations becomes prohibitively large. 100,000 equations are not uncommon in the simulation of chemical plants. Special techniques have been developed to decompose these large systems into smaller sets, using techniques like partitioning and tearing, as well as sequencing of equations in a way which reduces the computational effort. Let us consider a simple example:

$$F_1(x_1, x_3) = 0 \qquad \qquad \ldots(a)$$

$$F_2(x_2, x_4) = 0 \qquad \qquad \ldots(b)$$

$$F_3(x_2, x_4) = 0 \qquad \qquad \ldots(c)$$

$$F_4(x_1) = 0 \qquad \qquad \ldots(d) \qquad \ldots(3.65)$$

One can solve eq. 3.65 (d) *first* to obtain x_1, *then* solve eq. 3.65(a) for x_3, and then solve eqs. 3.65(b) and (c) together to give x_2 and x_4. Solving eq. 3.65 in this manner is much faster than solving all four equations simultaneously. The reader is referred to Westerberg et al. [25] for an excellent discussion of techniques to decompose sets of equations into subsets and sequences.

3.7 SPECIAL TECHNIQUES FOR OBTAINING ROOTS OF POLYNOMIALS

It was noted in sec. 2.1 that the equation

$$F_1(x) \equiv P_{N_1}(x) = x^{N_1} + \overline{a}_1 x^{N_1-1} + \overline{a}_2 x^{N_1-2} + ... + \overline{a}_{N_1-1}x + \overline{a}_{N_1} = 0 \qquad ...(3.66)$$

involving an N_1th-degree polynomial in x (note that the polynomial is written slightly differently than in eq. 2.7), has precisely N_1 roots. Even if the coefficients, $\overline{a}_i$, are all real some of the roots, α_i; $i = 1$, 2, ..., N_1, could occur as complex conjugate pairs. In addition, some roots could be equal (multiple roots). Such equations are commonly encountered in engineering and the characteristic equation of matrices (eq. 2.7) is an example. In chemical engineering, for example several equations of state used to estimate the values of the compressibility factor (see prob. 3.4) at given temperatures and pressures, are of this form. Often, we need to compute *all* the roots of such polynomials.

The procedure usually followed is to obtain the N_2 *real* roots first, using for example, the Newton-Raphson technique coupled with a search method. After a root is obtained *deflation* (see prob. 3.17 and later in this section) of the polynomial is carried out. For example, after obtaining the first root, α_1, we factor it out (analytically) of the polynomial:

$$P_{N_1-1}(x) = \frac{P_{N_1}(x)}{(x-\alpha_1)} \qquad ...(3.67)$$

and then continue to obtain the next root, α_2, using P_{N_1-1}. Several computer packages can perform deflation as well as account for multiple roots. After all the real roots have been factored out, an Nth degree polynomial is obtained, with N being *even*:

$$F(x) \equiv P_N(x) = x^N + a_1 x^{N-1} + a_2 x^{N-2} + ... + a_{N-1}x + a_N = 0 \qquad ...(3.68)$$

The N roots of this polynomial are all *complex* (conjugate pairs). One can continue to use the Newton-Raphson technique using complex arithmetic (with the initial estimate, $x^{(1)}$, being a complex number). The algorithm is the same as given in eq. 3.39, with $x^{(k)}$, $F[x^{(k)}]$ and $F'[x^{(k)}]$ being complex numbers or functions. This procedure also works on polynomials having complex coefficients, the roots of which would not necessarily be complex conjugates. Deflation using complex roots is usually inconvenient to apply.

A popular technique [7, 16] of finding the pairs of complex conjugate roots of $P_N(x)$ in eq. 3.68 is that of Lin [26] and Bairstow [27, 28]. This exploits the relationship

$$[x-(a+ib)][x-(a-ib)] = x^2 - 2ax + (a^2 + b^2) \qquad ...(3.69)$$

and attempts to find a quadratic *with real coefficients*, which is a factor of the polynomial, $P_N(x)$. The two complex conjugate roots can then be found using the analytical expression for the roots of a quadratic (having a negative discriminant). This method does away with the need for complex arithmetic. Multiple applications of the algorithm, coupled with deflation, can lead to the computation of all the roots of $P_N(x)$ two at a time. In order to discuss this method, we note that if we divide $P_N(x)$ by *any* quadratic

$$Q(x) \equiv x^2 + \beta x + \gamma \qquad ...(3.70)$$

we will get a new polynomial, $B_{N-2}(x)$, of degree $N-2$, and a remainder, $R(x)$, which would, in general, be a linear function of x (one degree lower than the quadratic). Thus,

$$P_N(x) = Q(x)B_{N-2}(x) + R(x) \qquad ...(3.71)$$

In this method, one attempts to find the values, $(\bar{\beta}, \bar{\gamma})$, of the two coefficients in $Q(x)$ such that the remainder, $R(x)$, becomes zero. For such a choice, $B_{N-2}(x)$ is the deflated form, $P_{N-2}(x)$, of the original polynomial, $P_N(x)$, and the roots of $x^2 + \bar{\beta}x + \bar{\gamma}$ are the two roots of $P_N(x)$.

If we write

$$B_{N-2}(x) = x^{N-2} + b_1 x^{N-3} + \ldots + b_{N-3}x + b_{N-2}$$

$$R(x) = \gamma_1 x + \gamma_2 \qquad \qquad \ldots(3.72)$$

and substitute the expressions for $P_N(x)$, $Q(x)$, $B_{N-2}(x)$ and $R(x)$ from eqs. 3.68, 3.70 and 3.72 into eq. 3.71, we obtain [upon equating coefficients of like powers of x on both sides of the equation]:

$$
\begin{aligned}
a_1 &= b_1 &&+ &&\beta \\
a_2 &= b_2 &&+ b_1 &&\beta + &&\gamma \\
a_3 &= b_3 &&+ b_2 &&\beta + b_1 &&\gamma \\
&\;\;. &&\;\;. \\
&\;\;. &&\;\;. \\
&\;\;. &&\;\;. \\
a_i &= b_i &&+ b_{i-1} &&\beta + b_{i-2} &&\gamma \\
&\;\;. &&\;\;. \\
&\;\;. &&\;\;. \\
&\;\;. &&\;\;. \\
a_{N-2} &= b_{N-2} &&+ b_{N-3} &&\beta + b_{N-4} &&\gamma \\
a_{N-1} &= &&\;\; b_{N-2} &&\beta + b_{N-3} &&\gamma + r_1 &&\ldots(a) \\
a_N &= &&&&b_{N-2} &&\gamma + r_2 &&\ldots(b) &&\ldots(3.73)
\end{aligned}
$$

Equation 3.73 can be written in a *general* form as

$$a_i = b_i + b_{i-1}\beta + b_{i-2}\gamma \; ; \quad i = 1, 2, \ldots, N \qquad \ldots(3.74)$$

with the following additional equations to complete the equivalence between eqs. 3.73 and 3.74:

$$
\begin{aligned}
b_{-1} &= 0 &&\ldots(a) \\
b_0 &= 1 &&\ldots(b) \\
b_{N-1} &= r_1 &&\ldots(c) \\
b_N &= r_2 - r_1\beta &&\ldots(d) &&\ldots(3.75)
\end{aligned}
$$

The introduction of two additional constants, b_{N-1} and b_N (in place of r_1 and r_2), is not essential, but is useful particularly in the technique of Bairstow.

If we want the remainder, $R(x)$, to be zero, r_1 and r_2 must be zero in eq. 3.73 and we will have to solve the following N nonlinear algebraic equations in the N variables, $b_1, b_2, \ldots, b_{N-2}, \beta, \gamma$:

$$
\begin{aligned}
F_1(\mathbf{b}, \beta, \gamma) &\equiv \beta + b_1 &&-a_1 &&= 0 \\
F_2(\mathbf{b}, \beta, \gamma) &\equiv \gamma + \beta b_1 + b_2 &&-a_2 &&= 0 \\
F_3(\mathbf{b}, \beta, \gamma) &\equiv \gamma b_1 + \beta b_2 + b_3 &&-a_3 &&= 0
\end{aligned}
$$

$$F_4\left(\mathbf{b},\beta,\gamma\right) \equiv \qquad \gamma b_2 + \beta b_3 + b_4 \qquad -a_4 \quad = 0$$

$$\vdots \qquad\qquad\qquad\qquad \vdots \qquad \vdots$$

$$F_{N-2}\left(\mathbf{b},\beta,\gamma\right) \equiv \qquad \gamma b_{N-4} + \beta b_{N-3} + b_{N-2} \; -a_{N-2} = 0$$

$$F_{N-1}\left(\mathbf{b},\beta,\gamma\right) \equiv \qquad \gamma b_{N-3} + \beta b_{N-2} \; -a_{N-1} = 0$$

$$F_N\left(\mathbf{b},\beta,\gamma\right) \equiv \qquad\qquad \gamma b_{N-2} \; -a_N \quad = 0 \qquad \ldots(3.76)$$

In more general form, the equation is written as

$$F_i\left(\mathbf{b},\beta,\gamma\right) \equiv \gamma b_{i-2} + \beta b_{i-1} + b_i - a_i = 0; \quad i = 1, 2, \ldots, N \qquad \ldots(3.77)$$

Lin [26] has suggested an adaptation of the successive substitutions algorithm to solve the above equations. Instead of assuming values for the entire set of variables (which is not required), the special structure of eq. 3.76 (or 3.77) is exploited to give the following procedure:

(*a*) Assume $\beta^{(k)}$, $\gamma^{(k)}$ ($k = 1$)

(*b*) Solve the first $N - 2$ equations in eq. 3.76 sequentially to give

$$b_1^{(k)} = a_1 - \beta^{(k)} \qquad\qquad\qquad\qquad \ldots(a)$$
$$b_2^{(k)} = a_2 - \beta^{(k)} b_1^{(k)} - \gamma^{(k)} \qquad\qquad \ldots(b)$$
$$b_3^{(k)} = a_3 - \beta^{(k)} b_2^{(k)} - \gamma^{(k)} b_1^{(k)} \qquad \ldots(c)$$
$$\vdots$$
$$b_i^{(k)} = a_i - \beta^{(k)} b_{i-1}^{(k)} - \gamma^{(k)} b_{i-2}^{(k)} \qquad \ldots(d)$$
$$\vdots$$
$$b_{N-2}^{(k)} = a_{N-2} - \beta^{(k)} b_{N-3}^{(k)} - \gamma^{(k)} b_{N-4}^{(k)} \qquad \ldots(e) \qquad \ldots(3.78)$$

The generalized version of this equation is given as

$$b_i^{(k)} = a_i - \beta^{(k)} b_{i-1}^{(k)} - \gamma^{(k)} b_{i-2}^{(k)}; \qquad i = 1, 2, \ldots, N - 2 \qquad \ldots(3.79)$$

Note the similarity of this to the Gauss-Seidel algorithm (eq. 1.28).

(*c*) use the last two equations in eq. 3.76 to update β and γ:

$$\gamma^{(k+1)} = \frac{a_N}{b_{N-2}^{(k)}} \qquad \ldots(a)$$

$$\beta^{(k+1)} = \frac{a_{N-1} - b_{N-3}^{(k)} \gamma^{(k)}}{b_{N-2}^{(k)}} \qquad \ldots(b) \qquad \ldots(3.80)$$

The algorithm is repeated until the values of β and γ converge to the values, $\bar{\beta}$ and $\bar{\gamma}$. At this point, one already has (in computer storage) the latest values of the coefficients, $b_i^{(k)}$; $k = 1, 2, \ldots, N - 2$, required to generate the deflated polynomial, $B_{N-2}(x)$. Deflation of $P_N(x)$ with $Q(x) = x^2 + \beta^{(k)}x + \gamma^{(k)}$

is, thus, simultaneously achieved. It is not surprising that this technique is first-order converging, since it is an adaptation of the successive substitutions technique.

The last two equations in eq. 3.73 can be used to give estimates of the remainder, $R(x)$, through the coefficients, r_1 and r_2, at the kth iteration:

$$b_{N-1}^{(k)} = r_1^{(k)} = a_{N-1} - b_{N-2}^{(k)}\beta^{(k)} - b_{N-3}^{(k)}\gamma^{(k)}$$

$$r_2^{(k)} = a_N - b_{N-2}^{(k)}\gamma^{(k)} = b_N^{(k)} + b_{N-1}^{(k)}\beta^{(k)} \qquad \qquad ...(3.81)$$

Example 3.9: Use Lin's technique with $\beta^{(1)} = -1$, $\gamma^{(1)} = 1$, to find the complex (conjugate) roots of the polynomial equation

$$P_4(x) = x^4 - 6x^3 + 15x^2 - 18x + 10 = 0$$

eq. 3.79 is easily written (using eq. 3.75) using $a_1 = -6$, $a_2 = 15$, $a_3 = -18$, $a_4 = 10$, as

$$b_1^{(k)} = a_1 - b_0\beta^{(k)} - b_{-1}\gamma^{(k)} = -6 - \beta^{(k)}$$

$$b_2^{(k)} = a_2 - b_1^{(k)}\beta^{(k)} - b_0\gamma^{(k)} = 15 - b_1^{(k)}\beta^{(k)} - \gamma^{(k)}$$

eq. 3.80 gives the equations for updating β and γ:

$$\gamma^{(k+1)} = \frac{a_4}{b_2^{(k)}} = \frac{10}{b_2^{(k)}}$$

$$\beta^{(k+1)} = \frac{a_3 - b_1^{(k)}\gamma^{(k)}}{b_2^{(k)}} = \frac{-18 - b_1^{(k)}\gamma^{(k)}}{b_2^{(k)}} \qquad \qquad ...(a)$$

eq. 3.81 gives

$$r_1^{(k)} = -18 - b_2^{(k)}\beta^{(k)} - b_1^{(k)}\gamma^{(k)} = b_3^{(k)}$$

$$r_2^{(k)} = 10 - b_2^{(k)}\gamma^{(k)} = b_4^{(k)} + b_3^{(k)}\beta^{(k)}$$

The following table gives the results for two iterations, correct to four decimal places, alongwith the exact values.

k Coefficients	1	2	3	10	Exact
$\gamma^{(k)}$	1	1.1111	1.3682	2.2853	2
$\beta^{(k)}$	-1	-1.4444	-1.7703	-2.0999	-2
$b_1^{(k)}$	-5	-4.5556	-4.2297	-3.900	-4
$b_2^{(k)}$	9	7.3088	6.1440	4.5249	5
$r_1^{(k)} = b_3^{(k)}$	-4	-2.3814	-1.3362	0.4146	0
$b_4^{(k)}$	-3	-1.5605	-0.7719	0.5301	0
$r_2^{(k)}$	1	1.8792	1.9508	-0.3392	0

Note the slow convergence to the correct values, γ and $\bar{\beta}$, corresponding to which the values of $b_i^{(k)}$ are also shown. The deflated polynomial and the quadratic are thus,

$$P_2(x) = x^2 - 4x + 5 = 0$$

$$Q(x) = x^2 - 2x + 2 = 0$$

The four roots can be easily calculated as $(1 \pm i)$ and $(2 \pm i)$. A slight increase in the rate of convergence can be obtained by using the most recent value, $\gamma^{(k+1)}$, in place of $\gamma^{(k)}$ in eq. (a) above, or in eq. 3.80(b). ∎

Bairstow [27, 28] has suggested a technique similar to that of Lin, using the Newton-Raphson method to compute $\beta^{(k+1)}$ and $\gamma^{(k+1)}$ from their kth iterate values. The equations are given as (see eqs. 3.77 and 3.75) before as:

$$b_i = a_i - \beta\, b_{i-1} - \gamma\, b_{i-2}\, ; \ i = 1, 2, ..., N \qquad ...(a)$$

$$r_1 = b_{N-1} \qquad\quad = 0 \qquad ...(b)$$

$$r_2 = b_N + \beta b_{N-1} = 0 \qquad ...(c) \qquad\qquad ...(3.82)$$

with b_{-1} and b_0 given by eqs. 3.75(a) and (b). Eqs. 3.82(b) and (c) can be expanded using a two-variable Taylor series to give

$$0 = r_1\left[\beta^{(k+1)}, \gamma^{(k+1)}\right] = r_1\left[\beta^{(k)}, \gamma^{(k)}\right] + \frac{\partial r_1}{\partial \beta}(\Delta\beta) + \frac{\partial r_1}{\partial \gamma}(\Delta\gamma)$$

$$0 = r_2\left[\beta^{(k+1)}, \gamma^{(k+1)}\right] = r_2\left[\beta^{(k)}, \gamma^{(k)}\right] + \frac{\partial r_2}{\partial \beta}(\Delta\beta) + \frac{\partial r_2}{\partial \gamma}(\Delta\gamma) \qquad ...(3.83)$$

where the left hand side is equated to zero, as is the standard practice for the Newton-Raphson method. In eq. 3.83, the derivatives are evaluated at $\beta^{(k)}$, $\gamma^{(k)}$, and the increments, $\Delta\beta$ and $\Delta\gamma$, can be used to give $\beta^{(k+1)}$, $\gamma^{(k+1)}$ using

$$\beta^{(k+1)} = \beta^{(k)} + \Delta\beta$$

$$\gamma^{(k+1)} = \gamma^{(k)} + \Delta\gamma \qquad ...(3.84)$$

Equation 3.83 can be simplified after substituting the expressions for r_1 and r_2 from eq. 3.82(b) and (c), to give

$$0 = b_{N-1} + \left(\frac{\partial b_{N-1}}{\partial \beta}\right)(\Delta\beta) + \left(\frac{\partial b_{N-1}}{\partial \gamma}\right)(\Delta\gamma)$$

$$0 = b_N + \beta b_{N-1} + \left[\frac{\partial b_N}{\partial \beta} + \beta\frac{\partial b_{N-1}}{\partial \beta} + b_{N-1}\right](\Delta\beta) + \left[\frac{\partial b_N}{\partial \gamma} + \beta\frac{\partial b_{N-1}}{\partial \gamma}\right](\Delta\gamma) \qquad ...(3.85)$$

where the superscripts (k) have been omitted for brevity. The coefficients, b_{N-1} and b_N, are obtained (as in Lin's technique) by solving eq. 3.82(a) *sequentially* from $i = 1$ to $i = N$, using initial estimates, $\beta^{(1)}$ and $\gamma^{(1)}$. The various derivatives in eq. 3.85 are then obtained using the sequential procedure discussed below.

Bairstow developed a sequential computational technique for obtaining the various partial derivatives required in eq. 3.85. Using eq. 3.82(a) and differentiating it partially with respect to β first, gives (note that the a_i are constant, but the b_i depend on both β and γ):

$$-\frac{\partial b_1}{\partial \beta} = 1$$

$$-\frac{\partial b_2}{\partial \beta} = b_1 \quad + \beta \frac{\partial b_1}{\partial \beta}$$

$$-\frac{\partial b_3}{\partial \beta} = b_2 \quad + \beta \frac{\partial b_2}{\partial \beta} \quad + \gamma \frac{\partial b_1}{\partial \beta}$$

.
.

$$-\frac{\partial b_i}{\partial \beta} = b_{i-1} + \beta \frac{\partial b_{i-1}}{\partial \beta} + \gamma \frac{\partial b_{i-2}}{\partial \beta}$$

.
.

$$-\frac{\partial b_N}{\partial \beta} = b_{N-1} + \beta \frac{\partial b_{N-1}}{\partial \beta} + \gamma \frac{\partial b_{N-2}}{\partial \beta} \qquad \ldots(3.86)$$

If we define

$$d_{i-1} \equiv -\frac{\partial b_i}{\partial \beta}; \quad i = 1, 2, \ldots, N \qquad \ldots(3.87)$$

we can rewrite eq. 3.86 as

$$d_i \equiv -\frac{\partial b_{i+1}}{\partial \beta} = b_i - \beta d_{i-1} - \gamma d_{i-2}; \quad i = 0, 1, \ldots, N-1 \qquad \ldots(3.88)$$

with

$$d_{-1} = 0$$

$$d_{-2} = 0 \qquad \ldots(3.89)$$

used to complete the definitions. A sequential application of eq. 3.88 gives $\dfrac{\partial b_{N-1}}{\partial \beta}$ and $\dfrac{\partial b_N}{\partial \beta}$ required in eq. 3.85.

A similar procedure can be used to obtain the derivatives with respect to γ. From eq. 3.82(a), we have

$$-\frac{\partial b_1}{\partial \gamma} = 0$$

$$-\frac{\partial b_2}{\partial \gamma} = 1 \quad + \beta \frac{\partial b_1}{\partial \beta}$$

$$-\frac{\partial b_3}{\partial \gamma} = b_1 \quad + \beta \frac{\partial b_2}{\partial \gamma} \quad + \gamma \frac{\partial b_1}{\partial \gamma}$$

.

$$-\frac{\partial b_i}{\partial \gamma} = b_{i-2} \quad + \beta \frac{\partial b_{i-1}}{\partial \gamma} + \gamma \frac{\partial b_{i-2}}{\partial \gamma}$$

.

.

.

$$-\frac{\partial b_N}{\partial \gamma} = b_{N-2} \quad + \beta \frac{\partial b_{N-1}}{\partial \gamma} + \gamma \frac{\partial b_{N-2}}{\partial \gamma} \qquad \qquad \ldots(3.90)$$

If we define (note the ingenuity)

$$d_{i-2} \equiv -\frac{\partial b_i}{\partial \gamma}; \quad i = 1, 2, \ldots, N \qquad \qquad \ldots(3.91)$$

with $d_{-2} = 0$ and $d_{-3} = 0$, as before, then eq. 3.90 can be written in *exactly* the same form (with $i = -1, 0, 1, \ldots, N-2$) as eq. 3.88. Thus, in a single application of eq. 3.88, one obtains *both* the derivatives of b_i with respect to β, as well as with respect to γ. Equation 3.85 can be rewritten in terms of d_i, as

$$b_{N-1} - d_{N-2}(\Delta\beta) - d_{N-3}(\Delta\gamma) = 0$$

$$b_N + \beta b_{N-1} + \left[b_{N-1} - d_{N-1} - \beta d_{N-2} \right](\Delta\beta) + \left[-d_{N-2} - \beta d_{N-3} \right](\Delta\gamma) = 0 \qquad \ldots(3.92)$$

The algorithm is, thus:

(*a*) assume values for $\beta^{(k)}$ and $\gamma^{(k)}$ ($k = 1$)

(*b*) compute $b_1^{(k)}, b_2^{(k)}, \ldots, b_N^{(k)}$ sequentially [eqs. 3.82(*a*) and 3.75(*a*) and (*b*)]

(*c*) compute $d_0^{(k)}, d_1^{(k)}, \ldots, d_{N-1}^{(k)}$ sequentially [eqs. 3.88 and 3.89]

(*d*) evaluate ($\Delta\beta$) and ($\Delta\gamma$) using the analytical solution for simultaneous linear equations (eq. 3.92) in two variables, ($\Delta\beta$) and ($\Delta\gamma$).

(*e*) update $\beta^{(k+1)}$ and $\gamma^{(k+1)}$ [eq. 3.84]; continue until convergence of $\beta^{(k+1)}$ and $\gamma^{(k+1)}$ is achieved.

Example 3.10: Repeat example 3.9 from the same starting point, using Bairstow's second-order technique.

The expressions for $b_1^{(k)}, b_2^{(k)}, b_3^{(k)}$ and $b_4^{(k)}$, are the same as in example 3.9, and so the values of $b_i^{(1)}$ are identical. The equations for d_i are:

$$d_0^{(k)} = 1$$

$$d_1^{(k)} = b_1^{(k)} - \beta^{(k)}$$

$$d_2^{(k)} = b_2^{(k)} - \beta^{(k)} d_1^{(k)} - \gamma^{(k)}$$

$$d_3^{(k)} = b_3^{(k)} - \beta^{(k)} d_2^{(k)} - \gamma^{(k)} d_1^{(k)}$$

Starting from $\beta^{(1)} = -1$, $\gamma^{(1)} = 1$, and using the values of $b_i^{(1)}$, from the table in example 3.9, we obtain

$$\mathbf{d}^{(1)} = \begin{bmatrix} d_0^{(1)} & d_1^{(1)} & d_2^{(1)} & d_3^{(1)} \end{bmatrix} = \begin{bmatrix} 1 & -4 & 4 & 4 \end{bmatrix}$$

The equation for $\Delta\beta^{(k)}$ and $\Delta\gamma^{(k)}$ becomes

$$-4 - 4\left(\Delta\beta\right)^{(k)} + 4\left(\Delta\gamma\right)^{(k)} = 0$$

$$1 - 4\left(\Delta\beta\right)^{(k)} - 8\left(\Delta\gamma\right)^{(k)} = 0$$

Hence,

$$\Delta\gamma^{(k)} = \frac{5}{12} = 0.4167$$

$$\Delta\beta^{(k)} = \frac{-7}{12} = -0.5833$$

and so

$$\beta^{(2)} = \beta^{(1)} + \Delta\beta^{(1)} = -1.5833$$

$$\gamma^{(2)} = \gamma^{(1)} + \Delta\gamma^{(1)} = 1.4167$$

which are closer to $\bar{\beta} = -2$ and $\bar{\gamma} = 2$ than the values $\beta^{(1)} = -1.4444$, $\gamma^{(1)} = 1.1111$ obtained using Lin's first-order algorithm. Further calculations give:

k	$\beta^{(k)}$	$\gamma^{(k)}$	$b_1^{(k)}$	$b_2^{(k)}$	$b_3^{(k)}$	$b_4^{(k)}$	$d_1^{(k)}$	$d_2^{(k)}$	$d_3^{(k)}$
1	−1	1	−5	9	−4	−3	−4	4	4
2	−1.5833	1.4167	−4.4167	6.5903	−1.3084	−1.4079	−2.8333	0.6875	3.7940
3	−1.9108	1.7990	−4.0892	5.3874	−0.3493	−0.3595	−2.1784	−0.5742	2.4726
6	−2.0000	2.0001	−3.9999	4.9997	2.025×10^{-5}	3.084×10^{-4}	−1.9998	−1.0000	1.9993

∎

Several other techniques for obtaining the roots of polynomials are available, and the reader is referred to some excellent texts [6, 7, 17, 28, 29] for details. These methods include Graeffe's [30] root-squaring technique, Bernoulli's method, Rutihauser's [32] Q-D (quotient-difference) method, Horner's [33] method, etc. Graeffe's method is popular since it gives approximate values of *all* the roots in a single application, but it has to be followed up by a different method to converge to accurate values of the roots. The Bairstow technique is probably one of the better methods.

3.8 ELEMENTS OF CATASTROPHE AND SINGULARITY THEORIES

In this section, some elements of catastrophe and singularity theories [34–38] are discussed. These techniques give an idea of the number of roots of nonlinear algebraic equations for a given set of parameter values. We shall limit our discussion to functions, $F(x)$, of a single variable only. An almost trivial example is the quadratic equation involving a single parameter, c:

$$F(x, c) = x^2 + 4x + c = 0 \qquad \qquad ...(3.93)$$

We know that the number of (real) roots of this function depends upon the value of the parameter c (see fig. 3.9*a* on page 89):

two (real) roots for $c < 4$
one root (two identical roots) for $c = 4$
no root for $c > 4$ ...(3.94)

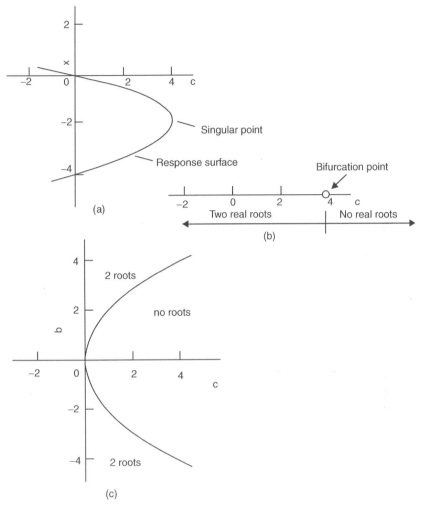

Fig. 3.9 (*a*) Response surface for $F(x, c) = x^2 + 4x + c = 0$ and (*b*) its bifurcation set. (*c*) Bifurcation set for $F(x, b, c) = x^2 + bx + c = 0$.

Similarly, the number of (real) roots for a function, $F(x, \mathbf{p})$, involving a single variable, x, and N parameters, $\mathbf{p} \equiv [p_1\ p_2...p_N]^T$, will depend on the values of these N parameters. An example of such a function (from chemical engineering) is the 'classic' [35] problem of the steady state operation of a non-adiabatic (or diabatic [35]) continuous flow stirred tank reactor (CSTR), in which an irreversible, exothermic, first order reaction, $A \rightarrow B$, is being carried out. The conversion, x, of the reactant can be written in terms of five parameters as [35]

$$F(x, \mathbf{p}) \equiv x - (1-x)Da \exp\left[\frac{Bx + a\theta_c Da}{1 + \alpha Da + (\alpha\theta_c Da + Bx)/\gamma}\right] = 0 \qquad ...(3.95)$$

with

$$\mathbf{p} \equiv \left[Da, B, \alpha, \theta_c, \gamma \right]^T \qquad \qquad ...(3.96)$$

In this equation, Da [$= Vk(T_f) / Q$] is the (dimensionless) Damkohler number, $B \left[= \dfrac{E}{RT_f} \dfrac{(-\Delta H_r) C_{Af}}{\rho C_p T_f} \right]$

is the dimensionless adiabatic temperature rise, $\alpha \left[= \dfrac{hA}{\rho C_p Vk(T_f)} \right]$ is the dimensionless heat transfer

coefficient, $\theta_c \left[= \dfrac{E}{RT_f} \dfrac{T_c - T_f}{T_f} \right]$ is the dimensionless coolant temperature, and $\gamma \left[= \dfrac{E}{RT_f} \right]$ is the

dimensionless activation energy [Ref. 35 gives the detailed nomenclature of the variables used here]. The equation for the dimensionless temperature can easily be written, and one form is given in prob. 3.25 (using different dimensionless groups than used in eq. 3.95).

The solution of eq. 3.93, $x(c) = -2 \pm \sqrt{4-c}$, is referred to as the response surface or the steady-state manifold. Figure 3.9(a) shows this manifold. This surface is quite smooth. It is easy to see that two solutions exist for $c < 4$ while none exist for $c > 4$. The point, $c = 4$, is referred to as a singular point of $F(x, c)$ (see fig. 3.9b). We next consider the simple quadratic function involving two parameters, F

$(x, b, c) \equiv x^2 + bx + c = 0$. The steady state manifold, $x(b, c) = \dfrac{\left(-b \pm \sqrt{b^2 - 4c} \right)}{2}$, can be visualized in

the three-dimensional x, b, c space with a small amount of effort. Again, there are two roots for certain

values of b and c $\left(\text{for } c < \dfrac{b^2}{4} \right)$ while no (real) roots exist if $c > \dfrac{b^2}{4}$. Thus, $x = \dfrac{-b}{2}, c = \dfrac{b^2}{4}$ represents

the locus of singular points in the x, b, c space, at which the number of roots changes suddenly from two to zero. Figure 3.9(c) shows a projection of this locus in the b, c space.

The solution, $x(\mathbf{p})$, of the general equation, $F(x, \mathbf{p}) = 0$, is referred to as the steady state manifold. It can be represented as a smooth surface in the $N + 1$ dimensional $(x, p_1, p_2, ..., p_N)$ space. The behaviour of these general surfaces (as for example eq. 3.95) is far more complex than that of the simple quadratic functions shown in fig. 3.9; there could be more than two real roots, and there could be several transitions where the number of roots changes suddenly. A problem of considerable interest to engineers is to find out exactly how many real roots, x, of this general function exist for a given set of parameter values.

A partial answer to this problem is provided by the implicit function theorem, which states that (under certain conditions [36]), the number of feasible (real) roots of $F(x, \mathbf{p})$ can change only when

$$F(x, \mathbf{p}) = 0 \qquad \qquad ...(a)$$

$$\frac{\partial F}{\partial x}(x, \mathbf{p}) = 0 \qquad \qquad ...(b) \qquad \qquad ...(3.97)$$

are satisfied simultaneously (this is a necessary but not sufficient condition). Points $[x, \mathbf{p}]$ on the steady-state manifold (*i.e.*, points which satisfy eq. 3.97(a) at which eq. 3.97(b) is simultaneously satisfied), are referred to as singular points, and form the *singular set*. Thus, for $F(x, c) = x^2 + 4x + c$, the singular set (a single point) is easily seen to be ($x = -2$, $c = 4$). Similarly, for $F(x, b, c) = x^2 + bx + c$, the singular set is the curve described parametrically by $[x = -b/2, b, c = b^2/4]$ in the x, b, c space. The projection, $f(\mathbf{p}) = 0$, of the singular set onto the parameter space is referred to as the *bifurcation or catastrophe set*. Note that the bifurcation set does not involve x. Figures 3.9(b) and (c), thus, represent the bifurcation sets of the two quadratic functions defined above. The number of solutions can change only when the parameter values cross the bifurcation set. Thus, the bifurcation set divides the parameter space into regions having different number of solutions. Often, two-dimensional cross sections of the bifurcation set are made for ease of visualization. Since there are five parameters in the classic CSTR problem (eq. 3.95), we fix values for any three (e.g., Da, B and α), and draw the cross-section of the bifurcation set using the remaining two parameters (γ–θ_c plots). Figure 3.10 shows the bifurcation set for *another* interesting problem in chemical reaction engineering, one which has been studied both theoretically and experimentally [37]. This is the co-oxidation of CO and ethane in air using a single catalyst (Pt/Al$_2$O$_3$) pellet. The state variable, x, is the temperature, T_p, of the catalyst pellet, while the parameters include the gas temperature (T_g), and CO (y_{CO} mole percent), C$_2$H$_6$ ($y_{C_2H_6}$), nitrogen (y_{N_2}) and oxygen (y_{O_2}) concentrations in the vapour phase for a given pellet. Figure 3.10 gives the T_g–y_{CO} projection of the bifurcation set with $y_{C_2H_6}$, y_{N_2} and y_{O_2} fixed at 4.25%, 72% and 19.95% (these are average values used in the experimental runs). The maximum number of *stable* steady states is found by experimentation to be four. Figure 3.11 [37] shows how the state variable, x ($\equiv T_p$), changes as a single parameter, T_g, called the bifurcation parameter, is varied (along AA' in fig. 3.10), keeping all the other parameters (y_{CO}, $y_{C_2H_6}$, y_{N_2}, y_{O_2}) fixed. Such x vs. p_i plots are referred to as *bifurcation diagrams*. Two hysteresis loops are observed in fig. 3.11, and the number of stable solutions changes from 1 to 2 to 1 to 2 to 1 as T_g increases from below about 130°C to above about 235°C. This information is used to identify the

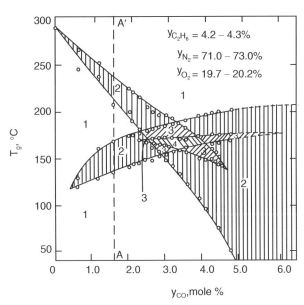

Fig. 3.10 Cross section of the bifurcation set for co-oxidation of CO and C$_2$H$_6$ in air on a single Pt/Al$_2$O$_3$ catalyst pellet. Circles indicate experimental data on the stable steady states. Number of steady states is as marked. [Reprinted from Ref. 37, copyright, 1985, with permission from Pergamon Press Ltd. Headington Hill Hall, Oxford OX3 OBW, UK]

regions in fig. 3.10. The ignition and extinction points (sudden increases and decreases in T_p as T_g is changed by small amounts) in fig. 3.11 are used for plotting the four experimental data points corresponding to $x_{CO} = 1.6\%$ in fig. 3.10. The locations of the four bifurcation points in fig. 3.11 can be obtained by solving eq. 3.97 (for a given y_{CO}, $y_{C_2H_6}$, y_{N_2}, y_{O_2}). Bifurcation diagrams for higher values of y_{CO} are more complex. Figure 3.12 [37] shows the bifurcation diagram for $y_{CO} = 2.6\%$. The number of stable steady states increases in the order $1 - 2 - 3 - 4 - 3 - 2 - 1$ as T_g increases from below 140°C to above 210°C. Again, this experimental information (ignition and extinction or bifurcation points) is used in the construction of the bifurcation set (fig. 3.10). Figure 3.10, thus, has been generated using the experimental results from the bifurcation plots. The intimate relationship between the bifurcation diagrams, the bifurcation set, and the number of *stable* steady state solutions of $F = 0$, is to be noted. It may be mentioned that even though the simultaneous solution of eqs. 3.97(a) and (b) for a given set of values of $y_{C_2H_6}$, y_{N_2} and y_{O_2} would give the T_g (y_{CO}) boundaries in fig. 3.10, in principle such a computational scheme is not very efficient and a better method [34] is available for generating cross-sections of the bifurcation set.

In this technique, we single out a parameter of interest, λ (the bifurcation parameter, as for example, T_g, in figs. 3.11 and 3.12), and look at the possible bifurcation diagrams (x *vs.* λ) for different values of the other parameters. Thus, eq. 3.97(a) is now rewritten as

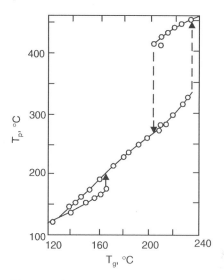

Fig. 3.11 Bifurcation diagram [x (= T_p) *vs.* T_g] for the co-oxidation of CO and C_2H_6 in air on a Pt/Al$_2$O$_3$ pellet [37]. Notation same as in fig. 3.10. $y_{CO} = 1.6\%$, $y_{C_2H_6} = 4.3\%$, $y_{C_2H_6} : y_{N_2} : y_{O_2} = 1: 17.3: 4.75$.
[Reprinted from Ref. 37, copyright 1985, with permission from Pergamon Press Ltd., Headington Hill Hall, Oxford, OX3 OBW, UK]

$$F\left(x, \lambda, \mathbf{p}^*\right) = 0 \qquad \qquad ...(3.98)$$

where $\mathbf{p}^*$ represents the remaining $N - 1$ parameters ($\mathbf{p} = [\lambda, \mathbf{p}^*]^T$). We find that the *qualitative* features of the bifurcation diagrams change when $\mathbf{p}^*$ crosses one of three hypersurfaces, called the hysteresis variety (HV), isola variety (IV) and the double limit variety (DLV) (not all of these three hypersurfaces need be present in all problems). These hypersurfaces are defined by the following equations:

HV:

$$F\left(x, \lambda, \mathbf{p}^*\right) = \frac{\partial F}{\partial x}\left(x, \lambda, \mathbf{p}^*\right) = \frac{\partial^2 F}{\partial x^2}\left(x, \lambda, \mathbf{p}^*\right) = 0 \qquad \ldots(a)$$

IV:

$$F\left(x, \lambda, \mathbf{p}^*\right) = \frac{\partial F}{\partial x}\left(x, \lambda, \mathbf{p}^*\right) = \frac{\partial F}{\partial \lambda}\left(x, \lambda, \mathbf{p}^*\right) = 0 \qquad \ldots(b)$$

DLV:

$$F\left(x_1, \lambda, \mathbf{p}^*\right) = F\left(x_2, \lambda, \mathbf{p}^*\right) = 0$$

$$\frac{\partial F}{\partial x}\left(x_1, \lambda, \mathbf{p}^*\right) = \frac{\partial F}{\partial x}\left(x_2, \lambda, \mathbf{p}^*\right) = 0 \qquad \ldots(c) \qquad \qquad \ldots(3.99)$$

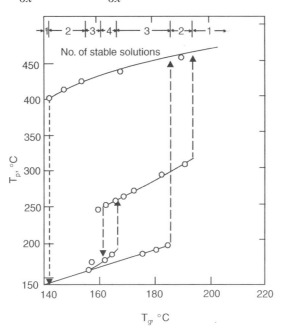

Fig. 3.12 Bifurcation diagram (T_p vs. T_g) for the co-oxidation of CO and C_2H_6 in air on a Pt/Al$_2$O$_3$ pellet [37]. Notation same as in fig. 3.11. $y_{CO} = 2.6\%$, $y_{C_2H_6} = 4.2\%$. [Adapted from Ref. 37]

When $\mathbf{p}^*$ crosses the HV hypersurface [$g(\mathbf{p})^* = 0$ satisfying the three equations 3.99(a)], an S-shaped curve (hysteresis) appears (or disappears) in the x vs. λ plots, as shown in fig. 3.13A (an inverse S-shaped curve could also appear [39, 40]). For any λ, thus, we could either have a single solution or three solutions, the middle one being unstable (note the similarity of the S-shaped curve in fig. 3.13A and one of the loops in fig. 3.11). In fact, the number of limit (or singular) points increases or decreases by two when we cross the HV hypersurfaces. Similarly, when $\mathbf{p}^*$ is changed such that it crosses the IV hypersurface either an isolated curve appears (or disappears), as in fig. 3.13B, or the bifurcation curve separates locally into two isolated curves, as in fig. 3.13C. Again the number of limit points changes by two when we cross the IV hypersurface. When $\mathbf{p}^*$ crosses the DLV, the nature of the bifurcation curve changes either as shown in fig. 3.13D or E. There is no change in the *number* of limit points as we cross the DLV hypersurface. The HV, IV and/or DLV, thus, divide the $\mathbf{p}^*$ space into several regions, each associated with a different kind of bifurcation behaviour. Knowledge of these regions in $\mathbf{p}^*$ space, and the kind of changes associated with each of the three varieties, helps one look for the right number of solutions of $F = 0$ for a given set of parameters. Alternatively, one could obtain the bifurcation diagram by computations for one set of parameter values in each (or some) of these regions.

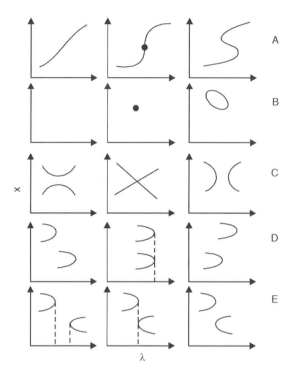

Fig. 3.13 Transitions of local bifurcation diagrams (x vs. λ) as $\mathbf{p}^*$ crosses the HV, IV or DLV hypersurfaces. [Reprinted from Ref. 38, copyright 1982, with permission from Pergamon Press Ltd., Headington Hill Hall, Oxford OX3 OBW, UK]

In the 'classic' CSTR problem described in eq. 3.95 we can use Da as the bifurcation parameter (hence, $\mathbf{p}^* = [B, \alpha, \theta_c, \gamma]^T$). The hysteresis and isola varieties are then hypersurfaces in the B, α, θ_c, γ space (the DLV does not exist for this case) [36, 38–40]. Figure 3.14 shows these varieties in the B–α space when $\theta_c = 0$, $\gamma \to \infty$ (schematic plots for other values of θ_c and γ are available in ref. 40). The x vs. Da bifurcation diagrams in the different regions of fig. 3.14 are also shown. The change in the number of bifurcation points by two as we cross the HV and IV curves is to be noted. For a given point in fig. 3.14, the values of B, α, θ_c and γ are known and x is a function of Da alone. If there are multiple solutions of x (Da), as for example, in zone d in fig. 3.14, we can use eqs. 97(a) and (b) to obtain the bifurcation points, $Da = Da_1$ and $Da = Da_2$ exactly, at which the number of roots changes suddenly. It is easily seen for this zone that for $0 < Da < Da_1$ and $Da > Da_2$, there is only one root, while for $Da_1 < Da < Da_2$, there are three. Bifurcation points for zones b, e and f in fig. 3.14 can similarly be obtained.

The technique of constructing the HV, IV and DLV hypersurfaces and inferring the kind of bifurcation diagrams in each zone is quite simple. It can be used even in situations where it is not possible to identify the singular points (using eq. 3.97) because of algebraic difficulties.

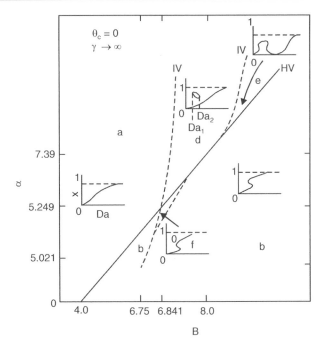

Fig. 3.14 Hysteresis (solid) and isola (dotted) varieties [39] for the classic CSTR problem (eq. 3.95) for $\theta_c = 0$, $\gamma \to \infty$ (not to scale). Schematic *x* vs. *Da* bifurcation patterns in the different regions [40] are also shown.

In closing, it may be added that methods also exist for determining the *maximum* number of solutions of $F = 0$, corresponding to a singular point of highest order (codimension) in the parameter space. Corresponding bifurcation diagrams in different regions of the parameter space near this singularity can also be easily determined using more advanced concepts (e.g., using the universal unfolding of the normal form which is contact equivalent to the function F). For the classic CSTR problem, such a study leads to two additional kinds of bifurcation diagrams (which cannot be found if $T_c > 2T_f/3$). The reader is referred to refs. 34–40 for a detailed discussion.

PROBLEMS

3.1 Write a general program using the successive substitutions technique for several variables, using eq. 3.32. Test it out on the cubic equation in 1 variable:

$$\lambda^3 - 6\lambda^2 + 11\lambda - 6 = 0$$

(see example 2.2). Can you obtain all the three roots, $[1\ \ 2\ \ 3]^T$ using $\lambda^{(k+1)} = (6 + 6\lambda^2 - \lambda^3)^{(k)}/11$. Study the convergence characteristics (sufficient condition) associated with this algorithm.

3.2 Use the program developed in prob. 3.1 to obtain the roots for (see prob. 2.4):

$$\lambda^3 + 6\lambda^2 + 10\lambda + 4 = 0$$

3.3 Consider the solution of [1]

$$F(x) = x^2 - 2 = 0$$

using the following forms (successive substitutions):

(i) $\quad x = x^2 + x - 2 \equiv f(x)$

(ii) $\quad x = \dfrac{x}{2} + \dfrac{1}{x} \equiv f(x)$

Try (i) with $x^{(1)} = 1$, and observe the *oscillations*. Study the convergence characteristics of the two choices of $f(x)$ above using the sufficient condition. Also plot $f(x)$ and a 45° line to study the convergence for the first algorithm starting with $(x)^{(1)} = 1$, and other choices for $x^{(1)}$.

*3.4 **Compressibility Factor Calculations:** The Soave-Redlich-Kwong (SRK) equation of state [41] is commonly used in chemical engineering to estimate the compressibility factor, Z. The set of equations are:

$$B = 0.08664 \frac{p_r}{T_r}$$

$$A = 0.42748 \frac{p_r}{T_r} F$$

$$F = \frac{1}{T_r} \left[1 + \left(0.480 + 1.574\omega - 0.176\omega^2\right)\left(1 - T_r^{1/2}\right) \right]^2$$

$$Z^3 - Z^2 + Z\left(A - B - B^2\right) - AB = 0$$

where

$$Z = \frac{pv}{RT}; \quad T_r = \frac{T}{T_c}; \quad p_r = \frac{p}{p_c}$$

(a) For *n-butane*, $T_c = 425.2$ K, $p_c = 37.5$ atm, $\omega = 0.193$ (constants) [41]. Make a general computer program (with input as ω, T_c, p_c and the temperature, T) so as to compute the molar volume, v, in cm³/mol $\left(R = 82.05 \dfrac{\text{atm cm}^3}{\text{mol K}}\right)$ at different values of the pressure, p (in atm). Use the Newton-Raphson technique, starting at different locations so as to get all the roots (starting estimates for roots *could* be $Z \sim 0.05$, 0.2, 0.9). Generate results for $T = 510.24$ K (one real solution) and for $T = 390$ K (3 solutions for certain p). Plot p on the y axis and v on the x axis. The qualitative features should be as shown in fig. P 3.4. Use $p_{\text{sat}}(T) = 20.8$ atm for *n-butane* at 390 K, to modify your p-v plot to make it physically meaningful (consistent with the phase rule [42]).

(b) Compare with values obtained from the original Redlich-Kwong equation for which

$$F = \frac{1}{T_r^{3/2}}$$

(c) Compare with results obtained from the Peng-Robinson equation [41]

$$B^* = 0.07780 \frac{p_r}{T_r}$$

$$A^* = \left(0.45724 \frac{p_r}{T_r}\right) F^*$$

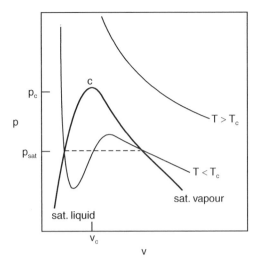

Fig. P 3.4 Schematic *p-v* plot for n-butane

$$F^* = \frac{1}{T_r}\left[1+\left(0.37464+1.54226\,\omega-0.26922\,\omega^2\right)\left(1-T_r^{1/2}\right)\right]^2$$

$$Z^3+\left(B^*-1\right)Z^2+\left(A^*-3B^{*2}-2B^*\right)Z-\left(A^*B^*-B^{*2}-B^{*3}\right)=0$$

(*d*) Also generate results using the van der Waal's equation of state:

$$B^*=\frac{1}{8}\left(\frac{p_r}{T_r}\right);\quad A^*=\frac{27}{64}\left(\frac{p_r}{T_r^2}\right)$$

$$Z^3-\left(1+B^*\right)Z^2+A^*Z-A^*B^*=0$$

3.5 The following nonlinear equations are obtained for steady state heat transfer (see prob. 6.12) in an infinite slab, with thermal conductivity given by a linear function of temperature:

$$\begin{bmatrix} 1 & 0 & 0 & 0 \\ 1 & -2 & 1 & 0 \\ 0 & 1 & -2 & 1 \\ 0 & 0 & 0 & 1 \end{bmatrix}\begin{bmatrix} \theta_1 \\ \theta_2 \\ \theta_3 \\ \theta_4 \end{bmatrix}=-a\begin{bmatrix} 0 \\ \dfrac{\theta_3^2+\theta_1^2-2\theta_1\theta_3}{4}+\theta_2\theta_3-2\theta_2^2+\theta_2\theta_1 \\ \dfrac{\theta_4^2+\theta_2^2-2\theta_2\theta_4}{4}+\theta_3\theta_4-2\theta_3^2+\theta_2\theta_3 \\ -1/a \end{bmatrix}$$

Write a computer code to solve this equation (appropriately recast) with *a* = 1, using successive substitutions. Compare with analytical results [1]:

$$\theta_1=0,\ \theta_4=1$$

$$\theta_2=-\frac{1}{a}+\frac{1}{a}\left[1+\frac{1}{3}\left(2a+a^2\right)\right]^{1/2}$$

$$\theta_3 = -\frac{1}{a} + \frac{1}{a}\left[1 + \frac{2}{3}\left(2a + a^2\right)\right]^{1/2}$$

If the thermal conductivity is independent of temperature, the right hand side in the above equations

should be replaced $[0\ \ 0\ \ 0\ \ 1]^T$, and the solution would be a linear profile: $\underline{\theta} = \begin{bmatrix} 0 & \dfrac{1}{3} & \dfrac{2}{3} & 1 \end{bmatrix}^T$. See

if your program gives this (see prob. 1.19). Notice that in the latter case, you are solving a set of linear algebraic equations and the Gauss-Seidel technique may be superior.

3.6 Consider the following nonlinear algebraic equation in a single variable (prob. 2.1)

$$F(\lambda) = \lambda^3 - 5\lambda^2 + 6\lambda - 1 = 0$$

Use $$\lambda = \lambda + F(\lambda) = f(\lambda)$$

(a) Start from $\lambda^{(0)} = 0$ and using the method of successive substitutions, compute upto $\lambda^{(3)}$. Repeat using $\lambda^{(0)} = 1$. Note how oscillation is observed in the latter case. Plot $f(x)$ and the 45° line to study how oscillations arise?

(b) Study the convergence criterion of the above choice of $f(\lambda)$, in the range $0 \le \lambda \le 3$ (using a plot), and see if convergence is *guaranteed*.

(c) Repeat part (a) using $\lambda^{(k+1)} = \left[\dfrac{-\lambda^3 + 5\lambda^2 + 1}{6}\right]^{(k)}$. Start with $\lambda^{(0)} = 0$, and note the slow

convergence to the first root.

*3.7 Flash Calculations: The equation characterizing an N-component flash [42] (in chemical engineering) at temperature T and pressure p (see fig. P 3.7) is

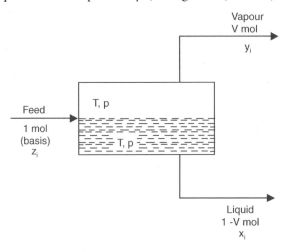

Fig. P 3.7 Notation for flash calculations

$$F = \sum_{i=1}^{N} \frac{z_i\left(K_i - 1\right)}{1 + V\left(K_i - 1\right)} = 0 \qquad \ldots(a)$$

where the $K_i\left(=\dfrac{y_i}{x_i}\right)$ are the K-factors, and are in general, functions of T, p, x_i and y_i; $i = 1, 2, \ldots,$

N [y_i and x_i are the mole fractions of component i in the vapour and liquid phase, respectively]. The corresponding expressions for the liquid and vapour compositions are

$$x_i = \frac{z_i}{1 + V\left(K_i - 1\right)}$$

$$y_i = K_i x_i; \quad i = 1, 2, \ldots, N \qquad \ldots (b)$$

For a feed specified by

i	Component	z_i	K_i (1 atm, 334.15 K)
1	n-hexane	0.250	1.694
2	ethanol	0.400	0.636
3	methylcyclopentane	0.200	1.668
4	benzene	0.150	1.070

use the Newton-Raphson iteration on eq. (*a*) to converge to the correct value of V at $p = 1$ atm and $T = 334.15$ K. Then obtain **x** and **y**. Note that K_i values themselves are functions of **x** and **y** (in addition to T and p), and so flash calculations require iterations on values of **x** and **y** and the use of packages to estimate K_i.

3.8 A finite difference technique applied to another problem in chemical engineering [irreversible 2nd-order reaction carried out isothermally in a porous catalyst slab with no external mass transfer resistance] leads to (see eq. 6.12 and prob. 6.7) the following set of algebraic equations

$$\begin{bmatrix} -2 & 2 & 0 & 0 & \cdot & \cdot & \cdot & 0 & 0 & 0 \\ 1 & -2 & 1 & 0 & \cdot & \cdot & \cdot & 0 & 0 & 0 \\ 0 & 1 & -2 & 1 & \cdot & \cdot & \cdot & 0 & 0 & 0 \\ \cdot & \cdot & \cdot & \cdot & & & & \cdot & \cdot & \cdot \\ \cdot & \cdot & \cdot & \cdot & & & & \cdot & \cdot & \cdot \\ 0 & 0 & 0 & 0 & \cdot & \cdot & \cdot & 1 & -2 & 1 \\ 0 & 0 & 0 & 0 & \cdot & \cdot & \cdot & 0 & 1 & -2 \end{bmatrix} \begin{bmatrix} C_1 \\ C_2 \\ C_3 \\ \cdot \\ \cdot \\ C_{N-1} \\ C_N \end{bmatrix}$$

$$\equiv \mathbf{BC} = \begin{bmatrix} AC_1^2 \\ AC_2^2 \\ \cdot \\ \cdot \\ AC_{N-1}^2 \\ AC_N^2 - 1 \end{bmatrix} \equiv \mathbf{f}(\mathbf{C})$$

or

$$\mathbf{C} = \mathbf{B}^{-1}\mathbf{f}(\mathbf{C})$$

where C_i are the dimensionless concentrations at several locations inside the slab, and A is proportional to the Thiele modulus. A successive substitutions method is used as follows:

$$\mathbf{C}^{(k+1)} = \mathbf{B}^{-1}\mathbf{f}\left(\mathbf{C}^{(k)}\right)$$

or

$$C_i^{(k+1)} = \sum_{j=1}^{N} \left(\mathbf{B}^{-1}\right)_{ij} f_j\left(\mathbf{C}^{(k)}\right)$$

Show that a sufficient condition for convergence is

$$\sum_{j=1}^{N} \left|\mathbf{B}^{-1}\right|_{ij} \leq \frac{1}{2A}; \quad i = 1, 2, ..., N$$

in the entire domain $(\mathbf{C}^{(1)}, \alpha)$. Hint: note that the dimensionless concentrations, C_i, are within the range [0, 1].

3.9 A finite element technique using orthogonal collocation gives (for the same ordinary differential equation as described in example 3.3; see prob. 6.36)

$$
\begin{bmatrix}
1 & 0 & 0 & 0 & 0 \\
11.1111 & -22.2222 & 11.1111 & 0 & 0 \\
1.0 & -4 & 7.5 & -6 & 1.5 \\
0 & 0 & 25 & -50 & 25 \\
0 & 0 & 2.5 & -10 & 7.5
\end{bmatrix}
\begin{bmatrix}
y_1 \\
y_2 \\
y_3 \\
y_4 \\
y_5
\end{bmatrix}
=
\begin{bmatrix}
1 \\
2y_2^3 \\
0 \\
2y_4^3 \\
-y_5^2
\end{bmatrix}
$$

Recast this into a successive substitutions form using eq. 3.32 and solve (on a computer, using different β).

3.10 Use eq. 3.31 to derive the sufficient condition for convergence (eq. 1.24) for Jacobi's algorithm (eq. 1.30). Thus, observe how diagonal dominance of the matrix $\mathbf{A}$ in the linear equation $\mathbf{Ax} = \mathbf{b}$, leads to convergence.

3.11 Starting with $x^{(1)} = 0.7$, obtain the first eight iterates using the Newton-Raphson technique on

$$F(x) = x - \frac{1}{3}e^x = 0 \quad \text{(example 3.5)}.$$

3.12 Write a program to obtain the N roots of the Legendre polynomials, $P_N(x)$, defined by the recursive relation:

$$P_0(x) = 1$$

$$P_1(x) = x$$

$$P_N(x) = \frac{2N-1}{N}xP_{N-1}(x) - \frac{N-1}{N}P_{N-2}(x); \quad n = 2, 3, ...$$

This forms a family of orthogonal polynomials [over $-1 \leq x \leq 1$], with respect to a weightage factor 1.0 (see Chapter 4, appendix 4A for details). Use the Newton-Raphson technique coupled with an incremental search technique with $N = 3$ and $N = 4$. It is known that all the roots lie in $-1 \leq x \leq 1$. These roots are used in chp. 4 to compute integrals.

3.13 Make a general program to obtain roots of a one-variable equation using incremental search coupled with the Newton-Raphson algorithm. Use this to solve problems 3.1, 3.2 and 3.6.

3.14 Obtain the multiple roots of

$$F(x) = \ln(x^2 + 1) - e^{0.4x} \cos(\pi x) = 0$$

using the Newton-Raphson technique with incremental search, as in prob. 3.13. This equation has infinite roots, so explore only $-5 \le x \le 5$.

3.15 A useful technique to obtain multiple roots is the method of deflation [8]. After obtaining one root, α_1, of $F(x) = 0$, we then work with a new function

$$F_1(x) \equiv \frac{F(x)}{(x - \alpha_1)}$$

and again use the Newton-Raphson technique (with derivatives obtained analytically or numerically) on $F_1(x)$ to obtain the other roots. Try this on $F(x) = x^3 - 6x^2 + 11x - 6 = 0$ (prob. 3.1). Do not deflate analytically using the technique described in sec. 3.6 for polynomials.

3.16 Solve [7], using the Newton-Raphson method starting from $[0.400 \quad 3.000]^T$

$$F_1(\mathbf{x}) = \frac{1}{2}\sin(x_1 x_2) - \frac{x_2}{4\pi} - \frac{x_1}{2} = 0$$

$$F_2(\mathbf{x}) = \left(1 - \frac{1}{4\pi}\right)\left(e^{2x_1} - e\right) + \frac{ex_2}{\pi} - 2ex_1 = 0$$

*3.17 **Compressor Calculations:** Find the ideal power required (per mol) to compress [42] methane from $p_{in} = 1.3605$ atm and $T_{in} = 4.44°C$ to $p_{final} = 5.44217$ atm. Assume the SRK equation (see prob. 3.4) to be valid with [41]

$$T_c = 190.6 \text{ K}, \quad p_c = 45.4 \text{ atm}, \quad \omega = 0.007$$

C_p (cal/mol–K) $= 4.598 + 0.01245T + 2.86 \times 10^{-6}T^2 - 2.703 \times 10^{-9}T^3$ (T in K). The molar entropy, s, and enthalpy, h, are given for an SRK gas as

$$s = s_0 + R\left[\ln\left(\frac{v - b}{v}\right) - \frac{\gamma}{b}\ln\left(\frac{v + b}{v}\right) + \ln\frac{v}{v^0}\right]$$

$$h = \left[\int_{298K}^{T} C_p dT\right] + T(s - s_0) + RT(Z - 1) + RT\left[-\ln\left(\frac{v - b}{v}\right) - \frac{\beta}{b}\ln\left(\frac{v + b}{v}\right) - \ln\frac{v}{v^0}\right]$$

$$\beta = 4.93396 \, bF ; \quad b = 0.0866404 \, RT_c/p_c$$

$$\gamma = -4.93396b \, F^{1/2}\left(0.480 + 1.574\omega - 0.176\omega^2\right)$$

$$v^0 = RT/(1 \text{ atm}); \quad s_0 = \int_{298 \text{ K}}^{T} \frac{C_p}{T}dT; \quad v = \frac{ZRT}{p}$$

with Z and other terms from prob. 3.4. Note that for an ideal compressor, $\Delta s = 0$ and power $= \Delta h$

[**Hint:** Use binary chop with $T_{final}^{(1)} = T_{in}$, and some ΔT, to obtain T_{final} such that $s_{final} = s_{in}$. Then compute h_{final}]   [**Ans:** $T = 105.55°C$, power $= 905.7$ cal/mol]

3.18 Recast the equations in prob. 3.5 in the Newton-Raphson form (eq. 3.56) and solve using the Gauss-Seidel method. Estimate the partial derivatives required in the Jacobian using a finite difference approximation:

$$\frac{\partial F_i}{\partial x_j} \cong \frac{1}{0.0001}\Big[F_i[x_1, x_2, ..., x_{j-1},\, x_j + 0.0001,\, x_{j+1}, ..., x_N] -$$

$$F_i[x_1, x_2, ..., x_{j-1},\, x_j,\, x_{j+1}, ..., x_N]\Big]$$

3.19 Consider the equation **BC = f(C)** given in prob. 3.8 (or prob. 3.9), in which several terms are linear in **C**. Apply the Newton-Raphson technique and show that it can be written in the following form:

$$\begin{bmatrix} b_{11}-2AC_1 & b_{12} & b_{13}...\, b_{1N} \\ b_{21} & b_{22}-2AC_2 & b_{23}...b_{2N} \\ . & & \\ . & & \\ . & & \\ b_{N1} & b_{\ N2} & ...b_{NN}-2AC_N \end{bmatrix}^{(k)} \mathbf{C}^{(k+1)} = \begin{bmatrix} -AC_1^2 \\ -AC_2^2 \\ . \\ . \\ . \\ -AC_{N-1}^2 \\ -AC_N^2 - 1 \end{bmatrix}^{(k)}$$

Note how this equation can be obtained by superposing the terms which are linear (which can be written by inspection, after practice) and those which are nonlinear.

3.20 The Crank-Nicholson technique (sec. 5.2) applied to $\dfrac{dy}{dx} = \dfrac{(1+x)^2}{y^2} + \dfrac{y}{1+x}$; $y(0) = 3$ [for which the analytical solution is $y = (x+1)[27 + 3\ln(1+x)]^{1/3}$, gives (at $t = 1$; $\Delta t = 0.1$) (see prob. 5.24)]:

$$y_{n+1} = 6.306568 + \frac{0.2205}{y_{n+1}^2} + \frac{y_{n+1}}{42}$$

Solve for y_{n+1} using the Newton-Raphson technique and compare this with the value $y_{n+1} = y\,[x = 1.1]$ from the given analytical solution. Note that algebraic equations arise in the solution of ordinary differential equations (initial value problems).

3.21 Solve $x^{20} - 1 = 0$ using $x^{(1)} = 1.5$ and a library subroutine using the Newton-Raphson method. Use a tolerance, ε, of 10^{-6}. See how many function evaluations are required. This equation gives problems with some techniques (see p. 245 in Ref. 8).

3.22 A higher (3rd) order Newton-Raphson technique gives [43]

$$x^{(k+1)} = x^{(k)} - \left\{ \frac{F\big[x^{(k)}\big]}{F'\big[x^{(k)}\big] - \dfrac{1}{2}\dfrac{F''\big[x^{(k)}\big]F\big[x^{(k)}\big]}{F'\big[x^{(k)}\big]}} \right\}$$

Obtain this algorithm by using an extra term on the right hand side in eq. 3.37, and

$$\Big[x^{(k+1)} - x^{(k)}\Big]^2 = \Big[x^{(k+1)} - x^{(k)}\Big]\left[\frac{-F\big[x^{(k)}\big]}{F'\big[x^{(k)}\big]} \right]$$

in this new term. Note that the (first order) Newton-Raphson expression (eq. 39) has been used to replace one of the $\{x^{(k+1)} - x^{(k)}\}$ terms above.

*3.23 **Multiplicity in CSTRs:** The following equation arises in chemical engineering relating the dimensionless temperature for the steady state operation of a non-adiabatic continuous flow stirred tank reactor, in which an irreversible, exothermic, first order reaction occurs (see eq. 3.95 for an equation for the conversion; note that the dimensionless variables used here are different from those in sec. 3.8):

$$y - y_{1b} = \phi\left[y_{ub} - y\right]\exp\left[\delta\left(\frac{y-1}{y}\right)\right]$$

where

$y_{1b} = (1 + \gamma y_a)/(1 + \gamma)$

$y_{ub} = (1 + \beta + \gamma y_a)/(1 + \gamma)$

$\quad y$ = dimensionless temperature of reactor effluent

$\quad y_a$ = dimensionless coolant temperature

$\quad \gamma$ = dimensionless heat transfer coefficient

$\quad \beta$ = dimensionless heat of reaction (Prater temperature)

$\quad \delta$ = dimensionless activation energy

$\quad \phi$ = dimensionless tank size parameter

The *a-priori* bounds on y are: $y_{1b} < y < y_{ub}$. *Caution*: depending on parameter values, the above equation may have multiple solutions. Find *all* solutions of the above equation for the set of parameters: $\beta = 0.4$, $\delta = 30$, $y_b = 1$, and

$\quad$ (*i*) $\gamma = 1$, $\phi = 0.07$

$\quad$ (*ii*) $\gamma = 1.6$, $\phi = 0.125$

using the Newton-Raphson algorithm. Terminate iterations when $|y^{(k+1)} - y^{(k)}| < 10^{-5}$.

3.24 An improvement of the multivariable Newton-Raphson technique (coupled with search techniques) is an algorithm of Brown [44]. Use the computer listing provided by him and solve $\mathbf{F}(\mathbf{x}) = \mathbf{0}$ as given in prob. 3.16. Find out the major improvements which Brown's algorithm offers.

3.25 A more useful *sufficient* condition for convergence of the Newton-Raphson technique has been provided by Lapidus [16]: If $F'(x)$ and $F''(x)$ do not change sign in the interval $[x^{(1)}, \alpha]$, and if $F[x^{(1)}]$ and $F''[x^{(1)}]$ have the same sign, the technique will always convergence to α. Study this condition for $F(x) \equiv x - \frac{1}{3}e^x = 0$, and find the limiting values of $x^{(1)}$ for which convergence is assured.

3.26 Use a computer package available to you to solve the Rosenbrock problem [24]:

$$F_1(\mathbf{x}) \equiv 10\left(x_2 - x_1^2\right) = 0$$

$$F_2(\mathbf{x}) \equiv 1 - x_1 = 0$$

starting with $\mathbf{x}^{(1)} = [-1.2 \quad 1]^T$. The solution is $\mathbf{x} = [1 \quad 1]^T$.

3.27 Obtain the four complex (conjugate) roots of

$$F(x) = x^4 - 10x^3 + 39x^2 - 70x + 50$$

$$= [x - (3+i)][x - (3-i)][x - (2+i)][x - (2-i)] = 0$$

using both Lin's technique, as well as the Bairstow iteration. Use $\beta^{(1)} = \gamma^{(1)} = 0$. The factors are given for you to check your solutions.

3.28 Make a computer program using Bairstow's iteration for obtaining roots of a polynomial. Use this program to compute the two complex roots for the compressibility factor, Z in prob. 3.4, at $T = 510.24$ K and $p = 60$ atm (only one root is real under these conditions).

3.29 For turbulent flow of a fluid in a hydraulically smooth pipe, Prandtl's universal resistance law relates the friction factor, f, and the Reynolds number, Re, according to the following relationship [45]:

$$\frac{1}{\sqrt{f}} = -0.40 + 4.0 \log_{10}\left(Re\sqrt{f}\right)$$

Compute f for $Re = 10^5$, using the
(a) Newton-Raphson algorithm with $f^{(1)} = 0.01$
(b) Third order method described in prob. 3.22 with $f^{(1)} = 0.01$
(c) Bisection method; $f^{(1)} = 0.002$, $f^{(2)} = 0.01$
(d) Regula-falsi method, $f^{(1)} = 0.002$, $f^{(2)} = 0.01$
Compare the number of iterations required for convergence for all the methods. Terminate iterations when $|f^{(k+1)} - f^{(k)}| < 10^{-5}$.

***3.30** The mass balance equations for the following reactions taking place in a CSTR [18]:

$$A \xrightarrow{k_1} 2B$$

$$A \underset{k_3}{\overset{k_2}{\rightleftharpoons}} C$$

$$B \xrightarrow{k_4} D + C$$

is given by

$$F_1 = -C_A + C_{Ao} + \left[-k_1 C_A - k_2 C_A^{3/2} + k_3 C_C^2\right]\theta = 0$$

$$F_2 = -C_B + \left(2k_1 C_A - k_4 C_B^2\right)\theta = 0$$

$$F_3 = -C_C + \left(k_2 C_A^{3/2} - k_3 C_C^2 + k_4 C_B^2\right)\theta = 0$$

$$F_4 = -C_D + \left(k_4 C_B^2\right)\theta = 0$$

Use the Newton-Raphson technique to show that $[C_A \ C_B \ C_C \ C_D]$ are $[0.3189 \ 0.7839 \ 0.5350 \ 0.4916]$ for the following situation:

$$k_1 = 1.0 \ 1/s$$
$$k_2 = 0.2 \ \text{lit}^{1/2}/\text{mol}^{1/2} - s$$
$$k_3 = 0.05 \ \text{lit}/\text{mol} - s$$
$$k_4 = 0.4 \ \text{lit}/\text{mol} - s$$
$$\theta = 2 \ s$$
$$C_{Ao} = 1 \ \text{mol}/\text{lit}$$

3.31 Wegstein's Method [46] is another popular technique for the solution of algebraic equations, and is used in computer packages for steady state simulation of chemical plants (*e.g.*, Flowtran). For a one-variable case, $x = f(x)$, the algorithm is described by

$$x^{(2)} = f\left[x^{(1)}\right]$$

$$S \equiv \frac{f\left[x^{(k)}\right] - f\left[x^{(k-1)}\right]}{x^{(k)} - x^{(k-1)}}$$

$$x^{(k+1)} = \frac{f\left[x^{(k)}\right]}{1-S} + \frac{S}{S-1}x^{(k)}; \quad k = 2, 3, \ldots (a)$$

Figure P3.31 shows the graphical construction associated with this procedure, once a choice is made for $x^{(1)}$, with S as the slope of the line joining the points $[x^{(k)}, f(x^{(k)})]$ and $[x^{k-1}, f(x^{k-1})]$. Show that the graphical procedure is consistent with the above equations. Also note that at times, the new point $[x^{(k+1)}, f(x^{(k+1)})]$ may lie on the same side of the 45° line as the point $[x^{(k)}, f(x^{(k)})]$ and we need to *extrapolate* the line joining these two points to obtain its intersection with the 45° line. Instead of eq. (a) one uses

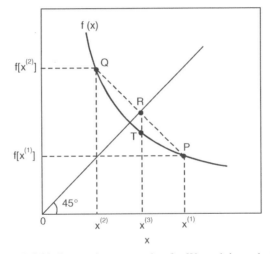

Fig. P 3.31 Geometric construction for Wegstein's method.

$$x^{(k+1)} = (1-q)f\left[x^{(k)}\right] + qx^{(k)}$$

with q given by $S/(S-1)$. In the bounded Wegstein method, if q goes outside $-5 \le q \le 0$, it is replaced by the bounds, -5 or 0. This technique has a 1.618 order convergence, and converges faster than the Newton-Raphson technique if the evaluation of derivatives required in the latter is time consuming.

The multivariate algorithm for $x_i = f_i(\mathbf{x})$; $i = 1, 2, \ldots, N$ is given by

$$x_i^{(2)} = f_i\left[\mathbf{x}^{(1)}\right]; \quad i = 1, 2, \ldots, N$$

$$S_i = \frac{f_i\left[\mathbf{x}^{(k)}\right] - f_i\left[\mathbf{x}^{(k-1)}\right]}{x_i^{(k)} - x_i^{(k-1)}}$$

$$q_i = \frac{S_i}{S_i - 1}$$

$$x_i^{(k+1)} = \left(1 - q_i\right) f_i \left[\mathbf{x}^{(k)}\right] + q_i x_i^{(k)}; \quad i = 1, 2, ..., N$$

3.32 Consider the equations characterizing the steady-state operation of a fluidized bed reactor (see prob. 5.22):

$$1.30\left(y_3 - y_1\right) + 1.04 \times 10^4 k y_2 = 0$$

$$1.88 \times 10^3 \left[y_4 - y_2 \left(1 + k\right)\right] = 0$$

$$1752 + 266.7 y_1 - 269.3 y_3 = 0$$

$$0.1 + 320 y_2 - 321 y_4 = 0$$

$$k = 0.0006 \exp\left(20.7 - \frac{15000}{y_1}\right)$$

Obtain *three* steady-state solutions.
[**Hint:** the three steady-state values of y_1 are 691, 759 and 915].

3.33 Consider the following coupled equations

$$x^2 + y^2 - 4 = 0$$

$$x^2 - y^2 - 1.5 = 0$$

(Do *not* eliminate variables to give $x^2 = 2.75$, $y^2 = 1.25$) Obtain the algorithm to solve for x and y using the 2-variable Newton-Raphson method. Obtain the inverse of the Jacobian analytically. Starting from $x = 1$, $y = 1$, obtain three iterates, and compare with the analytical solution.

3.34 Consider the system of equations

$$F_1\left(x_1, x_2\right) = 2x_1^2 - 5x_2^3 - 3 = 0$$

$$F_2\left(x_1, x_2\right) = 3x_1^3 + 2x_2^2 - 26 = 0$$

The following successive substitutions algorithm is used:

$$x_1^{(k+1)} = \left[x_1 + 2x_1^2 - 5x_2^3 - 3\right]^{(k)}$$

$$x_2^{(k+1)} = \left[3x_1^3 + x_2 + 2x_2^2 - 26\right]^{(k)}$$

where $\mathbf{x}^{(1)} = [1 \quad 1]^T$. Can you say whether you will be able to compute the roots based on the sufficient condition for convergence.

3.35 Solve using the Newton-Raphson technique:

$$y = 1 + 2\left(1.2 - y\right)^2 \exp\left[10\left(1 - \frac{1}{y}\right)\right]$$

Use $y^{(1)} = 1.05$. Obtain $y^{(2)}$ and $y^{(3)}$.

3.36 Derive a sufficient condition for convergence for the tridiagonal matrix using Jacobi's method (see prob. 1.20) for solving sets of linear equations.

3.37 A set of equations which arises quite often in the solution of certain types of second order ordinary differential equations is given by

$$\mathbf{Ax} = \mathbf{f(x)}$$

where the column matrix, $\mathbf{f}(\mathbf{x})$, is usually only a function of a few of the variables, for example,

$$f_i(\mathbf{x}) = f_i\left(x_{i-1}, x_i, x_{i+1}\right)$$

and $\mathbf{A}$ is a tridiagonal matrix. Apply the Newton-Raphson method to the ith equation of this set and obtain the algorithm in the form

$$\mathbf{B}\left[\mathbf{x}^{(k)}\right]\mathbf{x}^{(k+1)} = \mathbf{d}\left[\mathbf{x}^{(k)}\right]$$

prob. 3.19 is a special case of this more general system.

3.38 (*a*) An enterprising student decides to apply the Newton-Raphson technique in the form given by eq. 3.56:

$$\mathbf{A}^{(k)}\mathbf{x}^{(k+1)} = \mathbf{A}^{(k)}\mathbf{x}^{(k)} - \mathbf{F}\left[\mathbf{x}^{(k)}\right] \qquad \ldots(3.56)$$

to solve the equations in example 1.10:

$$\mathbf{F}(\mathbf{x}) = \begin{bmatrix} 2x_1 + x_2 + 0x_3 - 1 \\ 1x_1 + 2x_2 + 1x_3 - 2 \\ 0x_1 + 1x_2 + 1x_3 - 4 \end{bmatrix} = \begin{bmatrix} 0 \\ 0 \\ 0 \end{bmatrix}$$

starting with $\mathbf{x}^{(1)} = [1 \ 2 \ 1]^T$. Apply one iteration of the above NR algorithm and see what you get (do not compute $\mathbf{A}^{-1}$).

(*b*) Then consider the general case (without numbers) of linear, coupled algebraic equations, $\mathbf{Ax} - \mathbf{b} = \mathbf{0}$ and see what happens on applying eq. 3.56 to it.

Also see what the NR method (eq. 3.55) leads to when applied to $\mathbf{Ax} - \mathbf{b} = \mathbf{0}$. Comment on your answers.

REFERENCES

1. B.A. Finlayson, *Nonlinear Analysis in Chemical Engineering*, McGraw Hill, New York, 1980.

2. C.R. Wylie and L.C. Barrett, *Advanced Engineering Mathematics,* 5th ed., McGraw Hill, New York, 1982.

3. I. Newton, *Principia Mathematica,* Book I, Prop. XXXI, pp. 112–116; also, *Mathematical Principles of Natural Philosophy and His System of the World* (trans., F. Cajori), Berkeley, 1934.

4. J. Raphson, *Analysis Aequationum Universalis seu ad Aequationes Algebraices....*, London, 1st ed., 1690, 2nd ed., 1702.

   [Newton's original algorithm was slightly modified by Raphson. Incidentally, this was the first discussion of the method *in print*].

5. H.H. Goldstine, *A History of Numerical Analysis from the 16th, thru the 19th Century,* Springer Verlag, New York, 1977.

   [an excellent historical discussion]

6. A.S. Householder, *Principles of Numerical Analysis*, McGraw Hill, New York, 1953, p. 134.

7. B. Carnahan, H.A. Luther and J.O. Wilkes, *Applied Numerical Methods*, Wiley, New York, 1969.

8. J.R. Rice, *Numerical Methods, Software and Analysis : IMSL Reference Edition*, McGraw Hill, New York, 1983.

9. C.G. Broyden, *Math. Comp.* **19**, 577 (1965).

10. R.L. Burden and J.D. Faires, *Numerical Analysis*, 3rd ed., Prindle, Weber and Schmidt, Boston, MA, 1985.

11. J.K. Schubert, *Math. Comp.*, **24**, 33 (1970).

12. L.M. Naphtali and D.P. Sandholm, *AIChEJ*, **17**, 148 (1971).

13. *User's Manual, IMSL Math/Library,* Int. Math. Stat. Lib. Inc., Houston, 1989.

14. K. Hiebert, *ACM Trans, Math. Software*, **7**, 5 (1982).

15. S.D. Comte and C. deBoor, *Elementary Numerical Analysis*, 2nd ed., McGraw Hill, New York, 1972.
    [another excellent book at an elementary level]

16. L. Lapidus, *Digital Computation for Chemical Engineers*, McGraw Hill, New York, 1962.

17. M.L. James, G.M. Smith and J.C. Wolford, *Applied Numerical Methods for Digital Computation*, 3rd ed., Harper and Row, New York, 1985.

18. J.B. Riggs, *An Introduction to Numerical Methods for Chemical Engineers*, Texas Tech. University Press, Lubbock, TX, 1988.
    [a floppy disc full of programs also comes with the text]

19. D. Marquardt, *J. Soc. Indus. Appl. Math.*, **11**, 431 (1963).

20. K. Levenberg, *Q. Appl. Math.*, **2**, 164 (1944).

21. T.F. Edgar and D.M. Himmelblau, *Optimization of Chemical Processes*, McGraw Hill, New York, 1988.

22. G.S.G. Beveridge and R.S. Schechter, *Optimization: Theory and Practice,* McGraw Hill, New York, 1970.
    [Ref. Nos. 21 and 22 are excellent and popular texts on optimization techniques, with an emphasis on search techniques]

23. M.J.D. Powell in *Numerical Methods for Nonlinear Algebraic Equations*, P. Rabinowitz., ed., Gordon and Breach, New York, 1970.

24. G. Buzzi Ferraris and E. Tronconi, *Comp. Chem. Eng.,* **10**, 129 (1986).
    [an interesting paper, describing experiences with several packages, including their own, BUNSLI, in which a bidimensional search on the plane defined by the Newton-Raphson direction and the steepest descent direction, is used when the Newton-Raphson technique fails. If the Jacobian is near singular at any stage, a subset of linearly independent equations in fewer variables is solved to go to a new point]

25. A.W. Westerberg, H.P. Hutchison, R.L. Motard and P. Winter, *Process Flowsheeting*, Cambridge Univ. Press, Cambridge 1979.

26. S. Lin, *J. Math and Phys.*, **22**, 60 (1943).

27. L. Bairstow, *Investigations Relating to the Stability of the Aeroplane*, Reports and Memoranda, No. 154, of the Advisory Committee for Aeronautics, 1914.

28. G.E. Forsythe and C.B. Moler, *Computer Solution of Linear Algebraic Systems,* Prentice Hall, Englewood Cliffs, N.J. 1967.
    [a detailed discussion of various techniques is present in this classic text]

29. A.C. Aitken, *Proc. Roy. Soc. Edinburgh*, **46**, 289 (1926).

30. C.H. Graeffe, *Die Auflosung der hoheren Numerischen Gleichungen*, Zurich, 1837.

31. D. Bernoulli, *Comment. acad. sc. petrop.*, Vol III, pp. 85 (1728).

32. H. Rutihauser, *der Quotienten-Differenzen-Algorithms Mitteilungen aus dem Institut fur angew. Math.*, No. 7, Birkhauser, Basel and Stuttgart, 1956.

33. W.G. Horner, *Phil. Trans.,* **109**, 308 (1819).

34. D. Luss, *Chem. Eng. Educ.*, **20**, 12, 52 (1986).

35. L.F. Razon and R.A. Schmitz, *Chem. Eng. Sci.*, **42**, 1005 (1987).

36. V. Balakotaiah and D. Luss, *Chem. Eng. Sci.*, **39**, 865 (1984).

37. M.P. Harold and D. Luss, *Chem. Eng. Sci.*, **40**, 39 (1985).

38. V. Balakotaiah and D. Luss, *Chem. Eng. Sci.*, **37**, 1611 (1982).

39. V. Balakotaiah and D. Luss, *Chem. Eng. Commun.*, **13**, 111 (1981).

40. V. Balakotaiah and D. Luss, *Chem. Eng. Commun.*, **19**, 185 (1982).

41. B.E. Poling, J.M. Prausnitz and J. O'Connell, *The Properties of Gases and Liquids,* 5th ed., McGraw-Hill, New York, 2002.

[an excellent compendium of several equations to estimate thermodynamic and transport properties of fluids]

42. J.M. Smith, H.C. VanNess, and M. Abbott, *Introduction to Chemical Engineering Thermodynamics*, 7th ed., McGraw-Hill, New York, 2004.

[a popular text in Chemical Engineering Thermodynamics]

43. H.W. Richmond, *J. Lond. Math. Soc.*, **19**, 31 (1944).

44. K.M. Brown, in *Numerical Solution of Systems of Nonlinear Algebraic Equations*, G.D. Byrne and C.A. Hall, eds., Academic, New York, 1973.

45. R.B. Bird, W.E. Stewart and E.N. Lightfoot, *Transport Phenomena*, Wiley, New York, 2nd ed., 2001.

46. J.H. Wegstein, *Comm. ACM*, **1**, 9 (1958).

Chapter 4

Function Approximation

4.1 INTRODUCTION

There are several cases when we have information or data, y, available at several discrete locations (values of the independent variable, x). Examples include tabulated values of the properties of steam, trigonometric, logarithmic and other functions, etc. In fact, till the use of on-line measurement devices and recorders became popular, experimental results taken in a laboratory were available in a similar form. We may be required to interpolate/extrapolate these data, or may, at times, be interested in computing slopes or integrals of functions described by them. For example, we may measure the temperature, T, at several locations, x, in an infinite slab, $0 \leq x \leq L$, across which heat is being transferred at a steady rate. The rate of heat transfer across the surface would require the computation of the gradient, dT/dx, from the tabulated data on temperature. Similarly, computation of the mean temperature in the slab would require the evaluation of the integral, $\int_0^L T dx$, from the measured information. Before we can perform these operations, viz., interpolation, differentiation, and integration, on data available at discrete locations, we must 'fit' them by an analytical function. This chapter discusses several techniques for doing this.

4.2 LEAST SQUARES CURVE-FIT (LINEAR REGRESSION)

The simplest and probably the most popular technique is to fit the 'best' straight line

$$y = a_0 + a_1 x \qquad \qquad ...(4.1)$$

through a set of $n + 1$ data-points, (x_0, y_0), (x_1, y_1), ..., (x_n, y_n). Figure 4.1 shows some data from a filtration experiment (details given in example 4.1 later), and the best straight line (by visual examination) describing it. Most readers must have carried out such curve-fitting exercises fairly early in their careers. We develop here a method to estimate the constants, a_0 and a_1, in eq. 4.1 analytically.

The deviations of the data points in fig. 4.1 from the straight line are $y_i - (a_0 + a_1 x_i)$; $i = 0, 1, 2,...,$ n. These are referred to as *residuals*. The sum of the squares of these residuals (squares are used to avoid cancellation of positive and negative values on summing up) is written as

$$E \equiv \sum_{i=0}^{n} \left[y_i - \left(a_0 + a_1 x_i \right) \right]^2 \qquad \qquad ...(4.2)$$

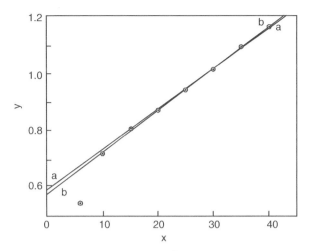

Fig. 4.1 Some data on filtration of a $CaCO_3$ slurry and the best straight line fits using (*a*) the visual method and (*b*) a straight line using regression analysis. $n + 1 = 8$. The data at $x = 5$ is neglected while drawing the best straight line. The best straight line using visual inspection was drawn before computations were made. Note how this method is not very good.

The above equation gives E as a function of two 'variables', a_0 and a_1. We would like to obtain values of a_0 and a_1 which would minimize this total error. This requires

$$\frac{\partial E}{\partial a_0} = -2\sum_{i=0}^{n}\left[y_i - \left(a_0 + a_1 x_i\right)\right] = 0$$

$$\frac{\partial E}{\partial a_1} = -2\sum_{i=0}^{n}\left\{x_i\left[y_i - \left(a_0 + a_1 x_i\right)\right]\right\} = 0 \qquad \ldots(4.3)$$

eq. 4.3 can be written as

$$a_0\left(n+1\right) + a_1\left(\Sigma x_i\right) = \left(\Sigma y_i\right)$$

$$a_0\left(\Sigma x_i\right) + a_1\left(\Sigma x_i^2\right) = \left[\Sigma\left(y_i x_i\right)\right] \qquad \ldots(4.4)$$

where the summations extend from $i = 0$ to n. The solution of these simultaneous equations in the two variables, a_0 and a_1, is

$$a_1 = \frac{\left(n+1\right)\Sigma\left(y_i x_i\right) - \left(\Sigma x_i\right)\left(\Sigma y_i\right)}{\left(n+1\right)\Sigma x_i^2 - \left(\Sigma x_i\right)^2} \qquad \ldots(a)$$

$$a_0 = -\frac{1}{n+1}\left[a_1\left(\Sigma x_i\right) - \left(\Sigma y_i\right)\right] \qquad \ldots(b) \qquad \ldots(4.5)$$

It can easily be confirmed that eq. 4.4 can be written in matrix form as

$$\mathbf{Aa} \equiv \left(\mathbf{X}^T\mathbf{X}\right)\mathbf{a} = \mathbf{X}^T\mathbf{y} \equiv \mathbf{b} \qquad \ldots(4.6)$$

where

$$\mathbf{X} \equiv \begin{bmatrix} 1 & x_0 \\ 1 & x_1 \\ \cdot & \cdot \\ \cdot & \cdot \\ \cdot & \cdot \\ 1 & x_n \end{bmatrix}$$

$$\mathbf{a} \equiv \begin{bmatrix} a_0 \\ a_1 \end{bmatrix}$$

$$\mathbf{y} \equiv \begin{bmatrix} y_0 \\ y_1 \\ \cdot \\ \cdot \\ \cdot \\ y_n \end{bmatrix} \qquad \qquad \qquad \qquad \ldots(4.7)$$

Equation 4.6 is in the same form as eq. 1.2, and the techniques described in chapter 1 can be used to solve it (though it is easier to obtain the solution analytically in this case). If the residuals are normally distributed about the linear eq. 4.1, then an estimate of the standard deviation, σ, for the regression line is given by [1]

$$\sigma = \left(\frac{\sum\limits_{i=0}^{n} \left[y_i - \left(a_0 + a_1 x_i \right) \right]^2}{(n+1) - 2} \right)^{1/2} \qquad \ldots(4.8)$$

One usually considers the fit to be good if σ is less than about one percent of the range of y_i (*i.e.*, the maximum value of $|y_i - y_j|$, $i \neq j$; $i, j = 0, 1, 2, \ldots, n$).

Example 4.1: Experimental data on constant pressure ($\Delta p = 38$ in. water) filtration of a 169.8 kg/cm^3 CaCO$_3$ slurry through a canvas medium of area 5.48×10^{-4} m^2, is given in the following Table [2]:

x_i	y_i
5	0.530
10	0.716
15	0.806
20	0.869
25	0.943
30	1.013
35	1.096
40	1.160

x in this case is the total volume, V(ml), of filtrate collected till time t (s), and y is t/V. As any chemical engineer knows, this process is described by the equation [3]

$$y = a_0 + a_1 x$$

where the constants, a_0 and a_1, are related to the resistance of the filter medium and to the specific cake resistance respectively. Obtain the best-fit values of a_0 and a_1. Neglect the first data point since it appears to the erroneous (see fig. 4.1).

The computations are quite simple:

$$n + 1 = 7$$

$$\sum x_i = 10 + 15 + ... + 40 = 175$$

$$\sum x_i^2 = 10^2 + 15^2 + ... + 40^2 = 5075$$

$$\sum y_i = 0.716 + 0.806 + ... + 1.160 = 6.603$$

$$\sum y_i x_i = (0.716 \times 10) + (0.806 \times 15) + ... + (1.160 \times 40) = 175.355$$

Hence

$$a_1 = \frac{(7 \times 175.355) - (175 \times 6.603)}{(7 \times 5075) - (175)^2} = 0.014686$$

$$a_0 = -\frac{1}{7}[(0.014686 \times 175) - 6.603] = 0.57614$$

and so

$$y = 0.57614 + 0.014686 x$$

These values can be used by a chemical engineer to evaluate the specific cake resistance [2, 3] as 5.1×10^8 m/kg for $CaCO_3$, which is quite low compared to the literature values ranging from $1.2 - 1.5 \times 10^{11}$ m/kg. ∎

At times data are better fit using an exponential expression

$$y = b_0 e^{b_1 x} \qquad ...(4.9)$$

Equation 4.5 can again be used if we transform this equation to the following form which is linear in the constants (a_0 and a_1):

$$\log y = \log b_0 + b_1 x = a_0 + a_1 x \qquad ...(4.10)$$

If the dependent variable, y, is a linear function of several variables, $x_1, x_2, ..., x_N$, we may wish to fit a set of data $(x_{1,0}, x_{2,0}, ... x_{N,0}, y_0), (x_{1,1}, x_{2,1}, ...x_{N,1}, y_1), ..., (x_{1,n}, x_{2,n}, ... x_{N,n}, y_n)$ to the following linear equation

$$y = a_0 + a_1 x_1 + a_2 x_2 + ... + a_N x_N \qquad ...(4.11)$$

in a least-squares manner, with $n > N$. Again, we can define the error, E, as (see eq. 4.2)

$$E = \sum_{i=0}^{n} \left[y_i - \left(a_0 + a_1 x_{1,i} + a_2 x_{2,i} + ... + a_N x_{N,i} \right) \right]^2 \qquad ...(4.12)$$

The minimum value of E will be obtained with choices of $a_0, a_1, ..., a_N$ given by

$$\frac{\partial E}{\partial a_0} = -2 \sum_{i=0}^{n} \left[y_i - \left(a_0 + a_1 x_{1,i} + a_2 x_{2,i} + ... + a_N x_{N,i} \right) \right] = 0$$

$$\frac{\partial E}{\partial a_1} = -2\sum_{i=0}^{n}\left\{x_{1,i}\left[y_i - \left(a_0 + a_1 x_{1,i} + \ldots + a_N x_{N,i}\right)\right]\right\} = 0$$

.
.

$$\frac{\partial E}{\partial a_N} = -2\sum_{i=0}^{n}\left\{x_{N,i}\left[y_i - \left(a_0 + a_1 x_{1,i} + \ldots + a_N x_{N,i}\right)\right]\right\} = 0 \qquad \ldots(4.13)$$

These equations can be rewritten in the following matrix form

$$
\begin{bmatrix}
n+1 & \sum x_{1,i} & \sum x_{2,i} & \cdots & \sum x_{N,i} \\
\sum x_{1,i} & \sum x_{1,i} x_{1,i} & \sum x_{2,i} x_{1,i} & \cdots & \sum x_{N,i} x_{1,i} \\
. \\
. \\
\sum x_{j,i} & \sum x_{1,i} x_{j,i} & \sum x_{2,i} x_{j,i} & \cdots & \sum x_{N,i} x_{j,i} \\
. \\
. \\
\sum x_{N,i} & \sum x_{1,i} x_{N,i} & \sum x_{2,i} x_{N,i} & \cdots & \sum x_{N,i} x_{N,i}
\end{bmatrix}
\begin{bmatrix}
a_0 \\ a_1 \\ . \\ . \\ a_j \\ . \\ . \\ a_N
\end{bmatrix}
=
\begin{bmatrix}
\sum y_i \\ \sum y_i x_{1,i} \\ . \\ . \\ \sum y_i x_{j,i} \\ . \\ . \\ \sum y_i x_{N,i}
\end{bmatrix}
\qquad \ldots(4.14)
$$

where all the summations extend from $i = 0$ to $i = n$. Equation 4.14 is referred to as the *normal* equations for linear regression. Again, it can be confirmed that, as in eq. 4.7, eq. 4.14 can be written in a matrix form as

$$\mathbf{Aa} \equiv \left(\mathbf{X}^T\mathbf{X}\right)\mathbf{a} = \mathbf{X}^T\mathbf{y} \equiv \mathbf{b} \qquad \ldots(4.15)$$

with

$$
\mathbf{X} \equiv
\begin{bmatrix}
1 & x_{1,0} & x_{2,0} & \cdots & x_{N,0} \\
1 & x_{1,1} & x_{2,1} & \cdots & x_{N,1} \\
. & . \\
. & . \\
. & . \\
1 & x_{1,n} & x_{2,n} & \cdots & x_{N,n}
\end{bmatrix}
\qquad \ldots(4.16)
$$

Matrices **a** and **y** are simple extensions of the matrices given in eq. 4.7:

$$
\mathbf{a} \equiv
\begin{bmatrix}
a_0 \\ a_1 \\ . \\ . \\ a_N
\end{bmatrix},
\quad
\mathbf{y} \equiv
\begin{bmatrix}
y_0 \\ y_1 \\ . \\ . \\ y_n
\end{bmatrix}
\qquad \ldots(4.17)
$$

If the y_i are normally distributed, the standard deviation is given by

$$\sigma = \left[\frac{\sum_{i=0}^{n} \left[y_i - \left(a_0 + a_1 x_{1,i} + a_2 x_{2,i} + ... + a_N x_{N,i} \right) \right]^2}{(n+1) - (N+1)} \right]^{1/2}$$

$$= \left[\frac{E}{n+1 - (N+1)} \right]^{1/2} \qquad ...(4.18)$$

At times, one is interested in fitting a set of $n+1$ data, (x_i, y_i), to a nonlinear equation (but with the coefficients, **a,** entering linearly) involving a set of N *linearly independent* functions

$$y = a_0 P_0(x) + a_1 P_1(x) + ... + a_N P_N(x) \qquad ...(4.19)$$

Examples include

$P_i(x) = x^i$ (polynomial expansion)

$P_i(x) = \sin(ix)$ or $\cos(ix)$ (Fourier expansion)

$P_i(x) = \exp[\alpha_i x]$, etc. $\qquad ...(4.20)$

Obviously, if the data is periodic, we would expect use of sin or cos functions to be better. Similarly, exponential functions would be better if the data have an exponential behaviour. The algorithm can be developed in a manner similar to that used in deriving eq. 4.14, and is left as an exercise (see prob. 4.1). A particularly fruitful choice of $P_i(x)$ is described in prob. 4.4. One usually keeps increasing the number, N, of functions till the standard deviation (given by the last term in eq. 4.18) does not change any more. Solution of the equations becomes more difficult for $N > 6$, however, since the determinant of the **A** matrix approaches zero as N increases.

If one is interested in fitting a general *nonlinear* function to a set of $n+1$ data points, (x_i, y_i), with the constants, **a,** entering nonlinearly in the expression for $y(x)$, one needs to use optimization techniques to minimize the error:

$$E \equiv \sum_{i=0}^{n} \left[y_i - y_{\text{calc}}(x_i) \right]^2 \qquad ...(4.21)$$

where $y_{\text{calc}}(x_i)$ is the computed value of y (using the model) corresponding to a value, x_i. A popular method is that of Box [4–6]. Details of this technique, which fall outside the scope of this text, are available elsewhere. Ref. 7 presents an interesting application of this technique to obtain three parameters in a fairly complex nonlinear kinetic model describing the polymerization of methyl-methacrylate in batch reactors.

4.3 NEWTON'S INTERPOLATION FORMULAE

The least squares technique is useful if one is trying to fit a low-order (in **a**) analytical function to a set of data with $n > N$. As shown in fig. 4.1, the fitted expression need not match with the data points *exactly.* Another possibility is to fit a polynomial of degree n to a set of $n+1$ data[*]. There are no degrees of freedom then, and we merely ensure that the polynomial passes through the data points exactly. A

---

[*] The Weierstrass approximation theorem states that if there is a function, $y(x)$, which is continuous in $a \le x \le b$, then we can approximate it by a polynomial, $p_n(x)$, of degree $n(\varepsilon)$ such that $|y(x) - p_n(x)| < \varepsilon$; $a \le x \le b$. Thus, we can, in principle, fit a 'good' polynomial to a set of data.

popular method of doing this is through the use of Newton's interpolation formulae. This is developed for the case where the values, y_0, y_1, y_2, ..., y_n, are known at equispaced values, x_0, x_1, x_2, ..., x_n, respectively, of the base points with $x_{i+1} - x_i \equiv \Delta x$.

We first define *forward differences* as follows:

$$\Delta y_i \equiv y_{i+1} - y_i \qquad \qquad ...(4.22)$$

Higher order forward differences can be easily written:

$$\Delta^2 y_i = \Delta\left(\Delta y_i\right) = \Delta\left(y_{i+1} - y_i\right) = \left(y_{i+2} - y_{i+1}\right) - \left(y_{i+1} - y_i\right)$$

$$= y_{i+2} - 2y_{i+1} + y_i$$

$$\Delta^j y_i = \Delta^{j-1} y_{i+1} - \Delta^{j-1} y_i \qquad \qquad ...(4.23)$$

We now define a dimensionless value of x by

$$\alpha \equiv \frac{x - x_0}{\Delta x} \qquad \qquad ...(4.24)$$

and write $y\left(x_0 + \alpha\Delta x\right)$ as a polynomial:

$$y\left(x_0 + \alpha\Delta x\right) = a_0 + a_1\alpha + a_2\alpha^2 + ... + a_n\alpha^n \qquad \qquad ...(4.25)$$

This involves $n + 1$ unknown coefficients, which can be determined by equating the analytical values at the base points, x_i, to the known values, y_i. Thus,

$$
\begin{aligned}
y\left(x_0\right) &= a_0 & &= y_0 \\
y\left(x_0 + \Delta x\right) &= a_0 + a_1 + a_2 + ... + a_n & &= y_1 \\
y\left(x_0 + 2\Delta x\right) &= a_0 + 2a_1 + 2^2 a_2 + ... + 2^n a_n & &= y_2 \\
&\;\vdots \\
y\left(x_0 + n\Delta x\right) &= a_0 + na_1 + n^2 a_2 + ... + n^n a_n & &= y_n
\end{aligned}
\qquad ...(4.26)
$$

or

$$
\mathbf{Aa} \equiv
\begin{bmatrix}
1 & 0 & 0 & 0 & \cdot & \cdot & \cdot & 0 \\
1 & 1 & 1 & 1 & \cdot & \cdot & \cdot & 1 \\
1 & 2 & 2^2 & 2^3 & \cdot & \cdot & \cdot & 2^n \\
\cdot & \cdot & \cdot & \cdot & & & & \cdot \\
\cdot & \cdot & \cdot & \cdot & & & & \cdot \\
\cdot & \cdot & \cdot & \cdot & & & & \cdot \\
1 & n & n^2 & n^3 & \cdot & \cdot & \cdot & n^n
\end{bmatrix}
\begin{bmatrix}
a_0 \\ a_1 \\ a_2 \\ \cdot \\ \cdot \\ \cdot \\ a_n
\end{bmatrix}
=
\begin{bmatrix}
y_0 \\ y_1 \\ y_2 \\ \cdot \\ \cdot \\ \cdot \\ y_n
\end{bmatrix}
= \mathbf{y} \qquad ...(4.27)
$$

Since $|\mathbf{A}| \neq 0$, we have a unique solution for $\mathbf{a}$ (and so the polynomial in eq. 4.25, passing through the distinct points $\alpha = 0, 1, 2, ..., n$, is uniquely determined). The values of $\mathbf{a}$ can be easily computed. The polynomial in eq. 4.25 so obtained can be written in a slightly different form (see prob. 4.5 and example 4.3) using the forward differences to give Newton's forward difference formula:

$$y\left(x_0 + \alpha\Delta x\right) = y_0 + \alpha\left(\Delta y_0\right) + \frac{\alpha(\alpha - 1)}{2!}\left(\Delta^2 y_0\right) + ... + \frac{\alpha(\alpha - 1)(\alpha - 2)...(\alpha - n + 1)\left(\Delta^n y_0\right)}{n!} + R \;...(a)$$

$$R = \frac{\alpha(\alpha-1)(\alpha-2)...(\alpha-n)}{(n+1)!} \Delta^{n+1} y[\xi(\alpha)]$$

$$= \frac{(\Delta x)^{n+1}}{(n+1)!} \alpha(\alpha-1)...(\alpha-n) y^{(n+1)}[\xi(\alpha)] \qquad ...(b) \qquad ...(4.28)$$

where the last term is an error or remainder term, with $y^{(n+1)}[\xi(\alpha)]$ being the $(n + 1)$th derivative of y evaluated at $x = \xi(\alpha)$, $x_0 < \xi(\alpha) < x_n$ (estimated values or bounds can be used, if available, to evaluate the error term). The relationship between $\Delta^{n+1} y(\xi)$ and $y^{(n+1)}(\xi)$ will be deduced in sec. 4.8. Obviously, if y is described *exactly* by a polynomial of degree n, eq. 4.28 will be exact, and the error term will be zero. Equation 4.28 is useful for interpolation of data, as well as for extrapolation, though care must be exercised in the latter case.

Example 4.2: The following table gives four values of y_i at $x_i = 1, 2, 3$ and 4. Obtain values of Δy_i, $\Delta^2 y_i$ and $\Delta^3 y_i$ at all possible base points. Also obtain a 3rd degree Newton forward difference formula (eq. 4.28) for interpolating values of y at any x. Make a plot of y vs. x.

The data as well as the forward differences are shown in a tabular format as

i	x_i	y_i	Δy_i	$\Delta^2 y_i$	$\Delta^3 y_i$
0	1	7			
			$\Delta y_0 = 10$		
1	2	17		$\Delta^2 y_0 = 26$	
			$\Delta y_1 = 36$		$\Delta^3 y_0 = 42$
2	3	53		$\Delta^2 y_1 = 68$	
			$\Delta y_2 = 104$		
3	4	157			

Note how easy it is to generate this table—any entry is obtained as the difference in the two neighbouring entries in the previous column.

Newton's forward difference formula (eq. 4.28) gives

$$y = 7 + 10\alpha + 26\frac{(\alpha^2 - \alpha)}{2} + 42\frac{(\alpha^2 - \alpha)(\alpha - 2)}{3!}$$

$$= 7 + 11\alpha - 8\alpha^2 + 7\alpha^3 ; \quad \alpha = x - 1 \qquad ...(a)$$

Note that the top entries along the sloping line in the above table are used in generating this equation. It can easily be checked that this equation correctly predicts values of y_i at $x_i = 1, 2, 3$ and 4. Figure 4.2 shows y obtained from this equation, as well as from $y = x^4 - 3x^3 + 6x^2 - 2x + 5$, which was used to generate the four values of y_i in the table. Note the differences between the interpolating function and the 'exact' function particularly for values of x beyond $1 \le x \le 4$. A higher order Newton's interpolation formula does, indeed, lead to $y = x^4 - 3x^3 + 6x^2 - 2x + 5$ (see prob. 4.6). ∎

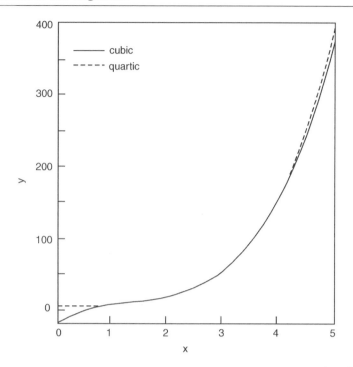

Fig. 4.2 Plot of eq. (*a*) in example 4.2 (solid curve). Also plotted is the exact function $y = x^4 - 3x^3 + 6x^2 - 2x + 5$ (dotted curve). The cubic is higher than the quartic in $1 < x < 2$ and $3 < x < 4$, and is lower in $2 < x < 3$, these differences being imperceptible on the graph above.

Example 4.3: Derive eq. 4.28.

An elegant derivation is given by Lapidus [1]. It uses the linear operators E and Δ defined by

$$E\,y(x) \equiv y(x + \Delta x) \quad \text{(shift-operator)}$$

$$\Delta y(x) \equiv y(x + \Delta x) - y(x) \quad \text{(forward-difference operator)}$$

Obviously,

$$E^2 y(x) = E\big[y(x + \Delta x)\big] = y(x + 2\Delta x), \text{ etc.}$$

and

$$\Delta y(x) = Ey(x) - y(x) = (E - 1)\,y(x)$$

This leads to the following relationship between the two operators:

$$E = 1 + \Delta$$

One can expand $(1 + \Delta)^\alpha$ as

$$E^\alpha = (1+\Delta)^\alpha = 1 + \alpha\Delta + \frac{\alpha(\alpha-1)}{2!}\Delta^2 + \frac{\alpha(\alpha-1)(\alpha-2)}{3!}\Delta^3 + \ldots$$

$$+ \ldots + \frac{\alpha(\alpha-1)\ldots(\alpha-n+1)}{n!}\Delta^n + \ldots$$

Thus,

$$y\left(x_0 + \alpha\Delta x\right) = E^\alpha y\left(x_0\right) = y_0 + \alpha\Delta y_0 + \frac{\alpha(\alpha-1)}{2!}\Delta^2 y_0 + \dots$$

The remainder can be inferred from the first neglected term as

$$R = \frac{\alpha(\alpha-1)(\alpha-2)\dots(\alpha-n)}{(n+1)!}\Delta^{n+1} y\left(\xi\right)$$

where ξ is some point between x_0 and x_n. ∎

An alternate procedure is to work with *backward differences,* defined by

$$\nabla y_i = y_i - y_{i-1} \qquad \dots(4.29)$$

Higher-order backward differences can be computed as

$$\nabla^2 y_i = \nabla\left(\nabla y_i\right) = \nabla\left(y_i - y_{i-1}\right) = \nabla y_i - \nabla y_{i-1}$$

$$= \left(y_i - y_{i-1}\right) - \left(y_{i-1} - y_{i-2}\right) = y_i - 2y_{i-1} + y_{i-2}$$

$$\nabla^j y_i = \nabla^{j-1} y_i - \nabla^{j-1} y_{i-1} \qquad \dots(4.30)$$

Once again, we define a dimensionless value of x as

$$\alpha \equiv \frac{x - x_n}{\Delta x} \qquad \dots(4.31)$$

(note the difference between this and the definition in eq. 4.24) and write $y(x_n + \alpha\Delta x)$ as

$$y(x) \equiv y\left(x_n + \alpha\Delta x\right) = a_0 + a_1\alpha + a_2\alpha^2 + \dots + a_n\alpha^n \qquad \dots(4.32)$$

We can obtain the $(n+1)$ coefficients, a_i, by forcing the polynomial in eq. 4.32 to pass through the $(n+1)$ data points $(x_n, y_n), (x_{n-1}, y_{n-1}), \dots, (x_0, y_0)$, *i.e.*, making the residual zero at these base points. This leads to

$$y\left(x_n + \alpha\Delta x\right) = y_n + \alpha\left(\nabla y_n\right) + \frac{\alpha(\alpha+1)}{2!}\nabla^2 y_n + \dots + \frac{\alpha(\alpha+1)\dots(\alpha+n-1)}{n!}\nabla^n y_n + R \qquad \dots(a)$$

$$R = \frac{\alpha(\alpha+1)(\alpha+2)\dots(\alpha+n)}{(n+1)!}\nabla^{n+1} y\left[\xi(\alpha)\right]$$

$$= \frac{\alpha(\alpha+1)\dots(\alpha+n)}{(n+1)!}(\Delta x)^{n+1} y^{(n+1)}\left[\xi(\alpha)\right]; \; x_0 \le \xi \le x_n \qquad \dots(b) \quad \dots(4.33)$$

This is Newton's backward difference formula. Equation 4.33 can be derived in a manner similar to that used in example 4.3 (see prob. 4.9). It may be emphasized that if we have a set of data, $(x_0, y_0), (x_1, y_1), \dots, (x_n, y_n)$, and we wish to fit an *n*th *degree* polynomial using either eq. 4.28 or eq. 4.33, we shall get the same final results. This is because a unique *n*th-degree *polynomial* passes through a set of $n+1$ points. On the other hand, if we have $n + j$ $(j > 1)$ data points, we can choose several different *n*th-degree polynomials passing through them. In the latter case, one prefers to use data at base points nearest the value of x at which we wish to evaluate y.

Example 4.4: Using Newton's backward difference formula, fit a 3rd-degree polynomial through the four data points given in example 4.2.

i	x_i	y_i	∇y_i	$\nabla^2 y_i$	$\nabla^3 y_i$
0	1	7			
			$\nabla y_1 = 10$		
1	2	17		$\nabla^2 y_2 = 26$	
			$\nabla y_2 = 36$		$\nabla^3 y_3 = 42$
2	3	53		$\nabla^2 y_3 = 68$	
			$\nabla y_3 = 104$		
3	4	157			

eq. 4.33 gives

$$y(x_3 + \alpha) = 157 + 104\alpha + \frac{\alpha^2 + \alpha}{2} \times 68 + \frac{(\alpha^2 + \alpha)(\alpha + 2)}{6} \times 42 + R$$

or

$$y(4 + \alpha) = 157 + 104\alpha + 34\alpha^2 + 34\alpha + 7\alpha^3 + 21\alpha^2 + 14\alpha + R$$

$$= 157 + 152\alpha + 55\alpha^2 + 7\alpha^3 + R$$

Note that this expression looks different from eq. (*a*) in example 4.2. This is because $\alpha = x - 4$ here, while α was $x - 1$ in example 4.2. It can easily be shown that *both* these equations reduce to

$$y(x) = -19 + 48x - 29x^2 + 7x^3$$

thus confirming the uniqueness of the polynomial fit of the same degree to identical data points. ∎

One could also fit an nth-degree polynomial through the data points (x_{n+1}, y_{n+1}), (x_n, y_n), ..., (x_1, y_1), to obtain (see prob. 4.11)

$$y(x_n + \alpha\Delta x) = y_{n+1} + (\alpha - 1)(\nabla y_{n+1}) + \frac{(\alpha - 1)\alpha}{2!}\nabla^2 y_{n+1} + ...$$

$$... + \frac{(\alpha - 1)\alpha(\alpha + 1)(\alpha + 2)...(\alpha + n - 2)}{n!}\nabla^n y_{n+1} + R \qquad ...(4.34)$$

where α is related to x by eq. 4.31.

Many similar interpolation formulae using either forward or backward differences can be derived, but we have presented some which are used later in developing expressions for evaluating derivatives and integrals. Central difference formulae can also be developed, and the reader is referred to Lapidus [1] for details.

4.4 NEWTON'S DIVIDED DIFFERENCE INTERPOLATION POLYNOMIAL

We now extend Newton's interpolation formulae involving forward/backward differences, to cases where the base points are *not* evenly spaced. Once again, it is assumed that we have a set of $(n + 1)$ data points, (x_0, y_0), (x_1, y_1), ..., (x_n, y_n). We define *finite divided differences* as follows:

$$y[x_0] \equiv y_0$$

$$y[x_1, x_0] \equiv \frac{y_1 - y_0}{x_1 - x_0}$$

$$y[x_2, x_1, x_0] \equiv \frac{y[x_2, x_1] - y[x_1, x_0]}{x_2 - x_0}$$

$$y[x_n, x_{n-1}, ..., x_0] \equiv \frac{y[x_n, x_{n-1}, ..., x_1] - y[x_{n-1}, x_{n-2}, ..., x_0]}{x_n - x_0} \qquad ...(4.35)$$

These are referred to as 0th, 1st, 2nd, ..., nth order finite-divided differences. One can easily deduce (see prob. 4.13) that

$$y[x_n, x_{n-1}, ..., x_0] = \frac{y_n}{(x_n - x_0)(x_n - x_1)...(x_n - x_{n-1})}$$

$$+ \frac{y_{n-1}}{(x_{n-1} - x_0)(x_{n-1} - x_1)...(x_{n-1} - x_{n-2})(x_{n-1} - x_n)}$$

$$+ ...$$

$$+ \frac{y_0}{(x_0 - x_1)(x_0 - x_2)...(x_0 - x_n)}$$

$$= \sum_{i=0}^{n} \frac{y_i}{\prod_{\substack{j=0 \\ j \neq i}}^{n} (x_i - x_j)} \qquad ...(4.36)$$

It can also be deduced that the order of the arguments in $y[x_n, x_{n-1}, ..., x_0]$ is immaterial (see prob. 4.13).

Newton's fundamental formula gives $y(x)$ in terms of a polynomial of nth degree as

$$y(x) = y_0 + (x - x_0)y[x_1, x_0] + (x - x_0)(x - x_1)y[x_2, x_1, x_0] + ...$$

$$... + (x - x_0)(x - x_1)...(x - x_{n-1})y[x_n, x_{n-1}, ..., x_1, x_0] + R_n(\xi)$$

$$R_n(\xi) = (x - x_0)(x - x_1)...(x - x_n)y[\xi, x_n, x_{n-1}, ..., x_0]; \ x_0 \leq \xi \leq x_n \qquad ...(4.37)$$

where $R_n(\xi)$ is the remainder. The polynomial is observed to be of degree n because of its last term. By substituting $x = x_0, x_1, ..., x_n$ in this polynomial, we obtain:

$$x = x_0, \ y(x) = y_0$$

$$x = x_1, \ y(x) = y_0 + (x_1 - x_0)y[x_1, x_0] = y_0 + (x_1 - x_0)\frac{y_1 - y_0}{x_1 - x_0} = y_1$$

$$x = x_2, \; y(x) = y_0 + (x_2 - x_0) y[x_1, x_0] + (x_2 - x_0)(x_2 - x_1) y[x_2, x_1, x_0]$$

$$= y_0 + (x_2 - x_0)\frac{y_1 - y_0}{x_1 - x_0} + (x_2 - x_0)(x_2 - x_1) \times$$

$$\left[\frac{y_2}{(x_2 - x_0)(x_2 - x_1)} + \frac{y_1}{(x_1 - x_2)(x_1 - x_0)} + \frac{y_0}{(x_0 - x_2)(x_0 - x_1)} \right]$$

$$= y_0 + \frac{x_2 - x_0}{x_1 - x_0} y_1 - \frac{x_2 - x_0}{x_1 - x_0} y_0 - \frac{x_2 - x_0}{x_1 - x_0} y_1 - \frac{x_2 - x_1}{x_0 - x_1} y_0 + y_2$$

$$= y_2, \text{ etc.} \hspace{4cm} ...(4.38)$$

i.e., the polynomial passes through the $n + 1$ data points (x_0, y_0), (x_1, y_1), ..., (x_n, y_n) (and so is uniquely determined). We can obtain an expression for the remainder, $R_n(\xi)$. We have (using interchangeability of arguments and the definition of the divided differences):

$$R_n(\xi) = \{y(\xi) - y_0\} - (\xi - x_0) y[x_1 - x_0] - (\xi - x_0)(\xi - x_1) y[x_2, x_1, x_0] - ...$$

$$- (\xi - x_0)(\xi - x_1)...(\xi - x_{n-1}) y[x_n, x_{n-1}, ..., x_0]$$

$$= (\xi - x_0) y[\xi, x_0] - (\xi - x_0) y[x_1 - x_0] - (\xi - x_0)(\xi - x_1) y[x_2, x_1, x_0] -$$

$$... - (\xi - x_0)(\xi - x_1)...(\xi - x_{n-1}) y[x_n, x_{n-1}, ..., x_0]$$

$$= (\xi - x_0)\{y[\xi, x_0] - y(x_1, x_0)\} - ...$$

$$= (\xi - x_0)\{y[\xi, x_0] - y(x_0, x_1)\} - ...$$

$$= (\xi - x_0)(\xi - x_1) y[\xi, x_0, x_1] - (\xi - x_0)(\xi - x_1) y[x_2, x_1, x_0] - ...$$

$$= (\xi - x_0)(\xi - x_1)\{y[\xi, x_0, x_1] - y[x_0, x_1, x_2]\} - ...$$

$$= (\xi - x_0)(\xi - x_1)(\xi - x_2) y[\xi, x_0, x_1, x_2] - ...$$

.

.

.

$$= (\xi - x_0)(\xi - x_1)(\xi - x_2)...(\xi - x_n) y[\xi, x_n, x_{n-1}, ..., x_1, x_0] \hspace{2cm} ...(4.39)$$

Example 4.5: Consider the following data (see example 4.2)

i	x_i	y_i
0	1	7
1	3	53
2	4	157
3	6	857

Express the divided differences, $y[x_0]$, $y[x_0, x_1]$, $y[x_0, x_1, x_2]$ in a tabular form and find the 3rd-degree polynomial which fits these 4 data points.

eq. 4.35 leads to:

i	x_i	$y_i = y[x_i]$	$y[x_{i+1}, x_i]$	$y[x_{i+2}, x_{i+1}, x_i]$	$y[x_{i+3}, x_{i+2}, x_{i+1}, x_i]$
0	1	7			
			$y[x_1, x_0] = 23$		
1	3	53		$y[x_2, x_1, x_0] = 27$	
			$y[x_2, x_1] = 104$		$y[x_3, x_2, x_1, x_0] = 11$
2	4	157		$y[x_3, x_2, x_1] = 82$	
			$y[x_3, x_2] = 350$		
3	6	857			

Notice the similarity with the table in example 4.2. The 3rd-degree polynomial passing through the given set of four data points is given by eq. 4.37 as

$$y(x) = 7 + 23(x-1) + 27(x-1)(x-3) + 11(x-1)(x-3)(x-4)$$

$$= -67 + 124x - 61x^2 + 11x^3$$

It is easy to see that this polynomial passes through the four data points given. As in the case of the forward/backward difference formulae one could fit several different polynomials of degree $< n$ to a set of $n + 1$ data points. ∎

4.5 LAGRANGIAN INTERPOLATION (UNEQUAL INTERVALS)

The Lagrangian interpolation formula can be written as

$$y(x) = a_0 (x - x_1)(x - x_2)...(x - x_n) + a_1 (x - x_0)(x - x_2)(x - x_3)...(x - x_n) + ...$$

$$+ a_j (x - x_0)(x - x_1)...(x - x_{j-1})(x - x_{j+1})...(x - x_n) + ...$$

$$+ a_n (x - x_0)...(x - x_{n-1}) + R \qquad ...(a)$$

$$R = \frac{(x - x_0)(x - x_1)...(x - x_n)}{(n+1)!} y^{(n+1)}[\xi(x)]; \quad x_0 \le \xi(x) \le x_n \qquad ...(b) \qquad ...(4.40)$$

with $a_0, a_1, ..., a_n$ being obtained by forcing the residuals at the $n + 1$ base points to be zero. Equation 4.40 is a particularly convenient form of an *n*th degree polynomial expression for $y(x)$. It is easy to observe that if $x = x_0$, all terms except the first vanish in eq. 4.40, and we obtain

$$y_0 = a_0 (x_0 - x_1)(x_0 - x_2)...(x_0 - x_n) \qquad ...(4.41)$$

Similarly, forcing the residual to be zero at $x = x_j$ leads to

$$y_j = a_j (x_j - x_0)(x_j - x_1)...(x_j - x_{j-1})(x_j - x_{j+1})...(x_j - x_n) \qquad ...(4.42)$$

These equations can be used to determine $a_0, a_1, ..., a_n$. This leads to

$$y(x) = \frac{(x - x_1)(x - x_2)...(x - x_n)}{(x_0 - x_1)(x_0 - x_2)...(x_0 - x_n)} y_0 + ...$$

$$+\frac{(x-x_0)(x-x_1)...(x-x_{j-1})(x-x_{j+1})...(x-x_n)}{(x_j-x_0)(x_j-x_1)...(x_j-x_{j-1})(x_j-x_{j+1})...(x_j-x_n)}y_j+...$$

$$+\frac{(x-x_0)(x-x_1)...(x-x_{n-1})}{(x_n-x_0)...(x_n-x_{n-1})}y_n$$

$$=\sum_{j=0}^{n}\left[\prod_{\substack{i=0\\i\neq j}}^{n}\frac{(x-x_i)}{(x_j-x_i)}\right]y_j$$

$$\equiv\sum_{j=0}^{n}L_j^{(n)}(x)y_j \qquad\qquad ...(4.43)$$

where $L_j^{(n)}(x)$, the jth Lagrangian coefficient function, is the nth degree polynomial in x in this case and depends on the location of all the $(n+1)$ base points.

It must be emphasized that the nth degree polynomial obtained from eq. 4.43 will be identical to that obtained from Newton's fundamental formula using divided differences (eq. 4.37), provided the $n+1$

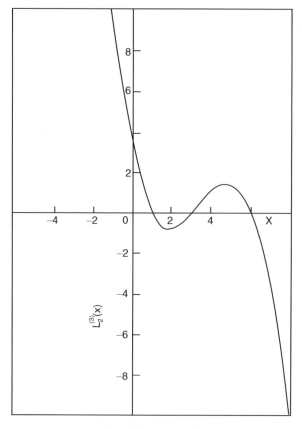

Fig. 4.3 Plot of $L_2^{(3)}(x)=-\dfrac{(x-1)(x-3)(x-6)}{6}$, as used in example 4.6.

data points used for these two applications are identical. However, eq. 4.43 is quite convenient to use and program for, on a computer. Newton's formulae have the advantage, however, that one can make use of the previous computations (for obtaining an nth degree polynomial) if we wish to fit a higher degree, $(n+1)$, polynomial. For the Lagrangian formulation, we will have to repeat the entire calculation. Moreover, since subtraction of numbers having similar magnitudes is involved in the Lagrangian interpolation scheme, round-off errors could pose problems for high-degree polynomials [1].

Figure 4.3 shows a plot of one of the Lagrangian coefficient functions, relevant to example 4.6. It is noted that the nth degree polynomial, $L_j^{(n)}(x)$, has n roots (where the functions are zero) at $x = x_0, x_1, \ldots, x_{j-1}, x_{j+1}, \ldots, x_n$, and has a value of unity at $x = x_j$.

Example 4.6: Consider the data of example 4.5 again. Fit a third degree polynomial through these points, using the Lagrangian interpolation formula. Simplify and check if this is the same as the polynomial obtained in the previous example.

The data is shown again

i	x_i	y_i
0	1	7
1	3	53
2	4	157
3	6	857

eq. 4.43 leads to

$$y(x) = 7\frac{(x-3)(x-4)(x-6)}{(1-3)(1-4)(1-6)} + 53\frac{(x-1)(x-4)(x-6)}{(3-1)(3-4)(3-6)}$$

$$+157\frac{(x-1)(x-3)(x-6)}{(4-1)(4-3)(4-6)} + 857\frac{(x-1)(x-3)(x-4)}{(6-1)(6-3)(6-4)}$$

$$= 7L_0^{(3)}(x) + 53L_1^{(3)}(x) + 157L_2^{(3)}(x) + 857L_3^{(3)}(x)$$

or

$$y(x) = -\frac{7}{30}(x-3)(x-4)(x-6) + \frac{53}{6}(x-1)(x-4)(x-6)$$

$$-\frac{157}{6}(x-1)(x-3)(x-6) + \frac{857}{30}(x-1)(x-3)(x-4)$$

$$= -\frac{7}{30}(x^3 - 13x^2 + 54x - 72) + \frac{53}{6}(x^3 - 11x^2 + 34x - 24)$$

$$-\frac{157}{6}(x^3 - 10x^2 + 27x - 18) + \frac{857}{30}(x^3 - 8x^2 + 19x - 12)$$

$$= 11x^3 - 61x^2 + 124x - 67$$

which is the same polynomial as in example 4.5. Note that $L_j^{(3)}(x)$ are third degree polynomials here. ∎

The nth degree polynomial obtained using any of the techniques discussed so far has an error associated with it which can be estimated using the first omitted term. The Chebyshev economization technique (also referred to as telescoping a power series) [1, 8] uses the set of Chebyshev polynomials to transform this series into an equivalent one of a lower degree (obviously, with different coefficients), but with a similar error as before. Details can be found in Refs. 1 or 8.

4.6 PADÉ APPROXIMATIONS

It was observed in fig. 4.2 that the approximating polynomial, $y = 7 + 11\alpha - 8\alpha^2 + 7\alpha^3$ (with $\alpha = x - 1$), oscillated about the 'exact' curve. Such oscillations are quite common when we use polynomial approximations to curve-fit data. A better approximation of a function, $f(x)$, in this regard is a rational-function approximation, $y(x)$, of degree $n + m$, given by

$$y(x) = \frac{a_0 + a_1 x + a_2 x^2 + ... + a_n x^n}{1 + b_1 x + b_2 x^2 + ... + b_m x^m} \cong f(x) \qquad ...(4.44)$$

There are $n + m + 1$ coefficients to be determined. The Padé technique chooses these coefficients to satisfy the following conditions

$$
\begin{aligned}
y(0) &= f(0) \\
y'(0) &= \frac{df}{dx}(0) \\
&\quad . \\
&\quad . \\
&\quad . \\
y^{(n+m)}(0) &= \frac{d^{n+m} f(x)}{dx^{n+m}}\bigg|_{x=0} \qquad ...(4.45)
\end{aligned}
$$

It is obvious that the Padé approximation, $y(x)$, for $m = 0$ is identical to a Taylor expansion of $f(x)$, about $x = 0$ [*i.e.*, the Maclaurin expansion of $f(x)$]. In fact, this provides an easier method of evaluating the coefficients, a_i and b_i, than does eq. 4.45, as illustrated in example 4.7.

Example 4.7: Obtain the $n = 2$, $m = 1$ approximation to e^x, using the Maclaurin expansion for this function.

The Maclaurin expansion of e^x is given by

$$f(x) = e^x = 1 + x + \frac{1}{2!}x^2 + \frac{1}{3!}x^3 + \frac{1}{4!}x^4 + ... = \sum_{i=0}^{\infty} \frac{x^i}{i!}$$

We have, for $n = 2$, $m = 1$

$$y(x) = \frac{a_0 + a_1 x + a_2 x^2}{1 + b_1 x}$$

Thus,

$$f(x) - y(x) = \sum_{i=0}^{\infty} \frac{x^i}{i!} - \frac{a_0 + a_1 x + a_2 x^2}{1 + b_1 x}$$

Table 4.1 Padé Approximants to e^x

$m\downarrow$	$n\to 0$	1	2	3
0	$\dfrac{1}{1}$	$\dfrac{1+x}{1}$	$\dfrac{1+x+\frac{1}{2}x^2}{1}$	$\dfrac{1+x+\frac{1}{2}x^2+\frac{1}{6}x^3}{1}$
1	$\dfrac{1}{1-x}$	$\dfrac{1+\frac{1}{2}x}{1-\frac{1}{2}x}$	$\dfrac{1+\frac{2}{3}x+\frac{1}{6}x^2}{1-\frac{1}{3}x}$	$\dfrac{1+\frac{3}{4}x+\frac{1}{4}x+\frac{1}{24}x^3}{1-\frac{1}{4}x}$
2	$\dfrac{1}{1-x+\frac{1}{2}x^2}$	$\dfrac{1+\frac{1}{3}x}{1-\frac{2}{3}x+\frac{1}{6}x^2}$	$\dfrac{1+\frac{1}{2}x+\frac{1}{12}x^2}{1-\frac{1}{2}x+\frac{1}{12}x^2}$	$\dfrac{1+\frac{3}{5}x+\frac{3}{20}x^2+\frac{1}{60}x^3}{1-\frac{2}{5}x+\frac{1}{20}x^2}$
3	$\dfrac{1}{1-x+\frac{1}{2}x^2-\frac{1}{6}x^3}$	$\dfrac{1+\frac{1}{4}x}{1-\frac{3}{4}x+\frac{1}{4}x^2-\frac{1}{24}x^3}$	$\dfrac{1+\frac{2}{5}x+\frac{1}{20}x^2}{1-\frac{3}{5}x+\frac{3}{20}x^2-\frac{1}{60}x^3}$	$\dfrac{1+\frac{1}{2}x+\frac{1}{10}x^2+\frac{1}{120}x^3}{1-\frac{1}{2}x+\frac{1}{10}x^2-\frac{1}{120}x^3}$
4	$\dfrac{1}{1-x+\frac{1}{2}x^2-\frac{1}{6}x^3+\frac{1}{24}x^4}$	$\dfrac{1+\frac{1}{5}x}{1-\frac{4}{5}x+\frac{3}{10}x^2-\frac{1}{15}x^3+\frac{1}{120}x^4}$	$\dfrac{1+\frac{1}{3}x+\frac{1}{30}x^2}{1-\frac{2}{3}x+\frac{1}{5}x^2-\frac{1}{30}x^3+\frac{1}{300}x^4}$	$\dfrac{1+\frac{3}{7}x+\frac{1}{14}x^2+\frac{1}{210}x^3}{1-\frac{4}{7}x+\frac{1}{7}x^2-\frac{4}{210}x^3+\frac{1}{840}x^4}$

$$= \frac{\left(\sum_{i=0}^{\infty} \frac{x^i}{i!}\right)(1+b_1 x) - \left(a_0 + a_1 x + a_2 x^2\right)}{1+b_1 x}$$

$$= \frac{(1-a_0) + (1+b_1 - a_1)x + \left(\frac{1}{2!}+b_1 - a_2\right)x^2 + \sum_{i=3}^{\infty}\left[\frac{1}{i!}+\frac{b_1}{(i-1)!}\right]x^i}{1+b_1 x} \quad \ldots(a)$$

It can be shown (p. 393 in Ref. 10) that if we wish $[f - y]^{(k)}(0) = 0$; $k = 0, 1, 2, \ldots, n + m$, as in eq. 4.45, $f(x) - y(x)$ must have a root of multiplicity $n + m + 1$ at $x = 0$, *i.e.*, we should only have terms $x^{n+m+1}, x^{n+m+2}, \ldots$, etc., in the numerator of eq. (a) above. For our present example, this gives

$$1 - a_0 = 0$$

$$1 + b_1 - a_1 = 0$$

$$\frac{1}{2!} + b_1 - a_2 = 0$$

$$\frac{1}{3!} + \frac{b_1}{2!} = 0$$

This leads to

$$a_0 = 1 \qquad a_1 = \frac{2}{3} \qquad a_2 = \frac{1}{6} \qquad b_1 = -\frac{1}{3}$$

or

$$y(x) = \frac{1 + \frac{2}{3}x + \frac{1}{6}x^2}{1 - \frac{1}{3}x} \cong e^x \qquad \ldots(b)$$

Padé approximations for e^x are quite useful (see Chapter 5), and some low-order expressions are listed in table 4.1.

Values obtained from eq. (b) are compared with exact values of e^x as well as with values from the 3rd degree Maclaurin expansion, for $0 \le x \le 2.0$ below:

x	e^x	Padé (eq. b)	3rd degree Macaurin
0	1.000000	1.000000	1.000000
0.25	1.284025	1.284091	1.283854
0.50	1.648721	1.650000	1.645833
0.75	2.117000	2.125000	2.101563
1.00	2.718282	2.750000	2.666667
1.25	3.490343	3.589286	3.356771
1.50	4.481689	4.750000	4.187500
1.75	5.754603	6.425000	5.174479
2.00	7.389056	9.000000	6.333333

The Padé approximants are observed to be better for $0 \le x \le 1$. It can be shown [10, 11] that if we express the Padé approximation in the form of a continued division, we can save on the total number of multiplications and divisions required as well (as compared to evaluation of e^x using a Maclaurin series of degree $n + m$). This explains the popularity of this technique, even though it is less convenient to work with than polynomial approximations.

The Padé approximation for a matrix function, $\mathbf{f}(x)$, defined by

$$\mathbf{f}(x) \equiv \begin{bmatrix} f_{11}(x) & f_{12}(x) & \cdots & f_{1N}(x) \\ f_{21}(x) & \cdots & & \cdot \\ \cdot & & & \cdot \\ \cdot & & & \cdot \\ \cdot & & & \cdot \\ f_{N1}(x) & \cdots & \cdots & f_{NN}(x) \end{bmatrix} \qquad \ldots(4.46)$$

can be written in terms of two matrix polynomials (note the analogy with eq. 4.44).

$$\mathbf{f}(x) \cong \left[\mathbf{I} + \mathbf{b}_1 x + \mathbf{b}_2 x^2 + \ldots + \mathbf{b}_m x^m \right]^{-1} \left[\mathbf{a}_0 + \mathbf{a}_1 x + \ldots + \mathbf{a}_n x^n \right] \qquad \ldots(4.47)$$

where $\mathbf{I}$ is an $N \times N$ unit diagonal matrix, and $\mathbf{a}_0, \mathbf{a}_1, \ldots, \mathbf{a}_n, \mathbf{b}_1, \ldots, \mathbf{b}_m$, are $N \times N$ matrices of constants, which may be determined by using equations similar to that given in eq. 4.45.

One now defines an exponential function of a matrix [12] by

$$e^{x\mathbf{B}} \equiv \mathbf{I} + x\mathbf{B} + \frac{1}{2!}x^2\mathbf{B}\mathbf{B} + \frac{1}{3!}x^3\mathbf{B}\mathbf{B}\mathbf{B} + \ldots \qquad \ldots(4.48)$$

where $\mathbf{B}$ is a matrix of constants:

$$\mathbf{B} = \begin{bmatrix} B_{11} & B_{12} & \cdots & B_{1N} \\ \cdot & & & \cdot \\ \cdot & & & \cdot \\ \cdot & & & \cdot \\ B_{N1} & B_{N2} & \cdots & B_{NN} \end{bmatrix} \qquad \ldots(4.49)$$

This function is such that

$$\frac{d}{dx}e^{x\mathbf{B}} = \mathbf{0} + \mathbf{B} + x\mathbf{B}\mathbf{B} + \frac{x^2}{2!}\mathbf{B}\mathbf{B}\mathbf{B} + \ldots$$

$$= \mathbf{B}\left\{ \mathbf{I} + x\mathbf{B} + \frac{x^2}{2!}\mathbf{B}\mathbf{B} + \ldots \right\}$$

$$= \mathbf{B}e^{x\mathbf{B}} \qquad \ldots(4.50)$$

a form which is similar to that for ordinary exponentials (there are other similarities too). Padé approximation to $e^{x\mathbf{B}}$ can also be found, and some of them are given here:

$$e^{x\mathbf{B}} \cong \mathbf{I} + x\mathbf{B}$$

$$e^{x\mathbf{B}} \cong \{\mathbf{I} - x\mathbf{B}\}^{-1}\mathbf{I}$$

$$e^{x\mathbf{B}} \cong \left\{\mathbf{I} - \frac{1}{2}x\mathbf{B}\right\}^{-1}\left\{\mathbf{I} + \frac{1}{2}x\mathbf{B}\right\}; \text{ etc.} \qquad \qquad \ldots(4.51)$$

The similarity between these expressions and the Padé approximations of e^x given in table 4.1 can be noted. In fact, we can adapt table 4.1 and write other Padé forms of $e^{x\mathbf{B}}$ almost by inspection of the corresponding forms in that table.

4.7 CUBIC SPLINE APPROXIMATIONS

It was pointed out earlier that polynomial approximants to a set of $n + 1$ data points have oscillatory characteristics. The higher the degree of the polynomial, the more oscillatory is its behaviour. Padé approximants were introduced to overcome this problem, but they are inconvenient to work with. An alternate technique which exploits the simplicity of the polynomial expansions and yet avoids their oscillatory nature, is the (lower order) cubic (or equivalent) spline approximation. Figure 4.4 shows how a curve, $f(x)$, can be approximated by a set of n cubics, $S_i(x)$, over smaller subintervals of x:

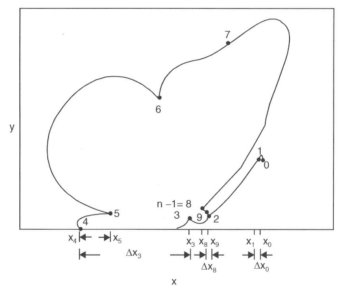

Fig. 4.4 Cubic spline approximation to a function $f(x)$ described by a set of $n + 1$ data points, $n = 9$. Coordinates of ith point are x_i, y_i, $i = 0, 1, \ldots, n$.

$$S_0(x) = a_{0,0} + a_{1,0}(x - x_0) + a_{2,0}(x - x_0)^2 + a_{3,0}(x - x_0)^3$$

$$S_1(x) = a_{0,1} + a_{1,1}(x - x_1) + a_{2,1}(x - x_1)^2 + a_{3,1}(x - x_1)^3$$

.

.

$$S_i(x) = a_{0,i} + a_{1,i}(x - x_i) + a_{2,i}(x - x_i)^2 + a_{3,i}(x - x_i)^3$$

.

.

$$S_{n-1}(x) = a_{0,n-1} + a_{1,n-1}(x - x_{n-1}) + a_{2,n-1}(x - x_{n-1})^2 + a_{3,n-1}(x - x_{n-1})^3 \qquad \ldots(4.52)$$

There are a total of $4n$ coefficients to be determined. The commonly used conditions for evaluating them are:

(a) $S_i(x_i)$ $= y_i$; $i = 0, 1, 2, ..., n-1$

(b) $S_{n-1}(x_n)$ $= y_n$

(c) $S_{i+1}(x_{i+1})$ $= S_i(x_{i+1})$; $i = 0, 1, 2, ..., n-2$

(d) $\dfrac{dS_{i+1}}{dx}(x_{i+1}) \equiv S'_{i+1}(x_{i+1}) = S'_i(x_{i+1})$; $i = 0, 1, 2, ..., n-2$

(e) $\dfrac{d^2 S_{i+1}}{dx^2}(x_{i+1}) \equiv S''_{i+1}(x_{i+1}) = S''_i(x_{i+1})$; $i = 0, 1, 2, ..., n-2$ ...(4.53)

These conditions ensure the cubic splines not only to be continuous (condition in eq. 4.53 (c)) but also be 'smooth' at the ends of the subintervals (conditions in eqs. 4.53 (d) and (e)). Also, conditions 4.53 (a) and (b) ensure that the set of N cubic splines fit the set of data points, (x_0, y_0), (x_1, y_1), ..., (x_n, y_n). Equation 4.53 provides only $4n - 2$ equations for the $4n$ coefficients, and we need two more. These are usually chosen as

$$S''_0(x_0) = S''_{n-1}(x_n) = 0 \qquad ...(4.54)$$

which are referred to as free boundary conditions. If we know values of $\dfrac{df}{dx}$ at x_0 and x_n, we can use

$$S'_0(x_0) = f'(x_0); \quad S'_{n-1}(x_n) = f'(x_n) \qquad ...(4.55)$$

These are referred to as clamped boundary conditions.

eq. 4.53 and the free boundary conditions in eq. 4.54 can be used with eq. 4.52 to give

$y_i = a_{0,i}$; $i = 0, 1, 2, ..., n-1$ ...(a)

$$a_{0, i+1} = a_{0, i} + a_{1, i}(\Delta x_i) + a_{2, i}(\Delta x_i)^2 + a_{3, i}(\Delta x_i)^3 \qquad ...(c)$$
$$a_{1, i+1} = a_{1, i} + 2a_{2, i}(\Delta x_i) + 3a_{3, i}(\Delta x_i)^2 \qquad ...(d) \quad \left. \right\} \; i = 0, 1, ..., n-2$$
$$a_{2, i+1} = a_{2, i} + 3a_{3, i}(\Delta x_i) \qquad ...(e)$$

$y_n = a_{0, n-1} + a_{1, n-1}(\Delta x_{n-1}) + a_{2, n-1}(\Delta x_{n-1})^2 + a_{3, n-1}(\Delta x_{n-1})^3$ ...(b)

$a_{2, 0} = 0$ ...(f)

$2a_{2, n-1} + 6a_{3, n-1}(\Delta x_{n-1}) = 0$ ...(g) ...(4.56)

where eqs. 4.56 (a) – (e) are obtained from eqs. 4.53 (a) – (e) respectively, and eqs. 4.56 (f) and (g) stem from eq. 4.54. We can eliminate $a_{1,i}$ and $a_{3,i}$ from these equations to give (see prob. 4.22)

$$a_{2, 0} = 0 \qquad ...(a)$$

$$(\Delta x_{i-1})a_{2, i-1} + 2(\Delta x_i + \Delta x_{i-1})a_{2, i} + (\Delta x_i)a_{2, i+1}$$

$$= \frac{3}{\Delta x_i}\left(a_{0,\,i+1} - a_{0,i}\right) - \frac{3}{\Delta x_{i-1}}\left(a_{0,i} - a_{0,\,i-1}\right);$$

$$i = 1,\,2,\,\dots,\,n-2 \qquad\qquad \dots(b)$$

$$\frac{1}{3}\left(\Delta x_{n-2}\right)a_{2,\,n-2} + \frac{2}{3}\left[\Delta x_{n-2} + \Delta x_{n-1}\right]a_{2,\,n-1}$$

$$= \frac{y_n}{\Delta x_{n-1}} - \left(\frac{1}{\Delta x_{n-1}} + \frac{1}{\Delta x_{n-2}}\right)a_{0,\,n-1} + \frac{1}{\Delta x_{n-2}}a_{0,n-2} \qquad \dots(c)\ \ \dots(4.57)$$

These equations can easily be written in matrix form as

$$\mathbf{A}\mathbf{a}_2 = \mathbf{b} \qquad\qquad \dots(4.58)$$

where $\mathbf{a}_2 \equiv [a_{2,0} \quad a_{2,1} \ \dots \ a_{2,\,n-1}]^T$, and $\mathbf{b}$ involves $a_{0,i}$, which can be obtained from eq. 4.56a. Once all the $a_{2,i}$ are obtained from eq. 4.58 (note the near tridiagonal form of $\mathbf{A}$), we can evaluate the $a_{3,i}$ and $a_{1,i}$ from eq. 4.56 using:

$$a_{3,\,i} = \frac{1}{3\left(\Delta x_i\right)}\left(a_{2,\,i+1} - a_{2,i}\right); \quad i = 0,\,1,\,\dots,\,n-2$$

$$a_{3,n-1} = -\frac{a_{2,n-1}}{3\left(\Delta x_{n-1}\right)}$$

$$a_{1,i} = \frac{1}{\Delta x_i}\left(a_{0,i+1} - a_{0,i}\right) - \frac{\Delta x_i}{3}\left(2a_{2,i} + a_{2,i+1}\right); \quad i = 0,\,1,\,\dots,\,n-2$$

$$a_{1,\,n-1} = \frac{y_n - a_{0,\,n-1}}{\Delta x_{n-1}} - a_{2,\,n-1}\left(\Delta x_{n-1}\right) - a_{3,\,n-1}\left(\Delta x_{n-1}\right)^2 \qquad \dots(4.59)$$

This completes the determination of the n cubic splines describing $f(x)$. A similar set of equations for the coefficients can be obtained if we use the clamped boundary conditions given in eq. 4.55.

Example 4.8: Fit a set of 2 cubic splines to a half ellipse described by $f(x) = +\frac{1}{3}\left[25 - 4x^2\right]^{1/2}$ (see fig. 4.5). Choose the three data points ($n = 2$) as $(-2.5, 0)$, $(0, 1.67)$ and $(2.5, 0)$. Use the free boundary conditions.

The splines are

$$S_0(x) = a_{0,\,0} + a_{1,\,0}(x + 2.5) + a_{2,\,0}(x + 2.5)^2 + a_{3,0}(x + 2.5)^3$$

$$S_1(x) = a_{0,\,1} + a_{1,\,1}x + a_{2,1}x^2 + a_{3,1}x^3$$

eq. 4.56(a) gives

$$a_{0,0} = 0$$

$$a_{0,1} = 1.667$$

eq. 4.57 leads to (with $\Delta x_0 = \Delta x_1 = 2.5$)

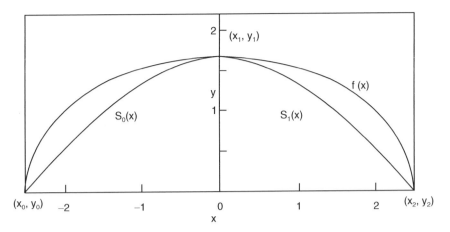

Fig. 4.5 A half-ellipse defined by $f(x) = +\frac{1}{3}[25 - 4x^2]^{1/2}$ and the two cubic splines, $S_0(x)$ and $S_1(x)$, computed in example 4.8.

$$\begin{bmatrix} 1 & 0 \\ 0.83 & 3.33 \end{bmatrix} \begin{bmatrix} a_{2,0} \\ a_{2,1} \end{bmatrix} = \begin{bmatrix} 0 \\ -0.8a_{0,1} + 0.4a_{0,0} \end{bmatrix} = \begin{bmatrix} 0 \\ -1.33 \end{bmatrix}$$

or

$$a_{2,0} = 0$$

$$a_{2,1} = -0.4$$

eq. 4.59 gives

$$a_{3,0} = \frac{a_{2,1} - a_{2,0}}{7.5} = -0.0533$$

$$a_{3,1} = -\frac{a_{2,1}}{7.5} = +0.0533$$

$$a_{1,0} = 1.0$$

$$a_{1,1} = 0$$

The cubic spline approximation to $f(x) = +\frac{1}{3}[25 - 4x^2]^{1/2}$ using three data points is, thus,

$$S_0(x) = (x + 2.5) - 0.0533(x + 2.5)^3; \quad -2.5 \le x \le 0$$

$$S_1(x) = 1.667 - 0.4x^2 + 0.0533x^3; \quad 0 \le x \le 2.5$$

These are plotted in fig. 4.5. The deviation is quite large, but the use of more spline functions would improve the fit. ∎

A similar fit of cubic splines can be performed on the butterfly shown in fig. 4.4, with the indicated set of $n + 1 = 10$ data points (see prob. 4.23). An interesting study was made by Wei [13], who found that it required over thirty terms in a least-squares (using Fourier Sine series; see eq. 4.20) analysis to obtain a diagram resembling an elephant (so much for the statement that we can fit an elephant with five constants!). prob. 4.25 explores a fit of an elephant using cubic splines.

4.8 DIFFERENTIATION FORMULAE

Once a set of data-points is approximated by a continuous function using any of the previous techniques, it becomes easy to obtain derivatives. For example, for equispaced base points, one can use Newton's forward difference formula (eq. 4.28) to give

$$\frac{dy}{dx} = \frac{dy}{d\alpha}\frac{d\alpha}{dx} = \frac{dy}{d\alpha}\frac{1}{\Delta x}$$

$$= \frac{1}{\Delta x}\left[\Delta y_0 + \frac{2\alpha-1}{2!}\Delta^2 y_0 + \frac{3\alpha^2-6\alpha+2}{3!}\Delta^3 y_0 +...+ \frac{(\Delta x)^{n+1}}{(n+1)!} y^{n+1}(\xi) P_n(\alpha)\right] \qquad ...(4.60)$$

where $P_n(\alpha)$ is a polynomial of degree n. Similarly,

$$\frac{d^2 y}{dx^2} = \frac{1}{(\Delta x)^2}\frac{d^2 y}{d\alpha^2} = \frac{1}{(\Delta x)^2}\left[\Delta^2 y_0 + (\alpha-1)\Delta^3 y_0 +...\right] \qquad ...(4.61)$$

Usually, one is interested in estimating the derivatives at $x = x_0$ (*i.e.*, $\alpha = 0$). eqs. 4.60 and 4.61 lead to

$$y'(x_0) = \frac{1}{\Delta x}\left[\Delta y_0 - \frac{1}{2}\Delta^2 y_0 + \frac{1}{3}\Delta^3 y_0 - \frac{1}{4}\Delta^4 y_0 +...\right] \qquad ...(a)$$

$$y''(x_0) = \frac{1}{(\Delta x)^2}\left[\Delta^2 y_0 - \Delta^3 y_0 + \frac{11}{12}\Delta^4 y_0 - \frac{5}{6}\Delta^5 y_0 + \frac{137}{180}\Delta^6 y_0 -...\right] \qquad ...(b) \qquad ...(4.62)$$

Since we can renumber base points starting from any one of them, we have from eq. 4.62a

$$y'(x_i) = \frac{1}{\Delta x}\left[\Delta y_i - \frac{1}{2}\Delta^2 y_i +...\right]$$

$$= \left[\frac{y_{i+1} - y_i}{\Delta x}\right] - \left[\frac{1}{2}\frac{y_{i+2} - 2y_{i+1} + y_i}{\Delta x}\right] +... \qquad ...(4.63)$$

The first term on the right is the finite difference form of $y'(x_i)$, while inclusion of the second term gives a more accurate expression for this derivative.

Eq. 4.62 (with only the first terms) also leads to

$$\Delta y_i \cong (\Delta x) y'(x_i)$$

$$\Delta^2 y_i \cong (\Delta x)^2 y''(x_i)$$

.

.

$$\Delta^j y_i \cong (\Delta x)^j y^{(j)}(x_i) \qquad ...(4.64)$$

a fact that has already been made use of in eq. 4.28. We can similarly derive expressions for y', y'', etc., using the backward differences:

$$y_i' = \frac{1}{\Delta x}\left[\nabla + \frac{\nabla^2}{2} + \frac{\nabla^3}{3} + \frac{\nabla^4}{4} + \dots\right]y_i$$

$$y_i'' = \frac{1}{(\Delta x)^2}\left[\nabla^2 + \nabla^3 + \frac{11}{12}\nabla^4 + \frac{5}{6}\nabla^5 + \frac{137}{180}\nabla^6 + \dots\right]y_i \qquad \dots(4.65)$$

.
.
.

the error terms can easily be obtained (see prob. 4.26). For eq. 4.62a, we get

$$y'(x_i) = \frac{1}{\Delta x}\left[\Delta y_i - \frac{1}{2}\Delta^2 y_i + \dots + \frac{(-1)^{n-1}}{n}\Delta^n y_i\right] + \left[\prod_{\substack{k=0 \\ k\neq i}}^{n}(x_i - x_k)\right]\frac{y^{(n+1)}(\xi_i)}{(n+1)!} \qquad \dots(4.66)$$

In order to reduce the truncation errors in eq. 4.66, one is tempted to use small values of Δx [so that $(x_i - x_k)_{max}$ is small]. This, however, leads to subtraction of nearly equal numbers in the computation of the forward differences, leading to a loss of significant figures. Division of the less accurate estimate of y_i' by the small Δx value magnifies the error further. So, reduction of Δx does not necessarily lead to an improvement in the numerical value of y_i' using eq. 4.66, or its equivalent.

If we have data available at base points which are not equispaced, we can obtain numerical estimates of y_i' using a similar technique applied to the Lagrangian interpolation function, eq. 4.43. This leads to

$$y'(x) = \sum_{j=0}^{n} L_j^{(n)'}(x)y_j + R'(x) \qquad \dots(4.67)$$

where $R(x)$ is given in eq. 4.40, and has the same form as derived in prob. 4.26. We have therefore,

$$y_k' = \sum_{j=0}^{n} L_j^{(n)'}(x_k)y_j + \left[\prod_{\substack{j=0 \\ j\neq k}}^{n}(x_k - x_j)\right]\frac{y^{(n+1)}(\xi_k)}{(n+1)!} \qquad \dots(4.68)$$

The three-point Lagrangian formula is quite popular. For base points, x_0, x_1 and x_2, the derivatives of the three coefficient functions required in eq. 4.68 are given by

$$L_0^{(2)'}(x_k) = \frac{2x_k - x_1 - x_2}{(x_0 - x_1)(x_0 - x_2)}$$

$$L_1^{(2)'}(x_k) = \frac{2x_k - x_0 - x_2}{(x_1 - x_0)(x_1 - x_2)}$$

$$L_2^{(2)'}(x_k) = \frac{2x_k - x_0 - x_1}{(x_2 - x_0)(x_2 - x_1)}; \quad k = 0, 1, 2 \qquad \dots(4.69)$$

Example 4.9: Obtain y_1' for the data of example 4.6. Use eqs. 4.68 and 4.69 and the first three data points.

i	x_i	y_i
0	1	7
1	3	53
2	4	157
3	6	857

The derivative functions are

$$L_0^{(2)'}(x_1) = \frac{2x_1 - x_1 - x_2}{(x_0 - x_1)(x_0 - x_2)} = \frac{x_1 - x_2}{(x_0 - x_1)(x_0 - x_2)} = \frac{-1}{(-2)(-3)} = \frac{-1}{6}$$

$$L_1^{(2)'}(x_1) = \frac{2x_1 - x_0 - x_2}{(x_1 - x_0)(x_1 - x_2)} = \frac{1}{(2)(-1)} = -\frac{1}{2}$$

$$L_2^{(2)'}(x_1) = \frac{2x_1 - x_0 - x_1}{(x_2 - x_0)(x_2 - x_1)} = \frac{x_1 - x_0}{(x_2 - x_0)(x_2 - x_1)} = \frac{2}{(3)(1)} = \frac{2}{3}$$

Eq. 4.68 gives

$$y'(x_1) = -\frac{1}{6} \times 7 - \frac{1}{2} \times 53 + \frac{2}{3} \times 157 - \frac{1}{3} y^{(3)}(\xi_1)$$

$$= 77 - \frac{1}{3} y^{(3)}(\xi_1)$$

We had seen in example 4.2 that the data were generated using

$$y(x) = x^4 - 3x^3 + 6x^2 - 2x + 5$$

The exact value of $y'(x_1)$ is 61. Since $y^{(3)}(x) = 24x - 18$, the bounds for $y^{(3)}(\xi_1)$ are 6 to 78. The error term for our estimated value of $y_1' = 77$ is thus between -2 to -26. The actual error of $61 - 77 = -16$ lies inside this range. If $y(x)$ were unknown, as it would be in most cases of interest, estimates of $y^{(3)}(\xi_1)$ would be difficult to obtain.

We could have renumbered the base points and taken the last three data points in the table above, to obtain a different estimate for $y'(3)$. ∎

4.9 INTEGRATION FORMULAE OR QUADRATURES

The interpolation formulae obtained in the earlier sections of this chapter can be used to derive integration formulae. For example, if we have a set of $n + 1$ data, (x_0, y_0), (x_1, y_1), ..., (x_n, y_n), at equispaced base points, we can fit an nth degree polynomial through them (for example, using eq. 4.28), and use the latter for integration purposes. Thus,

$$\int_{x_0}^{x_1} f(x)\,dx = \int_{x_0}^{x_1} y(x)\,dx = (\Delta x) \int_{\alpha=0}^{\alpha=1} \left[y_0 + \alpha \Delta y_0 + \frac{\alpha^2 - \alpha}{2!} \Delta^2 y_0 \right.$$

$$+\frac{\alpha^3-3\alpha^2+2\alpha}{3!}\Delta^3 y_0 +...+ \frac{\alpha(\alpha-1)...(\alpha-n+1)}{n!}\Delta^n y_0 \Bigg] d\alpha$$

$$+\frac{(\Delta x)^{n+2}}{(n+1)!}\int_0^1 \alpha(\alpha-1)...(\alpha-n) f^{(n+1)}\big[\xi(\alpha)\big] d\alpha$$

$$=(\Delta x)\Bigg[y_0 +\frac{1}{2}\Delta y_0 -\frac{1}{12}\Delta^2 y_0 +\frac{1}{24}\Delta^3 y_0 -...\Bigg]$$

$$+\frac{(\Delta x)^{n+2}}{(n+1)!} f^{(n+1)}(\xi)\int_0^1 \alpha(\alpha-1)...(\alpha-n) d\alpha$$

$$\equiv (\Delta x)\Bigg[\frac{y_0+y_1}{2} -\frac{1}{12}\big(y_2 -2y_1 +y_0\big)+\frac{1}{24}\Delta^3 y_0 -...\Bigg]$$

$$+\frac{C(\Delta x)^{n+2}}{(n+1)!} f^{(n+1)}(\xi) \qquad\qquad ...(4.70)$$

where C is a constant equal to $-\dfrac{1}{6}$ for $n = 1$, and ξ is a number in $[x_0, x_n]$. The form of eq. 4.70 which is most popular is that for $n = 1$:

$$\int_{x_0}^{x_1} f(x)\,dx = \frac{\Delta x}{2}\big(y_0 +y_1\big)-\frac{(\Delta x)^3}{12} f''(\xi); \; x_0 \le \xi \le x_1 \qquad\qquad ...(4.71)$$

This is known as the *trapezoidal rule,* since the first term is the area of the trapezoid formed between the x-axis and the two data points, (x_0, y_0) and (x_1, y_1). If $f(x)$ is a polynomial of first degree (or lower), the error term (due to truncation) is zero. However, round off errors could still be present. Higher order formulae for the integral over $x_0 \le x \le x_1$ using data points beyond $x = x_1$ can also be derived.

We could, similarly, obtain

$$\int_{x_0}^{x_2} f(x)\,dx = (\Delta x) \int_{\alpha=0}^{2}\Bigg[y_0 +\alpha\Delta y_0 +\frac{\alpha^2-\alpha}{2!}\Delta^2 y_0 +\frac{\alpha^3-3\alpha^2+2\alpha}{3!}\Delta^3 y_0 +...\Bigg] d\alpha$$

$$+\frac{(\Delta x)^{n+2}}{(n+1)!}\int_0^2 \alpha(\alpha-1)...(\alpha-n) f^{(n+1)}\big[\xi(\alpha)\big] d\alpha$$

$$=(\Delta x)\Bigg[2y_0 +2\Delta y_0 +\frac{1}{3}\Delta^2 y_0 +0\Delta^3 y_0 -\frac{1}{90}\Delta^4 y_0 +...\Bigg]$$

$$+\frac{(\Delta x)^{n+2}}{(n+1)!} f^{(n+1)}(\xi)\int_0^2 \alpha(\alpha-1)...(\alpha-n) d\alpha$$

$$= \left[\frac{(\Delta x)}{3}(y_0 + 4y_1 + y_2) - \frac{(\Delta x)}{90}\Delta^4 y_0 + ... \right] + E \qquad ...(4.72)$$

The error, E, for $n = 3$, is obtained as $-(\Delta x)^5 f^{(4)}(\xi)/90$. This gives

$$\int_{x_0}^{x_2} f(x)\,dx = \frac{\Delta x}{3}(y_0 + 4y_1 + y_2) - \frac{(\Delta x)^5}{90}f^{(4)}(\xi); \quad x_0 \le \xi \le x_3 \qquad ...(4.73)$$

which is known as *Simpson's rule*. Note the higher degree of accuracy $[(\Delta x)^5]$ as compared to the trapezoidal rule $[(\Delta x)^3]$. In this method, we are fitting a quadratic (parabola) through the three data points, (x_0, y_0), (x_1, y_1) and (x_2, y_2), and estimating the area under this curve [really speaking, we are fitting a cubic to four data points, but the value of the integral is the same]. It may be noted that ξ lies between x_0 and x_3 since we are fitting a polynomial (cubic) to points (x_0, y_0), (x_1, y_1), (x_2, y_2) and (x_3, y_3), even though we are obtaining the integral only between (x_0, y_0) and (x_2, y_2).

We can continue this procedure to give

$$\int_{x_0}^{x_3} f(x)\,dx = \frac{3(\Delta x)}{8}(y_0 + 3y_1 + 3y_2 + y_3) - \frac{3}{80}(\Delta x)^5 f^{(4)}(\xi); \quad x_0 \le \xi \le x_3 \quad ...(a)$$

$$\int_{x_0}^{x_4} f(x)\,dx = \frac{2(\Delta x)}{45}(7y_0 + 32y_1 + 12y_2 + 32y_3 + 7y_4) - \frac{8}{945}(\Delta x)^7 f^{(6)}(\xi);$$

$$x_0 \le \xi \le x_5 \quad ...(b) \qquad ...(4.74)$$

Note the sudden jump in the degree of accuracy at every two steps. It is easy to see why eq. 4.74a is less popular than eq. 4.73. The above set of equations is referred to as *closed Newton-Cotes* integration formulae, the word closed referring to the fact that values of y at the two end points of the integration domain are used. These formulae can be written in terms of a weighted sum of values of y_i as

$$\int_{x_0}^{x_2} f(x)\,dx = \sum_{i=0}^{n} w_i y_i \qquad ...(4.75)$$

where w_i are weightage factors associated with values of y_i. Since the Lagrangian interpolation formula gives the same polynomial when applied to equispaced base points as does Newton's forward difference formula, no new results are obtained from the former.

Low-order Newton-Cotes formulae are preferred for integration since the curve-fit polynomials associated with them are less oscillatory in nature. Multiple applications of eqs. 4.71 and 4.73 to a set of data points give *composite* formulae:

$$\int_{x_0}^{x_n} f(x)\,dx = \frac{\Delta x}{2}\left[y_0 + 2y_1 + 2y_2 + 2y_3 + ... + 2y_{n-1} + y_n \right] - \frac{(\Delta x)^3}{12}\sum_{i=0}^{n-1} f''(\xi_i);$$

$$x_i \le \xi_i \le x_{i+1} \qquad ...(a)$$

$$\int_{x_0}^{x_n} f(x)\,dx = \frac{\Delta x}{3}\left[y_0 + 4y_1 + 2y_2 + 4y_3 + 2y_4 + 4y_5 + ... + 4y_{n-1} + y_n \right]$$

$$-\frac{(\Delta x)^5}{90} \sum_{i=0}^{\frac{n}{2}-1} f^{(4)}(\xi_i); \quad x_{2i} \le \xi_i \le x_{2i+3} \qquad \dots(b) \quad \dots(4.76)$$

Equation 4.76(a) is obtained by fitting straight lines to the points (x_0, y_0) and (x_1, y_1) first, then to (x_1, y_1) and (x_2, y_2), and so on. Similarly, eq. 4.76(b) is obtained by computing the area under the parabola connecting (x_0, y_0), (x_1, y_1) and (x_2, y_2) first, then adding the area under the parabola connecting (x_2, y_2), (x_3, y_3) and (x_4, y_4), etc. It is necessary to have an odd number of base points for eq. 4.76(b) (*i.e.*, n is even). If μ_1 and μ_2 are locations in $x_0 \le x \le x_n$ (or x_{n+1}) such that

$$\sum_{i=0}^{n-1} f''(\xi_i) = nf''(\mu_1) = \frac{x_n - x_0}{\Delta x} f''(\mu_1)$$

$$\sum_{i=0}^{\frac{n}{2}-1} f^{(4)}(\xi_i) = \frac{n}{2} f^4(\mu_2) = \frac{x_n - x_0}{2\Delta x} f^4(\mu_2) \qquad \dots(4.77)$$

the errors associated with the composite formulae in eq. 4.76 are $-(\Delta x)^2 \times (x_n - x_0) f''(\mu_1)/12$ and $-(\Delta x)^4 (x_n - x_0) f^{(4)}(\mu_2)/180$, respectively.

Example 4.10: The dimensionless temperature of a fluid under steady, fully developed laminar flow in a cylindrical pipe, with walls heated electrically, is given by [p. 296 in Ref. 14]

$$\theta = -4Z - r^2 + \frac{r^4}{4} + \frac{7}{24}$$

where r is the dimensionless radius. The cup-mixing (bulk) dimensionless temperature is given by

$$\theta_b = \frac{\displaystyle\int_{r=0}^{1} \theta(1-r^2)r\,dr}{\displaystyle\int_{r=0}^{1} (1-r^2)r\,dr} = 4\int_{r=0}^{1} \theta(1-r^2)r\,dr$$

Generate values of θ at $Z = 0.5$ and $r = 0, 0.25, 0.5, 0.75, 1.0$, and use the composite Simpson's rule to estimate θ_b numerically.

Values of θ at $Z = 0.5$ are

i	r_i	θ_i
0	0	−1.7083
1	0.25	−1.7698
2	0.5	−1.9427
3	0.75	−2.1917
4	1.0	−2.4583

Hence $\theta_b = 4 \times \dfrac{0.25}{3} \times \left[(-1.7083 \times 0) + 4(-1.7698 \times 0.9375 \times 0.25) \right.$

$$+ 2(-1.9427 \times 0.75 \times 0.5) + 4(-2.1917 \times 0.4375 \times 0.75) + (-2.4583 \times 0)]$$

or

$$\theta_b = -1.9976$$

The analytically obtained value is $\theta_b = -4Z = -2$.   ∎

There are several cases where one has the flexibility of choosing the base-points. In example 4.10, we need not have chosen the base points, r_i, at equal spacings of 0.25 but instead, could have located them to give more accurate results. Similarly, while *designing* an experimental program, we may have a similar flexibility present (e.g., locating thermocouples to measure temperature in a metal slab at different locations or measuring concentrations at specified times while studying the progress of a reaction). In such situations, *Gaussian quadrature* (also referred to as Gauss-Legendre quadrature) gives more accurate results. The technique is described by

$$\int_{-1}^{1} f(z)\,dz = \sum_{i=0}^{n} w_i f(z_i) \qquad \ldots(4.78)$$

The values of the base points, z_i, and the weightage factors, w_i, are given in table 4.2. Any integral, $\int_a^b f^*(x)\,dx$, can be transformed into the form used in eq. 4.78 by defining

Table 4.2 Roots and Weightage Factors for the Gauss-Legendre Quadrature [8]*

n	Roots (z_i) of $P_{n+1}(z)$		Weightage Factors (w_i)
1	± 0.57735 02691 89626	$(=\pm 1/\sqrt{3})$	1.00000 00000 00000
2	0.00000 00000 00000		0.88888 88888 88889
	± 0.77459 66692 41483	$(=\pm\sqrt{3/5})$	0.55555 55555 55556
3	± 0.33998 10435 84856		0.65214 51548 62546
	± 0.86113 63115 94053		0.34785 48451 37454
4	0.00000 00000 00000		0.56888 88888 88889
	± 0.53846 93101 05683		0.47862 86704 99366
	± 0.90617 98459 38664		0.23692 68850 56189
5	± 0.23861 91860 83197		0.46791 39345 72691
	± 0.66120 93864 66265		0.36076 15730 48139
	± 0.93246 95142 03152		0.17132 44923 79170
9	± 0.14887 43389 81631		0.29552 42247 14753
	± 0.43339 53941 29247		0.26926 67193 09996
	± 0.67940 95682 99024		0.21908 63625 15982
	± 0.86506 33666 88985		0.14945 13491 50581
	± 0.97390 65285 17172		0.06667 13443 08688
14	0.00000 00000 00000		0.20257 82419 25561
	± 0.20119 40939 97435		0.19843 14853 27111
	± 0.39415 13470 77563		0.18616 10001 15562

(Contd.)

± 0.57097 21726 08539	0.16626 92058 16994
± 0.72441 77313 60170	0.13957 06779 26154
± 0.84820 65834 10427	0.10715 92204 67172
± 0.93727 33924 00706	0.07036 60474 88108
± 0.98799 25180 20485	0.03075 32419 96117

* Values given till ten decimal places (with two spaces interspersed to improve clarity)

$$z = \frac{2x - (a+b)}{(b-a)} \qquad \qquad \text{...(4.79)}$$

Example 4.11 shows how this technique leads to more accurate results.

Example 4.11: Compute the integral required for θ_b in example 4.10 using the Gauss-Legendre quadrature with $n = 2$.

We first transform the integral

$$z = \frac{2r-1}{1} = 2r - 1$$

or

$$r = \frac{z+1}{2}, \quad dr = \frac{dz}{2}$$

Thus,

$$\theta_b = 4 \int_{-1}^{1} \theta \left[1 - \left(\frac{1+z}{2} \right)^2 \right] \left[\frac{z+1}{2} \right] \frac{dz}{2}$$

$$= \frac{1}{4} \int_{-1}^{1} \theta \left[4 - (1+z)^2 \right] [1+z] dz$$

Using the Gauss-Legendre quadrature, we obtain (using values only till four decimal places)

$$\theta_b = \frac{1}{4} \left[0.5556 \left[\theta_0 \left\{ 4 - (1-0.7746)^2 \right\} (1-0.7746) \right] + 0.8889 \left[\theta_1 \left\{ 4 - (1+0)^2 \right\} \{1+0\} \right] \right.$$

$$\left. + 0.5556 \left[\theta_2 \left\{ 4 - (1+0.7746) \right\}^2 \{1+0.7746\} \right] \right]$$

$$= \frac{1}{4} \left[0.4946 \, \theta_0 + 2.6667 \, \theta_1 + 0.8389 \, \theta_2 \right]$$

The values of θ_i at the base points. z_i, are evaluated at $Z = 0.5$ using

$$\theta_i = -1.7083 - r_i^2 + \frac{r_i^4}{4}$$

The values are

i	z_i	$r_i = (1 + z_i)/2$	θ_i
0	−0.7746	0.1127	−1.72096
1	0	0.5	−1.94268
2	+0.7746	0.8873	−2.34064

Hence,

$$\theta_b = \frac{-7.99529}{4} = -1.9988$$

which is quite close to the analytical value of −2, and is more accurate than the value obtained in example 4.10. ∎

We now present the derivation of the Gaussian quadrature technique. We write the function $f(z)$ in eq. 4.78 using the Lagrangian interpolation formula (see eqs. 4.40 and 4.43)

$$f(z) = \sum_{i=0}^{n} f(z_i) L_i^{(n)}(z) + \frac{f^{(n+1)}[\xi(z)]}{(n+1)!} \prod_{i=0}^{n}(z - z_1) \qquad \ldots(4.80)$$

This can be integrated to give

$$\int_{-1}^{1} f(z)\,dz = \sum_{i=0}^{n} f(z_i) \int_{-1}^{1} L_i^{(n)}(z)\,dz + \frac{1}{(n+1)!} \int_{-1}^{1} f^{(n+1)}[\xi(z)] \prod_{i=0}^{n}(z - z_i)\,dz$$

$$\equiv \sum_{i=0}^{n} w_i f(z_i) + E \qquad \ldots(4.81)$$

The weightage factors, w_i, can easily be obtained by integrating the Lagrangian interpolating polynomials (eq. 4.43), once the base points, $z_0, z_1, \ldots z_n$, are known. The values of w_i in table 4.2 are precisely these integrals for the choices of z_i listed. If $f(z)$ is a polynomial of order n or lower, $E = 0$ for any set of base points.

The $n + 1$ base points are now selected such that the error, E, in eq. 4.81 is zero *even* if $f(z)$ is a polynomial of degree $2n + 1$ or less. With such an "optimal" choice of z_i, we obtain values of the integral having a (high) degree of accuracy of $2n + 1$ [*i.e.*, the results are exact if $f(z)$ is a polynomial of degree $2n + 1$ or less], using *only* $n + 1$ function evaluations, $f(z_0), f(z_1), \ldots, f(z_n)$. In contrast, the Newton-Cotes formulae give integrals having a degree of accuracy of only n or $n + 1$, using $n + 1$ function evaluations. It is convenient to work with the orthogonal Legendre polynomials, $P_i(z)$ (see appendix 4A for details). We can express the terms in the error, E, in eq. 4.81, in terms of these polynomials as

$$\prod_{i=0}^{n}(z - z_i) = \sum_{i=0}^{n+1} b_i P_i(z) \qquad \ldots(a)$$

$$\frac{1}{(n+1)!}f^{(n+1)}\big[\xi(z)\big]=\sum_{j=0}^{n}c_{j}P_{j}(z) \qquad\qquad \ldots(b)^{*} \qquad \ldots(4.82)$$

Since $\prod_{i=0}^{n}(z-z_{i})$ is a polynomial of degree $n+1$, the highest degree of the Legendre polynomial to be used should be $n+1$, and this is reflected in eq. 4.82a. Similarly, if $f(z)$ is a polynomial of degree $2n+1$, $f^{(n+1)}$ will be a polynomial of degree n, and so the highest degree Legendre function to be used in its expansion should be n, as in eq. 4.82b. The error, E, in eq. 4.81, is thus written as

$$E=\int_{-1}^{1}\sum_{i=0}^{n+1}\sum_{j=0}^{n}b_{i}c_{j}P_{i}(z)P_{j}(z)dz$$

$$=\sum_{i=0}^{n+1}\sum_{j=0}^{n}b_{i}c_{j}\int_{-1}^{1}P_{i}(z)P_{j}(z)dz$$

$$=\sum_{j=0}^{n}b_{j}c_{j}\int_{-1}^{1}P_{j}^{2}(z)dz \qquad\qquad \ldots(4.83)$$

The last step in eq. 4.83 follows from the fact that the Legendre polynomials are orthogonal with respect to a weightage function of unity. We wish E to be zero [since $f(z)$ has been taken as a polynomial of degree $2n+1$]. This can be achieved if we choose (without loss of generality; we cannot choose all the c_i to be zero since then eq. 4.82b will be inconsistent [a function of z on the LHS and zero on the RHS]) for algebraic convenience

$$b_{0}=b_{1}=b_{2}=\ldots=b_{n}=0 \qquad\qquad \ldots(4.84)$$

This makes E as zero. Using this in eq. 4.82a gives

$$b_{n+1}P_{n+1}(z)=(z-z_{0})(z-z_{1})\ldots(z-z_{n}) \qquad\qquad \ldots(4.85)$$

Since $P_{n+1}(z)$ is a polynomial of degree $n+1$, eq. 4.85 suggests that $z_0, z_1, \ldots z_n$ are the $n+1$ roots of $P_{n+1}(z)$ [if $z=z_i$, eq. 4.85 gives $P_{n+1}(z_i)=0$, and so z_i is a root of $P_{n+1}(z)$].

In summary, if we choose the base points $z_0, z_1, \ldots, z_n$ as the roots of $P_{n+1}(z)$, then eq. 4.81 gives the value of the integral with an accuracy of degree $2n+1$, using only $n+1$ function evaluations. Table 4.2 lists the roots of $P_{n+1}(z)$ for *several* values of n, and the corresponding values of $\int_{-1}^{1}L_{i}^{(n)}(z)dz\big(=w_{i}\big)$. The error for the integral of *general* function, $f(z)$, for such a choice of base points is given by [8]

$$\int_{-1}^{1}f(z)dz=\sum_{i=0}^{n}w_{i}f(z_{i})+\frac{2^{2n+3}\big[(n+1)!\big]^{4}f^{(2n+2)}(\xi)}{(2n+3)\big[(2n+2)!\big]^{3}}; \qquad -1\le\xi\le1 \qquad \ldots(4.86)$$

---

* $\dfrac{f^{(n+1)}[\xi]}{(n+1)!}$ is replaced by $\dfrac{f^{(n+1)}(z)}{(n+1)!}$ since if we make the latter as zero for any general z, E will be zero for any ξ.

If instead of $\int_{-1}^{1} f(z)\,dz$, we had to compute $\int_{0}^{\infty} e^{-z} f(z)\,dz$, it is more convenient to use the Gauss-Laguerre quadrature which gives

$$\int_{0}^{\infty} e^{-z} f(z)\,dz = \sum_{i=0}^{n} w_i f(z_i) \qquad \ldots(4.87)$$

where the z_i are $n + 1$ roots of the $(n + 1)$th degree Laguerre polynomial. This equation gives exact values of the integral if $f(z)$ is a polynomial of degree $2n + 1$ or lower. We have, similarly, Gauss-Hermite and Gauss-Chebyshev quadratures for evaluating integrals of the type $\int_{-\infty}^{\infty} e^{-z^2} f(z)\,dz$ and $\int_{-1}^{1} \frac{1}{\sqrt{(1 - z^2)}} f(z)\,dz$, respectively. The values of the base points and the corresponding weightage functions are available in Ref. 8. The development of the algorithms is similar to that presented above.

4.10 EXTRAPOLATION TECHNIQUE OF RICHARDSON AND GAUNT

This method appears to go back in history to the days of Archimides, even though formally it is attributed to Richardson and Gaunt. A study of eq. 4.60 for derivatives, and eq. 4.70 for integrals suggests that we can obtain a numerical estimate for a quantity, Q, as

$$Q = V(\Delta x) + C_1 (\Delta x)^n + C_2 (\Delta x)^{n+1} + \ldots \qquad \ldots(4.88)$$

where $V(\Delta x)$ is the estimate of Q using Δx, accurate to degree $n - 1$. We can use a value of $\dfrac{\Delta x}{2}$ to obtain another slightly more accurate estimate, $V\left(\dfrac{\Delta x}{2}\right)$, for the *same* quantity, Q. Thus,

$$Q = V\left(\frac{\Delta x}{2}\right) + C_1 \left(\frac{\Delta x}{2}\right)^n + C_2 \left(\frac{\Delta x}{2}\right)^{n+1} + \ldots \qquad \ldots(4.89)$$

It is assumed that C_1 and C_2 do not change. Multiplying eq. 4.89 by 2^n and subtracting eq. 4.88 leads to

$$Q = \left[\frac{2^n V\left(\dfrac{\Delta x}{2}\right) - V(\Delta x)}{2^n - 1} \right] - \frac{C_2 (\Delta x)^{n+1}}{2 \times (2^n - 1)} \qquad \ldots(4.90)$$

The term in brackets is a more accurate estimate of Q than the two earlier estimates, $V(\Delta x)$ and $V\left(\dfrac{\Delta x}{2}\right)$. In this manner, we can use two applications of a low-order formula to give an estimate of a higher order. In fact, we can continue this procedure with values Δx, $\dfrac{\Delta x}{2}$ and $\dfrac{\Delta x}{4}$, to give estimates correct to $O(\Delta x)^{n+2}$, etc.

Example 4.12: Develop an extrapolation procedure using the composite trapezoidal rule. This is known as Romberg's integration procedure.

We had from eq. 4.76a (adapted)

$$\int_a^b f(x)\,dx = \frac{\Delta x}{2}\left[f(a)+2\sum_{i=1}^{n-1} f(x_i)+f(b)\right]-\frac{(\Delta x)^2 (b-a)}{12}f''(\mu_1)$$

An alternate expression for the error term has been given by Ralston and Rabinowitz [11] as

$$\int_a^b f(x)\,dx = \frac{\Delta x}{2}\left[f(a)+2\sum_{i=1}^{n-1} f(a+i\Delta x)+f(b)\right]-\frac{(\Delta x)^2}{12}\left[f'(b)-f'(a)\right]+\frac{b-a}{720}(\Delta x)^4 f^{(4)}(\mu)$$

or

$$Q = V(\Delta x)-\frac{(\Delta x)^2}{12}\left[f'(b)-f'(a)\right]+O(\Delta x)^4$$

Note the slightly different form of the error terms than in eq. 4.88. The technique of Richardson and Gaunt leads to

$$Q = \frac{4V\left(\dfrac{\Delta x}{2}\right)-V(\Delta x)}{3}+O(\Delta x)^4$$

Romberg suggested a neat scheme to estimate the integral using $\Delta x, \dfrac{\Delta x}{2}, \dfrac{\Delta x}{4}, \dfrac{\Delta x}{8}$, etc., thus juxtaposing the base points and saving on the computational effort. He also used these improved estimates of Q [accurate to $O(\Delta x)^4$] to obtain still more accurate values, correct to $O(\Delta x)^6$, etc.

APPENDIX 4A

Orthogonal Polynomials and Functions

A set of $n + 1$ polynomials (or functions), $P_0(x)$, $P_1(x)$, ..., $P_i(x)$, ..., $P_n(x)$, is defined to be orthogonal with respect to a weightage factor, $W(x)$ over a range $a \leq x \leq b$, if

$$\int_a^b W(x) P_i(x) P_j(x) dx = 0 \qquad\qquad i \neq j$$

$$= \text{positive value}, \quad i = j \qquad\qquad ...(A\ 4.1)$$

A very popular family is the set of Legendre polynomials (of the first kind). For this, $W(x) = 1$, $a = -1$, $b = +1$. The first few polynomials of this set are given by

$$P_0(x) = 1$$

$$P_1(x) = x$$

$$P_2(x) = \frac{1}{2}\left(3x^2 - 1\right)$$

$$P_3(x) = \frac{1}{2}\left(5x^3 - 3x\right)$$

$$P_4(x) = \frac{1}{8}\left(35x^4 - 30x^2 + 3\right)$$

$$iP_i(x) = (2i-1)x P_{i-1}(x) - (i-1)P_{i-2}(x); \qquad i = 2, 3, ... \qquad ...(A\ 4.2)$$

Note that $P_i(x)$ is a polynomial of degree i. It is easy to see that eq. A4.1 is satisfied, and that

$$\int_{-1}^1 P_i^2(x) dx = \frac{2}{2i+1} \qquad\qquad ...(A\ 4.3)$$

Similarly, the set of Laguerre polynomials, $\mathcal{L}_i(x)$, is given {with $W(x) = e^{-x}$, $a = 0$, $b = \infty$} by

$$\mathcal{L}_0(x) = 1$$

$$\mathcal{L}_1(x) = -x + 1$$

$$\mathcal{L}_2(x) = x^2 - 4x + 2$$

$$\mathcal{L}_3(x) = -x^3 + 9x^2 - 18x + 6$$

$$\mathcal{L}_i(x) = (2i - x - 1)\mathcal{L}_{i-1}(x) - (i-1)^2 \mathcal{L}_{i-2}(x); \quad i = 2, 3, ... \qquad ...(A\ 4.4)$$

Again, $\mathcal{L}_i(x)$ is observed to be a polynomial of degree i. Other sets of orthogonal polynomials or functions [with respect to various $W(x)$, a, b] are discussed in mathematics texts [16]. In fact, Fourier sine and cosine series are written in terms of a set of orthogonal functions, $\sin\left(\dfrac{i\pi x}{2L}\right)$ or $\cos\left(\dfrac{i\pi x}{2L}\right)$, with $W(x) = 1$, $a = 0$, $b = 2L$.

Orthogonal polynomials have several interesting properties and uses, and some of these are elaborated here without proof [16]:

(a) If the orthogonal polynomial, $P_i(x)$ $[i \geq 1]$, is of degree i (as in the two examples presented above), then it has i *distinct* roots [solutions of $P_i(x) = 0$] *all* lying between $a \leq x \leq b$. Roots of the Legendre polynomials defined in eq. A4.2 are listed in table 4.2.

(b) Any polynomial, $y(x)$, of degree n, can be written *uniquely* in terms of an orthogonal set, $P_0(x)$, $P_1(x)$, ..., $P_n(x)$ [when $P_i(x)$ is a polynomial of degree i] as

$$y(x) = a_0 P_0(x) + a_1 P_1(x) + \ldots + a_n P_n(x) \qquad \ldots(A\ 4.5)$$

The coefficients can be determined by exploiting the orthogonality property

$$\int_a^b W(x) y(x) P_j(x) dx = \sum_{i=0}^n a_i \int_a^b W(x) P_i(x) P_j(x) dx$$

$$= a_j \int_a^b W(x) P_j^2(x) dx \qquad \ldots(A\ 4.6)$$

and so

$$a_j = \frac{\displaystyle\int_a^b W(x) P_j(x) y(x) dx}{\displaystyle\int_a^b W(x) P_j^2(x) dx} \qquad \ldots(A\ 4.7)$$

PROBLEMS

4.1 Obtain the algorithm for obtaining linear regression values of the coefficients a_0, a_1, ..., a_n in eq. 4.19, when applied to a set of $n + 1$ data points, (x_0, y_0), (x_1, y_1), ..., (x_n, y_n). Note that when $P_i(x)$ are monomials, *i.e.*, $P_i(x) = x^i$, the matrix **A** becomes 'striped'. Such striped matrices have $|\mathbf{A}| \to 0$ for $n \geq 6$.

4.2 The Antoine equation for the vapour pressure of any pure compound is written as [17]

$$\ln p_{sat} = a - \frac{b}{T + c}$$

where a, b and c are constants for that compound. Re-express this equation as

$$\ln p_{sat} = \left(a - \frac{b}{c}\right) + \left(\frac{a}{c}\right) T - \frac{1}{c} T \ln p_{sat}$$

or as

$$y = a_0 + a_1 x + a_2 (xy)$$

Develop the linear regression expressions for obtaining the constants a_0, a_1, and a_2 (and thus a, b and c) from a set of $n + 1$ $(T_i, p_{sat,i})$ data. You may assume (xy) to be an 'independent' group to enable you to apply (pseudo) linear regression.

4.3 Make a program to compute a least squares fit to a set of data using eq. 4.14. Test it out on the data of example 4.1. Then use the results of prob. 4.2 to obtain the constants for the Antoine equation using vapour pressure data on acetone [18]

T (K)	p_{sat} (bar)
259.2	0.04267
273.4	0.09497
290.1	0.21525
320.5	0.74449
350.9	2.01571
390.3	5.655
446.4	17.682
470.6	26.628
508.1	47.000

4.4 *Forsythe's Method* [19]

One of the problems associated with the use of the technique described in prob. 4.1 (least squares fit to a polynomial, $y = a_0 + a_1x + a_2x^2 + ... + a_Nx^N$) is that the **a** must be recomputed over and over again as we vary N (to find the right number of terms in the polynomial). This is overcome by the use of the following set of polynomials:

$$P_{-1}(x) = 0$$
$$P_0(x) = 1$$
$$P_1(x) = (x - \alpha_1)P_0(x)$$
$$P_2(x) = (x - \alpha_2)P_1(x) - \beta_1 P_0(x)$$

.

.

$$P_{j+1}(x) = (x - \alpha_{j+1})P_j(x) - \beta_j P_{j-1}(x)$$

These polynomials are orthogonal to each other *under summation, i.e.,*

$$\sum_{i=0}^{n} P_j(x_i)P_k(x_i) = 0 ; \quad j \neq k$$

Assuming that we have a set of mutually orthogonal polynomials, $P_{-1}(x)$, $P_0(x)$, ..., $P_j(x)$, use the recursion relation for $P_{j+1}(x)$ and compute values of α_{j+1} and β_j which will make it orthogonal to $P_j(x)$ and $P_{j-1}(x)$. Then show that $P_{j+1}(x)$ is orthogonal to all earlier $P_k(x)$.

[**Hint:** You can show that $\sum_{i=0}^{n} x_i P_j(x_i)P_k(x_i) = 0$, $k < j-1$, by using the recursion formula for

$P_{k+1}(x_i)$ in $\sum_{i=0}^{n} P_j(x_i)P_{k+1}(x_i)$].

For such a choice of polynomials in

$$y = a_0 + a_1 P_1(x) + a_2 P_2(x) + ... + a_N P_N(x)$$

obtain the expressions for **a** for a least squares fit to a given set of $n + 1$ data points (x_i, y_i).

4.5 Solve eq. 4.27 for $n = 1$ and $n = 2$ and confirm eq. 4.28.

4.6 Add two more data points, $(x_4 = 5, y_4 = 395)$ and $(x_5 = 6, y_5 = 857)$, to the table in example 4.2. Compute the various forward differences. Also compute $\Delta^4 y_i$ and $\Delta^5 y_i$. Obtain the highest order Newton forward difference formula possible. Transform from α into x and check against the polynomial used to generate the values of y_i.

4.7 Curve fit data points generated using $y = 2\sin(\pi x)$ for $0 \le x \le 1$, by a 2nd degree polynomial using eq. 4.28. Plot the exact function as well as the polynomial fit for this range of x to see the deviations. A Fourier sine series would have been the best choice for this case. Estimate the error at $x = 0.25$.

4.8 The following table [20] gives the effect of the aromatics concentration, C_A, on the rate, r_A, of coke formation on a metal plate during pyrolysis of naphtha in a jet stirred reactor, at 1083 K.

$10^4 C_A$ (kmol/m^3)	$10^2 r_A$ kg/m^2–hr
1.79	0.28
2.03	0.32
2.22	0.36
2.47	0.40
2.97	0.49
3.39	0.59
4.95	0.99
7.37	1.55
9.01	2.00
9.83	2.25
10.07	2.60

Determine the order of the reaction using the expression

$$r_A = k C_A^n$$

and a least squares fit (note that you can rearrange this equation as $y = \ln r_A = \ln k + n \ln C_A \equiv a_0 + a_1 x$).

4.9 Derive eq. 4.33 using a procedure similar to that used in example 4.3 [**Hint:** Show that $E^{-1} = -\nabla$. Then obtain $E^\alpha y_n = y(x_n + \alpha \Delta x)$].

4.10 Use the results of example 4.3 to obtain

$$y(x) \equiv y(x_1 + \alpha \Delta x) = y_1 + \alpha \Delta y_1 + \frac{\alpha^2 - \alpha}{2} \Delta^2 y_1 + \dots$$

Apply this formula to obtain a second degree polynomial passing through the data points (x_1, y_1), (x_2, y_2) and (x_3, y_3) in example 4.2.

4.11 Derive eq. 4.34 using a procedure similar to that used in prob. 4.9. Also develop expressions for $y(x)$ using *second* degree polynomials (eqs. 4.33 and 4.34) involving backward differences. Use the data in example 4.2, and choose $n = 3$ when using eq. 4.33, and $n = 2$ when using eq. 4.34. Find out the base points at which these two polynomials give a residual of zero. Express the two polynomials in terms of x, and show that they are identical.

4.12 Consider the Legendre polynomial [from the set, $P_n(x)$, which are orthogonal over $-1 \le x \le 1$ with weightage factor 1.0]:

$$P_3(x) = \frac{1}{2}(5x^3 - 3x)$$

Generate values of $P_3(x)$ at the five base points (±1, ±0.5, 0). Fit a polynomial of degree = 2 through (some of) these points, using Newton's forward difference formula. Use forward differences corresponding to $x_0 = -1$.

4.13 Deduce eq. 4.36 {**Hint:** Obtain expressions for $y[x_2, x_1, x_0]$ in terms of y_2, y_1, and y_0, and generalize}. Also show that $y[x_2, x_1, x_0] = y[x_0, x_1, x_2]$, etc., and that the order of the arguments is unimportant.

4.14 Consider the set of five data points (alternate entries) given in prob. 4.3. Generate a table of all divided differences, and fit *a* third degree polynomial corresponding to the first entries in your table. Check if your polynomial replicates your data points.

4.15 (*a*) Add another data point ($x_4 = 7$, $y_4 = 1657$) to the table of example 4.5. Complete the table for divided differences. Fit a polynomial of fourth degree to the data and see if it is the same as that used to generate these data points ($y = x^4 - 3x^3 + 6x^2 - 2x + 5$). Note how results in example 4.5 can be used, and only one new term needs to be computed. (*b*) Instead of using the top diagonal terms in the polynomial expansion, show that if we follow any path through this table, terminating in the same *highest order* difference, we will end up getting the same polynomial.

4.16 Show that for equispaced base points, Newton's divided difference interpolating formula reduces to Newton's forward difference formula.

4.17 Show that the Lagrangian interpolation formula of 2nd degree applied to equispaced data points, (x_0, y_0), ($x_0 + \Delta x$, y_1), and ($x_0 + 2\Delta x$, y_2), gives the same results as Newton's forward difference formula (This equivalence is true for higher degree formulae also).

4.18 Use the Legendre polynomial given in prob. 4.12 to generate a set of four data points corresponding to base points, $x = -1.0$, -0.6, 0.3, 1.0. Then fit a 3rd degree polynomial to it using Lagrangian interpolation. You should be able to get the exact polynomial in this case.

4.19 Using Lagrangian interpolation, obtain an appropriate third degree polynomial for the vapour pressure of acetone (see data in prob. 4.3) which could be used for 259.2 K $\leq T \leq$ 320.5 K.

4.20 Deduce the $n = 3$, $m = 2$ Padé approximation of e^x. Write down the corresponding approximation of $e^{x\mathbf{B}}$.

4.21 Use the Maclaurin series for $\sin x$ and obtain a Padé approximation for this function with $n = 2$, $m = 2$. Also write series expressions for $\sin(x\mathbf{B})$ and $\cos(x\mathbf{B})$, and show that $\dfrac{d}{dx}\sin(x\mathbf{B}) = \mathbf{B}\cos(x\mathbf{B})$, and $\dfrac{d}{dx}\cos(x\mathbf{B}) = -\mathbf{B}\sin(x\mathbf{B})$. Write the Padé approximation ($n = 2$, $m = 2$) for $\sin(x\mathbf{B})$.

4.22 Derive eqs. 4.57 and 4.59.

4.23 Expand the butterfly shown in fig. 4.4 on a graph sheet. Using the coordinates of the 10 data points shown, make a computer program to evaluate the cubic splines. Compare the results obtained at intermediate points with the diagram. Comment on the fit, particularly at points where there are discontinuities in the slopes. A better fit would be obtained if we fit several sets of splines—one set over each range where $f'(x)$ is continuous.

4.24 Take a semicircle given by $f(x) = +\sqrt{9 - (x-5)^2}$, with center at $x = 5$, $y = 0$, and radius of 3. Take three data points, (2, 0), (5, 3) and (8, 0). Obtain the cubic splines, $S_0(x)$ and $S_1(x)$.

4.25 Figure P4.25 shows a computer version of an elephant from the ancient caves of Ajanta (India). The coordinates of its 34 data points can be obtained easily. Make a general computer code which can perform a

(a) least squares polynomial fit on the 34 points shown, using degree, *N*, of the polynomial (see prob. 4.1) as 5 and 8.

(b) cubic-spline fit with 33 cubic functions.

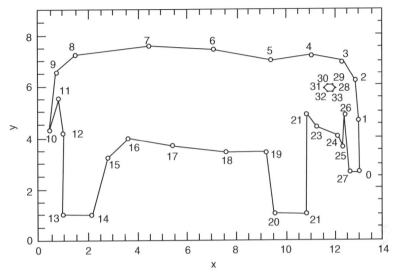

Fig. P 4.25

Compare the results obtained. Also see Wei [13], who fitted a least-squares Fourier sine series to the same data. Several graphics softwares on PCs have programs for polynomial and cubic spline fits to data points and you may wish to use these.

[This problem is due to Prof. A. Varma]

4.26 By substituting the expression for α, show that the error term in Newton's forward difference formula is

$$R(x) = \frac{(x - x_0)(x - x_1)...(x - x_n)}{(n+1)!} y^{(n+1)}(\xi)$$

Thus show that the error for the corresponding differentiation formula (eq. 4.62*a*) is

$$\left| \frac{dR}{dx} \right|_{x=x_i} = \frac{y^{n+1}(\xi)}{(n+1)!} \prod_{\substack{k=0 \\ k \neq i}}^{n} (x_i - x_k); \quad i = 0, 1, ..., n$$

4.27 Apply the three-point Lagrangian interpolation formula for evaluating derivatives (eq. 4.68) to a set of three equispaced base points, x_0, $x_0 + \Delta x$, and $x_0 + 2\Delta x$, and show that

$$y_0' = \frac{1}{2(\Delta x)}\left[-3y_0 + 4y_1 - y_2\right] + \frac{(\Delta x)^2}{3} y^{(3)}(\xi_0)$$

This is useful to obtain fluxes at a boundary in a heat transfer problem using temperatures at three locations.

4.28 Obtain $\dfrac{dp_{sat}}{dT}(290.1 \text{ K})$ using the first, third and fifth data points in prob. 4.3, and the three-point Lagrangian formula.

4.29 Use Newton's forward difference formula for estimating $\dfrac{df}{dx}$ correct to $O\,(\Delta x)^2$ to evaluate $\dfrac{df}{dx}$ at $x = -0.1$ for the following data:

x	-0.3	-0.1	0.1	0.3
$f(x)$	-0.20431	-0.08993	0.11007	0.39569

4.30 Given the following table (generated using $y = 3t^4 + 2t$)

t	y
0	0
0.5	1.1875
1.0	5.0000
1.5	18.1875
2.0	52.0000
2.5	122.1875
3.0	249.0000

Estimate $\dfrac{d^2 y}{dt^2}$ numerically at $t = 1.5$, using Newton's *forward* difference formula correct to $O(\Delta t)$. How does the value improve if you take one more term, *i.e.*, correct to $O\,(\Delta t)^2$. Compare with the *analytical* value of $y''(1.5) = 81$.

4.31 Derive an expression for $\dfrac{dy}{dt}$ using Newton's *backward* difference formula (eq. 4.65) applied to points $y_n,\ y_{n-1}, y_{n-2},\ \dots$. Obtain $y'\,(1.5)$ using data of prob. 4.30, correct to $O\,(\Delta t)$ using this formula.

4.32 Use the composite trapezoidal rule with $\Delta x = 0.2$ to evaluate

$$\int_1^2 (x \ln x)\, dx$$

Compare your results with the analytical value. Note $\int (x \ln x)\, dx = \dfrac{x^2}{2}\left[\ln x - \dfrac{1}{2}\right]$.

4.33 *Open Newton-Cotes Integration Formula:* Expand $f(x)$ using Newton's forward difference formula, in terms of y_1, Δy_1, $\Delta^2 y_1$, etc. Then use this to evaluate $\int_{x_0}^{x_2} f(x)\, dx$ (using up to terms involving Δy_1) as

$$\int_{x_0}^{x_2} f(x)\, dx = 2(\Delta x)\, y_1 + \frac{(\Delta x)^3}{3} f''(\xi);\ x_0 \le \xi \le x_2$$

This is known as the mid-point rule. Interpret this formula graphically. Higher order formulae can similarly be obtained. These produce results which are usually inferior to those obtained for the closed formulae.

4.34 Use the 3 point ($n = 2$) Gauss-Legendre formula to estimate $\int_{1}^{2}(x \ln x)\,dx$ after reducing it to the

form $\int_{-1}^{1} f(z)\,dz$. Compare with the value from prob. 4.32.

4.35 Use the Gauss-Legendre quadrature to evaluate the double integral $\int_{-1}^{1}\int_{-1}^{1}\sin^{2}(xy)\,dx\,dy$. Give

your answer correct to four decimal places. Use 3 points in the x direction and 2 points in the y direction. Remember that the values of x, y are in *radians*. Use an *intuitive* extension of the $1 - D$ formula (also see prob. 4.39).

4.36 Let $f(x) = 3x^{2}e^{x} + 2x^{4}$. Obtain $\dfrac{df}{dx}$ at $x = 2.0$ using eq. 4.63 with $\Delta x = 0.2$ as well as with $\Delta x = 0.1$. Use Richardson's extrapolation procedure to obtain a better estimate from these values. Compare with the analytical value.

4.37 Use the method in prob. 4.35 to obtain

$$\int_{-1}^{1}\int_{-1}^{1}x^{2}y^{2}\,dx\,dy$$

using the same number of points for evaluation of the integral as in prob. 4.35. Compare with the analytical value of the integral of $\dfrac{4}{9}$. Do not separate the integrals over x and y (see prob. 4.39 also).

4.38 Let $f(x) = 3x^{2}e^{x} + 2x^{4}$. Approximate $f(2.03)$ using Lagrangian polynomials of degree two, using $x_0 = 2$, $x_1 = 2.06$ and $x_2 = 2.10$. Compare the results with the exact value from the equation itself.

4.39 Deduce a 2-*dimensional* Newton interpolation formula for a function, $f(x, y)$, in terms of forward differences defined by

$$\Delta_x f_0 \equiv f\left(x_0 + \Delta x, y_0\right) - f\left(x_0, y_0\right)$$

$$\Delta_y f_0 \equiv f\left(x_0, y_0 + \Delta y\right) - f\left(x_0, y_0\right)$$

Write *only* upto linear terms in x and y directions, and use

$$\alpha \equiv \frac{x - x_0}{\Delta x} \quad \text{and} \quad \beta \equiv \frac{y - y_0}{\Delta y}$$

Use this formula to deduce an expression for the double-integral $\int_{x_0}^{x_0+\Delta x}\int_{y_0}^{y_0+\Delta y} f(x, y)\,dx\,dy$. This

formula is the $2 - D$ extension of the 1-dimensional trapezoidal rule derived in the text. Compare with the 1-D rule. Extend this formula to write the composite 2-D expression for

$$\int\limits_{x_0}^{x_0+n\Delta x} \int\limits_{y_0}^{y_0+m\Delta y} f(x, y)\,dx\,dy$$

in terms of values of f defined by

$$f_{ij} \equiv f(x_0 + i\Delta x, y_0 + j\Delta y)$$

$$i = 0, 1, 2, ..., n$$

$$j = 0, 1, 2, ..., m$$

4.40 Evaluate the integral

$$I = \int\limits_{0}^{\infty} e^{-z} z^3 \, dz$$

using the Gauss-Laguerre two-point quadrature formula for $n = 1$. The values of z_0 and z_1 are given [8] by

$$z_0 = 0.58579$$

$$z_1 = 3.41421$$

Obtain expressions for w_0 and w_1, in terms of z_0 and z_1, and use them to evaluate numerical values of w_0 and w_1, for use in evaluating the above integral, The analytical value of I is 6.0.

$$\left[\mathbf{Hint:} \int\limits_{a}^{b} u(x)v'(x)\,dx = u(x)v(x)\Big|_{a}^{b} - \int\limits_{a}^{b} v(x)u'(x)\,dx \right]$$

REFERENCES

1. L. Lapidus, *Digital Computation for Chemical Engineers,* McGraw-Hill, New York, 1962.
2. S.K. Gupta, unpublished data.
3. W.L. McCabe, J.C. Smith and P. Harriot, *Unit Operations of Chemical Engineering,* 7th ed., McGraw-Hill, New York, 2004.
4. M. Box, *Computer J.,* **8**, 42 (1965).
   [Presents a very popular technique for curve-fitting models to data].
5. G.S.G. Beveridge and R.S. Schechter, *Optimization: Theory and Practice,* McGraw-Hill, New York, 1970.
6. T.F. Edgar, D.M. Himmelblau and L.S. Lasdon, *Optimization of Chemical Processes,* 2nd ed., McGraw-Hill, New York, 2001.
7. V. Ravikumar and S.K. Gupta, *Polymer,* **32**, 3233 (1991).
8. B. Carnahan, H.A. Luther and J.O. Wilkes. *Applied Numerical Techniques,* Wiley, New York, 1969.
9. H. Padé, *Ann. Sci. Ec. Norm. Sup.,* Paris, **9**, 1 (1892).
10. R.L. Burden and J.D. Faires, *Numerical Analysis,* 3rd ed., Prindle, Weber and Schmidt, Boston, 1985.
11. A. Ralston and P. Rabinowitz, *A First Course in Numerical Analysis,* 2nd ed., McGraw-Hill, New York, 1978.
12. N.R. Amundson, *Mathematical Methods in Chemical Engineering: Matrices and their Applications,* Prentice Hall, Englewood Cliffs, N.J., 1966.

13. J. Wei, *Chemtech,* **5,** 128 (1975).
    [An interesting paper which shows the results of a least-squares fit for an elephant]
14. R.B. Bird, W.E. Stewart and E.N. Lightfoot, *Transport Phenomena,* 2nd ed., Wiley, New York, 2001.
15. L.F. Richardson and J.A. Gaunt, *Phil. Trans. Roy. Soc. Lon.,* **226A,** 299 (1927).
16. H.S. Mickley, T.K. Sherwood and C.E. Reid, *Applied Mathematics in Chemical Engineering,* 2nd ed., McGraw-Hill, New York, 1957.
17. B.E. Poling, J.M. Prausnitz and J.O' Connell, *The Properties of Gases and Liquids,* 5th ed., McGraw-Hill, New York, 2002.
18. D. Ambrose, C.H.S. Sprake and R. Townsend, *J. Chem. Thermo.,* **6,** 693(1974).
19. G.E. Forsythe, *SIAM J,* **5,** 74 (1957).
20. D. Sahu and D. Kunzru, *Can. J. Chem. Eng.,* **66,** 808 (1988).

Chapter 5

Ordinary Differential Equations: Initial Value Problems

5.1 INTRODUCTION

In several situations one obtains a set of N first order ordinary differential equations (ODEs) in N variables, $y_1, y_2, ..., y_n$:

$$\frac{dy_1}{dt} = f_1\left(y_1, y_2, ..., y_N\right)$$

$$\vdots \qquad\qquad\qquad\qquad ...(5.1)$$

$$\frac{dy_N}{dt} = f_N\left(y_1, y_2, ..., y_N\right)$$

with conditions given on *all* the N variables at the *same* value of t, say at $t = 0^*$ (this is what makes this an initial value problem, (IVP)):

$$\text{at} \quad t = 0: \quad y_1 = y_{1,0}$$

$$\vdots \qquad\qquad\qquad\qquad ...(5.2)$$

$$y_N = y_{N,0}$$

In matrix notation, these equations can be rewritten as

$$\frac{d\mathbf{y}}{dt} = \mathbf{f}(\mathbf{y}) \qquad\qquad ...(a)$$

$$\mathbf{y}(t = 0) = \mathbf{y}_0 \qquad\qquad ...(b) \qquad\qquad ...(5.3)$$

Examples where such equations are obtained in engineering include the modeling of batch reactors (or plug-flow reactors) in chemical engineering, or the dynamic modeling of units whose steady state operation is described by algebraic equations. In addition, partial differential equations obtained in the dynamic modeling of some engineering units, can be reduced to a set of ODE-IVPs by the use of various numerical techniques like the finite difference technique, the orthogonal collocation technique, etc. Sometimes even nonlinear algebraic equations are transformed into ODE-IVPs and then integrated to steady state to give their solutions. Thus, we see that ordinary differential equations-initial value

---

There is no loss of generality by assuming the values of y to be specified at $t = 0$ instead of at $t = t_0$.

problems (ODE-IVPs) are encountered quite often in engineering practice. This chapter deals with methods of obtaining the solutions, **y** (*t*), of these equations.

It may be mentioned that at times, higher-order ordinary differential equations can be reduced to a set of first order ODEs by a transformation of variables. For example, a tabular reactor with axial mixing (TRAM) is described in chemical engineering by [1]:

$$\frac{1}{Pe}\frac{d^2c}{dx^2} - \frac{dc}{dx} - R(c) = 0 \qquad \qquad ...(5.4)$$

where *Pe* is the Peclet number, *c* is the dimensionless concentration of the reactant, *x* is the dimensionless axial location, and *R* (*c*) is a dimensionless rate of reaction term. Equation 5.4 can be reduced to a set of two first order ODE-IVPs by defining a new variable y_1:

$$\frac{dc}{dx} = y_1 \qquad \qquad ...(a)$$

$$\frac{1}{Pe}\frac{dy_1}{dx} - y_1 - R(c) = 0 \qquad \qquad ...(b) \qquad \qquad ...(5.5)$$

These equations are of the same form as eq. 5.1, with *x* being the independent variable and **y** = $[y_1 \quad c]^T$. Obviously, we would need conditions on both *c* as well as $\frac{dc}{dx}$ (or y_1) at *x* = 0 for eq. 5.5 to be an initial value problem (Danckwerts' boundary conditions are usually applied—these, however, lead to a boundary value problem, see Chapter 6). The characteristic of the IVPs is that *all* the dependent variables, **y** (*t*), have their conditions specified at the same value of the independent variable, *t*. Chapter 6 discusses techniques to solve boundary-value problems (BVPs) in which the conditions on the dependent variables are not specified at the same value of the independent variable.

There are several techniques which have been developed to solve ODE-IVPs. These are described for a single dependent variable system first, and then generalized for cases involving several dependent variables.

5.2 EXPLICIT ADAMS-BASHFORTH TECHNIQUES

Several techniques can be developed by the use of Newton's backward difference formula (eq. 4.33). We consider the simple ODE-IVP[**]:

[**] If we had, instead

$$\frac{dy}{dt} = f(t, y) \qquad \qquad ...(a)$$

we could define two variables $y_1 = t$, $y_2 = y$, and write

$$\frac{dy_1}{dt} = 1$$

$$\frac{dy_2}{dt} = f(y_1, y_2) \qquad \qquad ...(b)$$

with
$$\mathbf{y}(0) = \begin{bmatrix} 0 & y_0 \end{bmatrix}^T \qquad \qquad ...(c)$$

We have, thus, reduced eq. (a) to the same form as eq. 5.1. A similar transformation is made if *t* occurs *explicitly* in the functions in eq. 5.1. A set of *N* + 1 ODEs in $[y_1\ y_2\ ...\ y_{N+1}]$ can be written, with $y_{N+1} \equiv t$, $f_{N+1} = 1$, $y_{N+1}(0) = 0$.

$$\frac{dy}{dt} = f(y) \equiv y'(y)$$

$$y(0) = y_0 \qquad \qquad ...(5.6)$$

As in chapter 4, we discretize the variable, t, using equal intervals, Δt ($\equiv h$), called the step size or interval of integration, and define

$$t_i = i(\Delta t) = ih$$

$$y_i = y(t = t_i)$$

$$y_i' = y'(t = t_i); \quad i = 0, 1, 2, ... \qquad \qquad ...(5.7)$$

The ODE in eq. 5.6 can easily be integrated between $t = t_n$ and $t = t_{n+1} = t_n + h$ as follows (it is assumed that one has already computed the points $y_0, y_1, y_2, ..., y_n$):

$$\int_{t_n}^{t_{n+1}} \frac{dy}{dt} dt = y_{n+1} - y_n = \int_{t_n}^{t_{n+1}} f(y) dt = \int_{t_n}^{t_{n+1}} y'(y) dt \qquad \qquad ...(5.8)$$

Since y' is a function of y, it is not known in $t_n \leq t \leq t_{n+1}$, and needs to be estimated. One possibility is to use a polynomial approximation to $y'(y)$ in $t_n \leq t \leq t_{n+1}$ using points $(t_n, y_n), (t_{n-1}, y_{n-1}), ..., (t_{n-j}, y_{n-j})$ [and so, points $(t_n, y_n'),(t_{n-1}, y_{n-1}'),..., (t_{n-j}, y_{n-j}')$] computed previously. Newton's backward difference formula (eq. 4.33) can be used for this purpose. Using the dimensionless time, α, defined by eq. 4.31:

$$\alpha = \frac{t - t_n}{h} \qquad \qquad ...(5.9)$$

we obtain from eq. 5.8

$$y_{n+1} - y_n = h \int_{\alpha=0}^{1} y'(\alpha) d\alpha \qquad \qquad ...(5.10)$$

The function $y'(y)$ or $y'(\alpha)$ required in the integrand of eq. 5.10 can be written using eq. 4.33 as

$$y'(\alpha) = \left[1 + \alpha\nabla + \frac{\alpha(\alpha+1)}{2!}\nabla^2 + ... + \frac{\alpha(\alpha+1)...(\alpha+j-1)}{j!}\nabla^j \right] y_n' + R(\alpha) \qquad \qquad ...(5.11)$$

It may be cautioned that eq. 5.11 is obtained by curve-fitting a jth-degree polynomial to the $(j + 1)$ points $(t_n, y_n'), (t_{n-1}, y_{n-1}'),..., (t_{n-j}, y_{n-j}')$, and extrapolating it in, $t_n \leq t \leq t_{n+1}$ for use in eq. 5.10. The expression in eq. 5.11 is *not* obtained by curve-fitting a jth-degree polynomial to $(t_n, y_n), (t_{n-1}, y_{n-1})$, ... (t_{n-j}, y_{n-j}), and then differentiating it analytically, as done for obtaining eq. 4.65.

On using eq. 5.11 in eq. 5.10 and performing the integration (noting that $\nabla y_n', \nabla^2 y_n', ..., \nabla^j y_n'$ are independent of α), we obtain

$$y_{n+1} = y_n + h \left[1 + \frac{1}{2}\nabla + \frac{5}{12}\nabla^2 + \frac{3}{8}\nabla^3 + ... + c_j\nabla^j \right] y_n' + h \int_{\alpha=0}^{1} R(\alpha) d\alpha \qquad \qquad ...(5.12)$$

We can truncate the above formula at different points (corresponding to different values of *j*) and evaluate the corresponding error terms. For example, for $j = 0$ [fitting a 0th-degree polynomial, *i.e.*, a constant, to the point (t_n, y_n'); *i.e.*, assuming $y'(\alpha) = y_n'$ in $t_n \leq t \leq t_{n+1}$, see fig. 5.1], we obtain

$$y_{n+1} = y_n + hy_n' + \frac{h^2}{2}y''(\xi) = y_n + hf(y_n) + \frac{h^2}{2}f'(\xi); \quad y_n \leq \xi \leq y_{n+1} \qquad \dots(5.13)$$

The error term in this equation is easily obtained using $R(\alpha) = \alpha h(y'')_\xi$ (eq. 4.33b) in the integral in eq. 5.12. The only difference here is the range of ξ, which extends to y_{n+1} now since $y'(\alpha)$ in eq. 5.11 is being extrapolated to this point. The results for other values of *j* can be obtained similarly, and some popular formulae are given below:

$j = 0$ (first-order Adams-Bashforth technique or explicit Euler technique)

$$y_{n+1} = y_n + hf(y_n) + \frac{h^2}{2}f'(\xi); \quad y_n \leq \xi \leq y_{n+1} \qquad \dots(a)$$

$j = 1$ (second-order Adams-Bashforth technique, see fig. 5.1)

$$y_{n+1} = y_n + \frac{h}{2}\left[3f(y_n) - f(y_{n-1})\right] + \frac{5h^3}{12}f''(\xi); \quad y_{n-1} \leq \xi \leq y_{n+1} \qquad \dots(b)$$

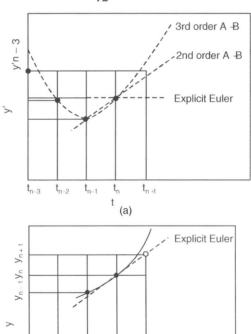

Fig. 5.1 Graphical representation of some low-order Adams-Bashforth (AB) methods. Points (t_n, y_n), (t_{n-1}, y_{n-1}), ... are values already computed. (*a*) (t_{n+1}, y_{n+1}) is predicted by using different approximations to y' in $t_n \leq t \leq t_{n+1}$, as shown. (*b*) shows the explicit Euler technique to be based on the tangent at the computed (t_n, y_n). Note that the computed points will not be the same for different techniques (as shown above) due to the different truncation errors present.

$j = 3$ (fourth-order Adams-Bashforth technique)

$$y_{n+1} = y_n + \frac{h}{24}\left[55f(y_n) - 59f(y_{n-1}) + 37f(y_{n-2}) - 9f(y_{n-3})\right]$$

$$+\frac{251}{720}h^5 f^{(4)}(\xi); \quad y_{n-3} \le \xi \le y_{n+1} \qquad \qquad ...(c) \qquad ...(5.14)$$

These form part of the Adams-Bashforth family of techniques. Several points can be noted about these:

(*a*) the right-hand-side of these equations do not incorporate the unknown variable, y_{n+1} (in contrast to the techniques discussed in sec. 5.3), and so we can compute y_{n+1} quite easily (and without any trial and error) if we know all the *previous* points. Such techniques are known as *explicit* techniques.

(*b*) the error terms in eq. 5.14, referred to as [2] *local truncation errors,* LTE (due to truncation of the series), are observed to decrease from order h^2 [denoted by $O\ (h^2)$] for the explicit Euler method, to $O\ (h^5)$ for the fourth order technique (h is obviously much smaller than unity). Other authors [3–5] define the LTE slightly differently. It may be noted that the order, r, of the technique is associated with an LTE of $O\ (h^{r+1})$. There is another way to looking at the order of a technique. If the solution, $y\ (t)$, is an $(r + 1)$th degree polynomial in t, an rth-order technique will give exact results, provided there are no round-off errors.

(*c*) starting from $(t_0 = 0,\ y_0)$ we can obtain $(t = h,\ y_1)$ in a single step using the explicit Euler technique. This point can then be used with a further application of the algorithm to obtain $(t = 2h,\ y_2)$. The procedure can be continued to generate more points, $y_3,\ y_4,\ ...,$ sequentially. We thus *march forward* in variable t. As opposed to this, the two-step second order Adams-Bashforth algorithm, when applied to $n = 0$ and $n = 1$, gives

$$y_1 = y_0 + \frac{h}{2}\left(3y_0' - y_{-1}'\right) \qquad \qquad ...(a)$$

$$y_2 = y_1 + \frac{h}{2}\left(3y_1' - y_0'\right) \qquad \qquad ...(b) \qquad ...(5.15)$$

Obviously, y_{-1}' is undefined, and creates starting problems. Similar problems are encountered in all other higher order algorithms of this family. The method used to overcome this problem is to start with the lowest-order technique (explicit Euler method) at t_0 and generate y_1. Using y_0 and y_1, the second order technique is used to generate y_2. The third order technique can now be used to compute y_3, etc. Since the LTEs of the low-order techniques used initially are high, much smaller integration step sizes should be used with them than for the higher order methods, to minimize the overall error. Appropriate juxtaposition of the step-sizes is also required for this sequential *marching method.*

(*d*) the Adams-Bashforth algorithms can be seen to relate $y_{n+1} - y_n$ to a weighted-average value of the slopes at different locations, multiplied by the integration step size. For example, the fourth-order method can be written as

$$y_{n+1} = y_n + h\left[\beta_1 y_n' + \beta_2 y_{n-1}' + \beta_3 y_{n-2}' + \beta_4 y_{n-3}'\right] \qquad \qquad ...(5.16)$$

where the β are the weightage factors.

(*e*) the explicit Euler technique is observed to have a finite-difference form for y_n':

$$y_n' = \frac{y_{n+1} - y_n}{h} = \frac{y(t_n + h) - y(t_n)}{(t_n + h) - (t_n)} \qquad \qquad ...(5.17)$$

Example 5.1: Use the explicit Euler technique with $h = 0.025$ to integrate $y' = -3y : y_0 = 1$ upto $t = 0.25$. Compare with the exact value of 0.47237 at this point.

We have

$$y_{n+1} = y_n - 3hy_n = (1 - 3h) y_n = 0.925 y_n$$

$\therefore$ $y_1 = 0.925$ at $t = 0.025$

         $y_2 = 0.925^2 = 0.855625$ at $t = 0.05$

         $y_3 = 0.925^3 = 0.7914531$ at $t = 0.075$

         $y_4 = 0.925^4 = 0.7320941$ at $t = 0.1$

         $y_{10} = 0.925^{10} = 0.45858$ at $t = 0.25$

The exact value of y_{10} is 0.47237.   ■

It can be observed that $y_{1,\,exact} = 0.9277434$. The error in this is seen to be 0.002744. The LTE can be estimated since the analytical solution is known, $y_{exact} = e^{-3t}$. We estimate the LTE as $\dfrac{h^2}{2} y''(\xi) = 0.0028125 e^{-3t} < 0.0028125$. This is about the same as obtained above. The Euler technique underestimates y_1 for this case.

Use of $h = 0.25$ would give $y\,(t = 0.25) = 0.25$, with the error being substantially higher.

5.3 IMPLICIT ADAMS-MOULTON TECHNIQUES

The explicit techniques discussed above have certain limitations, discussed in sec. 5.9, which make them unsuitable for several important applications. Implicit techniques are then used. One family of such techniques is the Adams-Moulton set. In this case, we use eq. 4.34 instead of eq. 4.33 to estimate $y'(\alpha)$ in the range $t_n \le t \le t_{n+1}$:

$$y'\left(\frac{t - t_n}{h}\right) = y'(\alpha) = \left[1 + (\alpha - 1)\nabla + \frac{(\alpha - 1)\alpha}{2!}\nabla^2 + \ldots\right.$$

$$\left. + \frac{(\alpha - 1)\alpha(\alpha + 1)\ldots(\alpha + j - 2)}{j!}\nabla^j \right] y'_{n+1} + R(\alpha) \qquad \ldots(5.18)$$

This means we are fitting a jth-degree polynomial through the $(j + 1)$ points $\left(t_{n+1}, y'_{n+1}\right), \left(t_n, y'_n\right),$ $\left(t_{n-1}, y'_{n-1}\right), \ldots, \left(t_{n-j+1}, y'_{n-j+1}\right),$ and using it in eq. 5.10.

This leads to

$$y_{n+1} = y_n + h\left[1 - \frac{1}{2}\nabla - \frac{1}{12}\nabla^2 - \frac{1}{24}\nabla^3 - \ldots\right] y'_{n+1} + h \int_{\alpha=0}^{1} R(\alpha)\,d\alpha \qquad \ldots(5.19)$$

The following common techniques are obtained for different values of j:

$j = 0$ (implicit Euler technique)

$$y_{n+1} = y_n + h f\left(y_{n+1}\right) - \frac{h^2}{2} f'(\xi); \qquad y_n \le \xi \le y_{n+1} \qquad \ldots(a)$$

$j = 1$ (Crank-Nicholson technique, trapezoid rule for ODE-IVPs, etc.)

$$y_{n+1} = y_n + \frac{h}{2}\left[f\left(y_{n+1}\right) + f\left(y_n\right)\right] - \frac{h^3}{12}f''(\xi); \quad y_n \leq \xi \leq y_{n+1} \quad \dots(b)$$

$j = 3$ (fourth-order Adams-Moulton technique)

$$y_{n+1} = y_n + \frac{h}{24}\left[9f\left(y_{n+1}\right) + 19f\left(y_n\right) - 5f\left(y_{n-1}\right) + f\left(y_{n-2}\right)\right]$$

$$-\frac{19}{720}h^5 f^{(4)}(\xi); \quad y_{n-2} \leq \xi \leq y_{n+1} \qquad \dots(c) \qquad \dots(5.20)$$

It is easy to see that in the implicit Euler technique, we are assuming that $y' = y'\left(y_{n+1}\right)$ in the entire range $t_n \leq t \leq t_{n+1}$. Since the values of only $y_0, y_1, \dots, y_n$ are known at the time of applying eq. 5.20, this poses a problem—the unknown y_{n+1} appears on both sides of the algorithms in eq. 5.20 (this is why these are called implicit techniques). Techniques described in chapter 3 need to be used to obtain iterative solutions of y_{n+1} *at every step of integration*, as illustrated in example 5.2 below. Again, it is observed that a method of order, r, has an LTE of 0 (h^{r+1}).

Example 5.2: Integrate $y' = \sin y$; $y_0 = 2$; using $h = 0.05$ in the implicit Euler technique, to compute y_1.

We have from eq. 5.20(a)

$$y_{n+1} = y_n + h \sin\left(y_{n+1}\right)$$

The nonlinear algebraic equation can be written in the form of eq. 3.1 (with variable, y_{n+1}, to be solved for) as

$$F\left(y_{n+1}\right) \equiv y_{n+1} - h\sin\left(y_{n+1}\right) - y_n = 0$$

We could solve this equation using the successive substitutions technique, one form of which is (see prob. 5.4 for convergence criterion)

$$y_{n+1}^{(k+1)} = h\sin\left[y_{n+1}^{(k)}\right] + y_n; \quad k = 1, 2, \dots$$

Alternatively, it can be solved by using the Newton-Raphson method:

$$y_{n+1}^{(k+1)} = y_{n+1}^{(k)} - \frac{F\left[y_{n+1}^{(k)}\right]}{F'\left[y_{n+1}^{(k)}\right]} = y_{n+1}^{(k)} + \frac{h\sin\left[y_{n+1}^{(k)}\right] + y_n - y_{n+1}^{(k)}}{1 - h\cos\left[y_{n+1}^{(k)}\right]} \qquad \dots(a)$$

The general equation for other implicit techniques is discussed in prob. 5.5. Equation (a) above is used with $n = 0$, $h = 0.05$, $y_0 = 2$ to give

$$y_1^{(k+1)} = y_1^{(k)} + \frac{0.05\sin\left[y_1^{(k)}\right] + 2 - y_1^{(k)}}{1 - 0.05\cos\left[y_1^{(k)}\right]}$$

Starting with a value of $y_1^{(0)} = 2(= y_0)$, we obtain the following iterates

k	$y_1^{(k)}$
0	2.0000000
1	2.0445381
2	2.0444944
3	2.0444944

or, $y_1 = 2.0444944$. A similar iteration is necessary *at every stage of integration* to obtain $y_2, y_3, \dots$, etc. ∎

Several of the comments made regarding the explicit Adams-Bashforth techniques in sec. 5.2 apply to the implicit methods as well. The errors decrease as higher order techniques are used. Starting problems exist for higher order algorithms as well. And finally, these algorithms can be expressed in terms of weighted-average slopes at several locations.

It was mentioned in chp. 4 that several interpolation formulae can be written. Corresponding to each of these, we can derive an integration algorithm. Some of these are discussed in the next section.

5.4 GENERAL MULTISTEP INTEGRATION METHODS (FOR MULTIVARIABLE ODE-IVPs)

The algorithms for integrating the single (dependent) variable ODE-IVPs as discussed in secs. 5.2 and 5.3 can easily be generalized for the multivariable case of eq. 5.3. Thus, the multivariable Adams-Bashforth (4th order) algorithm is given by

$$\mathbf{y}_{n+1} = \mathbf{y}_n + \frac{h}{24}\left[55\mathbf{y}_n' - 59\mathbf{y}_{n-1}' + 37\mathbf{y}_{n-2}' - 9\mathbf{y}_{n-3}'\right] + O(h^5) \qquad \qquad \text{...(5.21)}$$

where

$$\mathbf{y}_n = \begin{bmatrix} y_1(t_n) & y_2(t_n) & \cdots & y_N(t_n) \end{bmatrix}^T$$

$$\mathbf{y}_n' = \begin{bmatrix} f_1(\mathbf{y}_n) & f_2(\mathbf{y}_n) & \cdots & f_N(\mathbf{y}_n) \end{bmatrix}^T \qquad \qquad \text{...(5.22)}$$

etc. The multivariable forms of the other algorithms described in the earlier two sections can be similarly written. In fact, all these techniques are part of a more general multistep algorithm described by

$$\mathbf{y}_{n+1} = \alpha_0 \mathbf{y}_{n+1} + \alpha_1 \mathbf{y}_n + \alpha_2 \mathbf{y}_{n-1} + \dots + \alpha_k \mathbf{y}_{n-k+1}$$

$$+ h\left[\beta_0 \mathbf{y}_{n+1}' + \beta_1 \mathbf{y}_n' + \dots + \beta_k \mathbf{y}_{n-k+1}'\right] + O(h^q) \qquad \qquad \text{...(5.23)}$$

where $\alpha_0, \alpha_1, \alpha_2, ..., \alpha_k, \beta_0, \beta_1, ..., \beta_k$ are constants characterizing a particular method. Thus, the fourth-order Adams Bashforth method has $k = 4$, $\alpha_1 = 1$, $\alpha_0 = \alpha_2 = \alpha_3 = \alpha_4 = 0$, $\beta_0 = 0$, $\beta_1 = \dfrac{55}{24}$, $\beta_2 = \dfrac{-59}{24}$, $\beta_3 = \dfrac{37}{24}$, $\beta_4 = \dfrac{-9}{24}$. Table 5.1 summarizes several multistep algorithms and includes some others not already described. It is to be noted that algorithms with $\beta_0 \neq 0$ are implicit techniques, while those with $\beta_0 = 0$ are explicit methods. Equation 5.23 expresses $\mathbf{y}_{n+1}$ as a weighted average of several previous values, $\mathbf{y}_n, \mathbf{y}_{n-1}, ...,$ etc., and h *times* the weighted average of the slopes at several locations.

Example 5.3: Consider the following ODE-IVP

$$\begin{bmatrix} y_1' \\ y_2' \end{bmatrix} = \begin{bmatrix} -100 & 0 \\ 2 & -1 \end{bmatrix}\begin{bmatrix} y_1 \\ y_2 \end{bmatrix} = \begin{bmatrix} -100y_1 \\ 2y_1 - y_2 \end{bmatrix} = \begin{bmatrix} f_1(\mathbf{y}) \\ f_2(\mathbf{y}) \end{bmatrix}$$

with

$$\mathbf{y}_0 = \begin{bmatrix} 2 & 1 \end{bmatrix}^T$$

Use the explicit Euler technique with $h = 0.02$ to obtain $\mathbf{y}(t_1 = 0.02)$ at the end of one time interval. We have

$$\begin{bmatrix} y_1 \\ y_2 \end{bmatrix}_{t_1} = \begin{bmatrix} y_1 \\ y_2 \end{bmatrix}_{t_0=0} + 0.02 \begin{bmatrix} -100y_1 \\ 2y_1 - y_2 \end{bmatrix}_{t_0}$$

$$= \begin{bmatrix} 2 \\ 1 \end{bmatrix} + 0.02 \begin{bmatrix} -100 \times 2 \\ 2 \times 2 - 1 \end{bmatrix} = \begin{bmatrix} -2 \\ 1.06 \end{bmatrix}$$

The analytical solution is

$$\begin{bmatrix} y_1 \\ y_2 \end{bmatrix}_{exact} = \begin{bmatrix} 2e^{-100t} \\ \dfrac{103}{99}e^{-t} - \dfrac{4}{99}e^{-100t} \end{bmatrix}$$

and so

$$\begin{bmatrix} y_1 \\ y_2 \end{bmatrix}_{t_1,\ exact} = \begin{bmatrix} 0.27067 \\ 1.014335 \end{bmatrix}$$

The results are substantially in error, particularly for y_1. This is due to the large value of h used. A more elaborate discussion of the integration of this ODE is presented in sec. 5.9. ∎

5.5 PREDICTOR-CORRECTOR TECHNIQUES

It was observed in example 5.2 that implicit techniques involve the unknown variables, y_{n+1}, on the right hand side, usually as a nonlinear function. The Newton-Raphson technique (or the successive substitutions method) was used to solve for y_{n+1}. A popular and simple method to go around this problem is to first *predict* a value, $\bar{y}_{n+1}$, of y_{n+1} using an explicit algorithm, and use it on the right hand side of an implicit technique (usually having the same order LTE) to improve the estimate. Thus, the fourth order Adams-Bashforth technique can be used as a predictor equation, and the fourth order Adams-Moulton technique can be used as a corrector. This predictor-corrector (PC) combination is, thus

$$P: \bar{y}_{n+1} = y_n + \frac{h}{24}\left[55f(y_n) - 59f(y_{n-1}) + 37f(y_{n-2}) - 9f(y_{n-3})\right]$$

$$C: y_{n+1} = y_n + \frac{h}{24}\left[9f(\bar{y}_{n+1}) + 19f(y_n) - 5f(y_{n-1}) + f(y_{n-2})\right] \qquad \ldots(5.24)$$

This combination avoids the use of trial and error. In fact, one could use the value of y_{n+1} so predicted on the right-hand side of the corrector equation and improve the estimate of y_{n+1} further, somewhat akin to the successive substitutions technique. This combination is referred to as PC^2, etc. The multivariable combination can be similarly written. As for the individual algorithms, start-up problems exist for the PC combinations too. A very popular PC combination is the Milne-Simpson technique (see table 5.1):

$$P: \bar{y}_{n+1} = y_{n-3} + \frac{4h}{3}\left[2f(y_n) - f(y_{n-1}) + 2f(y_{n-2})\right] + \frac{14}{45}h^5 f^{(4)}(\xi)$$

$$C: y_{n+1} = y_{n-1} + \frac{h}{3}\left[f(\bar{y}_{n+1}) + 4f(y_n) + f(y_{n-1})\right] - \frac{h^5}{90}f^{(4)}(\xi) \qquad \ldots(5.25)$$

This has lower LTEs than eq. 5.24 but is less stable.

Table 5.1 Some Algorithms for Integrating ODE-IVPs

Technique	$q-1$ [**]	α_0	α_1	α_2	α_3	α_4	α_5	α_6	β_0	β_1	β_2	β_3	β_4	β_5	β_6	Comments
ADAMS BASHFORTH	1	0	1	0	0	0	0	0	0	1	0	0	0	0	0	Explicit Euler
"	2	0	1	0	0	0	0	0	0	$\frac{3}{2}$	$\frac{-1}{2}$	0	0	0	0	
"	3	0	1	0	0	0	0	0	0	$\frac{23}{12}$	$\frac{-16}{12}$	$\frac{5}{12}$	0	0	0	
"	4	0	1	0	0	0	0	0	0	$\frac{55}{24}$	$\frac{-59}{24}$	$\frac{37}{24}$	$\frac{-9}{24}$	0	0	
"	5	0	1	0	0	0	0	0	0	$\frac{1901}{720}$	$\frac{-2774}{720}$	$\frac{2616}{720}$	$\frac{-1274}{720}$	$\frac{251}{720}$	0	
"	6	0	1	0	0	0	0	0	0	$\frac{4277}{1440}$	$\frac{-7923}{1440}$	$\frac{9982}{1440}$	$\frac{-7298}{1440}$	$\frac{2877}{1440}$	$\frac{-475}{1440}$	
ADAMS MOULTON	1	0	1	0	0	0	0	0	1	0	0	0	0	0	0	Implicit Euler
"	2	0	1	0	0	0	0	0	$\frac{1}{2}$	$\frac{1}{2}$	0	0	0	0	0	Crank Nicholson
"	3	0	1	0	0	0	0	0	$\frac{5}{12}$	$\frac{8}{12}$	$\frac{-1}{12}$	0	0	0	0	
"	4	0	1	0	0	0	0	0	$\frac{9}{24}$	$\frac{19}{24}$	$\frac{-5}{24}$	$\frac{1}{24}$	0	0	0	
"	5	0	1	0	0	0	0	0	$\frac{251}{720}$	$\frac{646}{720}$	$\frac{-264}{720}$	$\frac{106}{720}$	$\frac{-19}{720}$	0	0	
"	6	0	1	0	0	0	0	0	$\frac{475}{1440}$	$\frac{1427}{1440}$	$\frac{-798}{1440}$	$\frac{482}{1440}$	$\frac{-173}{1440}$	$\frac{27}{1440}$	0	

(Contd.)

Technique	$q-1$ [**]	α_0	α_1	α_2	α_3	α_4	α_5	α_6	β_0	β_1	β_2	β_3	β_4	β_5	β_6	Comments
Nystrom explicit	2	0	0	1	0	0	0	0	0	2	0	0	0	0	0	mid-point rule
"	3	0	0	1	0	0	0	0	0	$\frac{7}{3}$	$\frac{-2}{3}$	$\frac{1}{3}$	0	0	0	
"	4	0	0	1	0	0	0	0	0	$\frac{8}{3}$	$\frac{-5}{3}$	$\frac{4}{3}$	$\frac{-1}{3}$	0	0	
"	5	0	0	1	0	0	0	0	0	$\frac{269}{190}$	$\frac{-266}{190}$	$\frac{294}{190}$	$\frac{-146}{190}$	$\frac{29}{190}$	0	
Nystrom implicit	1	0	0	1	0	0	0	0	2	0	0	0	0	0	0	
"	2	0	0	1	0	0	0	0	0	2	0	0	0	0	0	(explicit)
"	4	0	0	1	0	0	0	0	$\frac{1}{3}$	$\frac{4}{3}$	$\frac{1}{3}$	0	0	0	0	
Hermite explicit	3	0	-4	5	0	0	0	0	0	4	2	0	0	0	0	
"	5	0	-18	9	10	0	0	0	0	9	18	3	0	0	0	
Hermite implicit	3	$\frac{1}{2}$	0	$\frac{1}{2}$	0	0	0	0	$\frac{-1}{4}$	0	$\frac{-1}{4}$	0	0	0	0	
Milne explicit	4	0	0	0	0	1	0	0	0	$\frac{8}{3}$	$\frac{-4}{3}$	$\frac{8}{3}$	0	0	0	
"	6	0	0	0	0	0	0	1	0	$\frac{33}{10}$	$\frac{-42}{10}$	$\frac{78}{10}$	$\frac{-42}{10}$	$\frac{33}{10}$	0	
Milne implicit	4	0	0	1	0	0	0	0	$\frac{1}{3}$	$\frac{4}{3}$	$\frac{1}{3}$	0	0	0	0	Simpson's method
"	6	0	0	0	0	1	0	0	$\frac{14}{45}$	$\frac{64}{45}$	$\frac{24}{45}$	$\frac{64}{45}$	$\frac{14}{45}$	0	0	

[*] adapted from Ref. 6
[**] LTE $= O\,(h^q)$

5.6 RUNGE-KUTTA METHODS

Another very popular family of integration techniques for ODE-IVPs is the Runge-Kutta (RK) set of algorithms. These are explicit, one step, highly accurate techniques which do not have the starting problems associated with the multistep algorithms. The second order RK technique for a single ODE-IVP is discussed first, and then the algorithms for higher order techniques are presented. The equation to be integrated is slightly more general than eq. 5.6:

$$\frac{dy}{dt} = f(t, y); \quad y(t = 0) = y_0 \qquad \qquad ...(5.26)$$

We write the solution, y_{n+1}, at $t = t_{n+1}$ in terms of the value, y_n, of y at time, t_n, as

$$y_{n+1} = y_n + h\phi(t_n, y_n, h) \qquad \qquad ...(5.27)$$

The function, ϕ, is an increment function and is some approximation to y' in the interval $t_n \leq t \leq t_{n+1}$. Equation 5.27 is to be written as an *explicit* equation, *i.e.*, if we know the value of y_n, we can easily compute the value, y_{n+1}, after an interval, h, without any trial and error. Thus, we can easily *march forward* in time starting from the given initial condition, $y = y_0$ at $t = 0$. This is why these techniques, too, are sometimes referred to as marching techniques.

We can write the increment function, ϕ, as a weighted average of the slopes, $k_i = f(t_i, y_i)$, at two locations, in analogy with eq. 5.16:

$$y_{n+1} = y_n + h[ak_1 + bk_2] \qquad \qquad ...(5.28)$$

One location at which the slope is to be computed can be chosen as the known point (t_n, y_n). Thus, we choose

$$k_1 = f(t_n, y_n) \qquad \qquad ...(5.29)$$

The other location can be chosen somewhere inside the range $t_n \leq t \leq t_{n+1}$, $y_n \leq y \leq y_{n+1}$. We write

$$k_2 = f(t_n + ph, y_n + qhk_1) \qquad \qquad ...(5.30)$$

with p and q as constants to be determined in some 'optimal' manner. Figure 5.2 shows the locations of the points A and B at which the function, f, is evaluated to give the slopes k_1 and k_2, respectively.

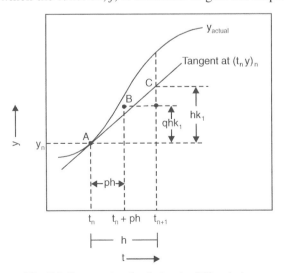

Fig. 5.2 Construction for 2nd-order RK technique

One can expand k_2 about the point (t_n, y_n) using a three term Taylor series:

$$k_2 = f\left(t_n + ph, y_n + qhk_1\right)$$

$$= f\left(t_n, y_n\right) + f_t\left(t_n, y_n\right)ph + f_y\left(t_n, y_n\right)qhk_1 + O\left(h^2\right) \qquad \text{...(5.31)}$$

where the subscripts t and y on f indicate the partial derivatives, *i.e.*, $f_t = \dfrac{\partial f}{\partial t}$ and $f_y = \dfrac{\partial f}{\partial y}$. Substituting

eqs. 5.29 and 5.31 in eq. 5.28 gives

$$y_{n+1} = y_n + h\left[af\left(t_n, y_n\right) + bf\left(t_n, y_n\right)\right] + h^2\left[bpf_t\left(t_n, y_n\right) + bqf\left(t_n, y_n\right)f_y\left(t_n, y_n\right)\right] + O\left(h^3\right) \text{ ...(5.32)}$$

A Taylor expansion of y_{n+1} about y_n can also be written as

$$y_{n+1} = y_n + hf\left(t_n, y_n\right) + \frac{h^2}{2!}f'\left(t_n, y_n\right) + \frac{h^3}{3!}f''\left(t_\xi, y_\xi\right) \qquad \text{...(5.33)}$$

where the primes denote (total) derivatives with respect to t. Using

$$f'\left(t_n, y_n\right) = \frac{df}{dt}\left(t_n, y_n\right) = \left[\frac{\partial f}{\partial t} + \frac{\partial f}{\partial y}\frac{dy}{dt}\right]_n = \left[f_t + f_y f\right]_n \qquad \text{...(5.34)}$$

in eq. 5.33, gives

$$y_{n+1} = y_n + hf\left(t_n, y_n\right) + \frac{h^2}{2!}f_t\left(t_n, y_n\right) + \frac{h^2}{2!}f_y\left(t_n, y_n\right)f\left(t_n, y_n\right) + \frac{h^3}{3!}f''\left(t_\xi, y_\xi\right) \qquad \text{...(5.35)}$$

We now have two equations for y_{n+1}—eqs. 5.32 and 5.35. Comparing the terms, we can write

$$a + b = 1$$

$$bp = \frac{1}{2}$$

$$bq = \frac{1}{2} \qquad \text{...(5.36)}$$

The choice of constants, a, b, p and q, in accordance with eq. 5.36, forces the algorithm in eq. 5.28 (which involves evaluating the function f at two locations, A and B, in fig. 5.2) to be accurate upto $O\left(h^3\right)$.

Because of the extra degree of freedom in eq. 5.36 (four unknowns, three equations), several choices of the four constants can be made. Some of the more popular choices and the corresponding algorithms are given below:

Improved or modified Euler's Method: $a = b = \dfrac{1}{2}$, $p = q = 1$:

$$y_{n+1} = y_n + h\left[\frac{1}{2}f\left(t_n, y_n\right) + \frac{1}{2}f\{t_n + h, y_n + hy'_n\}\right] + O\left(h^3\right) \qquad \text{...(a)}$$

Ralston's Method: $a = \dfrac{1}{3}$, $b = \dfrac{2}{3}$, $p = q = \dfrac{3}{4}$

$$y_{n+1} = y_n + h\left[\frac{1}{3}f(t_n, y_n) + \frac{2}{3}f\left\{t_n + \frac{3h}{4}, y_n + \frac{3h}{4}y_n'\right\}\right] + O(h^3) \qquad ...(b)$$

Heun's Method: $a = \dfrac{1}{4}$, $b = \dfrac{3}{4}$, $p = q = \dfrac{2}{3}$

$$y_{n+1} = y_n + h\left[\frac{1}{4}f(t_n, y_n) + \frac{3}{4}f\left\{t_n + \frac{2h}{3}, y_n + \frac{2h}{3}y_n'\right\}\right] + O(h^3) \qquad ...(c) \qquad ...(5.37)$$

where y_n' is the slope at point A in fig. 5.2 $\{y_n' \equiv f(t_n, y_n)\}$. The exact expressions for the LTE are available in ref. 6, but are quite cumbersome to use. In the entire family of second order Runge-Kutta algorithms, we note that the function, f, must be evaluated at two locations to march from t_n to t_{n+1}. Also, it may be noted that these techniques are explicit, *i.e.*, knowing (t_n, y_n), one computes $f(t_n, y_n)$, then computes f at the second location which is now known [e.g., at $t_n + \dfrac{3h}{4}$, $y_n + \dfrac{3h}{4}f(t_n, y_n)$ in Ralston's method], and finally computes y_{n+1}, without any trial and error involved.

The graphical interpretation of eq. 5.37(a) is quite informative. The explicit Euler technique is used to predict point C in fig. 5.2. Then a line is drawn from point A, having a slope equal to the mean value of the slopes at points A and C. This line gives the value of y_{n+1} at t_{n+1}. It may be noted that there is a unique first order RK method, which is identical to the explicit Euler technique, in contrast to a variety of higher order RK methods which are available.

The extension to higher order algorithms is similar. There are more free parameters which can be selected somewhat arbitrarily, than the single parameter in the second order algorithm. A popular version for integrating $\dfrac{dy}{dt} = f(t, y)$ is the fourth order Runge-Kutta-Gill [7] technique. It is given by

$$y_{n+1} = y_n + h\left[ak_1 + bk_2 + ck_3 + dk_4\right] + O(h^5)$$

$$= y_n + h\left[\frac{1}{6}k_1 + \frac{1 - \dfrac{\sqrt{2}}{2}}{3}k_2 + \frac{1 + \dfrac{\sqrt{2}}{2}}{3}k_3 + \frac{1}{6}k_4\right]$$

$$k_1 = f(t_n, y_n) \equiv y_n'$$

$$k_2 = f\left(t_n + \frac{h}{2}, y_n + \frac{h}{2}k_1\right)$$

$$k_3 = f\left[t_n + \frac{h}{2}, y_n + \left(\frac{\sqrt{2}}{2} - \frac{1}{2}\right)hk_1 + \left(1 - \frac{\sqrt{2}}{2}\right)hk_2\right]$$

$$k_4 = f\left[t_n + h, y_n - \frac{\sqrt{2}}{2}hk_2 + \left(1 + \frac{\sqrt{2}}{2}\right)hk_3\right] \qquad ...(5.38)$$

Again, the expression for the LTE for this technique [6] is quite complicated; in fact, this is one of the major drawbacks of the RK algorithms. A single-step application of eq. 5.38 requires four function evaluations (which usually consume the largest amount of computer time). The popularity of the Runge-Kutta-Gill algorithm stems from the fact that it minimizes round-off (not LTE) errors, as compared to the other fourth-order algorithms [6].

Example 5.4: Use the Runge-Kutta-Gill technique to integrate the following ODE-IVP

$$\frac{dy}{dt} = 4.25713 \times 10^{-12}\, y^{2.010101}; \quad y_0 = 10^9$$

This is an empirical equation [8, 9] for the world's population, y, as a function of time, t (year). $t_0 = 0$ represents the base year, 1840 AD. Integrate this equation (by hand) for one step, using $h = 2$ yr. Also, make a computer program to predict y in 1975 using this technique. Use $h = 2$ yr in the program.

We have

$$f(t, y) = f(y) = 4.25713 \times 10^{-12}\, y^{2.010101}$$

We follow eq. 5.38 to give, sequentially

$$k_1 = 4.25713 \times 10^{-12} \times \left(10^9\right)^{2.010101} = 5.248388 \times 10^6$$

$$k_2 = 4.25713 \times 10^{-12} \times \left[10^9 + \frac{2}{2} \times 5.248388 \times 10^6\right]^{2.010101}$$

$$= 5.303904 \times 10^6$$

$$k_3 = 4.25713 \times 10^{-12} \times \left[10^9 + 0.207 \times 2 \times 5.248388 \times 10^6 + 0.293 \times 2 \times 5.303904 \times 10^6\right]^{2.010101}$$

$$= 5.304249 \times 10^6$$

$$k_4 = 4.25713 \times 10^{-12} \times \left[10^9 - 0.707 \times 2 \times 5.303904 \times 10^6 + 1.707 \times 2 \times 5.304249 \times 10^6\right]^{2.010101}$$

$$= 5.36091 \times 10^6$$

$$y_1 = 10^9 + 2\left[\frac{1}{6} \times 5.248388 + 0.09767 \times 5.303904 + 0.569 \times 5.304249 + \frac{1}{6} \times 5.36091\right] \times 10^6$$

$$= 1.010609 \times 10^9$$

A computer program with $h = 2$ yr gives the following results

Year, AD	t (yr.)	y_{RKG}
1840	0	1×10^9
1860	20	1.11735×10^9
1880	40	1.26610×10^9
1900	60	1.46085×10^9
1920	80	1.72689×10^9
1940	100	2.11228×10^9
1960	120	2.72088×10^9
1975	135	3.47452×10^9 (interpolated)
2032	192	∞ (!!)

Note that the analytical solution, $y_{exact} = [8.11131 \times 10^{-10} - 4.30013 \times 10^{-12} \, t]^{-0.99}$ predicts $y = \infty$ in 2028.63 AD (doomsday!). The numerical solution for 1975 compares well with the analytical solution of $y = 3.473$ billion which, in turn, compares well with the actual population of 3.97 billion. ∎

For the more general case where there are N dependent variables:

$$\frac{d\mathbf{y}}{dt} = \mathbf{f}(t, \mathbf{y}); \quad \mathbf{y}(t = 0) = \mathbf{y}_0 \qquad \ldots(5.39)$$

a fourth order Runge-Kutta algorithm (classical form [6]) is given by:

$$\mathbf{y}_{n+1} = \mathbf{y}_n + h\left[\frac{1}{6}\mathbf{k}_1 + \frac{1}{3}\mathbf{k}_2 + \frac{1}{3}\mathbf{k}_3 + \frac{1}{6}\mathbf{k}_4\right] + O(h^5)$$

$$\mathbf{k}_1 = \mathbf{f}\left[t_n, \mathbf{y}_n\right]$$

$$\mathbf{k}_2 = \mathbf{f}\left[t_n + \frac{h}{2}, \mathbf{y}_n + \frac{h}{2}\mathbf{k}_1\right]$$

$$\mathbf{k}_3 = \mathbf{f}\left[t_n + \frac{h}{2}, \mathbf{y}_n + \frac{h}{2}\mathbf{k}_2\right]$$

$$\mathbf{k}_4 = \mathbf{f}\left[t_n + h, \mathbf{y}_n + h\mathbf{k}_3\right] \qquad \ldots(5.40)$$

The equivalent multivariable form for the Runge-Kutta-Gill algorithm can easily be written by analogy with eq. 5.40.

Example 5.5: Integrate, by hand, the ODE-IVPs of example 5.3, using $h = 0.02$ and eq. 5.40.

The ODE-IVPs are

$$\mathbf{y}' \equiv \begin{bmatrix} y_1' \\ y_2' \end{bmatrix} = \begin{bmatrix} -100y_1 \\ 2y_1 - y_2 \end{bmatrix} = \mathbf{f}(t, \mathbf{y}) = \mathbf{f}(\mathbf{y}); \quad \begin{bmatrix} y_{1,0} \\ y_{2,0} \end{bmatrix} = \begin{bmatrix} 2 \\ 1 \end{bmatrix}$$

We have, according to eq. 5.40

$$\mathbf{k}_1 = \begin{bmatrix} -100 \times 2 \\ 2 \times 2 - 1 \end{bmatrix} = \begin{bmatrix} -200 \\ 3 \end{bmatrix}$$

$$\mathbf{k}_2 = \mathbf{f}\begin{bmatrix} 2 + 0.01 \times (-200) \\ 1 + 0.01 \times (3) \end{bmatrix} = \mathbf{f}\begin{bmatrix} 0 \\ 1.03 \end{bmatrix} = \begin{bmatrix} -100 \times 0 \\ 2 \times 0 - 1.03 \end{bmatrix} = \begin{bmatrix} 0 \\ -1.03 \end{bmatrix}$$

$$\mathbf{k}_3 = \mathbf{f}\begin{bmatrix} 2 + 0.01 \times 0 \\ 1 - 0.01 \times 1.03 \end{bmatrix} = \mathbf{f}\begin{bmatrix} 2 \\ 0.9897 \end{bmatrix} = \begin{bmatrix} -100 \times 2 \\ 2 \times 2 - 0.9897 \end{bmatrix} = \begin{bmatrix} -200 \\ 3.0103 \end{bmatrix}$$

$$\mathbf{k}_4 = \mathbf{f}\begin{bmatrix} 2 + 0.02 \times (-200) \\ 1 + 0.02 \times (3.0103) \end{bmatrix} = \mathbf{f}\begin{bmatrix} -2 \\ 1.060206 \end{bmatrix} = \begin{bmatrix} -100 \times (-2) \\ 2 \times (-2) - 1.060206 \end{bmatrix}$$

$$= \begin{bmatrix} 200 \\ -5.060206 \end{bmatrix}$$

Hence

$$\left[\begin{matrix} y_1 \\ y_2 \end{matrix}\right]_{t=0.02} = \left[\begin{matrix} 2 \\ 1 \end{matrix}\right] + \frac{0.02}{6}\left\{\left[\begin{matrix} -200 \\ 3 \end{matrix}\right] + 2\left[\begin{matrix} 0 \\ -1.03 \end{matrix}\right] + 2\left[\begin{matrix} -200 \\ 3.0103 \end{matrix}\right] + \left[\begin{matrix} 200 \\ -5.060206 \end{matrix}\right]\right\}$$

$$= \left[\begin{matrix} 0.66667 \\ 1.006334646 \end{matrix}\right]$$

which is a tremendous improvement over the results obtained in example 5.3 using the explicit Euler technique. Of course, the amount of computational effort spent is far larger in this case.   ∎

As is evident from example 5.5, higher order RK techniques involve several evaluations of the function, $f(t, y)$. These are usually complicated, and require considerable computer time. In fact, one can get an idea of the computer time required by different RK algorithms simply by looking at the number of function evaluations per step of size, h. It is easy to see that the fourth-order RK method of eq. 5.40 requires four *sets* of function calculations. The following table gives some details [4] on other RK algorithms:

No. of function evaluations per step	2	3	4	5	6	7	8	9
Best LTE*	$O(h^3)$	$O(h^4)$	$O(h^5)$	$O(h^5)$	$O(h^6)$	$O(h^7)$	$O(h^7)$	$O(h^8)$

The reason why the fourth-order RK algorithms are more popular than the fifth-order ones is obvious from this table. The advantage due to the slight improvement in the accuracy corresponding to the fifth-order RK techniques is far outweighed by the additional function calculation. It has also been found [10] for example, that often the use of the fourth-order RK method with a step size h, leads to more accurate results than, for example, the use of four applications of the explicit Euler technique with step size $\frac{h}{4}$ (the number of function calculations being four in both cases).

Another very popular RK technique is that of Fehlberg [11]. For the multivariable problem (eq. 5.39), the Runge-Kutta-Fehlberg technique gives two estimates of $\mathbf{y}_{n+1}$ using only six sets of function evaluations:

$$\mathbf{y}_{n+1} = \mathbf{y}_n + h\left[\frac{25}{216}\mathbf{k}_1 + \frac{1408}{2565}\mathbf{k}_3 + \frac{2197}{4104}\mathbf{k}_4 - \frac{1}{5}\mathbf{k}_5\right] + O(h^5) \qquad ...(a)$$

$$\overline{\mathbf{y}}_{n+1} = \mathbf{y}_n + h\left[\frac{16}{135}\mathbf{k}_1 + \frac{6656}{12825}\mathbf{k}_3 + \frac{28561}{56430}\mathbf{k}_4 - \frac{9}{50}\mathbf{k}_5 + \frac{2}{55}\mathbf{k}_6\right] + O(h^6) \quad ...(b)$$

$$\mathbf{k}_1 = \mathbf{f}\left[t_n, \mathbf{y}_n\right]$$

$$\mathbf{k}_2 = \mathbf{f}\left[t_n + \frac{h}{4}, \mathbf{y}_n + \frac{1}{4}\mathbf{k}_1\right]$$

$$\mathbf{k}_3 = \mathbf{f}\left[t_n + \frac{3h}{8}, \mathbf{y}_n + \frac{3}{32}\mathbf{k}_1 + \frac{9}{32}\mathbf{k}_2\right]$$

---

* The best LTE is the lowest LTE for all possible algorithms of a given order RK method.

$$\mathbf{k}_4 = \mathbf{f}\left[t_n + \frac{12h}{13}, \mathbf{y}_n + \frac{1932}{2197}\mathbf{k}_1 - \frac{7200}{2197}\mathbf{k}_2 + \frac{7296}{2197}\mathbf{k}_3\right]$$

$$\mathbf{k}_5 = \mathbf{f}\left[t_n + h, \mathbf{y}_n + \frac{439}{216}\mathbf{k}_1 - 8\mathbf{k}_2 + \frac{3680}{513}\mathbf{k}_3 - \frac{845}{4104}\mathbf{k}_4\right]$$

$$\mathbf{k}_6 = \mathbf{f}\left[t_n + \frac{h}{2}, \mathbf{y}_n - \frac{8}{27}\mathbf{k}_1 + 2\mathbf{k}_2 - \frac{3544}{2565}\mathbf{k}_3 + \frac{1859}{4104}\mathbf{k}_4 - \frac{11}{40}\mathbf{k}_5\right] \qquad \dots(5.41)$$

The technique uses some common locations for the fourth and sixth order RK estimates, and thus saves on time (if some of the points were not chosen common to both, ten function evaluations would have been required). *Both* values of $\mathbf{y}_{n+1}$, as given by eqs. 5.41 a and b, are evaluated at any step, and then a numerical estimate of the error is made using these values (see sec. 5.8 for details). If the estimated error is less than the desired value, the value of h used in the next stage is increased. If, however, the error exceeds the desired value, a lower value of h is used and the calculation repeated. Sec. 5.8 provides a detailed discussion of techniques for step-size control to meet desired tolerances.

5.7 SEMI-IMPLICIT RUNGE-KUTTA TECHNIQUES

The explicit RK techniques can be written in the following general form

$$\mathbf{y}_{n+1} = \mathbf{y}_n + h\sum_{i=1}^{r} w_i \mathbf{k}_i \qquad \dots(a)$$

$$\mathbf{k}_i = \mathbf{f}\left(t_n + b_i h, \mathbf{y}_n + \sum_{j=1}^{i-1} a_{ij} h\,\mathbf{k}_j\right) \qquad \dots(b) \qquad \dots(5.42)$$

where r, w_i, b_i and a_{ij} are constants. A sequential computation of k_i is made. The Runge-Kutta-Gill technique (eq. 5.38) can be rewritten concisely using this form as [6]

	b_i	$j = 1$	$j = 2$	$j = 3$	$j = 4$
$i = 1$	0	0	0	0	$-$
$i = 2$	$\dfrac{1}{2}$	$\dfrac{1}{2}$	0	0	$-$
$i = 3$	$\dfrac{1}{2}$	$\dfrac{\sqrt{2}}{2} - \dfrac{1}{2}$	$1 - \dfrac{\sqrt{2}}{2}$	0	$-$
$i = 4$	1	0	$-\dfrac{\sqrt{2}}{2}$	$1 + \dfrac{\sqrt{2}}{2}$	$-$
$b_i \diagdown w_j$		$\dfrac{1}{6}$	$\dfrac{1 - \dfrac{\sqrt{2}}{2}}{3}$	$\dfrac{1 + \dfrac{\sqrt{2}}{2}}{3}$	$\dfrac{1}{6}$

$$\dots(5.43)$$

where the element in the box are a_{ij}.

A variety of techniques have been developed, known as *semi-implicit RK methods* [12–15] which have an extra term in the summation of eq. 5.42(*b*). These are written (slightly differently) as

$$\mathbf{y}_{n+1} = \mathbf{y}_n + \sum_{i=1}^{r} w_i \mathbf{k}_i$$

$$\mathbf{k}_i = h\mathbf{f}\left(t_n + b_i h, \mathbf{y}_n + \sum_{j=1}^{i} a_{ij} \mathbf{k}_j \right) \qquad \text{...(5.44)}$$

The $\mathbf{k}_i$, then, need to be computed iteratively (since they also occur on the right-hand-side of the equation). This increases the amount of the computations, but has advantages in certain cases of importance, as discussed in secs. 5.9 and 5.10. These techniques are discussed for the case when the ODE-IVPs are as given in eq. 5.3, *i.e.*, when there is no explicit dependence of the function $\mathbf{f}$ on t.

Rosenbrock [16] expanded the function

$$\mathbf{k}_i = h\mathbf{f}\left(\mathbf{y}_n + \sum_{j=1}^{i} a_{ij} \mathbf{k}_j \right) \qquad \text{...(5.45)}$$

about $\left(\mathbf{y}_n + \sum_{j=1}^{i-1} a_{ij} \mathbf{k}_j \right)$ using the multivariable Taylor series [see eq. (*c*) in example 3.7]

$$\mathbf{f}\left[\left(\mathbf{y}_n + \sum_{j=1}^{i-1} a_{ij} \mathbf{k}_j \right) + a_{ij} \mathbf{k}_j \right] = \mathbf{f}\left(\mathbf{y}_n + \sum_{j=1}^{i-1} a_{ij} \mathbf{k}_j \right) + a_{ii} \mathbf{A}\left(\underline{\xi}_i \right) \mathbf{k}_i \qquad \text{...(5.46)}$$

where $\mathbf{A}\left(\underline{\xi}_i \right)$ is the Jacobian of f at location $\underline{\xi}_i$ lying in $\left[\mathbf{y}_n + \sum_{j=1}^{i-1} a_{ij} \mathbf{k}_j, \mathbf{y}_n + \sum_{j=1}^{i} a_{ij} \mathbf{k}_j \right]$. eqs. 5.45 and 5.46 lead to

$$\mathbf{k}_i = h\mathbf{f}\left[\mathbf{y}_n + \sum_{j=1}^{i-1} a_{ij} \mathbf{k}_j \right] + a_{ii} h\mathbf{A}\left(\underline{\xi}_i \right) \mathbf{k}_i \qquad \text{...(5.47)}$$

or

$$\mathbf{k}_i = h\left\{ \mathbf{I} - a_{ii} h\mathbf{A}\left(\underline{\xi}_i \right) \right\}^{-1} \mathbf{f}\left[\mathbf{y}_n + \sum_{j=1}^{i-1} a_{ij} \mathbf{k}_j \right] \qquad \text{...(5.48)}$$

where $\mathbf{I}$ is an $N \times N$ unit (diagonal) matrix (N is the number of variables in $\mathbf{y}$). Some simplified forms of eq. 5.48 have been suggested by different workers. These are expanded using the Taylor series and binomial expansions, and compared to a Taylor series expansion of $\mathbf{y}_{n+1}$ around $\mathbf{y}_n$ to give equations for the various coefficients (some degrees of freedom exist here too, as in the explicit RK methods). A particularly efficient technique is *Michelsen's* [13] *third-order method*:

$$\mathbf{y}_{n+1} = \mathbf{y}_n + \sum_{i=1}^{3} w_i \mathbf{k}_i + O\left(h^4 \right)$$

$$\mathbf{k}_1 = h\left[\mathbf{I} - a_1 h \mathbf{A}(\mathbf{y}_n)\right]^{-1} \mathbf{f}(\mathbf{y}_n)$$

$$\mathbf{k}_2 = h\left[\mathbf{I} - a_1 h \mathbf{A}(\mathbf{y}_n)\right]^{-1} \mathbf{f}(\mathbf{y}_n + b_2 \mathbf{k}_1)$$

$$\mathbf{k}_3 = \left[\mathbf{I} - a_1 h \mathbf{A}(\mathbf{y}_n)\right]^{-1} (b_{31}\mathbf{k}_1 + b_{32}\mathbf{k}_2)$$

$$w_1 = 1.0376095, \quad w_2 = 0.8349303 \quad w_3 = 1.0$$

$$a_1 = 0.43586659 \quad b_2 = 0.75$$

$$b_{31} = -0.6302021, \quad b_{32} = -0.2423378 \qquad \qquad \dots (5.49)$$

Note the use of the Jacobian at the known location, $\mathbf{y}_n$. Also note the use of the same coefficient, a_{ii}, in the equation for $\mathbf{k}_1$, $\mathbf{k}_2$ and $\mathbf{k}_3$. This enables one to solve $\mathbf{k}_1$, $\mathbf{k}_2$ and $\mathbf{k}_3$ using a single LU decomp of $\mathbf{I} - a_1 h \mathbf{A}(\mathbf{y}_n)$, and performing three sets of fore-and-aft sweeps with different right-hand-sides (thus, the matrix need not be inverted). Also, the different form for $\mathbf{k}_3$ in eq. 5.49 than in eq. 5.48 is to be noted.

Michelsen's method is an improvement over the techniques developed by Rosenbrock [16] and Caillaud and Padmanabhan [15]. Prokopakis and Seider [12] have provided an excellent review of the various semi-implicit RK techniques, and have also presented a second-order technique with *adjustable* coefficients to improve the accuracy.

Example 5.6: Simplify Michelsen's technique for the single ODE-IVP

$$\frac{dy}{dt} = f(y); \quad y(t = 0) = y_0$$

The algorithm can easily be written as

$$y_{n+1} = y_n + w_1 k_1 + w_2 k_2 + w_3 k_3 + O(h^4)$$

$$k_1 = \frac{hf(y_n)}{1 - a_1 h f'(y_n)}$$

$$k_2 = \frac{hf(y_n + b_2 k_1)}{1 - a_1 h f'(y_n)}$$

$$k_3 = \frac{b_{31} k_1 + b_{32} k_2}{1 - a_1 h f'(y_n)}$$

Note that there is no trial and error involved, in contrast to implicit techniques of the Adams-Moulton family. This is why these techniques are referred to as semi-implicit. ∎

5.8 STEP-SIZE CONTROL AND ESTIMATES OF ERROR

While integrating ODE-IVPs, we usually specify an error criterion, ε, and adjust the step size, h_n, used to obtain $\mathbf{y}_{n+1}$ from $\mathbf{y}_n$ to satisfy this requirement. Several techniques have been used, and two are being described here. The first technique proceeds along the lines discussed in sec. 4.9, and has been used by Michelsen [13], and several other workers. Values of $\mathbf{y}_{n+1}$ are obtained, once with a single step size of

h_n, and then with two steps, each of size $\dfrac{h_n}{2}$. These values of $\mathbf{y}_{n+1}$ so obtained can be represented by $\mathbf{y}_{n+1}\,(h_n)$ and $\mathbf{y}_{n+1}\!\left(\dfrac{h_n}{2}\right)$, respectively. Obviously, if h_n is small enough, these two estimates will be identical. Their difference,

$$\mathbf{E}_n \equiv \mathbf{y}_{n+1}\!\left(\frac{h_n}{2}\right) - \mathbf{y}_{n+1}\,(h_n) \qquad \qquad ...(5.50)$$

gives an idea of the error. This could be compared to the permissible error, ε (ε could also depend on the variable, y_i), to give an error parameter:

$$q \equiv \underset{i}{\text{Max}}\left|\frac{E_{n,\,i}}{\varepsilon}\right| \qquad \qquad ...(5.51)$$

where the maximum over all the N variables, y_i, is obtained. Obviously, if $q > 1$, $\mathbf{y}_{n+1}$ is unacceptable, and the computations must be repeated with smaller values of the step size, $\dfrac{h_n}{2}$ and $\dfrac{h_n}{4}$ [only the latter needs to be computed, since $\mathbf{y}_{n+1}\!\left(\dfrac{h_n}{2}\right)$ has already been evaluated]. The procedure of halving the step size is continued till $q < 1$.

If the error parameter, however, is found to be less than unity, the results, $\mathbf{y}_{n+1}\,(h_n)$ and $\mathbf{y}_{n+1}\!\left(\dfrac{h_n}{2}\right)$, are used to generate an even better estimate using the extrapolation technique of Richardson and Gaunt (eq. 4.90). The step size, h_{n+1}, to be used in the *next* step (to generate $\mathbf{y}_{n+2}$) can be then increased to speed-up the computations while still maintaining the errors within the specified bound. The error using Michelsen's scheme can be *approximated* (for the worst variable) by

$$E_n \sim \text{C}h_n^4$$

$$E_{n+1} \sim \text{C}h_{n+1}^4 \qquad \qquad ...(5.52)$$

(this is an approximation because the coefficient of h^4 would really be different for the two steps). Since we would like $E_{n+1} \cong \varepsilon$, and since $E_n \sim q\,\varepsilon$ (eq. 5.51), we have

$$\left(\frac{h_{n+1}}{h_n}\right)^4 \sim \left(\frac{E_{n+1}}{E_n}\right) \sim \frac{1}{q} \qquad \qquad ...(5.53)$$

or

$$h_{n+1} \cong h_n \left(\frac{1}{q}\right)^{\frac{1}{4}} \qquad \qquad ...(5.54)$$

Since so many approximations have been made, and since we would not like to choose h_{n+1} too large (and then halve it to come within the error tolerance in the next step), we like to be conservative in increasing the step size. Michelsen suggests that we use

$$h_{n+1} = h_n \text{Min} \left\{ \frac{1}{\sqrt{2}} \left(\frac{1}{q} \right)^{\frac{1}{4}}, 3 \right\} \qquad \qquad ...(5.55)$$

i.e., we increase h_{n+1} to at most three times h_n, even if we could increase it by a larger factor. The term $\frac{1}{\sqrt{2}}$ is another safety factor. A similar procedure can be written for other integration techniques.

There is another method for step size adaptation which is quite commonly used. It is illustrated for a single dependent variable case with respect to the R-K-Fehlberg (RKF) technique. Starting with a value of y_n and h_n, two estimates, $y_{n+1} \left[O\left(h_n^5 \right) \right]$ and $\bar{y}_{n+1} \left[O\left(h_n^6 \right) \right]$, are obtained using the fourth and sixth order equations (eqs. 5.41 a and b). The error of y_{n+1} (per unit step size) with respect to the "true" value, $y\left(t_{n+1} \right)$ can be written as

$$E_n \equiv \underbrace{\frac{y\left(t_{n+1} \right) - y_{n+1}}{h_n}}_{O\left(h_n^4 \right)} = \underbrace{\frac{y\left(t_{n+1} \right) - \bar{y}_{n+1}}{h_n}}_{O\left(h_n^5 \right)} + \underbrace{\left[\frac{\bar{y}_{n+1} - y_{n+1}}{h_n} \right]}_{O\left(h_n^r \right)} \qquad ...(5.56)$$

Thus, the last term (in brackets) on the right-hand-side of eq. 5.56 must be of $O\left(h_n^4 \right)$, *i.e.*, $r = 4$, and can give a good idea of the error for the fourth-order RKF formula:

$$E_n \equiv \frac{y\left(t_{n+1} \right) - y_{n+1}}{h_n} \cong \frac{\bar{y}_{n+1} - y_{n+1}}{h_n} \qquad \qquad ...(5.57)$$

The two numerical estimates $\bar{y}_{n+1}$ and y_{n+1} can, thus, be used to estimate E_n. If $| E_n |$ so estimated exceeds the tolerance, ε, the calculations are rejected, and a new, smaller value, $h_{n, new}$, is used to reevaluate y_{n+1}. This is obtained as follows. Using eq. 5.52 we have, with $| E_{n, new} | = \varepsilon$ and eq. 5.57,

$$|E_n| \sim Ch_n^4$$

$$|E_{n, new}| \sim Ch_{n, new}^4$$

therefore
$$h_{n, new} = h_n \left[\left| \frac{E_{n, new}}{E_n} \right| \right]^{\frac{1}{4}} = h_n \left[\frac{\varepsilon h_n}{|\bar{y}_{n+1} - y_{n+1}|} \right]^{\frac{1}{4}} \qquad ...(5.58)$$

The use of $h_{n, new}$ should, hopefully, lead to estimates of y_{n+1} and $\bar{y}_{n+1}$ which satisfy the error requirements. In fact, we use a more conservative estimate of $h_{n, new}$:

$$h_{n, new} = 0.84 h_n \left[\frac{\varepsilon h_n}{|\bar{y}_{n+1} - y_{n+1}|} \right]^{\frac{1}{4}} \qquad \qquad ...(5.59)$$

We must note that the tolerance, ε used in Michelsen's example and that in the RKF technique, differ slightly in terms of interpretation.

If $|E_n|$ computed using eq. 5.57 is less than the tolerance, the better value of $O(h_n^6)$ is accepted, and the step size, h_{n+1}, required for computing y_{n+2} is estimated using

$$h_{n+1} = \text{Min} \left\{ 0.84 h_n \left[\frac{\varepsilon h_n}{\left| \bar{y}_{n+1} - y_{n+1} \right|} \right]^{\frac{1}{4}}, 4 h_n \right\} \qquad \ldots (5.60)$$

This leads to higher values of h_{n+1} so that computations are speeded up without sacrificing accuracy.

5.9 STABILITY OF ALGORITHMS

It was mentioned earlier that implicit techniques have certain advantages over explicit methods for integrating ODE-IVPs. This is illustrated with respect to the multistep algorithm. The multistep algorithm given in eq. 5.23 can be applied to the single equation (which has inherently bounded solutions for negative λs):

$$\frac{dy}{dt} = \lambda y \qquad \ldots (5.61)$$

to give (for $\alpha_0 = 0$)

$$\left(-1 + h\lambda\beta_0 \right) y_{n+1} + \left(\alpha_1 + h\lambda\beta_1 \right) y_n + \left(\alpha_2 + h\lambda\beta_2 \right) y_{n-1} + \ldots + \left(\alpha_k + h\lambda\beta_k \right) y_{n-k+1} = 0 \qquad \ldots (5.62)$$

The solution of this *difference equation* is discussed in detail in the text by Mickley, Sherwood and Reid [18], and is given by

$$y_{n+1} = C_1 \mu_1^{n+1} + C_2 \mu_2^{n+1} + \ldots + C_k \mu_k^{n+1} \qquad \ldots (5.63)$$

where μ_1, μ_2, ..., μ_k are the k roots (constants) of the following (polynomial) equation

$$\left(-1 + h\lambda\beta_0 \right) \mu^k + \left(\alpha_1 + h\lambda\beta_1 \right) \mu^{k-1} + \left(\alpha_2 + h\lambda\beta_2 \right) \mu^{k-2} + \ldots + \left(\alpha_k + h\lambda\beta_k \right) = 0 \qquad \ldots (5.64)$$

eq. 5.64 is known as the *characteristic equation* of the multistep algorithm. This equation is obtained by substituting $y_{n+1} = C\mu^{n+1}$, $y_n = C\mu^n$, $y_{n-1} = C\mu^{n-1}$, ..., $y_{n-k+1} = C\mu^{n-k+1}$ into eq. 5.62 and simplifying. *It is seen from eq. 5.63 that several numerical solutions for y_{n+1} exist, even though the ODE-IVP has a single analytical solution.* It turns out that only *one* of these solutions, say, $y_{n+1} = C_1\mu_1^{n+1}$, is the correct numerical approximation to the ODE-IVP in eq. 5.61. All other solutions corresponding to μ_2, μ_3, ..., μ_k in eq. 5.63 are spurious. Thus, we observe that use of the multistep algorithm could give not only the correct numerical approximation to the solution, but can also give *additional* solutions which are spurious. It is obviously necessary to ensure that the spurious terms do not overwhelm the correct one. Note that the principal root, μ_1, is a function of $h\lambda$, β_0, β_1, ..., β_k, α_1, α_2, ..., α_k (as are the other roots, too), since it is a solution of eq. 5.64, and so is technique-dependent. As long as we have

$$\left| \mu_1 \right| > \left| \mu_i \right|; \ i = 2, 3, \ldots, k \qquad \ldots (5.65)$$

we can see from eq. 5.63 that the spurious roots will die out as $n \to \infty$ (*i.e.*, as t increases). If this is not so, the spurious roots will gradually dominate and our numerical solution will be erroneous. In fact, these will have no relationship to the solution of the ODE-IVP. This is not desirable, and we must carefully avoid it, if possible. Fortunately, there are several techniques whose characteristic equation has a single root only and spurious roots pose no problem.

Example 5.7: Study the stability of the following algorithm (mid-point rule)

$$y_{n+1} = y_{n-1} + 2hy_n'$$

When applied to $\dfrac{dy}{dt} = \lambda y$, we obtain $y_{n+1} = y_{n-1} + 2h\lambda y_n$, which, on using $y_{n+1} = C\mu^{n+1}$, $y_n = C\mu^n$, $y_{n-1} = C\mu^{n-1}$, gives

$$\mu^2 - 2h\lambda\mu - 1 = 0$$

This gives the two roots as

$$\mu_1 = h\lambda + \sqrt{1 + h^2\lambda^2}$$

$$\mu_2 = h\lambda - \sqrt{1 + h^2\lambda^2}$$

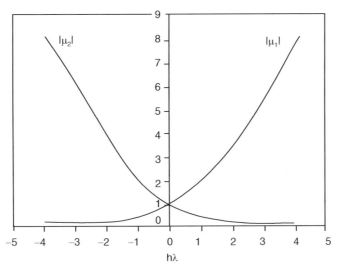

Fig. 5.3 The two roots of the characteristic equation for example 5.7.

The solutions of the difference equation are, thus,

$$y_{n+1} = C_1\mu_1^{n+1} + C_2\mu_2^{n+1}$$

It can easily be seen that the first of these, μ_1, is such the μ_1^n is an approximation to the exact solution, $y_n = C_2 e^{nh\lambda}$ (of the ODE-IVP, $y' = \lambda y$), while the second one has no relationship to it at all. μ_1, is thus, the principal root. fig. 5.3 shows that for $h\lambda < 0$,

$$\left|\mu_1\right| < 1$$

$$\left|\mu_2\right| > 1$$

while for $h\lambda > 0$, $\left|\mu_1\right| > \left|\mu_2\right|$. Thus, in this technique, the spurious roots will die out as $t \to \infty$ provided $\lambda > 0$, but would overpower the correct root if $\lambda < 0$ (when the ODE-IVP is inherently stable!). ■

It was observed in example 5.7 that the principal root, μ_1, should be an approximation to $e^{h\lambda}$. Indeed, it can be seen that there is an intimate relationship between the principal roots corresponding to several algorithms, and the various Padé approximations of $e^{h\lambda}$ (see table 4.1).

Example 5.8: Obtain the roots of the characteristic equation for the explicit and implicit Euler techniques, and for the Crank-Nicholson method. Check if these roots are Padé approximations of $e^{h\lambda}$. Also, study the principal root of eq. 5.37(*a*), a second order RK technique (improved Euler method).

Explicit Euler: $y_{n+1} = y_n + hy'_n$

Characteristic equation: $\mu - (1 + h\lambda) = 0$

There is only one principal root, $\mu_1 = 1 + h\lambda$, which is observed to be an approximation of $e^{h\lambda}$. The numerical solution of $y' = \lambda y$ using this technique will be obtained as $y_n = C_1(1 + h\lambda)^n$.

Implicit Euler: $y_{n+1} = y_n + hy'_{n+1}$

Characteristic equation: $1 - \mu + h\lambda\mu = 0$

or

$$\mu = \mu_1 = \frac{1}{1 - h\lambda}$$

Crank-Nicholson: $y_{n+1} = y_n + \dfrac{h}{2}(y'_{n+1} + y'_n)$

The characteristic equation gives a single root,

$$\mu_1 = \frac{1 + \dfrac{h\lambda}{2}}{1 - \dfrac{h\lambda}{2}}$$

In all these three cases, we obtain only one (principal) root. Also, μ_1 is indeed seen to be a Padé approximation (table 4.1) of $e^{h\lambda}$ in all these cases.

The characteristic equation for the improved Euler method (2nd order RK, eq. 5.37(*a*)) also leads to a single (principal) root (see prob. 5.6)

$$\mu_1 = 1 + h\lambda + \frac{1}{2}h^2\lambda^2$$

which is the ($n = 2$, $m = 0$) Padé approximation of $e^{h\lambda}$ (table 4.1)   ∎

It is observed that in the above example, the four techniques studied have no spurious roots which could have given wrong results. However, there is another reason, called *numerical instability*, which can give solutions which are meaningless. This is because of the propagation of the errors as t increases. To illustrate this, we apply the integration algorithm to the ODE-IVP: $\dfrac{dy}{dt} = \lambda y$; $y(0) = y_0$. The correct numerical solution (corresponding to the principal root, if there are several roots of the characteristic equation), $y_{n+1} = C_1\mu_1^{n+1}$, can be written in terms of y_n and y_0 as

$$y_{n+1} = \mu_1(C_1\mu_1^n) = \mu_1 y_n = \mu_1^{n+1} y_0 \qquad \ldots(5.66)$$

If there is a machine error (due to roundoff), e_0, in the value, y_0, read into a computer, we shall obtain

$$y_{n+1} = \mu_1^{n+1}(y_0 \mp e_0) \qquad \ldots(5.67)$$

assuming that no *other* error gets introduced during the computation of y_{n+1}. The error, as compared to the analytical solution, $y_{n+1} = y_0 e^{(n+1)h\lambda}$, is then

$$E_{n+1} = \left[e^{(n+1)h\lambda} - \mu_1^{n+1} \right] y_0 \pm \mu_1^{n+1} e_0 \qquad \ldots(5.68)$$

The term in brackets will not blow up since we have already stated that μ_1 must be an approximation of $e^{h\lambda}$. In fact, this term gives us an idea of the truncation error and also suggests that μ_1 must be a (Padé) approximation of $e^{h\lambda}$. The second term, $\mu_1^{n+1} e_0$, gives an idea of how the *initial* error gets *propagated* by the algorithm as t increases. Obviously, if $|\mu_1| < 1$, the error propagation will be unimportant. Hence, *numerical* stability of the integration algorithm requires that

$$|\mu_1| < 1 \qquad \ldots(5.69)$$

so that an error introduced at any stage dies out as t increases.

In general, λ in eq. 5.61 could be a complex number, but the above derivation still applies. One could, thus, plot the envelope defined by eq. 5.69 on the Argand diagram with the real and imaginary parts of $h\lambda$ as the axes. This plot could be used to find values of h which would give *stable* numerical results, as illustrated in the following example.

Example 5.9: Obtain the stability envelopes for the (*a*) explicit (*b*) implicit Euler and (*c*) Crank-Nicholson techniques.

(*a*) *Explicit Euler:* Example 5.8 and eq. 5.69 give the stability envelope as
$$| \mu_1 | = | 1 + h\lambda | < 1$$

This plots as a circle in the Argand diagram, as shown in fig. 5.4. If one were to use this algorithm to solve, say, $y' = -3y$, i.e., $\lambda = -3$, one should use $h \leq \dfrac{2}{3}$ to get stable numerical solutions, otherwise Re $(h\lambda) < -2$ and we will lie in the unstable region in fig. 5.4. If values of $h > \dfrac{2}{3} = 2/|\text{Re }\lambda|$ are used

Numerical and Exact Results for $y' = -3y$, $y_0 = 1$ using the Explicit Euler Technique

t	y_{exact}	y_{Euler}			
		$h = 0.025$	$h = 0.25$	$h = 0.5$	$h = 0.8$
0	1.00000	1.00000	1.00000	1.00000	1.00000
0.25	0.47237	0.45858	0.25000	–	–
0.50	0.22313	0.21030	0.062500	−0.50000	–
0.75	0.10540	0.096439	0.015625	–	–
0.80	0.090718	–	–	–	−1.40000
1.00	0.049787	0.044225	0.0039063	0.25000	–
1.25	0.023518	0.020281	0.00097656	–	–
1.50	0.011109	0.0093004	0.00024414	−0.12500	–
1.60	0.0082297	–	–	–	1.96000
1.75	0.0052475	0.0042650	0.000061035	–	–
2.00	0.0024788	0.0019559	0.000015259	0.062500	–
2.40	7.46586×10^{-4}	–	–	–	−2.74400
3.20	6.7729×10^{-5}	–	–	–	3.84160
4.00	6.144×10^{-6}	3.825×10^{-6}	0	0.0039063	−5.37824
4.80	5.57×10^{-7}	–	–	–	7.52954

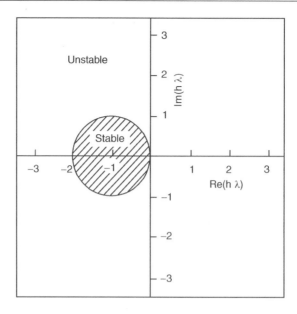

Fig. 5.4 Stability envelope for the explicit Euler technique

on a computer, errors magnify in time, and the solutions obtained are no good as observed from the numerical results given for $h = 0.8$.

Note that the accuracy worsens as h increases, but even with h as large as 0.25, the results show correct trends and do not blow up to infinity.

(b) *Implicit Euler*: Again, example 5.8 and eq. 5.69 give the stability condition as

$$|\mu_1| = \left|\frac{1}{1 - h\lambda}\right| < 1$$

It is observed that the entire left hand plane, $Re(h\lambda) < 0$, satisfies this equation (see fig. 5.5). In fact, all regions outside the circle $|1 - h\lambda| > 1$ satisfy this equation. Such techniques are called *A-stable* (algorithms having more than one root of the characteristic equation are said to be *A-stable* if *all* solutions, μ_i^n, of eq. 5.61 tend to zero as $t \to \infty$). One can obviously choose any (even large) value of h and integrate the ODE (which has bounded solutions if $Re \lambda < 0$), without errors propagating as t increases. Of course, the larger the value of h, the less accurate are the numerical solutions. It should now be clear why the implicit Euler technique is superior to the explicit form, even though both are accurate to $O(h^2)$. The price to be paid is the extra cost of iterative computation of the nonlinear algebraic equation at *each step*, as in example 5.2.

(c) *Crank-Nicholson*: The stability envelope can easily be written (μ_1 from example 5.8) as

$$|\mu_1| = \left|\frac{\left|1 + \dfrac{h\lambda}{2}\right|}{\left|1 - \dfrac{h\lambda}{2}\right|}\right| < 1$$

Again, this is satisfied for $Re(h\lambda) < 0$, and so this technique, too, is A-stable (see fig. 5.5). It is accurate to $O(h^3)$ and so is preferred over the implicit Euler method. ∎

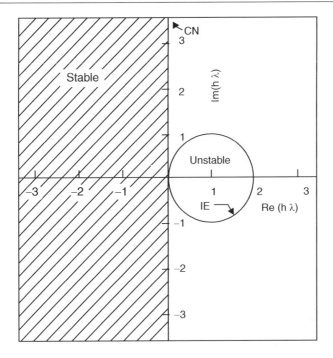

Fig. 5.5 Stability envelope of the implicit Euler (IE) technique (region inside circle represents unstable region). Also shown is the envelope for the Crank-Nicholson (CN) technique (the right half of the diagram is unstable). Shaded region is the stable-region for A-stable techniques.

Stability envelopes are available in texts [6, 19] for most techniques. Gear [19] shows the stability envelopes of the explicit Adams-Bashforth and the implicit Adams-Moulton techniques of different orders (see fig. 5.6). It is found that even enough the 1st and 2nd order Adams-Moulton techniques (implicit Euler and Crank Nicholson) are A-stable, higher order techniques of this family have restricted

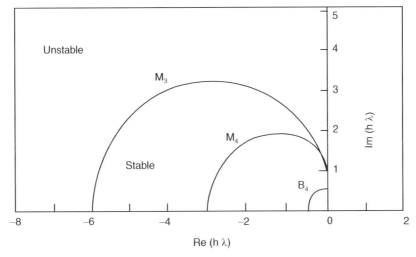

Fig. 5.6 Stability envelopes [19] for the fourth order Adams-Bashforth (B_4), and third (M_3) and fourth order (M_4) Adams-Moulton techniques. Only top part of Argand diagram shown due to symmetry about the real axis (see figs. 5.4 and 5.5 for complete diagram of other techniques).

regions of stability. These regions are larger than those of the Adams-Bashforth family of the same order.

Figure 5.7 shows some results for the explicit Runge-Kutta algorithms [6]. It is observed [6] that all forms of the RK technique of a given order have identical stability envelopes, provided the order ≤ 4. The envelope for the fifth order RK technique shown in fig. 5.7 is for a particular version known as the Nystron form [6]. As in example 5.9(a), we can easily find maximum values of h for which we will obtain meaningful numerical results while integrating the simple ODE-IVP, $y' = \lambda y;\ y(0) = y_0$.

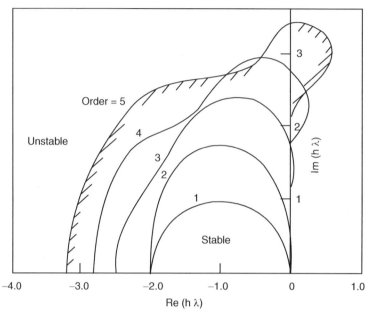

Fig. 5.7 Stability envelopes for the explicit R-K algorithms [6] of different orders. Only upper half of the Argand diagram shown, due to symmetry about the real axis. Note that the 1st order RK method is identical to the explicit Euler technique and their envelopes are the same [reprinted from ref. 6, copyright 1971, with permission from Academic Press Inc., Orlando, FL, USA]

It is observed that the explicit RK techniques have better stability characteristics than the explicit Euler technique. On the other hand, the semi-implicit RK methods, like Michelsen's technique (eq. 5.49) are found to be A-stable (see prob. 5.11).

Figure 5.8 shows stability envelopes [20] of a few Adams predictor-corrector (PC[1]) techniques of different orders. In these, the order of the explicit Adams-Bashforth predictor and that of the implicit Adams Moulton corrector are the same. It is observed that as the accuracy of these techniques improves, the stability worsens. This is in sharp contrast to the behaviour of the explicit RK algorithms where increasing the order leads to improvements in accuracy as well as stability.

The reason why we study the stability envelopes of integration algorithms using the simple ODE, $y' = \lambda y$, is that the conclusions obtained are general, and can be applied to the multivariable case, $\mathbf{y}' = \mathbf{f}(\mathbf{y})$ as well. We can linearize the multivariable equation using Taylor series to give

$$\mathbf{y}' = \mathbf{f}(\mathbf{y}) = \mathbf{f}(\mathbf{y}_n) + \mathbf{A}_n (\mathbf{y} - \mathbf{y}_n) \equiv \mathbf{A}_n \mathbf{y} + \mathbf{S}_n \qquad \ldots(5.70)$$

where $\mathbf{A}_n$ is the Jacobian matrix evaluated at time, t_n, and $\mathbf{S}_n = \mathbf{f}(\mathbf{y}_n) - \mathbf{A}_n \mathbf{y}_n$.

The multivariable Padé approximations of $\exp(h\,\mathbf{A}_n)$ (eq. 4.51) characterize the various numerical integration algorithms (see prob. 5.12). The requirement for stability for any algorithm applied to

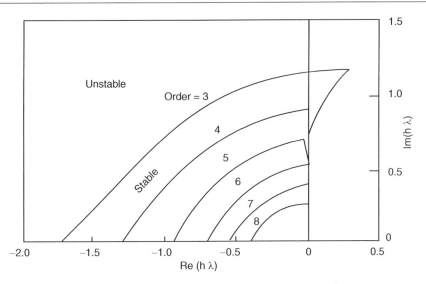

Fig. 5.8 Stability envelopes [6, 20] for the explicit Adams predictor-corrector (PC[1]) techniques of different orders. Upper half of the Argand diagram is shown due to symmetry about the real axis, as in figs. 5.6 and 5.7. The orders of the explicit and implicit versions used for any PC[1] set are the same.

eq. 5.70 can be shown to be (see pp. 40–42 in Ref. 3, for derivation):

$$\left|\mu_1\left(h\lambda_i\right)\right| < 1 \text{ for all } i = 1, 2, ..., N \qquad \qquad ...(5.71)$$

where λ_i are the N eigenvalues of the Jacobian, $\mathbf{A}_n$, evaluated at t_n and μ_1 is the principal root for the single (dependent) variable problem already discussed earlier in this section. Thus, figs. 5.4–5.7 can easily be used to find an appropriate value of h required by the various algorithms, when used in their more general, multidimensional forms. If the eigenvalues of $\mathbf{A}_n$ are real and satisfy $\lambda_i < 0$, so that the solutions, y_i (t), are bounded, then eq. 5.71 (plotted for *any* λ_i in figs. 5.4–5.7) leads to

$$h\left|\lambda_i\right|_{\max} < \left|p\right| \qquad \qquad ...(5.72)$$

In eq. 5.72, $|p|$ is the intercept of the stability envelope on the real axis of the Argand plot (*e.g.*, $|p| = 2$ for the explicit Euler technique, as shown in fig. 5.4). Since the Jacobian, $\mathbf{A}_n$, changes with time (unless eq. 5.1 is linear), this means that one must take h to be sufficiently small to ensure that eq. 5.72 is satisfied over the *entire* time domain, *i.e.*, $|\lambda_i|_{\max}$ should be the *largest value from among the N eigenvalues* in the *entire time domain* over which integration is to be carried out. Extension to the case of complex λ_i is quite easy. The choice of h should be such that $h\lambda_i$ lies in the stable region of the stability diagram for all i and t of interest.[*]

Example 5.10: Consider the following set of coupled ODE-IVPs:

$$\frac{dy_1}{dt} = -0.2y_1 + 0.2y_2 = f_1\left(t, \mathbf{y}\right) \qquad \qquad y_1(0) = 0$$

---

[*] It may be mentioned that the above method based on *local* linearization is not *always* valid, and that the eigenvalues of the 'frozen' Jacobian need not give valid information about error propagation (see K. Dekker and J.G. Verwer, *Stability of Runge-Kutta Methods for Stiff Nonlinear Differential Equations,* North Holland, Amsterdam, 1984, p. 12). A more rigorous theory of error-propagation in nonlinear ODE-IVPs is required.

$$\frac{dy_2}{dt} = 10y_1 - (60 + 0.125t) y_2 + 0.124t = f_2(t, \mathbf{y}) \qquad\qquad y_2(0) = 0$$

(for which analytical solutions are not available). We would like to integrate these equations from $t = 0$ to $t = 10$, using the 4th order explicit RK technique.

(a) Obtain the appropriate eigenvalues at $t = 0, 1, 5$ and 10 analytically.

(b) Suggest the largest value of h for which you expect stable solutions. You would use an h lower than that above for accuracy.

The Jacobian, $\mathbf{A}$, is given by

$$\mathbf{A} = \begin{bmatrix} \dfrac{\partial f_1}{\partial y_1} & \dfrac{\partial f_1}{\partial y_2} \\[2mm] \dfrac{\partial f_2}{\partial y_1} & \dfrac{\partial f_2}{\partial y_2} \end{bmatrix} = \begin{bmatrix} -0.2 & 0.2 \\ 10 & -(60 + 0.125t) \end{bmatrix}$$

The eigenvalues of $\mathbf{A}$ can be obtained using

$$\begin{vmatrix} -0.2 - \lambda & 0.2 \\ 10 & -60 - 0.125t - \lambda \end{vmatrix} = 0$$

This gives

$$\lambda_{1,2} = -(30.1 + 0.625t) \pm \left[895.985 + 3.90625 \times 10^{-3} t^2 + 3.7625t \right]^{\frac{1}{2}}$$

Values of $\lambda_{1,2}$ at different t are given by

t	λ_1	λ_2
0	−60.033	−0.167
1	−60.223	−0.167
5	−60.66	−0.1653
10	−61.286	−0.164

We, thus, see that

(a) the ODEs are inherently stable since Re $(\lambda_i) < 0$

(b) the maximum value of $|\lambda|$ is 61.286 for the domain of interest. From fig. 5.7, *any* 4th order RK technique should satisfy

$$h \,|\, \mathrm{Re}\, \lambda_i |_{\max} < 2.8$$

Thus, $h < 2.8/61.286 = 0.046$ for stability.   ∎

A numerical method for integrating ODE-IVPs is referred to as *strongly A-stable* [6, 12] if $|\mu_1| \to 0$ as $h\,|\, \mathrm{Re}\, \lambda_i| \to \infty$. While A-stability assures that errors do not propagate as t increases, strong A-stability assures that the solution of the difference equation approaches the true solution as the step size is increased. Michelsen's algorithm, for example, is strongly A-stable (see prob. 5.11).

Dahlquist [21] has deduced two interesting theorems, which we state here without proof. The first states that an *explicit k-step method*, (*e.g.*, Adams-Bashforth family) cannot be A-stable. The second states that the order of an A-stable linear multistep method cannot exceed two. The Crank-Nicholson technique is the most accurate A-stable, multistep method. Figure 5.6 shows that the higher order Adams-Moulton techniques are not A-stable and this is consistent with Dahlquist's second theorem.

5.10 STIFFNESS OF ODEs

The linearized form of the multivariable ODE-IVP, as given in eq. 5.70, has (analytical) solutions which are linear combination of terms [22]:

$$y_i = C_{i1}e^{\lambda_1 t} + C_{i2}e^{\lambda_2 t} + ... + C_{iN}e^{\lambda_N t} + \text{constant}; \quad i = 1, 2, ..., N \qquad ...(5.73)$$

where λ_i are the eigenvalues of A_n. As mentioned in the previous section, the value of h to be used in numerical integration is decided by the eigenvalue having the highest value of $|\text{Re }\lambda_i|$. On the other hand, the eigenvalue having the smallest $|\text{Re }\lambda_i|$ decides the time upto which $|y_i|$ is essentially nonzero, and so decides the value of t upto which we are interested in integrating the ODE-IVPs. A simple example illustrates this more clearly.

Example 5.11: Plot the analytical solutions for [23] (see example 5.3)

$$\begin{bmatrix} \dfrac{dy_1}{dt} \\ \dfrac{dy_2}{dt} \end{bmatrix} = \begin{bmatrix} -100 & 0 \\ 2 & -1 \end{bmatrix} \begin{bmatrix} y_1 \\ y_2 \end{bmatrix}$$

$$\mathbf{y}(0) = \begin{bmatrix} 2 \\ 1 \end{bmatrix}$$

The analytical solution is

$$\begin{bmatrix} y_1 \\ y_2 \end{bmatrix} = \begin{bmatrix} 2e^{-100t} \\ \dfrac{103}{99}e^{-t} - \dfrac{4}{99}e^{-100t} \end{bmatrix}$$

Figure 5.9 shows the variations of $y_1(t)$ and $y_2(t)$. It is observed that the e^{-100t} term, with $\lambda = -100$, leads to an early ($0 \le t \le 0.03$) and sharp decrease in y_1 and to a small maximum in y_2 at $t = 0.0137$. On the other hand, the e^{-t} term, with $\lambda = -1$, leads to slow change in y_2 (we need to reach $t = 4.64$ for y_2 to become 1 percent of the initial value of unity). If one uses the explicit Euler equation, one must use $h < \dfrac{2}{100} = 0.02$ to avoid problems of numerical instability. One must also integrate till about $t = 4.65$, so that y_2 reduces to about 0.01. Thus, the number of time steps to be used is about $\dfrac{4.65}{0.02} = 233$, and is determined approximately by the ratio known as the stiffness ratio [3], SR, defined by

$$SR \equiv \frac{|\text{Re }\lambda_i|_{max}}{|\text{Re }\lambda_i|_{min}} \qquad ...(5.74)$$

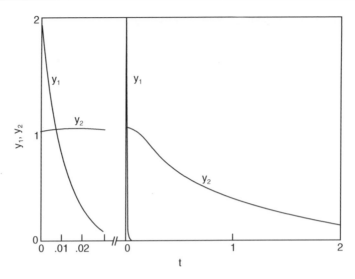

Fig. 5.9 y_1 and y_2 *vs.* t for example 5.11. y_2 has a slight maximum near $t \sim 0.02$.

■

Systems of ODE-IVPs for which the SR is large, are referred to as stiff. Alternatively, a system of ODE-IVPs is referred to as *stiff* if the (local) Jacobian contains at least one eigenvalue which does not contribute significantly over *most* of the domain of interest, as for example, the contribution of $\lambda = -100$ in example 5.11. It is obvious that ODE-IVPs characterized by high values of SR require significant amounts of computational effort due to the large number of integration steps.

For the more general case of eq. 5.1, the eigenvalues of the Jacobian are time dependent. The stiffness ratio, therefore, is also a function of time. An interesting example of multivariable ODE-IVPs where the SR is very large, as well as varies significantly with time, is [24]

$$\frac{dy_1}{dt} = 77.27\left(y_2 - y_1 y_2 + y_1 - 8.375 \times 10^{-6} y_1^2\right)$$

$$\frac{dy_2}{dt} = \frac{-y_2 - y_1 y_2 + y_3}{77.27}$$

$$\frac{dy_3}{dt} = 0.161\left(y_1 - y_3\right)$$

$$y(0) = \begin{bmatrix} 4 & 1.1 & 4 \end{bmatrix}^T \qquad \qquad \text{...(5.75)}$$

These equations represent mass balances for the Belousov reactions [involving a mixture of 1.25M, H_2SO_4, 0.0125M $KBrO_3$, 0.001M $Ce(NH_4)_2(NO_3)_5$ and 0.025M $CH_2 (COOH)_2$]. y_1, y_2 and y_3 are the dimensionless concentrations of the intermediates, $HBrO_2$, Br^- and Ce^{4+}. It is found that the *stiff variable* changes with time (see fig. 5.10), as does the stiffness ratio, which goes from about 70 at $t \cong 1.14$ to as high as 5×10^7 at $t \cong 14$. Figure 5.10 shows the integrated results [12] for a small range of t, obtained using a semi-implicit RK technique with adaptive mesh-sizes [12], as well as a GEAR program [19]. Obviously, algorithms using constant h are quite wasteful for integrating such equations, and methods to reduce the integration step, h, approximately when the SR increases (and increase it when the SR decreases) need to be used.

Special computer programs and algorithms are available [19] which are quite efficient for integrating such ODE-IVPs. In these general-purpose, versatile computer codes, both the step size as well as the order of the equation can be changed appropriately as the integration proceeds, based on the stiffness and the desired (specified) accuracy. Examples are GEAR (in IMSL), D02EBF (in NAG), EPISODE [25, 26], LSODE, etc. Most computer libraries have codes which are quite efficient, and use some

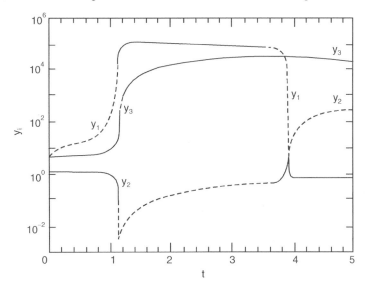

Fig. 5.10 Results for the Belousov reaction [12]. [reprinted from Ref. 12, copyright 1981, with permission from American Chemical Society, Washington DC 20036, USA]

adaptation of Gear's early program [27], DIFSUB. In this, use is made of special algorithms developed by Gear [19, 27, 28] for stiff ODE-IVPs, which we discuss in the next section.

5.11 GEAR'S TECHNIQUE FOR STIFF EQUATIONS

A very popular technique for integrating stiff ODE-IVPs is that of Gear [19, 27–29]. It comprises of multistep predictor and corrector equations. The kth-order technique is given (for a single dependent variable problem) by
E (explicit):

$$\overline{y}_{n+1} = \overline{\alpha}_1 y_n + \overline{\alpha}_2 y_{n-1} + ... + \overline{\alpha}_k y_{n-(k-1)} + h\overline{\beta}_0 y'_n \qquad ...(a)$$

I (implicit):

$$y_{n+1} = \alpha_1 y_n + \alpha_2 y_{n-1} + ... + \alpha_k y_{n-(k-1)} + h\beta_0 y'_{n+1} \qquad ...(b) \qquad ...(5.76)$$

Equation 5.76 is a special case of the more general multistep method given by eq. 5.23. Bars are used on the coefficients, $\overline{\alpha}_1, \overline{\alpha}_2, ..., \overline{\alpha}_k, \overline{\beta}_0$, of the explicit equation. These coefficients differ from those used in the implicit equation. Also, these sets of coefficients are different for Gear's method of different orders (superscript, k, has not been used on the coefficients for the sake of brevity).

One way of obtaining the coefficients of the explicit equation [17, 29] is to ensure that it gives exact results, $y(h)$ (in absence of round-off errors) for an ODE-IVP whose analytical solution is a polynomial of degree less than or equal to k. Thus, if $\overline{y}_{\text{exact}} = a_0$, we have from eq. 5.76 (a) [using $\overline{y}_{n+1} = y_n = ... = y_{n-k+1} = a_0$, $y'_n = 0$]:

$$a_0 = \bar{\alpha}_1 a_0 + \bar{\alpha}_2 a_0 + \ldots + \bar{\alpha}_k a_0 \qquad \ldots(5.77)$$

or

$$\bar{\alpha}_1 + \bar{\alpha}_2 + \ldots + \bar{\alpha}_k + 0\bar{\beta}_0 = 1 \qquad \ldots(5.78)$$

Similarly, on applying eq. 5.76 (a) to $\bar{y}_{\text{exact}} = a_0 + a_1 t$, we obtain [use $\bar{y}_{n+1} = a_0 + a_1 h$, $y_n = a_0$, $y_{n-1} = a_0 - a_1 h$, ..., $y_{n-k+1} = a_0 - a_1(k-1)h$, $y_n' = a_1$]:

$$a_0 + a_1 h = \bar{\alpha}_1 a_0 + \bar{\alpha}_2 (a_0 - a_1 h) + \bar{\alpha}_3 (a_0 - 2a_1 h) + \ldots + \bar{\alpha}_k \left[a_0 - a_1(k-1)h\right] + h\bar{\beta}_0 a_1$$

$$= a_0 \left[\bar{\alpha}_1 + \bar{\alpha}_2 + \ldots + \bar{\alpha}_k\right] - a_1 h \left[\bar{\alpha}_2 + 2\bar{\alpha}_3 + \ldots + (k-1)\bar{\alpha}_k\right] + a_1 h \bar{\beta}_0 \qquad \ldots(5.79)$$

which, on using eq. 5.78, simplifies to

$$0\bar{\alpha}_1 - \bar{\alpha}_2 - 2\bar{\alpha}_3 - 3\bar{\alpha}_4 - \ldots - (k-1)\bar{\alpha}_k + \bar{\beta}_0 = 1 \qquad \ldots(5.80)$$

It can easily be deduced that if $\bar{y}_{\text{exact}} = a_0 + a_1 t + a_2 t^2$, we will obtain, after using eqs. 5.78 and 5.80:

$$0\bar{\alpha}_1 + \bar{\alpha}_2 + 2^2 \bar{\alpha}_3 + 3^2 \bar{\alpha}_4 + \ldots + (k-1)^2 \bar{\alpha}_k = 1 \qquad \ldots(5.81)$$

This sequence can be continued till $\bar{y}_{\text{exact}} = a_0 + a_1 t + \ldots + a_k t^k$. The final set of equations can be written as

$$
\begin{bmatrix}
1 & 1 & 1 & 1 & \cdots & 1 & 0 \\
0 & -1 & -2 & -3 & \cdots & (-k-1) & 1 \\
0 & 1^2 & 2^2 & 3^2 & \cdots & (k-1)^2 & 0 \\
0 & -1^3 & -2^3 & -3^3 & \cdots & -(k-1)^3 & 0 \\
\cdot & & & & & & \\
\cdot & & & & & & \\
\cdot & & & & & & \\
0 & (-1)^k & (-2)^k & (-3)^k & \cdots & [-(k-1)]^k & 0
\end{bmatrix}
\begin{bmatrix}
\bar{\alpha}_1 \\ \bar{\alpha}_2 \\ \bar{\alpha}_3 \\ \bar{\alpha}_4 \\ \cdot \\ \cdot \\ \cdot \\ \bar{\alpha}_k \\ \bar{\beta}_0
\end{bmatrix}
=
\begin{bmatrix}
1 \\ 1 \\ 1 \\ 1 \\ \cdot \\ \cdot \\ \cdot \\ 1 \\ 1
\end{bmatrix}
\qquad \ldots(5.82)
$$

Equation 5.82 can be solved to obtain the values of the constants $\bar{\alpha}_1, \bar{\alpha}_2, \ldots, \bar{\alpha}_k, \bar{\beta}_0$, for a given value of k. Table 5.2(a) gives these constants for $k = 1, 2, \ldots, 6$.

We can similarly obtain the coefficients, $\alpha_1, \alpha_2, \ldots, \alpha_k, \beta_0$, for Gear's implicit equation, eq. 5.76(b), for different values of k (again, superscript k, indicating that α_i are different for different choices of k, is not used). The equation obtained *for the kth-order formula* (see prob. 5.13) is

$$
\begin{bmatrix}
1 & 1 & 1 & 1 & \cdots & 1 & 0 \\
0 & -1 & -2 & -3 & \cdots & -(k-1) & 1 \\
0 & 1^2 & 2^2 & 3^2 & \cdots & (k-1)^2 & 2 \\
0 & -1^3 & -2^3 & -3^3 & \cdots & -(k-1)^3 & 3 \\
\cdot & & & & & & \\
\cdot & & & & & & \\
\cdot & & & & & & \\
0 & (-1)^k & (-2)^k & (-3)^k & \cdots & [-(k-1)]^k & k
\end{bmatrix}
\begin{bmatrix}
\alpha_1 \\ \alpha_2 \\ \alpha_3 \\ \alpha_4 \\ \cdot \\ \cdot \\ \cdot \\ \alpha_k \\ \beta_0
\end{bmatrix}
=
\begin{bmatrix}
1 \\ 1 \\ 1 \\ 1 \\ \cdot \\ \cdot \\ \cdot \\ 1 \\ 1
\end{bmatrix}
\qquad \ldots(5.83)
$$

The coefficients can be solved for, and are listed for $k = 1, 2, ..., 6$, in table 5.2(b). Gear [27] also obtains the LTE when the kth-order explicit equation is used once (to go from t_{n-1} to t_n), and the kth-order implicit equation is iterated till convergence, as

$$\text{LTE} = \frac{h^{k+1} y_n^{(k+1)}}{k+1} + O\left(h^{k+2}\right) \qquad \qquad ...(5.84)$$

Table 5.2 (a) Coefficient for Gear's Explicit Equation

k	$\bar{\alpha}_1$	$\bar{\alpha}_2$	$\bar{\alpha}_3$	$\bar{\alpha}_4$	$\bar{\alpha}_5$	$\bar{\alpha}_6$	$\bar{\beta}_0$
1	1	0	0	0	0	0	1
2	0	1	0	0	0	0	2
3	$-\dfrac{3}{2}$	$\dfrac{6}{2}$	$-\dfrac{1}{2}$	0	0	0	$\dfrac{6}{2}$
4	$-\dfrac{10}{3}$	$\dfrac{18}{3}$	$-\dfrac{6}{3}$	$\dfrac{1}{3}$	0	0	$\dfrac{12}{3}$
5	$-\dfrac{65}{12}$	$\dfrac{120}{12}$	$-\dfrac{60}{12}$	$\dfrac{20}{12}$	$-\dfrac{3}{12}$	0	$\dfrac{60}{12}$
6	$-\dfrac{77}{10}$	$\dfrac{150}{10}$	$-\dfrac{100}{10}$	$\dfrac{50}{10}$	$-\dfrac{15}{10}$	$\dfrac{2}{10}$	$\dfrac{60}{10}$

(b) Coefficient for Gear's Implicit Equation

k	α_1	α_2	α_3	α_4	α_5	α_6	β_0
1	1	0	0	0	0	0	1
2	$\dfrac{4}{3}$	$-\dfrac{1}{3}$	0	0	0	0	$\dfrac{2}{3}$
3	$\dfrac{18}{11}$	$-\dfrac{9}{11}$	$\dfrac{2}{11}$	0	0	0	$\dfrac{6}{11}$
4	$\dfrac{48}{25}$	$-\dfrac{36}{25}$	$\dfrac{16}{25}$	$-\dfrac{3}{25}$	0	0	$\dfrac{12}{25}$
5	$\dfrac{300}{137}$	$-\dfrac{300}{137}$	$\dfrac{200}{137}$	$-\dfrac{75}{137}$	$\dfrac{12}{137}$	0	$\dfrac{60}{137}$
6	$\dfrac{360}{147}$	$-\dfrac{450}{147}$	$\dfrac{400}{147}$	$-\dfrac{225}{147}$	$\dfrac{72}{147}$	$-\dfrac{10}{147}$	$\dfrac{60}{147}$

The explicit-implicit pair is solved using a slightly different method that is common for PC techniques. If we subtract eq. 5.76(a) from eq. 5.76(b), we obtain

$$y_{n+1} = \bar{y}_{n+1} + \beta_0 \left[h y'_{n+1} - \left\{ \frac{\bar{\alpha}_1 - \alpha_1}{\beta_0} y_n + \frac{\bar{\alpha}_2 - \alpha_2}{\beta_0} y_{n-1} + ... + \frac{\bar{\alpha}_k - \alpha_k}{\beta_0} y_{n-(k-1)} + \frac{h\bar{\beta}_0}{\beta_0} y'_n \right\} \right]$$

$$\equiv \bar{y}_{n+1} + \beta_0 \left[h y'_{n+1} - \left\{ \gamma_1 y_n + \gamma_2 y_{n-1} + ... + \gamma_k y_{n-(k-1)} + h\delta_0 y'_n \right\} \right] \qquad ...(5.85)$$

where we have defined a new set of constants

$$\gamma_i \equiv \frac{(\overline{\alpha}_i - \alpha_i)}{\overline{\beta}_0}; \quad i = 1, 2, ..., k$$

$$\delta_0 = \frac{\overline{\beta}_0}{\beta_0} \qquad\qquad ...(5.86)$$

The term in brackets in eq. 5.85 $\gamma_1 y_n + \gamma_2 y_{n-1} + ... + \gamma_k y_{n-(k-1)} + h\delta_0 y'_n$, is written as $h\overline{\overline{y}}'_{n+1}$. Thus, eqs. 5.85 and 5.76 can be written as

$$\overline{y}_{n+1} = \overline{\alpha}_1 y_n + \overline{\alpha}_2 y_{n-1} + ... + \overline{\alpha}_k y_{n-k+1} + h\overline{\beta}_0 y'_n \qquad ...(a)$$

$$h\overline{\overline{y}}'_{n+1} = \gamma_1 y_n + \gamma_2 y_{n-1} + ... + \gamma_k y_{n-k+1} + h\delta_0 y'_n \qquad ...(b)$$

$$y_{n+1} = \overline{y}_{n+1} + \beta_0 \left(hy'_{n+1} - h\overline{\overline{y}}'_{n+1} \right) \equiv \overline{y}_{n+1} + \beta_0 b \qquad ...(c) \qquad ...(5.87)$$

The reason why we had used the definition in eq. 5.87(b) is clear when we look at eq. 5.87(c)—the terms in brackets in the latter equation are similar in interpretation.

$\overline{y}_{n+1}$ and $\overline{\overline{y}}'_{n+1}$ in eq. 5.87(c), can easily be obtained from eqs. 5.87(a) and (b). This leaves y_{n+1}, the unknown, as an implicit function, and iterative methods discussed in chp. 3 can be used to solve for it once the function, $y'(y)$, is available. Thus, Gear's technique, if used with the Newton-Raphson method, is not the conventional PC technique in which the estimate, $\overline{y}_{n+1}$, from the predictor is used on the right-hand side of the corrector, to get better estimates.

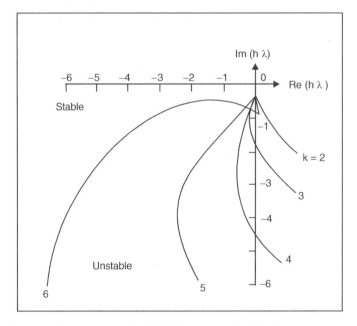

Fig. 5.11 Stability envelopes for Gear's method [19, 27]. Only lower half of the Argand diagram shown due to symmetry about the real axis. The envelope for $k = 1$ is the same as for the implicit Euler method (fig. 5.5).
[reprinted from Ref. 27, copyright, 1969, with permission from Elsevier Science Publishers BV, Amsterdam, Netherlands]

The stability envelopes for Gear's formulae are shown in fig. 5.11. It is observed that the 6th order method is stable (*i.e.*, round off errors die out) for Re $(h\lambda) < -6.1$. The 6th order method can also be shown to be *stable* and *accurate* in the rectangle described by $-6.1 < $ Re $(h\lambda) < $ approximately 0; $-0.5 \le$ Im $(h\lambda) \le 0.5$. Techniques having characteristics of stability and accuracy described by

stable   : Re $(h\lambda) < -D_1$ (region R_1)

stable and accurate   : $-D_1 < $ Re $(h\lambda) < D_2$; $-D_3 < $ Im $(h\lambda) < D_3$ (rectangle R_2)   ...(5.88)

(where D_1, D_2 and D_3 are real, positive constants), are referred to a *stiffly-stable* techniques. It is easy to see why stiffly-stable techniques are important. Eigenvalues for which $h\lambda_i$ lie in region R_1, die out soon, and so stability alone is important (so that round off errors do not increase without bounds) in region R_1. Eigenvalues for which $h\lambda_i$ are in zone R_2 give contributions which are substantial at high t, and we must ensure both stability (round off) as well as numerical accuracy in this region (note that fig. 5.11 only focuses on stability and *not* on accuracy). Gear's method for $k > 6$ are not stiffly-stable, and so are not used (there are other stiffly-stable methods of higher orders, though) [19].

Use of eq. 5.87(*c*) with the Newton-Raphson technique and an initial estimate $\left(\overline{y}_{n+1}\right)$ would give y_{n+1} on convergence. The procedure is similar to that described in example 5.2.

Equations 5.87(*a*) and (*b*) can be rewritten in matrix form as

$$\overline{\mathbf{Y}}_{n+1} \equiv \begin{bmatrix} \overline{y}_{n+1} \\ h\overline{y}'_{n+1} \\ y_n \\ y_{n-1} \\ y_{n-2} \\ \cdot \\ \cdot \\ \cdot \\ y_{n-(k-2)} \end{bmatrix} = \begin{bmatrix} \overline{\alpha}_1 & \overline{\beta}_0 & \overline{\alpha}_2 & \overline{\alpha}_3 & \cdots & \overline{\alpha}_{k-1} & \overline{\alpha}_k \\ \gamma_1 & \delta_0 & \gamma_2 & \gamma_3 & \cdots & \gamma_{k-1} & \gamma_k \\ 1 & 0 & 0 & 0 & \cdots & 0 & 0 \\ 0 & 0 & 1 & 0 & \cdots & 0 & 0 \\ 0 & 0 & 0 & 1 & \cdots & 0 & 0 \\ \cdot & & & & & & \\ \cdot & & & & & & \\ \cdot & & & & & & \\ 0 & 0 & 0 & 0 & \cdots & 1 & 0 \end{bmatrix} \begin{bmatrix} y_n \\ hy'_n \\ y_{n-1} \\ y_{n-2} \\ y_{n-3} \\ \cdot \\ \cdot \\ \cdot \\ y_{n-(k-1)} \end{bmatrix} \equiv \mathbf{BY}_n \qquad ...(5.89)$$

The first two equations here correspond to eqs. 5.87(*a*) and (*b*). The remaining equations in eq. 5.89 are mere identities (to be used later). Equation 5.87(*c*) (alongwith $k-1$ identities) can be written in matrix form as

$$\mathbf{Y}_{n+1} \equiv \begin{bmatrix} y_{n+1} \\ hy'_{n+1} \\ y_n \\ y_{n-1} \\ \cdot \\ \cdot \\ \cdot \\ y_{n-(k-2)} \end{bmatrix} = \begin{bmatrix} \overline{y}_{n+1} \\ h\overline{y}'_{n+1} \\ y_n \\ y_{n-1} \\ \cdot \\ \cdot \\ \cdot \\ y_{n-(k-2)} \end{bmatrix} + b \begin{bmatrix} \beta_0 \\ 1 \\ 0 \\ 0 \\ \cdot \\ \cdot \\ \cdot \\ 0 \end{bmatrix} \equiv \overline{\mathbf{Y}}_{n+1} + b\mathbf{C} \qquad ...(5.90)$$

Equations 5.89 and 5.90 can be used in the following sequence

$$\overline{\mathbf{Y}}_{n+1} = \mathbf{B}\mathbf{Y}_n \qquad \ldots(a)$$

$$G(b) = hy'_{n+1} - \left(h\overline{\overline{y}}'_{n+1} + b\right)$$

$$= hf\left[t_{n+1}, \overline{y}_{n+1} + b\beta_0\right] - \left[h\overline{\overline{y}}'_{n+1} + b\right] = 0 \qquad \ldots(b)$$

$$\mathbf{Y}_{n+1} = \overline{\mathbf{Y}}_{n+1} + b\mathbf{C} \qquad \ldots(c) \qquad \ldots(5.91)$$

where eq. 5.91(*b*) follows from eq. 5.87 (*c*). If we have the information at t_n, we can generate $\overline{\mathbf{Y}}_{n+1}$ using eq. 5.91(*a*), use the values of $\overline{y}_{n+1}$ and $\overline{\overline{y}}'_{n+1}$ so generated in eq. 5.91 (*b*) with a Newton-Raphson algorithm to evaluate *b*, and finally obtain $\mathbf{Y}_{n+1}$ (and thus information at t_{n+1}) using eq. 5.91 (*c*). Of course, there are start-up problems associated with this, and this is discussed later. Note that the function, *f*, is written explicitly as a function of *t* also.

Gear suggested a (linear) transformation of eq. 5.91 into a different form, first suggested by Nordsieck [30]. This form has the advantage that it can be used for estimating errors, and so enables easy step-size adjustments for meeting error constraints. In this, we use a vector, $\mathbf{Z}_{n+1}$, comprising of scaled derivatives of *y* at t_{n+1}:

$$\mathbf{Z}_{n+1} \equiv \begin{bmatrix} y_{n+1} \\ hy'_{n+1} \\ \dfrac{h^2}{2!}y''_{n+1} \\ \dfrac{h^3}{3!}y'''_{n+1} \\ \cdot \\ \cdot \\ \cdot \\ \dfrac{h^k}{k!}y^{(k)}_{n+1} \end{bmatrix} = \mathbf{T}\mathbf{Y}_{n+1} \qquad \ldots(5.92)$$

or

$$\mathbf{Y}_{n+1} = \mathbf{T}^{-1}\mathbf{Z}_{n+1} \qquad \ldots(5.93)$$

The transformation matrix, $\mathbf{T}^{-1}$ (or $\mathbf{T}$), can be deduced in a manner similar to that used for generating eqs. 5.82 and 5.83. Let us assume y_{exact} to be a polynomial of *k*th degree:

$$y_{exact} = a_0 + a_1 t + a_2 t^2 + \ldots + a_k t^k \qquad \ldots(5.94)$$

If we now take

$$t_{n+1} \quad = 0$$
$$t_n \quad = -h$$
$$t_{n-1} \quad = -2h$$
$$.$$
$$.$$
$$.$$
$$t_{n-(k-2)} \quad = -(k-1)h \qquad\qquad ...(5.95)$$

we obtain expressions for various terms in $\mathbf{Y}_{n+1}$ (see eq. 5.90) from eq. 5.94

$$y_{n+1} \quad = a_0$$

$$y_n \quad = a_0 - \quad ha_1 \quad + \quad h^2 a_2 - h^3 a_3 \quad +...+ \quad (-h)^k a_k$$

$$y_{n-1} \quad = a_0 - \quad 2ha_1 \quad + \quad 4h^2 a_2 - 8h^3 a_3 +...+ \quad 2^k (-h)^k a_k$$

$$.$$
$$.$$
$$.$$

$$y_{n-(k-2)} \quad = a_0 - \quad (k-1)ha_1 + \quad (k-1)^2 h^2 a_2 - \quad ...+ \quad (k-1)^k (-h)^k a_k \qquad ...(5.96)$$

Since we need to relate the various derivatives of y at t_{n+1} (in $\mathbf{Z}_{n+1}$) to the values, y_{n+1}, y_n, y_{n-1}, etc., we need to obtain expressions for these derivatives too. Equation 5.94 gives

$$y_{n+1} = a_0$$
$$y'_{n+1} = \left[a_1 + 2a_2 t + 3a_3 t^2 +...+ ka_k t^{k-1}\right]_{t=0} = a_1$$
$$y''_{n+1} = \left[2a_2 + 6a_3 t +...+ k(k-1)a_k t^{k-2}\right]_{t=0} = 2a_2$$
$$y'''_{n+1} = 6a_3$$
$$.$$
$$.$$
$$.$$
$$y^{(k)}_{n+1} = k!a_k \qquad\qquad ...(5.97)$$

We can substitute for the a_i from eq. 5.97 into eq. 5.96, to give

$$y_n = y_{n+1} - hy'_{n+1} + \frac{h^2}{2!}y''_{n+1} - \frac{h^3}{3!}y'''_{n+1} +...+ \frac{(-h)^k}{k!}y^{(k)}_{n+1}$$

$$y_{n-1} = y_{n+1} - 2hy'_{n+1} + \frac{4h^2}{2!}y''_{n+1} - \frac{8h^3}{3!}y'''_{n+1} +...+ \frac{2^k (-h)^k}{k!}y^{(k)}_{n+1}$$

.
.
.

$$y_{n-k+2} = y_{n+1} - (k-1)hy'_{n+1} + \frac{(k-1)^2}{2!}h^2 y''_{n+1} - \dots \qquad \dots(5.98)$$

We can now write these in matrix form (see eq. 5.93) to relate $\mathbf{Y}_{n+1}$ to $\mathbf{Z}_{n+1}$:

$$\mathbf{Y}_{n+1} = \begin{bmatrix} y_{n+1} \\ hy'_{n+1} \\ y_n \\ y_{n-1} \\ . \\ . \\ . \\ y_{n-(k-2)} \end{bmatrix} = \begin{bmatrix} 1 & 0 & 0 & 0 & \cdots & 0 \\ 0 & 1 & 0 & 0 & \cdots & 0 \\ 1 & -1 & 1 & -1 & \cdots & (-1)^k \\ 1 & -2 & 2^2 & -2^3 & \cdots & (-2)^k \\ . \\ . \\ . \\ 1 & -(k-1) & (k-1)^2 & -(k-1)^3 & \cdots & [-(k-1)]^k \end{bmatrix} \begin{bmatrix} y_{n+1} \\ hy'_{n+1} \\ \dfrac{h^2}{2!}y''_{n+1} \\ \dfrac{h^3}{3!}y'''_{n+1} \\ . \\ . \\ . \\ \dfrac{h^k}{k!}y^{(k)}_{n+1} \end{bmatrix} = \mathbf{T}^{-1}\mathbf{Z}_{n+1} \qquad \dots(5.99)$$

Matrix $\mathbf{T}^{-1}$ can easily be inverted to give $\mathbf{T}$.

eqs. 5.91 and 5.92 can now be used to relate the Nordsieck matrices at t_{n+1} and t_n as

Table 5.3 $(k+1) \times 1$ vector [19], **L**, in eq. 5.100

k	1	2	3	4	5	6
L	$\begin{bmatrix} 1 \\ 1 \end{bmatrix}$	$\begin{bmatrix} \frac{2}{3} \\ 1 \\ \frac{1}{3} \end{bmatrix}$	$\begin{bmatrix} \frac{6}{11} \\ 1 \\ \frac{6}{11} \\ \frac{1}{11} \end{bmatrix}$	$\begin{bmatrix} \frac{24}{50} \\ 1 \\ \frac{35}{50} \\ \frac{1}{5} \\ \frac{1}{50} \end{bmatrix}$	$\begin{bmatrix} \frac{120}{274} \\ 1 \\ \frac{225}{274} \\ \frac{85}{274} \\ \frac{15}{274} \\ \frac{1}{274} \end{bmatrix}$	$\begin{bmatrix} \frac{720}{1764} \\ 1 \\ \frac{1624}{1764} \\ \frac{735}{1764} \\ \frac{175}{1764} \\ \frac{21}{1764} \\ \frac{1}{1764} \end{bmatrix}$

$$\mathbf{Z}_{n+1} = \mathbf{T}\mathbf{Y}_{n+1} = \mathbf{T}\left(\overline{\mathbf{Y}}_{n+1} + b\mathbf{C}\right) = \mathbf{T}\left(\mathbf{B}\mathbf{Y}_n + b\mathbf{C}\right)$$

$$= \left(\mathbf{TBT}^{-1}\right)\mathbf{Z}_n + b\mathbf{TC}$$

$$\equiv \mathbf{PZ}_n + b\mathbf{L} \equiv \overline{\mathbf{Z}}_{n+1} + b\mathbf{L} \qquad \qquad \qquad \ldots(5.100)$$

where $\mathbf{P}$ is the Pascal upper triangular matrix given by

$$\mathbf{P} = \begin{bmatrix} 1 & 1 & 1 & 1 & \binom{4}{0} & \cdots & \binom{k-1}{0} & \binom{k}{0} \\ 0 & 1 & 2 & 3 & \binom{4}{1} & \cdots & \binom{k-1}{1} & \binom{k}{1} \\ 0 & 0 & \binom{2}{2} & \binom{3}{2} & \binom{4}{2} & \cdots & \binom{k-1}{2} & \binom{k}{2} \\ \cdot & & & & & & & \\ \cdot & & & & & & & \\ \cdot & & & & & & & \\ 0 & 0 & 0 & 0 & 0 & \cdots & 0 & \binom{k}{k} \end{bmatrix} \qquad \ldots(5.101)$$

[*i.e.*, $P_{ij} = \binom{j-1}{i-1} = \dfrac{(j-1)!}{\{(i-1)!(j-i)!\}}$ for $j \geq i$, and 0 otherwise]. The $(k+1) \times 1$ vector, $\mathbf{L}$, in eq. 5.100 is given for different order Gear techniques in table 5.3 Matrix $\overline{\mathbf{Y}}_{n+1}$ as defined in eq. 5.91(a) can be related to the matrix $\overline{\mathbf{Z}}_{n+1}$ defined in eq. 5.100 as follows:

$$\overline{\mathbf{Y}}_{n+1} = \mathbf{B}\mathbf{Y}_n = \mathbf{B}\mathbf{T}^{-1}\mathbf{Z}_n = \mathbf{T}^{-1}\left(\mathbf{TBT}^{-1}\right)\mathbf{Z}_n = \mathbf{T}^{-1}\mathbf{PZ}_n$$

$$= \mathbf{T}^{-1}\overline{\mathbf{Z}}_{n+1} \qquad \qquad \qquad \ldots(5.102)$$

On substituting the expanded forms of $\overline{\mathbf{Y}}_{n+1}$ and $\mathbf{T}^{-1}$ (eqs. 5.89 and 5.99) in eq. 5.102, we obtain

$$\overline{\mathbf{Y}}_{n+1} = \begin{bmatrix} \overline{y}_{n+1} \\ h\overline{\overline{y}}'_{n+1} \\ y_n \\ y_{n-1} \\ \cdot \\ \cdot \\ \cdot \\ y_{n-(k-2)} \end{bmatrix} = \begin{bmatrix} 1 & 0 & 0 & 0 & \cdots & 0 \\ 0 & 1 & 0 & 0 & \cdots & 0 \\ 1 & -1 & 1 & -1 & \cdots & (-1)^k \\ 1 & -2 & 2^2 & -2^3 & \cdots & (-2)^k \\ \cdot & & & & & \\ \cdot & & & & & \\ \cdot & & & & & \\ 1 & -(k-1) & (k-1)^2 & -(k-1)^3 & \cdots & [-(k-1)]^k \end{bmatrix} \begin{bmatrix} \overline{y}_{n+1} \\ h\overline{\overline{y}}'_{n+1} \\ \cdot \\ \cdot \\ \cdot \\ \cdot \\ \cdot \\ \cdot \end{bmatrix} \equiv \mathbf{T}^{-1}\overline{\mathbf{Z}}_{n+1} \qquad \ldots(5.103)$$

It is easy to see that the first two elements of $\mathbf{Z}_{n+1}$ will be $\bar{y}_{n+1}$ and $\bar{y}'_{n+1}$. Using analogy with eq. 5.99 we can see that the other terms in $\mathbf{Z}_{n+1}$ will be *some estimates* of higher order derivatives of y at t_{n+1}.

The procedure for integrating the single ODE-IVP, $y' = f(t, y)$; $y(0) = y_0$, using the kth order Gear technique can now be summarized as:

(*a*) Start with $\mathbf{Z}_n$ (starting problems discussed later in this section)

(*b*) Compute $\bar{\mathbf{Z}}_{n+1} = \mathbf{P}\mathbf{Z}_n$ (eq. 5.100)

(*c*) Obtain b by solving

$G(b) \equiv hf\left[t_{n+1}, \bar{y}_{n+1} + b\beta_0\right] - \left(h\bar{y}'_{n+1} + b\right) = 0$ (eq. 5.91*b*). Use $\bar{y}_{n+1}$ and $h\bar{y}'_{n+1}$ from $\bar{\mathbf{Z}}_{n+1}$. The Newton-Raphson method may be used to give

$$b^{(q+1)} = b^{(q)} - \frac{hf\left[t_{n+1}, \bar{y}_{n+1} + \beta_0 b^{(q)}\right] - \left(h\bar{y}'_{n+1} + b^{(q)}\right)}{h\beta_0 f_y\left[t_{n+1}, \bar{y}_{n+1} + \beta_0 b^{(q)}\right] - 1} \qquad ...(5.104)$$

(It is obvious that use of the Newton-Raphson technique for a multivariable problem would lead to the use of the Jacobian, $\mathbf{A}$).

(*d*) Compute $\mathbf{Z}_{n+1} = \bar{\mathbf{Z}}_{n+1} + b\mathbf{L}$ (eq. 5.100)

Most computer codes using Gear's technique incorporate automatic error estimation and adaptation of the step-size, h, and order, k, of the formula used. The elements of the vector, $\mathbf{Z}_{n+1}$, can be used to estimate the LTE of the kth-order Gear technique applied between t_n and t_{n+1}. Equations 5.84, 4.65 and the definition of the backward differences give

$$LTE_k(h) = \frac{h^{k+1}}{k+1} y_{n+1}^{(k+1)} = \frac{h^{k+1}}{k+1} \frac{\nabla^{k+1} y_{n+1}}{h^{k+1}} = \frac{1}{k+1} \nabla\left[\nabla^k y_{n+1}\right]$$

$$= \frac{1}{k+1} \nabla\left[k!(Z_{n+1})_{k+1,1}\right] = \frac{k!}{k+1} \nabla(Z_{n+1})_{k+1, 1}$$

$$= \frac{k!}{k+1}\left[(Z_{n+1})_{k+1, 1} - (Z_n)_{k+1, 1}\right] \qquad ...(5.105)$$

(The index, 1, is being used even though $\mathbf{Z}_{n+1}$ is a vector). Thus, an estimate of the LTE for the kth order Gear technique can be obtained using the last entries in $\mathbf{Z}_{n+1}$ and $\mathbf{Z}_n$. If LTE_k is below the specified tolerance, TOL, the computations are accepted, otherwise they are rejected. In either case, a new step size, $q_k h$, larger or smaller than h, is computed such that the LTE using this is approximately equal to TOL. Using the method described in sec. 5.8 (see eq. 5.58), we obtain

$$LTE_k(q_k h) = TOL = \frac{(q_k h)^{k+1}}{k+1} y_{n+1}^{(k+1)} = q_k^{k+1} LTE_k(h)$$

$$= q_k^{k+1} \frac{k!}{k+1}(\nabla Z_{n+1})_{k+1, 1} \qquad ...(5.106)$$

where $(\nabla Z_{n+1})_{k+1,1}$ is obtained using the last entries of $\mathbf{Z}_{n+1}$ and $\mathbf{Z}_n$, with $t_{n+1} = t_n + h$. On using a safety factor, we obtain from eq. 5.106

$$q_k = \frac{1}{1.2} \left[\frac{(k+1)\text{TOL}}{k!(\nabla Z_{n+1})_{k+1,1}} \right]^{\frac{1}{k+1}} \qquad \ldots(5.107)$$

In computer codes involving Gear's techniques, one also evaluates the step size required to satisfy the error tolerances with the $(k + 1)$th and $(k − 1)$th order techniques. The matrix $\mathbf{Z}_{n+1}$, can be used to estimate the error for a $(k − 1)$th order Gear technique, as

$$\text{LTE}_{k-1}(h) = \frac{h^k}{k} y_{n+1}^{(k)} = \frac{k!(Z_{n+1})_{k+1,1}}{k} \qquad \ldots(5.108)$$

If we would like the LTE using a step size $q_{k-1}h$ to be equal to TOL, we should use

$$q_{k-1} = \frac{1}{1.3} \left[\frac{(k)\text{TOL}}{k!(Z_{n+1})_{k+1,1}} \right]^{\frac{1}{k}} \qquad \ldots(5.109)$$

Once again, 1.3 is a safety factor [28] which is larger than used in eq. 5.107 so as to bias the technique towards continuing with the kth order technique. $(Z_{n+1})_{k+1,1}$ is the last entry of $\mathbf{Z}_{n+1}$ as evaluated for the kth-order technique with step size h. Similarly, we can find the step size, $q_{k+1}h$, to be used for a $(k + 1)$th order Gear technique so as to meet with the error tolerance. Since

$$\text{LTE}_{k+1}(h) = \frac{h^{k+2}}{k+2} y_{n+1}^{(k+2)} = \frac{\nabla^{k+2} y_{n+1}}{k+2} = \frac{k!}{k+2} \nabla^2 (Z_{n+1})_{k+1,1} \qquad \ldots(5.110)$$

we have

$$q_{k+1} = \frac{1}{1.4} \left[\frac{(k+2)\text{TOL}}{k!\nabla^2 (Z_{n+1})_{k+1,1}} \right]^{\frac{1}{k+2}} \qquad \ldots(5.111)$$

Values of $\nabla^2 [Z_{n+1}]_{k+1,1}$ can be obtained using backward differences of $\nabla[Z_{n+1}]_{k+1,1}$. The computer codes usually compute, q_k, q_{k-1} and q_{k+1} after some steps of integration of the ODE-IVP, and then choose the order of the Gear formulae to be used next from among these three (the order corresponding to the largest step size is selected). This reduces the computational time significantly, while maintaining the error-tolerance (since a variable step size is involved, the LTE per unit change in t is usually specified).

Another important aspect in the use of Gear's technique is the problem associated with starting-up (as well as after step size change). A first-order technique is used at $t = 0$. $\mathbf{Z}_0$ involves only two elements, y_0 and hy_0'. The former is the initial condition which is available, while the latter is evaluated as $hf(0, y_0)$. We can, therefore, evaluate $\mathbf{Z}_1 = [y_1 \quad hy_1']^T$. Thus, there are no starting problems with this choice of k. Whenever the error-control check suggests an increase in the order, we only need to add on an extra term in the $\mathbf{Z}$ matrix. For example, when we go from a kth order method to a $(k + 1)$th order method at, say, time t_n, we append an extra term, $\dfrac{h^{k+1} y_n^{(k+1)}}{(k+1)!} \left[= \dfrac{\nabla(Z_n)_{k+1,1}}{(k+1)} \right]$ to the computed $\mathbf{Z}_n$ matrix evaluated using order k. Since in most computer codes, one attempts to continue with this new order,

$k + 1$, for several steps, error computation using backward differences of this *new* entry in the $(k + 2)$nd row of $\mathbf{Z}_n$ poses no problem. Reduction of the order at t_n from k to $k - 1$ is associated with a simple dropping of the last term in $\mathbf{Z}_n$. [28]

The above discussion provides a glimpse of some important features associated with the use of Gear's technique, as applied to a *single* ODE-IVP, $y' = f(t, y)$; $y(0) = y_0$. The extension to a system of ODE-IVPs, $\mathbf{y}' = \mathbf{f}(t, \mathbf{y})$; $\mathbf{y}(0) = \mathbf{y}_0$, is fairly easy [19], and is discussed in prob. 5.14. The basic equations and techniques are quite similar to the one-variable case. However, we now have to evaluate $b_1, b_2, ..., b_N$ from N algebraic equations instead of a single b using eq. 5.91(b). The Jacobian, $\mathbf{A}$, of the function, $\mathbf{f}$, with respect to the N variables, $y_1, y_2, ..., y_N$, is required to obtain solutions for $\mathbf{b}$ (see prob. 5.15) using the Newton-Raphson technique. $\mathbf{A}$ may be obtained analytically or may be generated numerically.

Several of the features discussed in this section are incorporated in computer codes for integrating ODE-IVPs, as for example, in GEAR [19, 31], EPISODE [25, 26], LSODE, D02EBF (NAG library), etc. The reader is referred to detailed write-ups on these codes to get an idea of the variety of possibilities that are available.

Detailed comparisons of the various computer codes available for the solution of stiff ODE-IVPs, are available. Two particularly interesting studies are presented in refs. 10 and 32. In the former, the Robertson [14] problem (characterizing an autocatalytic reaction pathway):

$$\frac{dy_1}{dt} = -0.04 y_1 + 10^4 y_2 y_3$$

$$\frac{dy_2}{dt} = 0.04 y_1 - 10^4 y_2 y_3 - 3 \times 10^7 y_2^2$$

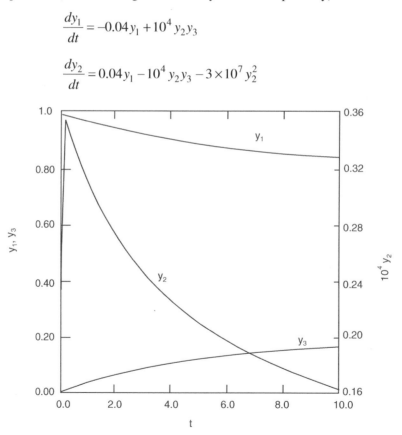

Fig. 5.12 Results [10] for the Robertson problem (eq. 5.112) [reprinted from ref. 10, copyright, 1984 with permission from John Wiley & Sons, Inc., New York, USA]

$$\frac{dy_3}{dt} = 3 \times 10^7 \, y_2^2$$

$$\mathbf{y}_0 = \begin{bmatrix} 1 & 0 & 0 \end{bmatrix}^T \qquad \qquad \dots(5.112)$$

is solved using six different computer codes, using several available options in each case. fig. 5.12 shows the "exact" results obtained using the semi-implicit RK technique of Caillaud and Padmanabhan [15]. The steep rise of y_3 near $t = 0$ is to be noted. This is an extremely stiff system, since one of the three eigenvalues of the Jacobian changes from -0.04 to -2450 when t increases from 0 to 0.02. In addition, one eigenvalue changes from -0.4 to -10^4 in the entire range of t. It was found [10] that *some* of the non-stiff (usually explicit) algorithms failed to give correct solutions. However, it was observed that the results from non-stiff algorithms, *when they were obtained*, matched well with those from stiff algorithms, but the computer times required were almost two orders of magnitude higher. The superiority of the stiff algorithms is thus clearly established. The reader is referred to this study [10] for more details.

Byrne et al. [32], similarly, provide an interesting comparison of two popular computer codes, EPISODE and GEAR. In the former, the step size can change from step to step, while in the latter, the step is kept constant for $k + 2$ consecutive *successful* steps (there are other differences too, see ref. 32). Because of this, EPISODE *usually* performs faster than GEAR for problems involving waves or active (rapidly varying) solutions. For simply decaying or linear problems, GEAR is usually faster. Detailed comparison of results obtained for four different problems solved using both these packages, has been provided.

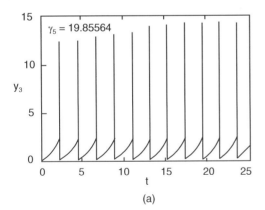
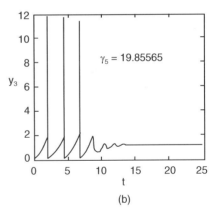

(a)   (b)

Fig. 5.13 Solution [33] of eq. 5.113 for two values of γ_5. [reprinted from ref. 33, copyright 1987, with permission from Pregamon Press, Ltd., Headington Hill Hall, Oxford 0X3 OBW, UK]

Chemburkar et al. [33] have recently studied the dynamics of a CSTR in which the reaction A $\rightarrow$ B $\rightarrow$ C takes place, using DGEAR (IMSL). The dimensionless mass and energy balance equations for this system can be written as

$$\frac{dy_1}{dt} = 1 - y_1 - \gamma_1 y_1 \exp\left(\frac{\gamma_2 y_3}{\gamma_2 + y_3}\right)$$

$$\frac{dy_2}{dt} = -y_2 + \gamma_1 y_1 \exp\left(\frac{\gamma_2 y_3}{\gamma_2 + y_3}\right) - \gamma_1 \gamma_3 y_2 \exp\left(\frac{\gamma_4 \gamma_2 y_3}{\gamma_2 + y_3}\right)$$

$$\frac{dy_3}{dt} = -y_3 - \gamma_5\left(y_3 - y_6\right) + \gamma_1\gamma_7 y_1 \exp\left(\frac{\gamma_2 y_3}{\gamma_2 + y_3}\right) + \gamma_1\gamma_7\gamma_3\gamma_8 y_2 \exp\left(\frac{\gamma_4\gamma_2 y_3}{\gamma_2 + y_3}\right) \quad \ldots(5.113)$$

where y_1 and y_2 are the dimensionless concentrations of A and B respectively, y_3 is the dimensionless temperature, t is the dimensionless time, and $\gamma_1 - \gamma_8$ are dimensionless parameters (see ref. 33 for definitions). For $\underline{\gamma} = [0.26 \ \infty \ 0.5 \ 1.0 \ \gamma_5 \ 0.0 \ 57.77 \ -0.426]^T$, and $y(0) = [0.0213 \ 0.0375 \ 4.629]^T$, they obtained solutions of eq. 5.113 using the computer program, DGEAR, and their results are shown in fig. 5.13 (these are near a 'limit point'). The sharp changes in y_3 (dimensionless temperature) reflect the stiffness of these equations. These workers also computed the chaotic oscillations of y_3 with time using a different set of values of $\underline{\gamma}$. It may be added that getting the exact heights of the sharp peaks requires storing and printing the y_i at very small intervals of t—a difficult task.

We are providing detailed results (*e.g.*, figs. 5.10, 5.12 and 5.13) and equations here for a few problems and urge the reader to get hands-on experience working with an available computer code with these equations as test-cases. A whole variety of research problems are being solved these days using these programs and one can get an idea of their extensive use while going through recent issues of any engineering journal. Problems involving optimization, parametric sensitivity, chaotic behaviour, control, etc., particularly, yield systems of ODE-IVPs which are stiff.

Example 5.12: The following set of mass and energy balance equations describe the high-pressure polymerization of ethylene [34] (to give low density polyethylene) in a plug-flow reactor (see ref. 34 for details—actually, the following equations are a simplified version of the equations in ref. 34):

$$\frac{dy_1}{dt} = -k_I y_1$$

$$\frac{dy_2}{dt} = -k_P y_2 y_3$$

$$\frac{dy_3}{dt} = 2k_I y_1 - k_T y_3^2$$

$$\frac{dy_4}{dt} = 2k_I y_1 + k_P y_2 y_3 - k_T y_3 y_4$$

$$\frac{dy_5}{dt} = 2k_I y_1 + k_P y_2 \left(2y_4 + y_3\right) - k_T y_3 y_5$$

$$\frac{dy_6}{dt} = \frac{1}{2} k_T y_3^2$$

$$\frac{dy_7}{dt} = k_T y_3 y_4$$

$$\frac{dy_8}{dt} = k_T \left[y_3 y_5 + y_4^2\right]$$

$$\frac{dy_9}{dt} = \beta_1 k_P y_2 y_3 + \beta_2 \left(\beta_3 - y_9\right)$$

$$y(0) = [0.002 \ 19.1071 \ 0 \ 0 \ 0 \ 0 \ 0 \ 0 \ 50]^T$$

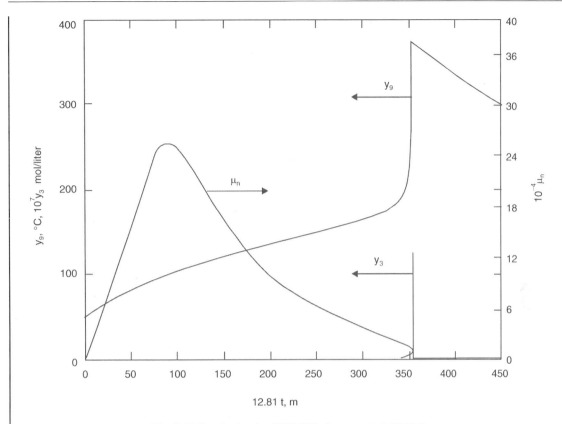

Fig. 5.14 Results for the ODE-IVPs in example 5.12 [34]

Use the following data for the rate constants, k_I, k_p and k_T, and the parameters, β_1, β_2, β_3, characterizing the physical properties and reactor variables:

$$k_I = 1.6 \times 10^{16} \exp\left[\frac{-38400}{\{1.987(y_9 + 273)\}}\right]$$

$$k_P = 5.888 \times 10^7 \exp\left[\frac{-5987}{\{1.987(y_9 + 273)\}}\right]$$

$$k_T = 1.3963 \times 10^9 \exp\left[\frac{+354}{\{1.987(y_9 + 273)\}}\right]$$

$$\beta_1 = 76.9231$$

$$\beta_2 = 0.06651$$

$$\beta_3 = 180$$

Integrate these equations using an available computer program for stiff ODE-IVPs. Some important variables are y_9 (temperature, °C), $1 - \dfrac{y_2}{y_{2,0}}$ (monomer conversion), $\dfrac{y_1}{y_{1,0}}$ (initiator conversion), y_3 (free radical concentration, mol/liter), and $\left[\dfrac{(y_4 + y_7)}{(y_3 + y_6)} \right]$ [number average chain length, μ_n (related to the molecular weight, of the polymer formed)] as a function of $12.81\,t$ (= axial position, m).

The program D02EBF in the NAG library is used to integrate these equations on a supermini HP9000/850S computer. The following program parameters are used:

N   = 9 (number of ODEs)

TOL   = 10^{-7} (error tolerance; lowering TOL did not lead to perceptible changes in the results)

IR   = 2 (results are required, correct to a fixed number of significant digits)

MPED = 0 (Jacobian calculated numerically)

The functions, $\mathbf{f}(t, \mathbf{y})$, were supplied in the subroutine FCN. Some results are shown in fig. 5.14, and some values of the temperature (y_9), free radical concentration (y_3), and average chain length (μ_n), are given below. Other quantities are available in ref. 34.

12.81t (m)	D02EBF			RK ($h = 10^{-3}$)
	y_9 (°C)	y_3 (mol/liter)	μ_n	y_9 (°C)
51.24	80.36802	9.17E-11	158930.0	80.368
102.48	103.688	1.14E-09	247587.7	103.693
153.72	121.8282	3.96E-09	157061.1	121.824
204.96	136.5822	9.73E-09	93175.55	136.576
256.2	150.036	2.08E-08	58039.41	150.034
307.44	166.2583	4.87E-08	35004.11	166.267
349.07	207.4913	3.23E-07	13242.79	207.649
352.275	227.3677	7.13E-07	8904.617	227.935
355.478	372.4867	6.68E-09	1460.006	*
358.68	369.8294	1.64E-09	1463.398	*
354.3406	**343.3893**	**1.25E-05**	**1547.79**	*

Note the sharp change in y_9 and y_3 near $12.81\,t \cong 350$ m. This is the region of stiffness. Results from a multivariable RKG program using a constant step size, $h = \Delta t = 10^{-3}$ (s), are also shown in the above table for y_9. The RKG technique is observed to fail when the equations become stiff. ∎

5.12 ODE-IVPs WITH COUPLED ALGEBRAIC EQUATIONS

Systems of ODE-IVPs solved in example 5.12 are encountered quite often in chemical engineering, and can be solved using techniques already described. At times, however, we may need to solve systems of ODE-IVPs which are coupled with nonlinear algebraic equations (differential algebraic equations, DAEs). A simple example involving only two dependent variables, $y(t)$ and $u(t)$, is

$$\frac{dy}{dt} = f(t, y, u); \quad y(0) = y_0 \qquad \qquad ...(a)$$

$$0 = g(t, y, u) \qquad \qquad ...(b) \qquad ...(5.114)$$

Such equations are encountered quite commonly in the solution of certain kinds of partial differential equations (see Chapter 7). If it is possible to express u in the terms of y *explicitly* using eq. 5.114 (b), we can reduce this system into a single ODE-IVP and integrate it easily. This was the case in example 5.12 where k_i and β_i could be easily substituted to give nine ODE-IVPs. If this substitution is not possible, we need to use new techniques. These are developed in this section. It may be cautioned that not all such systems of DAEs have solutions [29].

The method used [17, 29] is quite similar to that used in sec. 5.11, and is presented for the two-variable case described by eq. 5.114. The (estimated) value of u at $t = t_{n+1}$ can be written in terms of its values at earlier locations (for the kth order technique) as

$$\bar{u}_{n+1} = \eta_1 \mu_n + \eta_2 \mu_{n-1} + .. + \eta_{k+1} u_{n-k} \qquad ...(5.115)$$

Note the similarity of this equation to eq. 5.76. Also, note the absence of any derivative terms, u', in the above equation and the omission of superscript, k, on the coefficients, η_i. The coefficients, η_i, are obtained such that if $u(t)$ is a polynomial of degree k or less, eq. 5.115 gives exact results. Since the detailed procedure was presented in sec. 5.11 (eqs. 5.77–5.82), this is left as an exercise (prob. 5.16). The coefficients are obtained as

$$\begin{bmatrix} 1 & 1 & 1 & \cdots & 1 \\ 0 & -1 & -2 & \cdots & -k \\ 0 & (-1)^2 & (-2)^2 & \cdots & [-k]^2 \\ \cdot & & & & \\ \cdot & & & & \\ \cdot & & & & \\ 0 & (-1)^k & (-2)^k & \cdots & [-k]^k \end{bmatrix} \begin{bmatrix} \eta_1 \\ \eta_2 \\ \eta_3 \\ \cdot \\ \cdot \\ \cdot \\ \eta_{k+1} \end{bmatrix} = \begin{bmatrix} 1 \\ 1 \\ 1 \\ \cdot \\ \cdot \\ \cdot \\ 1 \end{bmatrix} \qquad ...(5.116)$$

The similarity with eq. 5.82 is to be noted again.
Equation 5.115 can be written in matrix form (in analogy with eq. 5.89) as

$$\bar{\mathbf{U}}_{n+1} \equiv \begin{bmatrix} \bar{u}_{n+1} \\ u_n \\ u_{n-1} \\ u_{n-2} \\ \cdot \\ \cdot \\ \cdot \\ u_{n-(k-1)} \end{bmatrix} = \begin{bmatrix} \eta_1 & \eta_2 & \eta_3 & \cdots & \eta_k & \eta_{k+1} \\ 1 & 0 & 0 & \cdots & 0 & 0 \\ 0 & 1 & 0 & \cdots & 0 & 0 \\ 0 & 0 & 1 & \cdots & 0 & 0 \\ \cdot & & & & & \\ \cdot & & & & & \\ \cdot & & & & & \\ 0 & 0 & 0 & \cdots & 1 & 0 \end{bmatrix} \begin{bmatrix} u_n \\ u_{n-1} \\ u_{n-2} \\ u_{n-3} \\ \cdot \\ \cdot \\ \cdot \\ u_{n-k} \end{bmatrix} = \mathbf{B}^* \mathbf{U}_n \qquad ...(5.117)$$

Similarly, an improved value, u_{n+1}, can be obtained from its estimate, $\bar{u}_{n+1}$, using the following equation

$$\mathbf{U}_{n+1} \equiv \begin{bmatrix} u_{n+1} \\ u_n \\ u_{n-1} \\ u_{n-2} \\ \cdot \\ \cdot \\ \cdot \\ \cdot \\ u_{n-(k-1)} \end{bmatrix} = \begin{bmatrix} \bar{u}_{n+1} \\ u_n \\ u_{n-1} \\ u_{n-2} \\ \cdot \\ \cdot \\ \cdot \\ \cdot \\ u_{n-(k-1)} \end{bmatrix} + d \begin{bmatrix} \beta_0 \\ 0 \\ 0 \\ 0 \\ \cdot \\ \cdot \\ \cdot \\ 0 \end{bmatrix} \equiv \bar{\mathbf{U}}_{n+1} + d\mathbf{C}^* \qquad \ldots(5.118)$$

Again, the analogy to eq. 5.90 is to be noted. β_0 is the same coefficient as used in eq. 5.90, and d is an unknown constant defined such that $\beta_0 d$ is the correction required to be made to $\bar{u}_{n+1}$ to give u_{n+1}. It is obvious that b and d must satisfy

$$g\left[t_{n+1}, y_{n+1}, u_{n+1}\right] = g\left[t_{n+1}, \ \bar{y}_{n+1} + b\beta_0, \bar{u}_{n+1} + d\beta_0\right] = 0 \qquad \ldots(a)$$

$$G(b) = hf\left[t_{n+1}, \bar{y}_{n+1} + b\beta_0, \bar{u}_{n+1} + d\beta_0\right] - \left(h\bar{y}_{n+1}' + b\right) = 0 \qquad \ldots(b) \qquad \ldots(5.119)$$

eq. 5.119(b) is an extension of eq. 5.91(b), and eq. 5.119(a) corresponds to the algebraic equation, eq. 5.114(b).

We now transform $\mathbf{U}_{n+1}$ to the Nordsieck form. We use the procedure followed in obtaining eq. 5.99 to give

$$\mathbf{U}_{n+1} = \begin{bmatrix} u_{n+1} \\ u_n \\ u_{n-1} \\ \cdot \\ \cdot \\ \cdot \\ u_{n-(k-1)} \end{bmatrix} = \begin{bmatrix} 1 & 0 & 0 & 0 & \cdots & 0 \\ 1 & -1 & 1 & -1 & \cdots & (-1)^k \\ 1 & -2 & 2^2 & -2^3 & \cdots & (-2)^k \\ \cdot & & & & & \\ \cdot & & & & & \\ \cdot & & & & & \\ 1 & -k & k^2 & -k^3 & \cdots & (-k)^k \end{bmatrix} \begin{bmatrix} u_{n+1} \\ hu'_{n+1} \\ \dfrac{h^2}{2!}u''_{n+1} \\ \cdot \\ \cdot \\ \cdot \\ \dfrac{h^k}{k!}u^{(k)}_{n+1} \end{bmatrix} \equiv \mathbf{T}^{*^{-1}}\mathbf{Z}^*_{n+1} \qquad \ldots(5.120)$$

Eqs. 5.120, 5.118, 5.117 and 5.120 again can be used sequentially to give

$$\mathbf{Z}^*_{n+1} = \mathbf{T}^*\mathbf{U}_{n+1} = \mathbf{T}^*\left\{\bar{\mathbf{U}}_{n+1} + d\mathbf{C}^*\right\} = \mathbf{T}^*\left\{\mathbf{B}^*\mathbf{U}_n + d\mathbf{C}^*\right\}$$

$$= \left(\mathbf{T}^*\mathbf{B}^*\mathbf{T}^{*^{-1}}\right)\mathbf{Z}^*_n + d\mathbf{T}^*\mathbf{C}^*$$

$$= \mathbf{P}\mathbf{Z}^*_n + d\mathbf{L} \equiv \bar{\mathbf{Z}}^*_{n+1} + d\mathbf{L} \qquad \ldots(5.121)$$

where use has been made of the equalities $\mathbf{T}^* \mathbf{B}^* \mathbf{T}^{*^{-1}} = \mathbf{P}$ [the $(k + 1) \times (k + 1)$ Pascal triangle] and $\mathbf{T}^* \mathbf{C}^* = \mathbf{L}$, the matrices encountered in sec. 5.11 [eq. 5.101 and table 5.3]. It can be deduced that

$$\overline{\mathbf{Z}}^*_{n+1} = \left[\overline{u}_{n+1} \quad h\overline{u}'_{n+1} \quad \frac{h^2 u''_{n+1}}{2!} \quad \cdots \quad \frac{h^k u^{(k)}_{n+1}}{k!} \right]^T$$

The procedure for solution is summarized as:

(a) Start with $\mathbf{Z}_n$, $\mathbf{Z}^*_n$ with $k = 1$. The starting values of the derivative of y at t_n can be generated as discussed in sec. 5.11. The value of u'_0 is taken as [29] zero.

(b) Compute $\overline{\mathbf{Z}}_{n+1} = \mathbf{PZ}_n$ (the derivation in sec. 5.11 is valid for eq. 5.114 also) and $\overline{\mathbf{Z}}^*_{n+1} = \mathbf{PZ}^*_n$. This gives values of $\overline{y}_{n+1}$, $h\overline{y}'_{n+1}$ (from $\overline{\mathbf{Z}}_{n+1}$) and $\overline{u}_{n+1}$ (from $\overline{\mathbf{Z}}^*_{n+1}$).

(c) Solve for b and d, using the two-variable Newton-Raphson technique in the equations

$$g\left[t_{n+1}, \overline{y}_{n+1} + b\beta_0, \overline{u}_{n+1} + d\beta_0 \right] = 0$$

$$G(b) = hf\left[t_{n+1}, \overline{y}_{n+1} + b\beta_0, \overline{u}_{n+1} + d\beta_0 \right] - \left(h\overline{y}'_{n-1} + b \right) = 0$$

(d) Use b and d so determined to obtain $\mathbf{Z}_{n+1}$ and $\mathbf{Z}^*_{n+1}$ using

$$\mathbf{Z}_{n+1} = \overline{\mathbf{Z}}_{n+1} + b\mathbf{L}$$

$$\mathbf{Z}^*_{n+1} = \overline{\mathbf{Z}}^*_{n+1} + d\mathbf{L}$$

More recently, Petzold and coworkers [35] have developed a modified version of the Gear technique for solving sets of DAEs of the more general form

$$\mathbf{G}\left[t, \mathbf{y}, \mathbf{y}' \right] = \mathbf{0}; \quad \mathbf{y}(0) = \mathbf{y}_0, \quad \mathbf{y}'(0) = \mathbf{y}'_0 \qquad \qquad \text{...(5.122)}$$

where $\mathbf{y}$ has N components, $y_1, y_2, ..., y_N$. The initial values of $\mathbf{y}_0$ and $\mathbf{y}'_0$ *must* be consistent, *i.e.*, they must satisfy the DAE, $\mathbf{G}[t, \mathbf{y}_0, \mathbf{y}'_0] = \mathbf{0}$ (the code can estimate $\mathbf{y}'_0$ starting from an initial guess too). In this code, the coefficients, $\alpha_1, \alpha_2, ...$ and α_k, in the implicit equation (eq. 5.76b) can be varied with time. This is known as the fixed *leading* coefficient method (if we divide eq. 5.76b by β_0 the *leading* coefficient of y_{n+1} is $\dfrac{1}{\beta_0}$, a constant), and has better stability characteristics than Gear's method.

Petzold and coworkers [35] have developed a computer package, DDASSL, which is very robust and is becoming quite popular. Details of the code are available in ref. 35. Example 5.12 can also be solved by DDASSL, with the equations for k_I, k_P and k_T used as algebraic equations. Identical results are obtained as with D02EBF. In chapter 7, we shall see how solutions of partial differential equations (reduced to a set of ODE-IVPs and algebraic equations using techniques described in Chapter 6) can be obtained using DDASSL.

Problem 5.30 illustrates the use of a DAE solver.

PROBLEMS

5.1 Deduce the second order Adams-Bashforth formula (eq. 5.14*b*), alongwith the error term.

5.2 Develop the third-order explicit Adam's integration formula for ODE-IVPs. If $y' = y - 2$; $y_0 = 1$, $y_1 = -0.7183$, $y_2 = -5.389$, $h = 1$, evaluate y_3 using this equation. Compare with the exact value of $y_3 = -18.085537$.

5.3 Derive eqs. 5.20 (*a*) and (*b*) along with the LTE term. You need to write the equation for R in eq. 4.34 (use analogy with eq. 4.33).

5.4 Consider the following successive substitutions form for the implicit Adams-Moulton techniques (see example 5.2)

$$y_{n+1}^{(k+1)} = w_n + h\beta_0 f\left[y_{n+1}^{(k)}\right]$$

Note that $w_n = y_n$, $\beta_0 = 1$ for the implicit Euler technique, and $w_n = y_n + \dfrac{h}{2}f(y_n)$, $\beta_0 = \dfrac{1}{2}$ for the Crank-Nicholson method. Use the sufficient condition for convergence of the successive substitutions technique to show that one will always converge to the solution, y_{n+1}, if $f'(y)$ is bounded, and if h is chosen small enough.

5.5 Consider the general form of the Adams-Moulton techniques (see prob. 5.4.)

$$y_{n+1} = w_n + h\beta_0 f\left[y_{n+1}\right]$$

where h, w_n and β_0 are known quantities. Obtain the general algorithm for computing $y_{n+1}^{(k+1)}$ using the Newton-Raphson technique.

5.6 Obtain the roots of the characteristic equation for eq. 5.37(*a*) and check your answer against that in example 5.8.

5.7 Consider the following ODE-IVP [4]

$$\begin{bmatrix} y'_1 \\ y'_2 \end{bmatrix} = \begin{bmatrix} 9y_1 + 24y_2 + 5\cos t - \dfrac{1}{3}\sin t \\ -24y_1 - 51y_2 - 9\cos t + \dfrac{1}{3}\sin t \end{bmatrix}$$

with $\mathbf{y}_0 = \begin{bmatrix} \dfrac{4}{3} & \dfrac{2}{3} \end{bmatrix}^T$. Make a computer program using a 4th-order RK technique to integrate this equation till large values of t. Try $h = 0.05$ and 0.1, and see how the latter choice leads to numerical instability. Compare the results using $h = 0.05$ with the analytical solution.

$$\mathbf{y} = \begin{bmatrix} 2e^{-3t} - e^{-39t} + \dfrac{1}{3}\cos t \\ -e^{-3t} + 2e^{-39t} - \dfrac{1}{3}\cos t \end{bmatrix}$$

5.8 Consider the simple looking ODE-IVP [5]

$$y' = 4y - 5e^{-t}; \quad y_0 = 1$$

Solve this ODE using a 4th order RK Gill program with $y_0 = 1$, 1.0001 and 0.9999, and see how round-off errors get propagated. Compare with the analytical solution of the ODE: $y = e^{-t} + Ce^{4t}$ [C obtained from the appropriate value of y_0]. Note that the ODE-IVP is inherently unstable only for $y_0 = 1$.

5.9 Consider the propagation of the initial round-off error, e_0, in eq. 5.68. Show that *this part of the error*, χ_{n+1}, can be expressed for the explicit Euler technique as

$$\frac{\chi_{n+1}}{\chi_n} = \mu_t = 1 + h\lambda$$

Thus, show why for $h = 0.5$ in example 5.9 (in the integration of $y' = -3y$; $y_0 = 1$) we observe oscillatory behaviour about the analytical solution. Similarly, show that such oscillations do not occur in the implicit Euler technique. What can you say about similar oscillations in the Crank-Nicholson technique.

5.10 A popular predictor-corrector combination uses the explicit Euler equation for predicting $\bar{y}_{n+1}$ and the Crank-Nicholson method to correct it. Deduce the stability condition (and plot the envelope) for this PC^1 combination. How do your results change for a PC^2 technique using these equations. Check if the characteristic roots of these combinations are Padé approximants of $e^{h\lambda}$. Note that other approximations could also be made for $e^{h\lambda}$. The implicit Norsett method [6] uses Hermite polynomials to approximate this exponential.

5.11 Obtain the stability condition for Michelsen's semi implicit RK technique [13], and thus show it to be A-stable. Is it strongly A-stable too?

5.12 Consider eq. 5.70. Check if the following equation is the analytical solution:

$$\mathbf{y}(t) = e^{t\mathbf{A}_n}\left[\mathbf{y}(t_n) + \mathbf{A}_n^{-1}\mathbf{S}_n\right] - \mathbf{A}_n^{-1}\mathbf{S}_n$$

[**Hint:** Use eq. 4.50 for $\dfrac{d\exp(t\mathbf{A}_n)}{dt}$]. Use this solution to relate $\mathbf{y}_{n+1}$ to $\mathbf{y}_n$. Replace $\exp(t\mathbf{A}_n)$ in this equation by the following Padé approximation (eq. 4.51)

$$\exp[h\mathbf{A}_n] = [\mathbf{I} + h\mathbf{A}_n]$$

to show that

$$\mathbf{y}_{n+1} \cong (\mathbf{I} + h\mathbf{A}_n)\mathbf{y}_n + h\mathbf{S}_n = \mathbf{y}_n + h(\mathbf{A}_n\mathbf{y}_n + \mathbf{S}_n)$$

$$= \mathbf{y}_n + h\mathbf{f}(\mathbf{y}_n)$$

which is the multivariable explicit Euler technique. Similar replacements of $\exp(h\mathbf{A}_n)$ by Padé approximations of different orders can lead to corresponding multivariable integration algorithms.

5.13 Deduce the first three equations in the matrix eq. 5.83.

5.14 Consider the multivariable set of ODE-IVPs

$$\frac{d\mathbf{y}}{dt} = \mathbf{f}(t, y); \; \mathbf{y}(t = 0) = \mathbf{y}_0$$

Generalize the derivation of Gear's algorithm of order k to show that the procedure would be given by

(a) Compute $\bar{\mathbf{Z}}_{n+1}$ using

$$\bar{\mathbf{Z}}_{n+1} \equiv \begin{bmatrix} \bar{y}_{1,\,n+1} & \bar{y}_{2,\,n+1} & \cdots & \bar{y}_{N,\,n+1} \\[4pt] h\bar{y}'_{1,\,n+1} & h\bar{y}'_{2,\,n+1} & \cdots & h\bar{y}'_{N,n+1} \\[4pt] \dfrac{h^2}{2!}\bar{y}''_{1,n+1} & \dfrac{h^2}{2!}\bar{y}''_{2,\,n+1} & \cdots & \dfrac{h^2}{2!}\bar{y}''_{N,n+1} \\[8pt] \dfrac{h^3}{3!}\bar{y}'''_{1,n+1} & \cdots & & \\[8pt] \cdot & & & \\ \cdot & & & \\ \cdot & & & \\[8pt] \dfrac{h^k}{k!}\bar{y}^{(k)}_{1,\,n+1} & \dfrac{h^k}{k!}\bar{y}^{(k)}_{2,\,n+1} & \cdots & \dfrac{h^k}{k!}\bar{y}^{(k)}_{N,n+1} \end{bmatrix} = \mathbf{P}\mathbf{Z}_n$$

where

$$\mathbf{Z}_n \equiv \begin{bmatrix} y_{1,\,n} & y_{2,\,n} & \cdots & y_{N,\,n} \\[4pt] hy'_{1,\,n} & hy'_{2,\,n} & \cdots & hy'_{N,n} \\[4pt] \dfrac{h^2}{2!}y''_{1,n} & \cdots & \cdots & \dfrac{h^2}{2!}y''_{N,n} \\[8pt] \dfrac{h^3}{3!}y'''_{1,n} & \cdots & & \\[8pt] \cdot & & & \\ \cdot & & & \\ \cdot & & & \\[8pt] \dfrac{h^k}{k!}y^{(k)}_{1,\,n} & \dfrac{h^k}{k!}y^{(k)}_{2,\,n} & \cdots & \dfrac{h^k}{k!}y^{(k)}_{N,n} \end{bmatrix}$$

The first subscript on $y_{i,\,j}$, $y^{(k)}_{i,\,j}$, $\bar{y}_{i,\,j}$ and $\bar{y}'_{i,\,j}$ indicates the ith variable ($i = 1, 2, ..., N$), while the second subscript on these indicates the value, t_j, at which they are to be evaluated. $\mathbf{P}$ is the Pascal matrix defined in eq. 5.101.

(b) Solve for $\mathbf{b} \equiv [b_1 \quad b_2 \quad ... \quad b_N]^T$ from

$$\mathbf{G}(\mathbf{b}) \equiv \begin{bmatrix} hf_1\,(t_{n+1},\overline{y}_{1,\,n+1}+\beta_0 b_1,\;\overline{y}_{2,\,n+1}+\beta_0 b_2,...,\;\overline{y}_{N,\,n+1}+\beta_0 b_N)\;\;-(h\overline{\overline{y}}'_{1,\,n+1}+b_1) \\ hf_2\,(t_{n+1},\overline{\mathbf{y}}_{n+1}+\beta_0\mathbf{b}) \qquad\qquad\qquad\qquad\qquad)-(h\overline{\overline{y}}'_{2,\,n+1}+b_2) \\ . \\ . \\ . \\ hf_N\,(t_{n+1},\overline{\mathbf{y}}_{n+1}+\beta_0\mathbf{b}) \qquad\qquad\qquad\qquad\qquad)-(h\overline{\overline{y}}'_{N,\,n+1}+b_N) \end{bmatrix} = \begin{bmatrix} 0 \\ 0 \\ . \\ . \\ . \\ 0 \end{bmatrix} \quad (a)$$

Here $\overline{\mathbf{y}}_{n+1} \equiv \begin{bmatrix} \overline{y}_{1,n+1} & \overline{y}_{2,\,n+1} & \cdots & \overline{y}_{N,\,n+1} \end{bmatrix}^T$. The values of $\overline{y}_{i,\,n+1}$ and $\overline{\overline{y}}'_{i,n+1}$ are available from $\overline{\mathbf{Z}}_{n+1}$.

(c) Obtain $\mathbf{Z}_{n+1}$ from

$$\mathbf{Z}_{n+1} = \overline{\mathbf{Z}}_{n+1} + \mathbf{L}\mathbf{b}^T$$

where $\mathbf{Z}_{n+1}$ is defined similar to $\mathbf{Z}_n$ (with second subscript, n, replaced by $n+1$), and $\mathbf{L}$ is the same $(k+1) \times 1$ matrix as given in table 5.3.

The discussion on the single-variable problem following eq. 5.105 holds for the multivariable case as well. The LTEs for *all* N variables can be evaluated using the entries in $\mathbf{Z}_{n+1}$. The L_2 norm of the LTEs (or the maximum LTE) may now be used to change the step size. The matrix multiplications required are performed by a technique using successive additions in most GEAR programs [19], to save on computer time.

5.15 Apply the multivariable Newton-Raphson technique to eq. (a) in prob. 5.14 to obtain the following equation to evaluate $\mathbf{b}$:

$$\mathbf{b}^{(k+1)} = \mathbf{b}^{(k)} - \left[h\beta_0\mathbf{A}^{(k)} - \mathbf{I} \right]^{-1} \mathbf{G}\big(\mathbf{b}^{(k)}\big)$$

where $\mathbf{A}^{(k)}$ is the Jacobian of $\mathbf{f}$ (*i.e.*, $A_{ij} = \dfrac{\partial f_i}{\partial y_j}$), evaluated at location, k. A variant of Newton's technique involving the Frechét derivative of $\mathbf{G}$ is actually used in the most GEAR computer codes [32].

5.16 Derive eq. 5.116.

5.17 Solve (using a calculator) for four time intervals (*i.e.*, till $t = 4h$)

$$\frac{dy}{dt} = y;\; y_0 = 1$$

using $h = 0.1$. Use a second-order Adams-Bashforth predictor and the Crank-Nicholson corrector. In the *first* time interval only, use the explicit Euler equation as the predictor (with $h = 0.1$) to avoid start-up problems. Compare all the computed values of y with the analytical solution, $y = e^t$.

5.18 Use the second order Runge-Kutta algorithm:

$$y_{n+1} = y_n + hf\left[t_n + \frac{h}{2},\; y_n + \frac{1}{2}hf_n \right]$$

and apply to $y' = \lambda y$, where λ is negative. Observe how the ratio, $\dfrac{y_{n+1}}{y_n}$, from this algorithm gives a Padé approximation of $\exp(h\lambda)$. Relate this observation to eqs. 5.66 and 5.68.

5.19 Two of the several Padé approximants of e^x are

$$e^x = \frac{1 + \dfrac{1}{3}x}{1 - \dfrac{2}{3}x + \dfrac{1}{6}x^2} \quad \text{and} \quad \frac{1 + \dfrac{2}{3}x + \dfrac{1}{6}x^2}{1 - \dfrac{1}{3}x}$$

For a single-variable ODE-IVP: $y' = f(y)$; $y(0) = y_0$, deduce *corresponding* integration algorithms (hint: see prob. 5.18). Express your answer in a Runge-Kutta form. Does this problem have a unique answer?

5.20 Solve the following ODEs [3] *as a coupled set* numerically

$$y_1' = -y_1$$

$$y_2' = -100 y_2$$

$$y_3' = -y_3$$

with $\mathbf{y_0} = [1 \ \ 1 \ \ 1]^T$. Use ODE-IVP integration packages (either available in a library, or your own) based on

(*a*) a 4th (or higher) order RK method with constant h values. Run the program with $h = 0.1, 0.05, 0.03, 0.028, 0.027$ and 0.01. Comment on your results.

(*b*) a GEAR package. See the effect of the error tolerance on the results. Gain experience with the use of this package by running it with different options.

Compare with the analytical solution in both cases.

5.21 Consider the equation [6]

$$y' = -200\left[y^3 - F(t) \right] + \frac{dF(t)}{dt}; \ y_0 = 10$$

$$F(t) = 10 - (10 + t)e^{-t}$$

Obtain the range of eigenvalues of the Jacobian, and so obtain the upper limit for the value of h to be used in an explicit RK technique. Make a program using the 4th order RK Gill technique for a single (dependent) variable and obtain numerical results for $0 < t < 15$.

5.22 The following set of equations [23] describes the dynamic behaviour of a fluidized-bed reactor (in chemical engineering)

$$\frac{dy_1}{dt} = 1.30(y_3 - y_1) + 1.04 \times 10^4 k y_2$$

$$\frac{dy_2}{dt} = 1.88 \times 10^3 \left[y_4 - y_2(1 + k) \right]$$

$$\frac{dy_3}{dt} = 1752 + 266.7 y_1 - 269.3 y_3$$

$$\frac{dy_4}{dt} = 0.1 + 320y_2 - 321y_4$$

where $k = 0.0006 \, \exp\left(20.7 \frac{15000}{y_1}\right)$ and $\mathbf{y}_0 = [759.167 \quad 0 \quad 600 \quad 0.1]^T$. y_1 and y_3 represent the temperatures of the particle and fluid phases, and y_2 and y_4 represent the partial pressures of the reactant in these two phases, respectively. Solve these equations using a GEAR package. Note that three steady-state solutions are possible (corresponding to $y_1 = 691$, 759 and 915; see prob. 3.34), and by choosing $y_{1,0} = 759.167$, we are studying the response to a step change from the middle (unstable) steady state. These equations are *very* stiff, with the stiffness ratio $\cong 10^6$. Start from other values of $\mathbf{y}_0$, and see how your results converge to the stable-steady states.

5.23 The dimensionless diffusion equation $\frac{\partial c}{\partial t} = \frac{\partial^2 c}{\partial x^2}$; $c(0, t) = c(1, t) = 0$; c $(x, 0)$ specified; is often

integrated using the method of lines with a second-order finite difference approximation for $\frac{\partial^2 c}{\partial x^2}$

(see Chapter 7). The PDEs are thereby transformed into a set of ODE-IVPs given below

$$
\begin{bmatrix} \dfrac{dc_1}{dt} \\ \cdot \\ \cdot \\ \cdot \\ \cdot \\ \cdot \\ \cdot \\ \dfrac{dc_n}{dt} \end{bmatrix}
= n^2
\begin{bmatrix}
-2 & 1 & 0 & 0 & & 0 & 0 & 0 \\
1 & -2 & 1 & 0 & & 0 & 0 & 0 \\
0 & 1 & -2 & 1 & & 0 & 0 & 0 \\
 & & & \cdot & & & & \\
 & & & & \cdot & & & \\
 & & & & & \cdot & & \\
0 & 0 & 0 & 0 & \cdot & 1 & -2 & 1 \\
0 & 0 & 0 & 0 & \cdot & \cdot & 0 & 1 & -2
\end{bmatrix}
\begin{bmatrix} c_1 \\ c_2 \\ c_3 \\ \cdot \\ \cdot \\ \cdot \\ c_{n-1} \\ c_n \end{bmatrix}
$$

where $c_1(t)$, ..., $c_n(t)$, are the concentrations at the n grid points. The eigenvalues of the above tridiagonal matrix are given in prob. 2.4.

If you wish to use a 5th order explicit Runge-Kutta method (Nystrom form) to integrate the above ODE-IVPs, what will be the largest choice of h you would use for $n = 10$, 100 and 1000.

5.24 Make a computer program using the Crank-Nicholson technique along with the Newton-Raphson method and solve

$$\frac{dy}{dt} = \frac{(1+t)^2}{y^2} + \frac{y}{1+t}; \quad y_0 = 3$$

Solve for y (t) till $t = 1.1$, using $h = 0.1$, and compare with the analytical results given in prob. 3.22.

5.25 Obtain the largest value of h to get stable solutions of the ODE-IVP of example 5.4. Note that the

ODE-IVP is inherently *not* stable. We would like to have error propagation to be unimportant till about 1980 AD.

5.26 Jothi and Varma [36] study the operation of isothermal plug flow reactors in which CO, NO and O_2 (in automotive exhausts) react catalytically (iridium and rhodium). The dimensionless equations, in the absence of diffusional limitations, can be written as

$$\frac{dy_1}{dt} = kR(1-y_1)(1-y_2) + (S-R)(1-y_1)y_3$$

$$\frac{dy_2}{dt} = k(1-y_1)(1-y_2)$$

$$\frac{dy_3}{dt} = -(1-y_1)y_3$$

with $\mathbf{y}_0 = [0\ \ 0\ \ 1]^T$. y_1, y_2 and y_3 are the conversions of CO, NO and O_2, respectively, and t is a dimensionless reactor length. Integrate these for the following set of parameter values (upto $t = 5$):

$$k = 2$$
$$R = 0.33$$
$$S = 0.33$$

Use an RK computer package. Obtain results for several h, till halving the step size does not make much difference in the values of $\mathbf{y}$.

5.27 The polymerization of nylon 6 in a well-mixed, isothermal batch reactor [37] (in the absence of any vaporization) is described by the following equations:

$$\frac{dy_1}{dt} = -k_1y_1y_5 + k_1'y_2 - k_3y_1y_3 + k_3'(y_3 - y_2)$$

$$\frac{dy_2}{dt} = k_1y_1y_5 - k_1'y_2 - 2k_2y_2y_3 + 2k_2'y_5(y_3 - y_2) - k_3y_1y_2 + k_3'y_2$$

$$\frac{dy_3}{dt} = k_1y_1y_5 - k_1'y_2 - k_2y_3^2 + k_2'y_5(y_4 - y_3)$$

$$\frac{dy_4}{dt} = k_1y_1y_5 - k_1'y_2 + k_3y_1y_3 - k_3'(y_3 - y_2)$$

$$\frac{dy_5}{dt} = -k_1y_1y_5 + k_1'y_2 + k_2y_3^2 - k_2'y_5(y_4 - y_3)$$

The rate constants (catalyzed) are given in the following table:

$$k_i = A_i^o \exp\left[\frac{-E_i^o}{(1.987T)}\right] + A_i^c y_3 \exp\left[\frac{-E_i^c}{(1.987T)}\right]$$

$$k_i' = k_i \left[\exp\left(\frac{\Delta S_i}{1.987} - \frac{\Delta H_i}{1.987T}\right)\right]^{-1} ; \ i = 1, 2, 3$$

i	A_i^o	E_i^o	A_i^c	E_i^c	ΔH_i	ΔS_i
1	5.9874×10^5	1.9880×10^4	4.3075×10^7	1.8806×10^4	1.9180×10^3	-7.8846
2	1.8942×10^{10}	2.3271×10^4	1.2114×10^{10}	2.0670×10^4	-5.9458×10^3	9.4374×10^{-1}
3	2.8558×10^9	2.2845×10^4	1.6377×10^{10}	2.0107×10^4	-4.0438×10^3	-6.9457

T is the temperature in K. Integrate the ODE-IVPs using an RK computer code, with the following initial conditions $\mathbf{y}_0 = [8.8 \quad 0 \quad 0 \quad 0 \quad 0.177]^T$ and $T = 538K$. Plot $1 - \dfrac{y_1}{y_{1,0}}$ (caprolactam conversion) and $\dfrac{113 y_4}{y_3}$ (average molecular weight) as functions of t (t is in hr in the ODE-IVPs) for $0 \le t \le 12$.

5.28 Integrate the ODE-IVPs given in

    (*a*) eq. 5.75

    (*b*) eq. 5.112

    (*c*) eq. 5.113 (fig. 5.13a)

    (*d*) example 5.12

using a GEAR computer package. Check your results against those presented in this chapter.

5.29 Consider the 2nd order Gear implicit equation. Obtain its characteristic roots, and study its stability in terms of

    (*a*) spurious roots. Find out which root is the correct one;

    (*b*) propagation of round-off errors.

Hints: $(1 + x)^{\frac{1}{2}} = 1 + \dfrac{x}{2} - \dfrac{x^2}{8} + \ldots$

$$(1 - x)^{-1} = 1 + x + x^2 + x^3 + \ldots$$

Be careful about points where you get $\dfrac{a}{0}$ or $\dfrac{0}{0}$.

5.30 Solve the following set of DAEs for $10^{-6} \le t \le 10^6$:

$$\frac{dy_1}{dt} = -0.04 y_1 + 10^4 y_2 y_3$$

$$\frac{dy_2}{dt} = -0.04 y_1 - 10^4 y_2 y_3 - 3 \times 10^7 y_2^2$$

$$g(t) = y_1 \exp\left(3 \times 10^7 y_1 \; y_2 \; y_3\right) + y_2 + y_3 - 1 = 0$$

$$y_{1,0} = 1; \; y_{2,0} = 0; \; y_{3,0} = 10^{-3}$$

REFERENCES

1. G.F. Froment and K.B. Bischoff, *Chemical Reactor Analysis and Design*, 2nd. ed., Wiley, New York, 1990.
2. L. Lapidus, *Digital Computation for Chemical Engineers*, McGraw Hill, New York, 1962.
3. B.A. Finlayson, *Nonlinear Analysis in Chemical Engineering*, McGraw Hill, New York, 1980.
4. R.L. Burden and J.D. Faires, *Numerical Analysis*, 3rd. ed., Prindle, Weber and Schmidt, Boston, 1985.
5. J.R. Rice, *Numerical Methods, Software and Analysis: IMSL Reference Edition*, McGraw Hill, New York, 1983.
6. L. Lapidus and J.H. Seinfeld, *Numerical Solution of Ordinary Differential Equations*, Academic, New York, 1971.
7. S. Gill, *Proc. Cambridge Phil. Soc.*, **47**, 96 (1951).
8. H. von Foerster, P.M. Mora and L.W. Amiot, Science, **132**, 1291 (1960).
9. J. Serrin, *Science*, **189**, 86 (1975).
10. M.E. Davis, *Numerical Methods and Modeling for Chemical Engineers*, Wiley, New York, 1984.
11. E. Fehlberg, *Z. Angewandte Mathem. Mech.*, **44**, 17 (1964).
12. G.J. Prokopakis and W.D. Seider, *Ind. Eng. Chem., Fundam.*, **20**, 255 (1981).
13. M.L. Michelsen, *AIChEJ*, **22**, 594 (1976).
14. A.H. Robertson, in *Numerical Analysis,* J. Walsh, ed., Thompson Book Co., Washington, 1976, p. 178.
15. J.B. Caillaud and L. Padmanabhan, *Chem. Eng. J.*, **2**, 227(1971).
16. H.H. Rosenbrock, *Comput. J.*, **5**, 329 (1963).
17. C.D. Holland and A.I. Liapis, *Computer Methods for Solving Dynamic Separation Problems*, McGraw Hill, New York, 1983.
18. H.S. Mickley, T.K. Sherwood and C.E. Reid, *Applied Mathematics in Chemical Engineering*, 2nd ed., McGraw Hill, New York, 1957.
19. C.W. Gear, *Numerical Initial Value Problems in Ordinary Differential Equations,* Prentice Hall, Englewood Cliffs, N.J., 1971.
20. F.T. Krogh, *J.A.C.M.*, **13**, 374 (1966).
21. G. Dahlquist, *Proc. Symp. Appl. Math,* **15**, 147 (1963).
22. R. Bellman, *Introduction to Matrix Analysis*, 2nd ed., McGraw Hill, New York, 1960.
23. R.C. Aiken and L. Lapidus, *AIChEJ*, **20**, 368 (1974).
24. R.J. Field and R.M. Noyes, *J. Chem. Phys.*, **60**, 1877 (1974).
25. A.C. Hindmarsh and G.D. Byrne, Computer Documentation, UCID-30112, Rev. 1, Lawrence Livermore Laboratory, April 1977.
26. G.D. Byrne and A.C. Hindmarsh, in L. Lapidus and W.E. Schiesser, eds., *Numerical Methods for Differential Systems*, Academic, New York, 1976.
    [Refs. 25 and 26 give details of EPISODE]
27. C.W. Gear in A.J.H. Morrel, ed., *Information Processing*, **68**, North Holland, Amsterdam, 1969.
28. C.W. Gear, *Commun. ACM*, **14**, 176 (1971).
29. C.W. Gear, *IEEE Trans. Circuit Theory*, **CT18**, 89 (1971).
30. A. Nordsieck, *Math. Comp.*, **16**, 22 (1962).
31. User's Manual, *IMSL Library Math Library*, Int. Math. Stat. Lib. Inc., Houston, 1989.
32. G.D. Byrne, A.C. Hindmarsh, K.R. Jackson and H.G. Brown, *Comput. Chem. Eng.*, **1**, 133 (1977).
33. R.M. Chemburkar, O.E. Rossler and A. Varma, *Chem. Eng. Sci.*, **42**, 1507 (1987).
34. S.K. Gupta, M.V.G. Krishnamurthy and A. Kumar, *Polym. Eng. Sci.*, **25**, 37 (1985).
35. K.E. Brenan, S.L. Campbell and L.R. Petzold, *Numerical Solution of Initial-Value Problems in Differential Algebraic Equations,* North Holland, New York, 1989.
36. N. Jothi and A. Varma, *AIChEJ*, **27**, 848 (1981).
37. S.K. Gupta and A. Kumar, *Reaction Engineering of Step Growth Polymerization*, Plenum, New York, 1987.

Ordinary Differential Equations: Boundary Value Problems

6.1 INTRODUCTION

There is another class of ordinary differential equations, namely, boundary value problems (ODE-BVPs), which occurs quite frequently in engineering. In these, the boundary conditions on the dependent variables, **y**, are specified at two *different* values of the independent variable, x (note that we are using x instead of t here, since a spatial coordinate is usually involved). An example (from chemical engineering), mentioned in sec. 5.1 is the tubular reactor with axial mixing (TRAM), using the Danckwerts' boundary condition [1] (see eq. 5.4). The problem of diffusion cum reaction in a porous catalyst pellet (the classic Thiele [2] problem) also belongs to this category. For an isothermal spherical catalyst particle, this is described by [1, 2]

$$\frac{1}{x^2}\frac{d}{dx}\left(Dx^2\frac{dy}{dx}\right) - \mathcal{R}(y) = 0 \qquad \qquad \text{...}(a)$$

$$x = 0 \; : \; \frac{dy}{dx} = 0 \qquad \qquad \text{...}(b)$$

$$x = R \; : \; -D\frac{dy}{dx} = k_g\left(y - y_0\right) \qquad \qquad \text{...}(c) \qquad \text{...}(6.1)$$

where D is the effective diffusivity, k_g is the mass transfer coefficient of the fluid film surrounding the particle, R is the particle radius, y is the concentration of the reactant at radial location x, y_0 is the value of y outside the particle, and $\mathcal{R}(y)$ is a rate of reaction (mol reactant consumed per unit volume per second) term. Several heat and mass transfer problems are also described by ODE-BVPs. For example, the steady state heat conduction in an infinite slab of thickness, L, is described by

$$\frac{d}{dx}\left(k\frac{dy}{dx}\right) = 0$$

$$x = 0: y = y_0$$

$$x = L: y = y_1 \qquad \qquad \text{...}(6.2)$$

where k is the thermal conductivity of the material, y is the temperature, x is the distance from one surface of the slab (where the temperature is y_0) and y_1 is the temperature at the other face of the slab. Some more examples will be discussed as we proceed in this chapter.

Several techniques are available to solve these problems: finite difference, orthogonal collocation, orthogonal collocation on finite elements, Galerkin's technique on finite elements, etc. In all these the ODE-BVPs are reduced to a set of algebraic equations, and techniques discussed in Chapter 3 are used to solve the latter. These techniques are now discussed.

6.2 THE FINITE DIFFERENCE TECHNIQUE

Let us consider the following general form of a second-order ODE-BVP,*
ODE:

$$F\left(\frac{d^2y}{dx^2}, \frac{dy}{dx}, y, x\right) = 0 \qquad \ldots(a)$$

Boundary Conditions:

$$f_1\left(\frac{dy}{dx}, y, x\right) = 0 \text{ at } x = 0 \qquad \ldots(b)$$

$$f_2\left(\frac{dy}{dx}, y, x\right) = 0 \text{ at } x = 1 \qquad \ldots(c) \qquad \ldots(6.3)$$

Several ODE-BVPs of interest to engineers can be written in the above form.

The domain of x, $0 \le x \le 1$, is divided into $N + 1$ equispaced** *grid points* (see fig. 6.1), $x_1, x_2, \ldots,$

Fig. 6.1 The grid points used in the finite difference technique.

x_{N+1}, located such that

$$x_i = (i-1)\Delta x \equiv (i-1)\left(\frac{x_{N+1} - x_1}{N}\right); \quad i = 1, 2, \ldots, N+1 \qquad \ldots(6.4)$$

As in earlier chapters, we define the value of y at location x_i, as y_i:

$$y_i \equiv y(x_i) \qquad \ldots(6.5)$$

We then need to develop expressions for $\dfrac{d^2y}{dx^2}$ and $\dfrac{dy}{dx}$ at location, x_i, in terms of the values, y_i. A Taylor series representation is used for this purpose:

$$y_{i+1} = y(x_i + \Delta x) = y_i + \left.\frac{dy}{dx}\right|_{x_i}(\Delta x) + \frac{1}{2!}y_i''(\Delta x)^2 + \frac{1}{3!}y_i'''(\Delta x)^3 + \ldots \qquad \ldots(6.6)$$

---

* Procedures for higher order ODEs can be developed easily (see problems at the end of this chapter). See prob. 6.18.
** this is not necessary, but is quite common.

where $y_i^{(k)} \equiv \dfrac{d^k y}{dx^k}\Big|_{x_i}$. Similarly, we can write y_{i-1} as

$$y_{i-1} = y(x_i - \Delta x) = y_i - y_i'(\Delta x) + \frac{1}{2!} y_i''(\Delta x)^2 - \frac{1}{3!} y_i'''(\Delta x)^3 + \dots \qquad \dots (6.7)$$

Eqs. 6.6 and 6.7 can be used to give several equations for y_i':

$$\boxed{\frac{y_{i+1} - y_i}{\Delta x} = y_i'} + y_i'' \frac{(\Delta x)}{2} + \dots \left(\text{from eq. 6.6}\right) \qquad \dots (a)$$

$$\boxed{\frac{y_i - y_{i-1}}{\Delta x} = y_i'} - y_i'' \frac{(\Delta x)}{2} + \dots \left(\text{from eq. 6.7}\right) \qquad \dots (b)$$

$$\boxed{\frac{y_{i+1} - y_{i-1}}{2\Delta x} = y_i'} + \frac{y'''}{3!}(\Delta x)^2 + \dots \text{ (from eqs. 6.6 and 6.7)} \quad \dots (c) \qquad \dots (6.8)$$

Equations 6.8 $(a) - (c)$ give three formulae for y_i' in terms of the values of y at the grid points. These are shown in boxes. The first two are accurate to $O(\Delta x)$, while eq. 6.8(c) is accurate to $O\,[(\Delta x)^2]$ and so is more commonly used. The corresponding equations for y_i' when the grid points are not equispaced, can easily be derived (see prob. 6.1). It may be noted that eqs. 6.8 (a) and (b) are identical to eqs. 4.63 and 4.65. Equations 4.63 and 4.64 can be used to give yet another expression for y_i' (prob. 6.2) correct to $O\,[(\Delta x^2)]$

$$y_i' = \frac{-y_{i+2} + 4 y_{i+1} - 3 y_i}{2(\Delta x)} + \frac{1}{3} y_i'''(\Delta x)^2 \qquad \dots (6.9)$$

It may be noted that eq. 6.8(c) expresses y_i' in terms of values of y at points a step ahead and a step behind point i. In contrast, eq. 6.9 expresses y_i' in terms of values of y at points ahead of point i and so is known as a one-sided formula [3]. Several other expressions for y_i correct to $O\,(\Delta x)$ or $O\,[(\Delta x)^2]$ can be obtained similarly.

Equations 6.8(a) and (b) can be combined to give an equation for the second derivative, y_i'', at location i:

$$\boxed{\frac{y_{i+1} - 2 y_i + y_{i-1}}{(\Delta x)^2} = y_i''} + \frac{2 y_i''''(\Delta x)^2}{4!} \dots \qquad \dots (6.10)$$

Corresponding expressions for y_i'' when the grid points are not equispaced can easily be obtained. Similarly, expressions for y_i'' in terms of values of y at points lying only ahead of point i, or lying only behind point i, can be obtained (see prob. 6.3).

Equations 6.8(c) and 6.10 are the most popular forms used in the finite difference method (note that *both* of these are accurate to $O\,[(\Delta x)^2]$; *one usually avoids using formulae having different accuracies for the same independent variable*). These equations can be used to reduce eq. 6.3 to algebraic equations:

$$\mathbb{R}_i = F\left[\frac{y_{i+1} - 2y_i + y_{i-1}}{(\Delta x)^2}, \frac{y_{i+1} - y_{i-1}}{2(\Delta x)}, y_i, x_i\right] = 0; \quad i = 2, 3, ..., N \quad ...(a)$$

$$f_1\left[\frac{y_2 - y_0}{2(\Delta x)}, y_1, 0\right] = 0 \qquad\qquad ...(b)$$

$$f_2\left[\frac{y_{N+2} - y_N}{2(\Delta x)}, y_{N+1}, 1\right] = 0 \qquad\qquad ...(c) \qquad ...(6.11)$$

$\mathbb{R}_i$ is called the *residual* at point *i*. Eq. 6.11(*a*) forces the residual to be zero at each of the *internal* finite difference grid points. In another words, we choose the values of y_i such that the ODE-BVP is satisfied *exactly* at the internal grid points. Obviously, the larger the value of *N*, the more is the number of points at which we are forcing the ODE-BVP to be satisfied, and the closer is the numerical solution expected to be to the exact solution. Note that forcing the residual to be zero at a grid point does not imply that $y_i = y_{i,\ exact}$ at that point. Use of eq. 6.8(*c*) in the boundary conditions [eqs. 6.11(*b*) and (*c*)] leads to new variables, y_0 and y_{N+2}, values of *y* at *hypothetical* grid points. Thus, there are $N + 3$ unknowns and only $N + 1$ algebraic equations in eq. 6.11. Methods to account for these are discussed after example 6.1.

Example 6.1: An isothermal TRAM (tubular reactor with axial mixing) with an irreversible, second-order reaction taking place, is described (in chemical engineering) by

$$\frac{1}{Pe}\frac{d^2y}{dx^2} - \frac{dy}{dx} - Da\ y^2 = 0 \qquad 0 \le x \le 1$$

with boundary conditions

$$\frac{dy}{dx} = Pe(y - 1) \text{ at } x = 0$$

$$\frac{dy}{dx} = 0 \qquad\qquad \text{at } x = 1$$

Here, *y* is the dimensionless reactant concentration, *x* is the dimensionless axial position, *Pe* is the Peclet number for mass transfer and *Da* is the Damköhler number. Recast these equations into a finite difference form with $N = 3$ (four grid points, equispaced), with $Pe = 6$, $Da = 2$.

Equation 6.11 gives, for this case:

$$\frac{y_3 - 2y_2 + y_1}{6(\Delta x)^2} - \frac{y_3 - y_1}{2(\Delta x)} - 2y_2^2 = 0$$

$$\frac{y_4 - 2y_3 + y_2}{6(\Delta x)^2} - \frac{y_4 - y_2}{2(\Delta x)} - 2y_3^2 = 0$$

$$\frac{y_2 - y_0}{2(\Delta x)} = 6(y_1 - 1) \qquad\qquad ...(a)$$

$$\frac{y_5 - y_3}{2(\Delta x)} = 0 \qquad\qquad ...(b)$$

We have not substituted $\Delta x = \dfrac{1}{3}$. There are six unknowns, y_0 to y_5, and only four *algebraic* equations. So, we need two more equations to obtain unique solutions.

One possibility for obtaining two more algebraic equations to complete the set is to make the residual zero at the boundary points, $i = 1$ and $i = N + 1$, as well. This is illustrated below for example 6.1. ∎

Example 6.2: Obtain two more algebraic equations for the ODE-BVP of example 6.1, and eliminate y_0 and y_5. Solve to give the axial variation of y.

We have by making the residual zero at grid points 1 and 4:

$$\frac{y_2 - 2y_1 + y_0}{6(\Delta x)^2} - \frac{y_2 - y_0}{2(\Delta x)} - 2y_1^2 = 0$$

$$\frac{y_5 - 2y_4 + y_3}{6(\Delta x)^2} - \frac{y_5 - y_3}{2(\Delta x)} - 2y_4^2 = 0$$

On substituting Eqs. (*a*) and (*b*) of example 6.1:

$$y_0 = y_2 - 12(\Delta x)(y_1 - 1)$$

$$y_5 = y_3$$

into the above equations, we obtain

$$\frac{1}{3(\Delta x)^2} y_2 - \left[\frac{1}{3(\Delta x)^2} + \frac{2}{\Delta x} + 6\right] y_1 = 2y_1^2 - \left(6 + \frac{2}{\Delta x}\right)$$

$$\frac{1}{3(\Delta x)^2} y_3 - \frac{1}{3(\Delta x)^2} y_4 = 2y_4^2$$

It is common to substitute for the *hypothetical* values (y_0 and y_{N+2}) and obtain $N + 1$ equations for $y_1, y_2, ..., y_{N+1}$, rather than work with $N + 3$ equations in $y_0, y_1, ..., y_{N+2}$, where possible. The final equations can be written in matrix form as

$$\begin{bmatrix} -\left[\dfrac{1}{3(\Delta x)^2} + \dfrac{2}{\Delta x} + 6\right] & \dfrac{1}{3(\Delta x)^2} & 0 & 0 \\[2ex] \left[\dfrac{1}{6(\Delta x)^2} + \dfrac{1}{2(\Delta x)}\right] & -\dfrac{1}{3(\Delta x)^2} & \left[\dfrac{1}{6(\Delta x)^2} - \dfrac{1}{2(\Delta x)}\right] & 0 \\[2ex] 0 & \left[\dfrac{1}{6(\Delta x)^2} + \dfrac{1}{2(\Delta x)}\right] & -\dfrac{1}{3(\Delta x)^2} & \left[\dfrac{1}{6(\Delta x)^2} - \dfrac{1}{2(\Delta x)}\right] \\[2ex] 0 & 0 & \dfrac{1}{3(\Delta x)^2} & -\dfrac{1}{3(\Delta x)^2} \end{bmatrix} \begin{bmatrix} y_1 \\[2ex] y_2 \\[2ex] y_3 \\[2ex] y_4 \end{bmatrix}$$

$$
= \begin{bmatrix} 2y_1^2 - 6 - \dfrac{2}{\Delta x} \\[2mm] 2y_2^2 \\[1mm] 2y_3^2 \\[1mm] 2y_4^2 \end{bmatrix}
$$

or

$$
\mathbf{A}\,\mathbf{y} = \mathbf{f}\,(\mathbf{y})
$$

The generalization to larger values of N is quite simple. Note the tridiagonal form of the matrix, **A,** of constants. Also, note that all the nonlinear terms have been taken to the right hand side. The successive substitutions technique can now be used to give

$$
\mathbf{A}\mathbf{y}^{(k+1)} = \mathbf{f}\!\left(\mathbf{y}^{(k)}\right);\ k = 1,\,2,\,\dots
$$

Since **A** does not change with iteration number, we can use a single LU Decomp of **A** (using a special version to exploit its tridiagonal nature—see Thomas' method in example 1.7), and several fore-and-aft sweeps, with the right hand side being updated everytime. Alternatively, the Newton-Raphson technique can be used to give (see prob. 3.21) a procedure to obtain the solution, $\mathbf{y}$, for the general case with $N + 1$ grid points:

$$
\begin{bmatrix}
a-4y_1 & b & 0 & 0\dots\ 0 & 0 & 0 \\
c & -b-4y_2 & d & 0\dots\ 0 & 0 & 0 \\
0 & c & -b-4y_3 & d\dots\ 0 & 0 & 0 \\
\cdot & \cdot & \cdot & \cdot\ \ \cdot & \cdot & \cdot \\
\cdot & \cdot & \cdot & \cdot\ \ \cdot & \cdot & \cdot \\
0 & 0 & 0 & 0\dots\ c\ \ -b-4y_N & d \\
0 & 0 & 0 & 0\dots\ 0 & b & -b-4y_{N+1}
\end{bmatrix}^{(k)}
\begin{bmatrix} y_1 \\ y_2 \\ y_3 \\ \cdot \\ \cdot \\ y_N \\ y_{N+1} \end{bmatrix}^{(k+1)}
=
\begin{bmatrix} -2y_1^2 - e \\ -2y_2^2 \\ -2y_3^2 \\ \cdot \\ \cdot \\ -2y_N^2 \\ -2y_{N+1}^2 \end{bmatrix}^{(k)}
$$

where $a = -\left[\dfrac{1}{3(\Delta x)^2} + \dfrac{2}{\Delta x} + 6\right]$, $b = \dfrac{1}{3(\Delta x)^2}$, $c = \left[\dfrac{1}{6(\Delta x)^2} + \dfrac{1}{2(\Delta x)}\right]$, $d = \left[\dfrac{1}{6(\Delta x)^2} - \dfrac{1}{2(\Delta x)}\right]$, and

$e = \left[6 + \dfrac{2}{\Delta x}\right]$. The matrix on the left changes from iteration to iteration, and so LU decomp and sweep is not as useful. Thomas' algorithm or the Gauss-Seidel technique can be used to obtain solutions.

The numerical results for some values of N are given below (see prob. 6.4):

N	y_1	y_2	y_3	y_4	y_5	y_6	y_7	y_8
3	0.8273	0.5929	0.4550	0.3658	–	–	–	–
5	0.8296	0.6677	0.5548	0.4728	0.4130	0.3786	–	–
7	0.8304	0.7071	0.6133	0.5400	0.4817	0.4353	0.4006	0.3827

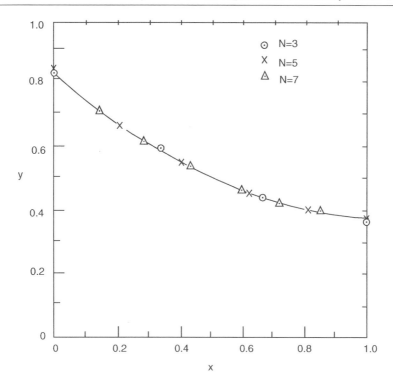

Fig. 6.2 Dimensionless concentration *vs.* axial location for the TRAM in example 6.2, using different numbers, $N + 1$, of grid points.

Figure 6.2 shows the results graphically for different values of N. Since the expressions used for y'' and y' are accurate upto $O[(\Delta x)^2]$, an increase in N (decrease in Δx) leads to reduction of errors. Usually, one increases N till the results become insensitive to further increases in its value. ■

Another method of taking care of boundary conditions is to use one-sided formulae for y_1' and/or y'_{N+1}. This is illustrated in prob. 6.5. For large N, the results are indistinguishable from that obtained using the earlier formulation involving hypothetical grid points, 0 and $N + 2$.

We saw in the previous discussion how to take care of boundary conditions involving y' [eqs. 6.3(b) and (c)]. Hypothetical points were introduced where required, and both the ODE-BVP as well as the boundary conditions were satisfied at the boundary points, $i = 1$ and/or $i = N + 1$. A somewhat similar situation arises in situations where there is symmetry of y about a certain value of x. An example (in chemical engineering) is diffusion cum reaction in an isothermal, porous, spherical catalyst pellet (Thiele [1,2] problem). This phenomenon is illustrated through the following ODE-BVP (see eq. 6.1)

$$\frac{1}{x^2}\frac{d}{dx}\left(x^2\frac{dy}{dx}\right) = \frac{d^2y}{dx^2} + \frac{2}{x}\frac{dy}{dx} = \phi^2 y^n \qquad \ldots(a)$$

$$\text{at } x = 0 : \left(\frac{dy}{dx}\right) = 0 \qquad \ldots(b)$$

$$\text{at } x = 1 : -\frac{dy}{dx} = Bi_m\left(y - 1\right) \qquad \ldots(c) \qquad \ldots(6.12)$$

Equation 6.12 is written in terms of dimensionless variables, in contrast to eq. 6.1. In eq. 6.12, y is the dimensionless concentration, n is the order of the irreversible reaction and ϕ and Bi_m are the (dimensionless) Thiele modulus and Biot number for mass transfer, respectively. The reactant concentration, y, is symmetrical about the centre, $x = 0$. If one has grid points $x_1 \,(= 0)$, $x_2, x_3, \ldots, x_{N+1}$ $(= 1)$, one obtains from eq. 6.12(b).

$$\frac{y_2 - y_0}{2(\Delta x)} = 0 \qquad \ldots (6.13)$$

where a hypothetical point, 0, has been introduced. The ODE-BVP (eq. 6.12a) can be used in its finite difference form at x_1 to give

$$\mathbb{R}_1 = \left[\frac{d^2 y}{dx^2} + \frac{2}{x}\frac{dy}{dx}\right]_{x_1} - \phi^2 y_1^n = 0 \qquad \ldots (6.14)$$

A problem arises here because $x = 0$ at point x_1, and the $\dfrac{2}{x}\left(\dfrac{dy}{dx}\right)$ term leads to 0/0 (using eq. 6.13)

at this location. L'Hospital's rule is used to get

$$\underset{x \to 0}{\text{Lim}} \frac{\dfrac{dy}{dx}}{x} = \frac{\dfrac{d^2 y}{dx^2}}{1} \qquad \ldots (6.15)$$

This gives on substitution into eq. 6.14

$$3y_1'' - \phi^2 y_1^n = 0 \qquad \ldots (6.16)$$

Equation 6.13 now gives

$$3\left(\frac{y_2 - 2y_1 + y_0}{(\Delta x)^2}\right) - \phi^2 y_1^n = \frac{6(y_2 - y_1)}{(\Delta x)^2} - \phi^2 y_1^n = 0 \qquad \ldots (6.17)$$

This can be solved with the other equations obtained by applying the finite difference technique to the ODE-BVP at the grid points, $x_2, x_3, \ldots, x_{N+1}$ (see prob. 6.6) to give the dimensionless concentration profile, $y(x)$, inside the catalyst pellet. Example 6.3 illustrates the use of these techniques for the classic problem (in chemical engineering) of reaction cum diffusion in a nonisothermal, porous, spherical catalyst pellet.

Example 6.3: The diffusion cum first-order irreversible reaction in a *non-isothermal,* porous, spherical catalyst particle is described by the following equation [1,3]:

$$\frac{d^2 y}{dx^2} + \frac{2}{x}\frac{dy}{dx} = \phi^2 \left\{ y \exp\left[\gamma - \frac{\gamma}{1 - \beta y + \beta(1-\delta)y_{N+1} + \beta\delta}\right] \right\} \equiv \phi^2 f(y)$$

$$x = 0: \frac{dy}{dx} = 0$$

$$x = 1: -\frac{dy}{dx} = Bi_m\left[y_{N+1} - 1\right] \qquad \ldots (a)$$

In the above equations, the common symbols have the same meaning as in eq. 6.12, y_{N+1} is the value of y at $x = 1$ [the $(N + 1)$th grid point in the finite-difference scheme], γ is the dimensionless activation energy, β is the dimensionless heat of reaction (Prater temperature), and δ is the ratio of the Biot numbers for mass and heat transfer (see ref. 3, sec. 4.5 for details). The dimensionless temperature, $T(x)$, is related to the dimensionless concentration, $y(x)$, by

$$T = 1 - \beta y + \beta y_{N+1}(1 - \delta) + \beta\delta \qquad \qquad ...(b)$$

Obtain the final equations for y_i, the concentration at grid point i, using the finite-difference scheme, with $N + 1$ equi-spaced grid points, $i = 1$ $(x = 0)$, 2, ..., $N + 1$ $(x = 1)$, located a distance $x\left(= \dfrac{1}{N}\right)$, apart.

At any grid point away from the two 'boundaries' of the problem, we have

$$\frac{y_{i+1} - 2y_i + y_{i-1}}{(\Delta x)^2} + \frac{2}{x_i}\frac{y_{i+1} - y_{i-1}}{2(\Delta x)} - \phi^2 f(y_i) = 0 ; \quad i = 2, 3, ..., N$$

where $$x_i = (i - 1)\Delta x$$

$$f(y_i) = y_i \exp\left[\gamma - \frac{\gamma}{1 - \beta y_i + \beta(1 - \delta)y_{N+1} + \beta\delta}\right]$$

The above equation can be written as

$$(1 + b_i)y_{i+1} + (-2)y_i + (1 - b_i)y_{i-1} = \phi^2 (\Delta x)^2 f(y_i) \qquad \qquad ...(c)$$

where

$$b_i = \frac{\Delta x}{x_i} = \frac{1}{i - 1}$$

At $x = 0$, we introduce a hypothetical grid point, $i = 0$, and get from the boundary condition and the ODE (and L'Hospital's rule as in eq. 6.15):

$$\frac{y_2 - y_0}{2(\Delta x)} = 0, \text{ or } y_0 = y_2$$

$$3\left(\frac{y_2 - 2y_1 + y_0}{(\Delta x)^2}\right) = \phi^2 f(y_1)$$

This simplifies to

$$6y_2 - 6y_1 = \phi^2 (\Delta x)^2 f(y_1) \qquad \qquad ...(d)$$

At $x = 1$ $(i = N + 1)$, we use a hypothetical grid point, $i = N + 2$, and use both the boundary condition and the ODE to give

$$-\frac{y_{N+2} - y_N}{2(\Delta x)} = Bi_m (y_{N+1} - 1), \text{ or } y_{N+2} = y_N - 2Bi_m (\Delta x)(y_{N+1} - 1)$$

$$\frac{y_{N+2} - 2y_{N+1} + y_N}{(\Delta x)^2} + \frac{2}{1}\frac{y_{N+2} - y_N}{2(\Delta x)} = \phi^2 f(y_{N+1})$$

This simplifies to

$$\left\{-2 - 2Bi_m(\Delta x)[1 + (\Delta x)]\right\} y_{N+1} + 2y_N = \phi^2 f(y_{N+1})(\Delta x)^2 - 2Bi_m(\Delta x)[1 + (\Delta x)] \quad \dots (e)$$

Equations $(c) - (e)$ can be written in matrix form as

$$
\begin{bmatrix}
-6 & 6 & 0 & 0 & \cdots & 0 & 0 & 0 \\
1-b_2 & -2 & 1+b_2 & 0 & \cdots & 0 & 0 & 0 \\
0 & 1-b_3 & -2 & 1+b_3 & \cdots & 0 & 0 & 0 \\
. & . & . & . & \cdots & . & . & . \\
. & . & . & . & \cdots & . & . & . \\
. & . & . & . & \cdots & . & . & . \\
. & . & . & . & \cdots & . & . & . \\
. & . & . & . & \cdots & . & . & . \\
. & . & . & . & \cdots & . & . & . \\
0 & 0 & 0 & 0 & \cdots & 1-b_N & -2 & 1+b_N \\
0 & 0 & 0 & 0 & \cdots & 0 & 2 & -2-Bi_m(\Delta x)(1+\Delta x)
\end{bmatrix}
\begin{bmatrix}
y_1 \\ y_2 \\ y_3 \\ . \\ . \\ . \\ . \\ . \\ . \\ y_N \\ y_{N+1}
\end{bmatrix}
$$

$$
=
\begin{bmatrix}
\phi^2 (\Delta x)^2 f(y_1) \\
\phi^2 (\Delta x)^2 f(y_2) \\
\phi^2 (\Delta x)^2 f(y_3) \\
. \\
. \\
. \\
. \\
. \\
. \\
\phi^2 (\Delta x)^2 f(y_N) \\
\phi^2 (\Delta x)^2 f(y_{N+1}) - 2Bi_m(\Delta x)(1+\Delta x)
\end{bmatrix}
$$

The results of problem 3.21 can now be used to give the Newton-Raphson algorithm for solving this nonlinear algebraic equation as

$$
\begin{bmatrix}
-6-\phi^2(\Delta x)^2 f'(y_1) & 6 & 0 & 0... \cdot 0\ 0 \\
1-b_2 & -2-\phi^2(\Delta x)^2 f'(y_2)\ 1+b_2 & 0... \cdot 0\ 0 \\
& \cdot & \cdot & \cdot\ \cdot\ \cdot\ \cdot \\
& \cdot & \cdot & \cdot\ \cdot\ \cdot\ \cdot \\
& \cdot & \cdot & \cdot\ \cdot\ \cdot\ \cdot \\
& \cdot & \cdot & \cdot\ \cdot\ \cdot\ \cdot \\
0 & 0 & 0\ 0... \cdot\ 2\ \xi
\end{bmatrix}^{(k)}
\begin{bmatrix}
y_1 \\
y_2 \\
\cdot \\
\cdot \\
\cdot \\
\cdot \\
y_{N+1}
\end{bmatrix}^{(k+1)}
$$

$$
=
\begin{bmatrix}
\phi^2(\Delta x)^2 \left[f(y_1) - y_1 f'(y_1) \right] \\
\phi^2(\Delta x)^2 \left[f(y_2) - y_2 f'(y_2) \right] \\
\cdot \\
\cdot \\
\cdot \\
\cdot \\
\phi^2(\Delta x)^2 \left[f(y_{N+1}) - y_{N+1} f'(y_{N+1}) \right] - 2 Bi_n (\Delta x)(1+\Delta x)
\end{bmatrix}^{(k)}
$$

where

$$
\xi \equiv -2 - Bi_m (\Delta x)(1+\Delta x) - \phi^2 (\Delta x)^2 f'(y_{N+1})
$$

and $f' = \dfrac{df}{dy}$ can easily be obtained. The tridiagonal nature of the matrix on the left hand side is to be noted (it changes with every iteration). Thomas' algorithm can be used to give solutions of this set of linear algebraic equations for any NR iteration.

Ferguson [4] provides numerical results [4, 5] for the case when $\beta = 0.6$, $\gamma = 20$, $\phi = 0.5$, $\delta = 1$, $Bi_m = \infty$ (and so $y_{N+1} = 1$, see prob. 6.8). Figure 6.3 shows these results. It is observed that for these parameter values, there correspond three *profiles*. This reflects the multiplicity of steady states that are possible for this case (extensions of concepts in sec. 3.8 can be used to study multiplicity for ODE-BVPs). The different profiles can be obtained from the Newton-Raphson algorithm using different starting profiles, $y^{(1)}(x)$, the middle solution, Q (in fig. 6.3) being the most difficult to get (an initial guess profile very close to the final solution, helps). More details on the solutions of the reaction-diffusion problem in catalysts and aspects of multiplicity are available in refs. 6 and 7, and an extensive review of the problem itself is provided by Aris [8].

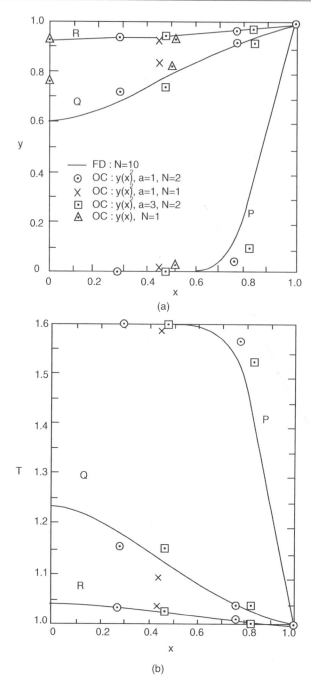

Fig. 6.3 Dimensionless concentration and temperature profiles, $y(x)$ and $T(x)$, for the reaction-diffusion problem of example 6.3. $\beta = 0.6$, $\gamma = 20$, $\phi = 0.5$, $\delta = 1$, $Bi_m = \infty$. Curve: FD results with $N = 10$. OC results also shown for various choices of trial functions (see examples 6.6 and 6.7). Note that $T = 1 + \beta - \beta y$.

   The values of $y(x)$ and $T(x)$ obtained at the grid points can be used to compute the effectiveness factor, η, given by

$$\eta = \frac{\text{Actual rate of consumption of reactant in the catalyst particle}}{\text{Rate of consumption of reactant if the entire catalyst particle were under ambient conditions}}$$

$$= 3\int_0^1 x^2 y(x)\exp\left[\gamma - \frac{\gamma}{T(x)}\right]dx$$

$$= 3\int_0^1 x^2 f(y)\,dx \qquad \qquad ...(f)$$

The integral can be evaluated using quadratures.

An alternate expression for η can also be used. This is given in terms of the flux at the outer surface (since all the reactant diffusing into the particle must react at steady state) [3]:

$$\eta = \frac{3}{\phi^2}\frac{dy}{dx}\bigg|_{x=1} \qquad \qquad ...(g)$$

Use of the integral to evaluate η is usually preferred when the finite difference method is used, since evaluation of derivatives involves more error. ∎

6.3 ORTHOGONAL COLLOCATION (OC)

A very popular technique for the solution of nonlinear ODE-BVPs is the orthogonal collocation method. This technique was developed sometimes during the early 1930s (see Chapter 1 of Ref. 5 for historical details) by Laczos [9], though his method is scarcely recognizable as the collocation method. Villadsen and Stewart [10] applied this technique for the first time to obtain solutions of boundary value problems. Since then, this technique has been used extensively to solve a whole variety of problems.

The technique owes part of its popularity to its simplicity. Let us consider the solution of the general second-order ODE-BVP in eq. 6.3 again. We first assume a solution, $y(x)$, in terms of a set of *trial* functions, $P_i(x)$:

$$y(x) = b_1 P_0(x) + b_2 P_1(x) + ... + b_{N+2}P_{N+1}(x) = \sum_{i=1}^{N+2} b_i P_{i-1}(x) \qquad ...(6.18)$$

In this equation, b_i are constant coefficients to be determined using the ODE-BVP and the boundary conditions. $P_i(x)$ are a set of trial functions which are *linearly independent* [11] in the domain of x ($0 \leq x \leq 1$), and are taken from a *complete* set [11] of such functions [any continuous function can be represented *exactly* as a linear combination of a set of *complete* functions; thus, $y(x)$ in eq. 6.18 becomes better as N increases]. Most often, the trial functions are also orthogonal over the domain of x, with respect to some weightage function, $W(x)$ (see Appendix 4A):

$$\int_0^1 W(x)P_i(x)P_j(x)\,dx = 0 ; \quad i \neq j; \ i,j = 0,1,2,...,N+1$$

$$= C_i; \quad i = j = 0,1,2,...,N+1 \qquad ...(6.19)$$

If $W(x) = 1$, $P_i(x)$ can easily be obtained using eq. A 4.7 as

$$P_0(x) = 1$$

$$P_1(x) = 2x - 1$$

$$P_2(x) = 6x^2 - 6x + 1$$

$$P_3(x) = 20x^3 - 30x^2 + 12x - 1, \dots \qquad \qquad \dots (6.20)$$

The orthogonal polynomial, $P_i(x)$, in eq. 6.20 is of degree i, and this set is referred to as the *shifted Legendre polynomials* (the Legendre polynomials are given in eq. A4.2). They form a complete and linearly independent set, and are one type of the more general Jacobi polynomials, $P_i^{(\alpha,\beta)}(x)$ [$P_i^{(\alpha,\beta)}(x)$ is an ith-degree polynomial too]. The latter are orthogonal over $0 \le x \le 1$ with respect to the weightage function $W(x) = (1-x)^\alpha x^\beta$, where α and β are constants. Detailed description of the various Jacobi polynomials, their properties, recursive formulae for generating them, methods to compute their roots, etc., are available in refs. 12 and 13.

At times, we could assume slightly different solutions for $y(x)$ than given in eq. 6.18. For example, if the boundary conditions for an ODE-BVP are

$$y(0) = 0$$
$$y(1) = 1 \qquad \qquad \dots (6.21)$$

we could assume a solution having the following form

$$y(x) = x + x(1-x) \sum_{i=1}^{N} b_i P_{i-1}(x) \qquad \qquad \dots (6.22)$$

This automatically satisfies the boundary conditions, and is of degree $(N+1)$; as is eq. 6.18. It is more convenient, however, not to pursue this line of approach, and instead, combine like-powered terms in x in eq. 6.18 [note that $P_i(x)$ contains monomials: 1, x, x^2, ..., x^i], and write the solution as

$$y(x) = d_1 + d_2 x + d_3 x^2 + d_4 x^3 + \dots + d_{N+2} x^{N+1} \qquad \qquad \dots (6.23)$$

The $N+2$ coefficients, $b_1, b_2, \dots, b_{N+2}$, have been replaced by an equal number of coefficients, $d_1, d_2, \dots, d_{N+2}$. It turns out [12] that the coefficients, b_i, decrease far more rapidly as i increases, than do the coefficients, d_i. However, eq. 6.23 is favoured since it leads to the handling of boundary conditions more directly and efficiently, as we see in the discussion below [12, 14]. Moreover, computer-oriented algorithms are easier to develop using eq. 6.23.

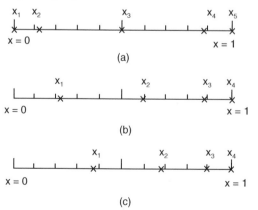

Fig. 6.4 Location of the OC points when (*a*) eq. 6.23 is used, $W(x) = 1$ in eq. 6.19; (*b*) eq. 6.32 is used with $W(x^2) = 1 - x^2$ in eq. 6.34; (*c*) eq. 6.32 is used with $W(x^2) = 1 - x^2$ in eq. 6.39. $N = 3$ in all three cases.

The $N + 2$ coefficients, d_i, $i = 1, 2, ..., N + 2$, in eq. 6.23 are evaluated by satisfying the two boundary conditions in eq. 6.3 at $x = x_1 = 0$, and $x = x_{N+2} = 1$ (see fig. 6.4a). In addition, we make the residual, $\mathbb{R}(x_i)$, zero at N distinct locations, $x_2, x_3, ..., x_{N+1}$, inside the interval, $0 < x < 1$. These points are referred to as collocation points. It is important to note that, in general the internal collocation points are not equispaced. In fact, Laczos [9] suggested as early as in 1938 that these be taken as roots of some orthogonal polynomial (he suggested the roots of Chebyshev polynomials to solve ODE-IVPs). In the present case, we shall take the N internal collocation points to be the roots of the Nth degree shifted Legendre polynomial, $P_N(x)$, given in eq. 6.20. This is why this technique is now referred to as the orthogonal collocation (OC) technique. Such a choice of OC points leads to the error, $|y_{\text{exact}}(x) - y(x)|$, being quite evenly distributed in the entire domain of x (see numerical results on the reaction-cum-diffusion problem in a cylindrical porous catalyst pellet in which a first order irreversible reaction is taking place, p. 186 in Ref. 12—the errors are much larger for equispaced collocation points). Moreover, such a choice of the OC points is optimal in the sense that values of the integral, $\int_0^1 \mathcal{F}(y)dx$ (which are often of interest, for example, for evaluating the mean value of y, or the effectiveness factor in the Thiele problem), evaluated using quadratures, are very accurately estimated. The locations of the OC points are given [5] as **x** in tables 6.1 and 6.2 for some values of N.

Table 6.1 Matrices for the Orthogonal Collocation technique [5] (non-symmetric)* $[0 \le x \le 1, W(x) = 1$ in eq. 6.19]

N + 2	x	w	A	B
3	$\begin{bmatrix} 0 \\ 0.5 \\ 1 \end{bmatrix}$	$\begin{bmatrix} \frac{1}{6} \\ \frac{2}{3} \\ \frac{1}{6} \end{bmatrix}$	$\begin{bmatrix} -3 & 4 & -1 \\ -1 & 0 & 1 \\ 1 & -4 & 3 \end{bmatrix}$	$\begin{bmatrix} 4 & -8 & 4 \\ 4 & -8 & 4 \\ 4 & -8 & 4 \end{bmatrix}$
4	$\begin{bmatrix} 0 \\ 0.21132 \\ 0.78868 \\ 1 \end{bmatrix}$	$\begin{bmatrix} 0 \\ \frac{1}{2} \\ \frac{1}{2} \\ 0 \end{bmatrix}$	$\begin{bmatrix} -7 & 8.196 & -2.196 & 1 \\ -2.732 & 1.732 & 1.732 & -0.7321 \\ 0.7321 & -1.732 & -1.732 & 2.732 \\ -1 & 2.196 & -8.196 & 7 \end{bmatrix}$	$\begin{bmatrix} 24 & -37.18 & 25.18 & -12 \\ 16.39 & -24 & 12 & -4.392 \\ -4.392 & 12 & -24 & 16.39 \\ -12 & 25.18 & -37.18 & 24 \end{bmatrix}$
5	$\begin{bmatrix} 0 \\ 0.11270 \\ 0.50000 \\ 0.88730 \\ 1 \end{bmatrix}$	$\begin{bmatrix} 0 \\ 0.27778 \\ 0.44444 \\ 0.27778 \\ 0 \end{bmatrix}$	use program in ref. 12 to generate these	

(Compiled from ref. 5)

* y given by eq. 6.23

Table 6.2 Values of x_i for the OC Technique [5]
[Roots of $P_N(x)$ or $P_N(x^2)$ in eqs. 6.19, 6.34($a = 1$), 6.42b ($a = 2$), and 6.39 ($a = 3$) respectively, $0 \le x \le 1$, $W(x)$ as listed]

N	eq. 6.23 for y; W (x) = 1 in	eq. 6.23 for y; W (x) = 1 − x² in		
	eq. 6.19	eq. 6.34 $a = 1$ planar geometry	eq. 6.42(b) $a = 2$ cylindrical geometry	eq. 6.39 $a = 3$ spherical geometry
1	0.5000000000	0.4472135955	0.5773502692	0.6546536707
2	0.2113248654	0.2852315165	0.3937651911	0.4688487935
	0.7886751346	0.7650553239	0.8030871524	0.8302238963
3	0.1127016654	0.2092992179	0.2976372952	0.3631174638
	0.5000000000	0.5917001814	0.6398959794	0.6771862795
	0.8872983346	0.8717401485	0.8875018095	0.8997579954
4	0.0694318442	0.1652789577	0.2389648430	0.2957581356
	0.3300094783	0.4779249498	0.5261587342	0.5652353270
	0.6699905218	0.7387738651	0.7639309081	0.7844834737
	0.9305681558	0.9195339082	0.9274913130	0.9340014304
5	0.0469100771	0.1365529329	0.1995240765	0.2492869301
	0.2307653450	0.3995309410	0.4449869862	0.4829098211
	0.5000000000	0.6328761530	0.6617966532	0.6861884691
	0.7692346551	0.8192793216	0.8339450062	0.8463475647
	0.9530899230	0.9448992722	0.9494550617	0.9533098466
6	0.0337652429	0.1163318689	0.1712204053	0.2153539554
	0.1693953068	0.3427240133	0.3848098228	0.4206380547
	0.3806904070	0.5506394029	0.5805038245	0.6062532055
	0.6193095931	0.7288685991	0.7474433215	0.7635196900
	0.8306046933	0.8678010538	0.8770597825	0.8850820442
	0.9662347571	0.9599350453	0.9627801781	0.9652459265
	$x_i, i = 2,3, ...,$ N+1 above; $x_1 = 0; x_{N+2} = 1$	$x_i, i = 1, 2, ..., N$ above; $x_{N+1} = 1$		

In order to evaluate the residuals, $\mathbb{R}(x_i)$, for eq. 6.3, we need expressions for the first and second derivatives of y. This is quite easy using the solution in eq. 6.23. We have from eq. 6.23.

$$y_i \equiv y\big|_{x_i} = 1d_1 + x_i d_2 + x_i^2 d_3 + x_i^3 d_4 + x_i^4 d_5 + ... + x_i^{N+1} d_{N+2}$$

$$y_i' \equiv \frac{dy}{dx}\bigg|_{x_i} = 0d_1 + 1d_2 + 2x_i d_3 + 3x_i^2 d_4 + 4x_i^3 d_5 + ... + (N+1)x_i^N d_{N+2}$$

$$y_i'' \equiv \frac{d^2y}{dx^2}\bigg|_{x_i} = 0d_1 + 0d_2 + 2d_3 + 6x_i d_4 + 12x_i^2 d_5 + ... + N(N+1)x_i^{N-1} d_{N+2} \qquad ...(6.24)$$

The values of y and its derivatives at locations, $x_1, x_2, ..., x_{N+2}$ (note that the two boundary points are included) can be written from eq. 6.24 in a matrix form as

$$\mathbf{y} \equiv \begin{bmatrix} y_1 \\ y_2 \\ y_3 \\ \cdot \\ \cdot \\ \cdot \\ \cdot \\ y_{N+2} \end{bmatrix} = \begin{bmatrix} 1 & x_1 & x_1^2 & x_1^3 & \cdots & x_1^{N+1} \\ 1 & x_2 & x_2^2 & x_2^3 & \cdots & x_2^{N+1} \\ \cdot & & & & & \\ \cdot & & & & & \\ \cdot & & & & & \\ \cdot & & & & & \\ 1 & x_{N+2} & x_{N+2}^2 & x_{N+2}^3 & \cdots & x_{N+2}^{N+1} \end{bmatrix} \begin{bmatrix} d_1 \\ d_2 \\ \cdot \\ \cdot \\ \cdot \\ \cdot \\ d_{N+2} \end{bmatrix} \equiv \mathbf{Qd} \qquad ...(a)$$

$$\mathbf{y}' \equiv \begin{bmatrix} y_1' \\ y_2' \\ \cdot \\ \cdot \\ \cdot \\ \cdot \\ y_{N+2}' \end{bmatrix} = \begin{bmatrix} 0 & 1 & 2x_1 & 3x_1^2 & \cdots & (N+1)x_1^N \\ 0 & 1 & 2x_2 & 3x_2^2 & \cdots & (N+1)x_2^N \\ \cdot & & & & & \\ \cdot & & & & & \\ \cdot & & & & & \\ \cdot & & & & & \\ 0 & 1 & 2x_{N+2} & 3x_{N+2}^2 & \cdots & (N+1)x_{N+2}^N \end{bmatrix} \begin{bmatrix} d_1 \\ d_2 \\ \cdot \\ \cdot \\ \cdot \\ \cdot \\ d_{N+2} \end{bmatrix} \equiv \mathbf{Cd} \quad ...(b)$$

$$\mathbf{y}'' \equiv \begin{bmatrix} y_1'' \\ y_2'' \\ \cdot \\ \cdot \\ \cdot \\ \cdot \\ \cdot \\ y_{N+2}'' \end{bmatrix} = \begin{bmatrix} 0 & 0 & 2 & 6x_1 & \cdots & N(N+1)x_1^{N-1} \\ 0 & 0 & 2 & 6x_2 & \cdots & N(N+1)x_2^{N-1} \\ \cdot & \cdot & \cdot & \cdot & & \cdot \\ \cdot & \cdot & \cdot & \cdot & & \cdot \\ \cdot & \cdot & \cdot & \cdot & & \cdot \\ \cdot & \cdot & \cdot & \cdot & & \cdot \\ \cdot & \cdot & \cdot & \cdot & & \cdot \\ 0 & 0 & 2 & 6x_{N+2} & \cdots & N(N+1)x_{N+2}^{N-1} \end{bmatrix} \begin{bmatrix} d_1 \\ d_2 \\ \cdot \\ \cdot \\ \cdot \\ \cdot \\ \cdot \\ d_{N+2} \end{bmatrix} \equiv \mathbf{Dd} \quad ...(c) \qquad ...(6.25)$$

where **Q**, **C** and **D** are $(N + 2) \times (N + 2)$ matrices of constants.

One could, in principle, use eq. 6.25 to evaluate the residuals of the second-order ODE-BVP of eq. 6.3, and solve for the coefficients, d_i (there will be 2 equations from the boundary conditions, and N residual equations, for the $N + 2$ coefficients, $d_1, d_2, ..., d_{N+2}$). It is more convenient [12, 14], however (and it also reduces the round-off errors [14]), to transform eq. 6.25 and express $\mathbf{y}'$ and $\mathbf{y}''$ in terms of

y, and then solve for y_1, y_2, ..., y_{N+2}. Equation 6.25(*a*) gives $\mathbf{d} = \mathbf{Q}^{-1}\mathbf{y}$, which may be substituted in eqs. 6.25(*b*) and (*c*) to give

$$
\mathbf{y'} = \begin{bmatrix} y_1' \\ y_2' \\ \cdot \\ \cdot \\ \cdot \\ \cdot \\ \cdot \\ y_{N+2}' \end{bmatrix} = \left(\mathbf{CQ^{-1}} \right)\mathbf{y} \equiv \mathbf{Ay} \qquad\qquad ...(a)
$$

$$
\mathbf{y''} = \begin{bmatrix} y_1'' \\ y_2'' \\ \cdot \\ \cdot \\ \cdot \\ \cdot \\ \cdot \\ y_{N+2}'' \end{bmatrix} = \left(\mathbf{DQ^{-1}} \right)\mathbf{y} \equiv \mathbf{By} \qquad\qquad ...(b) \qquad\qquad ...(6.26)
$$

($\mathbf{Q}^{-1}$ exists |5| if the OC points are distinct and the monomials 1, x, x^2, ..., x^{N+1} are linearly independent, as indeed they are). The matrices $\mathbf{A}$ and $\mathbf{B}$ are also a set of $(N + 2) \times (N + 2)$ constants and can be easily computed. They are given in table 6.1 for some values of N, and Villadsen and Michelsen [12] give computer programs which may be used to generate not only the location of the OC points, but these matrices as well (see appendix 6A of this chapter for details on the more general formulation of this technique in terms of Lagrangian interpolation polynomials). Table 6.2 gives the values of x_i which could be used to generate $\mathbf{A}$ and $\mathbf{B}$ for larger N.

The values of y_i' and y_i'' can be written (using a row by column multiplication of the matrices in eq. 6.26) as

$$
y_i' = A_{i1}y_1 + A_{i2}y_2 + ... + A_{i,N+2}y_{N+2} = \sum_{j=1}^{N+2} A_{ij}y_j
$$

$$
y_i'' = B_{i1}y_1 + B_{i2}y_2 + ... + B_{i,N+2}y_{N+2} = \sum_{j=1}^{N+2} B_{ij}y_j \qquad\qquad ...(6.27)
$$

The similarity of eq. 6.27 to eqs. 6.8(*c*) and 6.10 used in the finite difference technique, is to be noted. Once again, we have expressed y_i' and y_i'' as weighted averages of values of y at several locations. It must be noted that in the OC technique, values of y at *all* OC locations are used in the expressions for y_i' and y_i'', while in the finite difference technique, values of y at *only* the neighbouring locations are required.

The procedure to be used is now illustrated in the following examples.

Example 6.4: Obtain OC solutions for the isothermal TRAM of examples 6.1 and 6.2, using $N = 2$.

We have

$$\frac{1}{6}y'' - y' - 2y^2 = 0$$

$$y' = 6\,(y - 1) \text{ at } x = 0$$
$$y' = 0 \text{ at } x = 1$$

At the internal collocation points, we have

$$\frac{1}{6}\left[\sum_{j=1}^{4} B_{ij}y_j\right] - \sum_{j=1}^{4} A_{ij}y_j - 2y_i^2 = 0; \quad i = 2, 3$$

and at the two boundaries, we have

$$\sum_{j=1}^{4} A_{1j}y_j = 6\left(y_1 - 1\right)$$

$$\sum_{j=1}^{4} A_{4j}y_j = 0$$

Substituting the values of the matrix elements, we obtain

$$-7y_1 + 8.196y_2 - 2.196y_3 + y_4 = 6y_1 - 6 \qquad (i = 1)$$

$$\frac{1}{6}\left[16.39y_1 - 24y_2 + 12y_3 - 4.392y_4\right] - \left[-2.732y_1 + 1.732y_2\right.$$

$$\left. + 1.732y_3 - 0.7321y_4\right] = 2y_2^2 \qquad (i = 2)$$

$$\frac{1}{6}\left[-4.392y_1 + 12y_2 - 24y_3 + 16.39y_4\right] - \left[0.7321y_1 - 1.732y_2\right.$$

$$\left. - 1.732y_3 + 2.732y_4\right] = 2y_3^2 \qquad (i = 3)$$

$$-y_1 + 2.196y_2 - 8.196y_3 + 7y_4 = 0 \qquad (i = 4)$$

or, in matrix form,

$$\begin{bmatrix} -13 & 8.196 & -2.196 & 1 \\ 5.464 & -5.732 & 0.268 & 0 \\ -1.464 & 3.732 & -2.268 & 0 \\ -1 & 2.196 & -8.196 & 7 \end{bmatrix} \begin{bmatrix} y_1 \\ y_2 \\ y_3 \\ y_4 \end{bmatrix} = \begin{bmatrix} -6 \\ 2y_2^2 \\ 2y_3^2 \\ 0 \end{bmatrix}$$

Note that we do not get a tridiagonal matrix on the left, as we did in the case of the finite difference technique. The nonlinear terms and constants have been taken to the right hand side.

The Newton-Raphson technique can now be applied to this equation to give

$$\begin{bmatrix} -13 & 8.196 & -2.196 & 1 \\ 5.464 & -5.732-4y_2 & 0.268 & 0 \\ -1.464 & 3.732 & -2.268-4y_3 & 0 \\ -1 & 2.196 & -8.196 & 7 \end{bmatrix}^{(k)} \begin{bmatrix} y_1 \\ y_2 \\ y_3 \\ y_4 \end{bmatrix}^{(k+1)} = \begin{bmatrix} -6 \\ -2y_2^2 \\ -2y_3^2 \\ 0 \end{bmatrix}^{(k)}$$

Solution of this equation [starting from $y_i^{(1)} = 1 - x_i$] gives (see prob. 6.21)

$$\mathbf{y} = \begin{bmatrix} 0.8434 & 0.6676 & 0.4076 & 0.3883 \end{bmatrix}^T$$

at locations given by (see table 6.1)

$$\mathbf{x} = \begin{bmatrix} 0 & 0.2113 & 0.7887 & 1 \end{bmatrix}^T$$

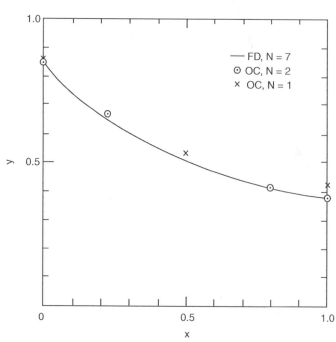

Fig. 6.5 Results for the isothermal TRAM of example 6.4. $\odot$: $N = 2$ OC results using eq. 6.23 for $y(x)$. Solid curve represents finite difference results for $N = 7$. Values of y at the common end points are

	FD ($N = 7$)	OC ($N = 2$)
$x = 0$	0.8304	0.8434
$x = 1$	0.3827	0.3883

These values are plotted in fig. 6.5 along with the $N = 1$ OC solution $[0.8569\ \ 0.5350\ \ 0.4276]^T$. It is observed that they agree well with the finite difference results with 8 grid points. It is observed that even low order OC solutions give results which are quite accurate. This is *often but not always so* (see ref. 16 for an interesting study on a polymerization reactor, where the finite difference technique is better than the OC method). ∎

Instead of using the OC procedure, we could assume a solution, $y(x)$, in terms of an appropriate set of sine or cosine functions (Fourier series representation). The trial functions in this case too, are orthogonal and form a complete and linearly independent set. However, the computational effort required is considerable, and we obtain results which are comparable in accuracy [12] to the results from the OC technique, provided the same number of terms are used. The ease with which the final algebraic equations can be written even for highly nonlinear ODE-BVPs, and the accuracy of even low-order solutions, explains why the orthogonal collocation technique has become so popular.

The solution, y_i, obtained using this technique can be used to estimate the slopes, y' at $x = 0$ or $x = 1$, using eq. 6.27 (these are of no interest in example 6.4, but would be of interest in problems where y_1 and y_{N+2} are specified). These slopes (related to fluxes) require values of y at *all* the locations, $x_1, x_2, ..., x_{N+2}$, and are quite accurate, in contrast to fluxes obtained using the finite difference technique, where y_1' can be estimated from values of y_2 alone (after eliminating the value, y_0, at the hypothetical point).

In several physical problems, we could be interested in computing integrals of the following type: $\int_0^1 \mathcal{F}(y)\,dx$. For example, we *could* be interested in the average concentration of the reactant in the *entire* isothermal TRAM of example 6.4:

$$\overline{y} = \int_0^1 y\,dx \qquad\qquad ...(6.28)$$

(this is not of too great an interest for the TRAM, unless the reactor suddenly solidifies, and we empty the entire contents of the reactor and measure the mean concentration!!). The computed values of y_i, $i = 1, 2, ..., N + 2$ can be used to estimate such an integral using an equation similar to that used in the Gauss-Legendre quadrature

$$I \equiv \int_0^1 \mathcal{F}(y)\,dx = \sum_{i=1}^{N+2} w_i \mathcal{F}(y_i) \qquad\qquad ...(6.29)$$

The values of the quadrature weightages, w_i, for low values of N are also given (as **w**) in table 6.1. Problem 6.22 illustrates how we can obtain **w** for larger values of N, using the locations, x_i. Appendix 6A of this chapter gives some details on how these quadrature weightages are determined for the more general case. It is sufficient to state that we obtain *exact* results for the integral, I (using the $N + 2$ values of y_i), provided $\mathcal{F}(y)$ is a polynomial degree $\leq 2N + 1$. In fact, the choice of the roots of $P_N(x)$ as the internal OC points is motivated by the desire to get accurate values of such integrals. There is a certain sense of optimality associated with obtaining accurate values of integrals using only $N + 2$ values of y, even though the function, $\mathcal{F}(y)$, may be of a higher degree than $N + 2$. A similar situation existed in the choice of the base points for the Gauss-Legendre quadrature (sec. 4.8). It could be argued that the optimal location of the internal OC points at the N roots of $P_N(x)$ based on the requirement of accurate values of integrals, may be non-optimal if we impose a different criterion of "quality", as for example, the maximum deviation $|y_{\text{exact}}(x) - y(x)|$. Villadsen and Michelsen [p. 147 in Ref. 12] study the isothermal Thiele problem with a first order irreversible reaction in a cylindrical geometry, using several different choices of the OC points, x_i (see appendix 6A) and find this to be so. However, they observe that if one choice of the x_i gives good results for integrals it does not perform too badly when a different criterion of quality is imposed. They recommend using higher values of N as a means of obtaining more accurate results, than exploring alternative sets of x_i. This appears to be the accepted practice.

Example 6.5: Compute the mean value of y of the entire contents of the TRAM of example 6.4. Compare the values obtained from the OC results with those from the finite difference method.

The finite difference results of example 6.2 can be used (for $N = 6$) with the composite Simpson's rule (eq. 4.76b) to give ($\Delta x = 1/6$)

$$\bar{y} = \int_0^1 y\,dx = \frac{1/6}{3}\left[y_1 + 4y_2 + 2y_3 + 4y_4 + 2y_5 + 4y_6 + y_7\right]$$

$$= \frac{1}{18}[0.8301 + 4\times0.6901 + 2\times0.5875 + 4\times0.5098$$

$$+ 2\times0.4499 + 4\times0.4053 + 0.3811] = 0.5393$$

The OC results give ($N = 2$)

$$\bar{y} = \int_0^1 y\,dx = w_1 y_1 + w_2 y_2 + w_3 y_3 + w_4 y_4$$

$$= 0\times0.8434 + 0.5\times0.6676 + 0.5\times0.4076 + 0\times0.3883$$

$$= 0.5376$$

We observe the mean value of y obtained from the lower order OC technique to be quite accurate. ∎

Several problems of interest in engineering are symmetrical about $x = 0$. For example, the isothermal reaction-cum-diffusion problem in a porous catalyst sphere (example 6.3 with $T = 1$) with a second-order irreversible reaction taking place is described by

$$\frac{d^2y}{dx^2} + \frac{2}{x}\frac{dy}{dx} = \phi^2 y^2$$

$$x = 0 : \frac{dy}{dx} = 0$$

$$x = 1 : -\frac{dy}{dx} = Bi_m(y-1) \qquad ...(6.30)$$

It can easily be seen that if we assume a solution, $y(x)$, as in eq. 6.23, we obtain (see prob. 6.23) [3] on substitution into eq. 6.30

$$d_2 = 0; \quad d_3 = \frac{d_1^2\phi^2}{6}; \quad d_4 = 0; \quad d_5 = \frac{d_1 d_3 \phi^2}{10}; \quad d_6 = 0; \quad ... \qquad ...(6.31)$$

The condition, $d_2 = 0$, simultaneously satisfies the boundary condition at $x = 0$. It is, thus, observed that $y(x)$ contains only even powers of x in this case. Such a simplification is *not* possible even if we define $x^* \equiv 1 - x$ (so that $\dfrac{dy}{dx^*} = 0$ at $x^* = 0$) in the isothermal TRAM in examples 6.1 and 6.2 (see prob. 6.23) and we must test this out by substitution, rather than use intuition.

In situations where we can show that odd powers of x are not present, we can save a considerable amount of computational effort (for the same accuracy, or get much higher accuracies for the same effort) by assuming the following solution:

$$y(x) = \overline{d}_1 + \overline{d}_2 x^2 + \overline{d}_3 x^4 + \overline{d}_4 x^6 + ... + \overline{d}_{N+1} x^{2N} = \sum_{i=1}^{N+1} \overline{b}_i P_{i-1}(x^2) \qquad ...(6.32)$$

$P_i(x^2)$ are part of another family of complete, linearly independent and orthogonal polynomials involving only even powers of x (we can, alternatively, transform variables using $u = x^2$):

$$P_i(x^2) = (-1)^i \left[1 - \overline{\gamma}_1 x^2 + \overline{\gamma}_2 x^4 - ... + (-1)^i \overline{\gamma}_i x^{2i} \right]; \quad i = 0, 1, 2, ..., N \qquad ...(6.33)$$

The values of $\overline{\gamma}_j$ for different $P_i(x^2)$ can easily be obtained (see appendix in chp. 4) from the orthogonality condition

$$\int_0^1 W(x) P_i(x^2) P_j(x^2) dx = C_i \delta_{ij}; \quad i, j = 1, 2, ..., N \qquad ...(6.34)$$

(where $\delta_{ij} = 0$ when $i \neq j$, and $\delta_{ii} = 1$). The N positive roots of $P_N(x^2)$ are selected as the *internal* collocation points, $x_1, x_2, ..., x_N$, and the $(N + 1)^{th}$ collocation point is selected at $x = 1$. This leads to an accurate determination of some integrals, as in the earlier OC formulation. There is no need for choosing any collocation point at $x = 0$ since the assumed solution in eq. 6.32 satisfies the BC at that point automatically. Two choices of the weightage function, $W(x)$, in eq. 6.34 are common. One is $W(x) = 1$, and the other is $W(x) = 1 - x^2$. The roots of $P_N(x^2)$ for the latter, which is more popular due to higher accuracy of low order OC results obtained, are given in table 6.2 (column corresponding to $a = 1$; planar geometry, see later). The placement of the corresponding OC points for $W(x) = 1 - x^2$, $N = 3$, are shown in fig. 6.4b. Note that the OC points in this case run from x_1 to x_{N+1}, as opposed to x_1 to x_{N+2} in the earlier case when eq. 6.23 was used, and there is no point at $x = 0$ in the present case.

The procedure, hereafter, is analogous to that used earlier. We can write

$$\mathbf{y} \equiv \begin{bmatrix} y_1 \\ y_2 \\ \cdot \\ \cdot \\ \cdot \\ \cdot \\ y_{N+1} \end{bmatrix} = \begin{bmatrix} 1 & x_1^2 & x_1^4 & \cdots & x_1^{2N} \\ 1 & x_2^2 & x_2^4 & \cdots & x_2^{2N} \\ \cdot \\ \cdot \\ \cdot \\ \cdot \\ 1 & x_{N+1}^2 & x_{N+1}^4 & \cdots & x_{N+1}^{2N} \end{bmatrix} \begin{bmatrix} \overline{d}_1 \\ \overline{d}_2 \\ \cdot \\ \cdot \\ \cdot \\ \cdot \\ \overline{d}_{N+1} \end{bmatrix} \equiv \mathbf{\overline{Q}\overline{d}} \qquad ...(a)$$

$$
\mathbf{y}' \equiv
\begin{bmatrix}
y_1' \\
y_2' \\
\cdot \\
\cdot \\
\cdot \\
\cdot \\
y_{N+1}'
\end{bmatrix}
=
\begin{bmatrix}
0 & 2x_1 & 4x_1^3 & \cdots & 2Nx_1^{2N-1} \\
0 & 2x_2 & 4x_2^3 & \cdots & 2Nx_2^{2N-1} \\
\cdot & & & & \\
\cdot & & & & \\
\cdot & & & & \\
\cdot & & & & \\
0 & 2x_{N+1} & 4x_{N+1}^3 & \cdots & 2Nx_{N+1}^{2N-1}
\end{bmatrix}
\begin{bmatrix}
\bar{d}_1 \\
\bar{d}_2 \\
\cdot \\
\cdot \\
\cdot \\
\cdot \\
\bar{d}_{N+1}
\end{bmatrix}
$$

$$
\equiv \bar{\mathbf{C}}\bar{\mathbf{d}} = \left(\bar{\mathbf{C}}\,\bar{\mathbf{Q}}^{-1}\right)\mathbf{y} \equiv \bar{\mathbf{A}}\mathbf{y} \qquad \qquad \dots(b)
$$

$$
\mathbf{y}'' \equiv
\begin{bmatrix}
y_1'' \\
y_2'' \\
\cdot \\
\cdot \\
\cdot \\
\cdot \\
y_{N+1}''
\end{bmatrix}
=
\begin{bmatrix}
0 & 2 & 12x_1^2 & \cdots & 2N(2N-1)x_1^{2N-2} \\
0 & 2 & 12x_2^2 & \cdots & 2N(2N-1)x_2^{2N-2} \\
\cdot & & \cdot & & \cdot \\
\cdot & & \cdot & & \cdot \\
\cdot & & \cdot & & \cdot \\
\cdot & & \cdot & & \cdot \\
0 & 2 & 12x_{N+1}^2 & \cdots & 2N(2N-1)x_{N+1}^{2N-2}
\end{bmatrix}
\begin{bmatrix}
\bar{d}_1 \\
\bar{d}_2 \\
\cdot \\
\cdot \\
\cdot \\
\cdot \\
\bar{d}_{N+1}
\end{bmatrix}
$$

$$
\equiv \bar{\mathbf{D}}\bar{\mathbf{d}} = \left(\bar{\mathbf{D}}\,\bar{\mathbf{Q}}^{-1}\right)\mathbf{y} \equiv \bar{\mathbf{B}}\mathbf{y} \qquad \dots(c) \qquad \dots(6.35)
$$

Integration formulae can be similarly given by

$$
\int_0^1 \mathcal{F}(y)\,dx = \sum_{i=1}^{N+1} \bar{w}_i \mathcal{F}(y_i) \qquad \qquad \dots(6.36)
$$

where (prob. 6.24)

$$
\bar{\mathbf{w}}^T = \begin{bmatrix} 1 & \dfrac{1}{3} & \dfrac{1}{5} & \cdots & \dfrac{1}{2N+1} \end{bmatrix} \left(\bar{\mathbf{Q}}\right)^{-1} \qquad \qquad \dots(6.37)
$$

The matrices $\mathbf{x}$, $\bar{\mathbf{A}}$, $\bar{\mathbf{B}}$ and $\bar{\mathbf{w}}$ are given in table 6.3 ($a = 1$; planar geometry; bars on the matrices are omitted in the table), for $N = 1$ and 2. For higher values of N, the locations, $\mathbf{x}$, of the OC points can be obtained from table 6.2, and the various matrices computed quite easily.

The choice of internal OC points as roots of $P_N(x^2)$ leads to *exact* estimates of the integral in eq. 6.36 if $\mathcal{F}(y)$ is of degree $2N$ (or lower), in x^2.

Example 6.6: Use the above formulation to solve, by orthogonal collocation, the *non*-isothermal reaction-diffusion problem (with parameter values of fig. 6.3) described in example 6.3. Note that we can show (prob. 6.23) that this equation, too, allows one to use only even powers of x in the solution. Use $N = 2$ with the matrices for $a = 1$.

We can write the OC forms for the equation in example 6.3 quite easily for $N = 2$ (bars on the matrix elements are being omitted):

$$i = 1 : \qquad \sum_{j=1}^{3} B_{1j} y_j + \frac{2}{x_1} \sum_{j=1}^{3} A_{1j} y_j = \phi^2 f(y_1)$$

$$i = 2 : \qquad \sum_{j=1}^{3} B_{2j} y_j + \frac{2}{x_2} \sum_{j=1}^{3} A_{2j} y_j = \phi^2 f(y_2)$$

$$i = 3 (BC) : \qquad \sum_{j=1}^{3} A_{3j} y_j = -Bi_m \left[y_3 - 1 \right]$$

On substitution the matrix elements from table 6.3, we obtain for $i = 1$

$$-4.740 y_1 + 5.677 y_2 - 0.9373 y_3 + \frac{2 \left[-1.753 y_1 + 2.508 y_2 - 0.7547 y_3 \right]}{0.2852}$$

$$= \phi^2 f(y_1)$$

or

$$-17.0331 y_1 + 23.2647 y_2 - 6.2297 y_3 = \phi^2 f(y_1)$$

Similarly, we obtain for $i = 2$ and 3

$$4.7392 y_1 - 24.9683 y_2 + 20.2308 y_3 = \phi^2 f(y_2)$$

$$1.792 y_1 - 8.791 y_2 + 7 y_3 = -Bi_m (y_3 - 1)$$

This can be written in matrix form as

$$\begin{bmatrix} -17.0331 & 23.2647 & -6.2297 \\ 4.7392 & -24.9683 & 20.2308 \\ 1.792 & -8.791 & Bi_m + 7 \end{bmatrix} \begin{bmatrix} y_1 \\ y_2 \\ y_3 \end{bmatrix} = \begin{bmatrix} \phi^2 f(y_1) \\ \phi^2 f(y_2) \\ Bi_m \end{bmatrix} \qquad \ldots (a)$$

with

$$f(y_i) = y_i \exp \left[\gamma - \frac{\gamma}{1 + \beta \delta + \beta (1 - \delta) y_3 - \beta y_i} \right]$$

The Newton-Raphson technique applied to this gives

$$\begin{bmatrix} -17.0331 - \phi^2 f'(y_1) & 23.2647 & -6.2297 \\ 4.7392 & -24.9683 - \phi^2 f'(y_2) & 20.2308 \\ 1.792 & -8.791 & Bi_m + 7 \end{bmatrix}^{(k)} \begin{bmatrix} y_1 \\ y_2 \\ y_3 \end{bmatrix}^{(k+1)}$$

$$= \begin{bmatrix} \phi^2 \left\{ f(y_1) - y_1 f'(y_1) \right\} \\ \phi^2 \left\{ f(y_2) - y_2 f'(y_2) \right\} \\ Bi_m \end{bmatrix}^{(k)} \qquad \ldots (b)$$

Table 6.3 OC Matrices for Symmetric Cases*
$[0 \le x \le 1, \quad W(x) = 1 - x^2$ in eqs. 6.34 $(a = 1)$, 6.42 (b) $(a = 2)$ and 6.39 $(a = 3)]$

N	x	w	A	B
			Planar geometry ($a = 1$)	
1	$\begin{bmatrix} 0.4472 \\ 1.0 \end{bmatrix}$	$\begin{bmatrix} 0.8333 \\ 0.1667 \end{bmatrix}$	$\begin{bmatrix} -1.118 & 1.118 \\ -2.500 & 2.500 \end{bmatrix}$	$\begin{bmatrix} -2.5 & 2.5 \\ -2.5 & 2.5 \end{bmatrix}$
2	$\begin{bmatrix} 0.2852 \\ 0.7651 \\ 1.0 \end{bmatrix}$	$\begin{bmatrix} 0.5549 \\ 0.3785 \\ 0.0667 \end{bmatrix}$	$\begin{bmatrix} -1.753 & 2.508 & -0.7547 \\ -1.371 & -0.6535 & 2.024 \\ 1.792 & -8.791 & 7 \end{bmatrix}$	$\begin{bmatrix} -4.740 & 5.677 & -0.9373 \\ 8.323 & -23.26 & 14.94 \\ 19.07 & -47.07 & 28 \end{bmatrix}$
			Cylindrical geometry ($a = 2$)	
1	$\begin{bmatrix} 0.5774 \\ 1.0 \end{bmatrix}$	$\begin{bmatrix} 0.375 \\ 0.125 \end{bmatrix}$	$\begin{bmatrix} -1.732 & 1.732 \\ -3 & 3 \end{bmatrix}$	$\begin{bmatrix} -6 & 6 \\ -6 & 6 \end{bmatrix}$
2	$\begin{bmatrix} 0.3938 \\ 0.8031 \\ 1.0 \end{bmatrix}$	$\begin{bmatrix} 0.1882 \\ 0.2562 \\ 0.0556 \end{bmatrix}$	$\begin{bmatrix} -2.540 & 3.826 & -1.286 \\ -1.378 & -1.245 & 2.623 \\ 1.715 & -9.715 & 8 \end{bmatrix}$	$\begin{bmatrix} -9.902 & 12.30 & -2.397 \\ 9.034 & -32.76 & 23.73 \\ 22.76 & -65.42 & 42.67 \end{bmatrix}$
			Spherical geometry ($a = 3$)	
1	$\begin{bmatrix} 0.6547 \\ 1.0 \end{bmatrix}$	$\begin{bmatrix} 0.2333 \\ 0.1 \end{bmatrix}$	$\begin{bmatrix} -2.291 & 2.291 \\ -3.5 & 3.5 \end{bmatrix}$	$\begin{bmatrix} -10.5 & 10.5 \\ -10.5 & 10.5 \end{bmatrix}$
2	$\begin{bmatrix} 0.4688 \\ 0.8302 \\ 1.0 \end{bmatrix}$	$\begin{bmatrix} 0.0949 \\ 0.1908 \\ 0.0476 \end{bmatrix}$	$\begin{bmatrix} -3.199 & 5.015 & -1.816 \\ -1.409 & -1.807 & 3.215 \\ 1.697 & -10.70 & 9 \end{bmatrix}$	$\begin{bmatrix} -15.67 & 20.03 & -4.365 \\ 9.965 & -44.33 & 34.36 \\ 26.93 & -86.93 & 60 \end{bmatrix}$

[Reprinted from ref. 5 with permission, copyright 1972, Academic Press Inc. Orlando, FL]
* Eq. 6.32 used for $y(x)$

The solutions for $\beta = 0.6$, $\gamma = 20$, $\phi = 0.5$, $\delta = 1$, $Bi_m = \infty$ (therefore $y_3 = 1$) (see fig. 6.3 points ⊙, and prob. 6.25) and $\mathbf{y}(P) = [-0.0101 \quad 0.05394 \quad 1]^T$, $\mathbf{y}(Q) = [0.7351 \quad 0.9287 \quad 1]^T$ and $\mathbf{y}(R) = [0.9381 \quad 0.9752 \quad 1]^T$ at $\mathbf{x} = [0.2852 \quad 0.7651 \quad 1]^T$. The multiplicity of the solutions is to be noted. The first and third solutions are normally quite easy to obtain [starting with $y^{(1)}(P) = 0$ and $y^{(1)}(R) = 1$], but we need to assume $y^{(1)}(Q)$ quite carefully $\{y^{(1)}(Q) = [0.68 \quad 0.91 \quad 1]^T\}$ to converge to the middle, unstable solution. Villadsen and Michelsen [12] discuss numerical procedures to get the unstable solution. The negative value of y for $y_1(P)$ is a result of rounding off of the $\mathbf{A}$ and $\mathbf{B}$ matrices. Figure 6.3 compares these results with the $N = 10$ finite difference solutions. Some discrepancy is observed.

The effectiveness factor, η, for the first of these three roots, $\mathbf{y}(P)$, is calculated as (see table 6.3 for $a = 1$)

$$\eta(P) = 3\int_0^1 x^2 f(y)dx = 3\left[w_1 x_1^2 f(y_1) + w_2 x_2^2 f(y_2) + w_3 x_3^2 f(y_3)\right]$$

$$= 3\left[0.5549 \times (0.2852)^2 \times f(y_1) + 0.3785 \times (0.7651)^2 \times f(y_2) + 0.0667 \times (1)^2 \times 1\right]$$

$$= 47.6610$$

The values of η for the second and third roots are $\eta(Q) = 3.2470$ and $\eta(R) = 1.3292$. These can be compared with the $N = 10$ FD results: $\eta(P) = 38.745$, $\eta(Q) = 3.5828$ and $\eta(R) = 1.3310$.

It can easily be seen that for the simple boundary condition, $y(x = 1) = 1$, the OC solution for $N = 1$ leads, in a similar manner, to (for y containing only even powers of x, and using the $a = 1$ matrices in table 6.3)

$$-7.5y_1 + 7.5 = \phi^2 y_1 \exp\left[\gamma - \frac{\gamma}{1 + \beta - \beta y_1}\right]$$

For the values of the parameters used above, we get

$$-30y_1 + 30 = y_1 \exp\left[20 - \frac{20}{1.6 - 0.6y_1}\right]$$

The solutions are $\mathbf{y}(P) = [0.01772 \quad 1]$, $\mathbf{y}(Q) = [0.8435 \quad 1]$ and $\mathbf{y}(R) = [0.9319 \quad 1]$, with $\eta(P) = 15.2176$, $\eta(Q) = 2.8476$, and $\eta(R) = 1.5217$ (see fig. 6.3). Note that even a low-order OC solution predicts the multiplicity of the profiles, even though it does not give very good estimates for the concentration profile or the effectiveness factor.

If instead of using the assumed solution, $y(x)$, in terms of even powers of x, we use eq. 6.23 and the matrices of table 6.1, we shall obtain for $N = 1$ [so that the same size matrix is obtained as in eq. (*a*) above]:

$$\begin{bmatrix} -3 & 4 & -1 \\ 0 & -8 & 8 \\ 1 & -4 & (3 + Bi_m) \end{bmatrix} \begin{bmatrix} y_1 \\ y_2 \\ y_3 \end{bmatrix} = \begin{bmatrix} 0 \\ \phi^2 f(y_2) \\ Bi_m \end{bmatrix} \qquad \ldots(c)$$

This gives a less accurate solution than given by eq. (*a*) above. The solutions for the same parameter values are again shown in fig. 6.3 (points $\triangle$). $\mathbf{y}(P)$ is observed to be -0.31 at $x = 0$, and is erroneous.

Values of the effectiveness factor are $\eta(P) = 16.1952$, $\eta(Q) = 3.3802$ and $\eta(R) = 1.4154$. The sensitivity of $\eta(P)$, particularly to the choice of the matrices, is to be noted. In fact, $\eta(P)$ values are also found to be quite sensitive to the value of N used in the finite difference method [$N = 4$, $\eta = 44.89$; $N = 10$, $\eta = 38.745$; $N = 20$, $\eta = 42.032$]. One *must*, therefore, ensure that large enough values of N are used in any numerical method. ∎

There is yet another way in which we can obtain OC solutions for the ODE-BVP in example 6.3. In this, we do not expand out the

$$\frac{1}{x^{a-1}} \frac{d}{dx}\left(x^{a-1} \frac{dy}{dx}\right)\left(\equiv \nabla^2 y \,; a = 3\right) \text{ term as } y'' + \frac{2y'}{x},$$

but work with $\nabla^2 y$ itself. Equations 6.35 (a) and (b) remain unchanged [except for the locations of the N internal OC points, since the weightage function, $W(x)$, in eq. 6.34 is different]. eq. 6.35(c) is replaced by

$$
\nabla^2 \mathbf{y} \equiv
\begin{bmatrix}
\nabla^2 y_1 \\
\nabla^2 y_2 \\
\cdot \\
\cdot \\
\cdot \\
\cdot \\
\nabla^2 y_{N+1}
\end{bmatrix}
=
\begin{bmatrix}
0 & 6 & 20x_1^2 & \cdots & (2i-2)(2i-1)x_1^{2i-4} & \cdots & 2N(2N+1)x_1^{2N-2} \\
0 & 6 & 20x_2^2 & \cdots & & \cdots & \\
\cdot & \cdot & \cdot & & & & \\
\cdot & \cdot & \cdot & & & & \\
\cdot & \cdot & \cdot & & & & \\
0 & 6 & 20x_{N+1}^2 & \cdots & & & 2N(2N+1)x_{N+1}^{2N-2}
\end{bmatrix}
\begin{bmatrix}
\bar{d}_1 \\
\bar{d}_2 \\
\cdot \\
\cdot \\
\cdot \\
\cdot \\
\bar{d}_{N+1}
\end{bmatrix}
$$

$$
\equiv \overline{\mathbf{D}}^* \bar{\mathbf{d}} \equiv \overline{\mathbf{B}}^* \mathbf{y} \qquad \qquad \dots(6.38)
$$

with $\nabla^2 y_i \equiv \left[\dfrac{1}{x^2} \dfrac{d}{dx}\left(x^2 \dfrac{dy}{dx} \right) \right]_{x_i}$. The internal OC points are the N positive roots of the orthogonal polynomial, $P_N(x^2)$, defined by an equation which differs slightly from eq. 6.34:

$$
\int_0^1 W(x)x^{a-1}P_i\left(x^2\right)P_j\left(x^2\right)dx = C_i \delta_{ij}; \quad i, j = 1, 2, \dots, N
$$

$$
a = 3 \qquad \qquad \dots(6.39)
$$

with $W(x)$ usually taken as 1 or $1 - x^2$. The integrals to be evaluated are usually of the form $\int_0^1 x^2 \mathcal{F}(x,y)dx$ (as in example 6.6 for obtaining the effectiveness factor), and are given by (note the presence of an x^2 term in the integrand, and its absence on the right hand side):

$$
\int_0^1 x^{a-1} \mathcal{F}(x, y)dx = \sum_{i=1}^{N+1} \bar{w}_i^* \mathcal{F}(x_i, y_i); \quad a = 3 \qquad \qquad \dots(6.40)
$$

where $\bar{\mathbf{w}}^*$ is now given by (see prob. 6.24)

$$
\bar{\mathbf{w}}^{*T} = \left[\frac{1}{3} \ \frac{1}{5} \ \frac{1}{7} \ \cdots \ \frac{1}{2N+3} \right] \overline{\mathbf{Q}}^{-1} \qquad \qquad \dots(6.41)
$$

Tables 6.3 (for $a = 3$, spherical geometry) gives the roots of the appropriate orthogonal polynomials for $W(x) = 1 - x^2$, and the matrices $\bar{\mathbf{w}}^*$, $\mathbf{A}^*$ and $\mathbf{B}^*$ for $N = 1$ and 2 (* and bars omitted). The roots of these polynomials for higher values of N are given in table 6.2 ($a = 3$, spherical geometry) and are shown in fig. 6.4c for $N = 3$. For higher value of N, the roots can be obtained from refs. 12 and 17. The corresponding matrices can be easily computed from these roots. Again, the choice of the internal OC points as roots of $P_N(x^2)$ as defined by eq. 6.39, leads to *exact* estimates of the integral in eq. 6.40 if $\mathcal{F}(x,y)$ is a polynomial of degree $2N$ or lower in x^2.

ODE-BVPs which involve cylindrical geometries $\left[\text{with } \nabla^2 y \equiv \dfrac{1}{x^{a-1}}\dfrac{d}{dx}\left(x^{a-1}\dfrac{dy}{dx}\right) \text{ terms; } a=2\right]$ and which can be shown to be symmetrical (*i.e.*, y is an even function of x), can be treated in a similar manner. Equations 6.38, 6.39, 6.40 and 6.41 are now replaced by

$$\nabla^2 \mathbf{y} \equiv \begin{bmatrix} \nabla^2 y_1 \\ \nabla^2 y_2 \\ \cdot \\ \cdot \\ \cdot \\ \nabla^2 y_{N+1} \end{bmatrix} = \begin{bmatrix} 0 & 4 & 16x_1^2 & \cdots & (2i-2)^2 x_1^{2i-4} & \cdots & (2N)^2 x_1^{2N-2} \\ 0 & 4 & 16x_2^2 & \cdots & & & \cdots \\ \cdot & \cdot & \cdot & \cdot & \cdot & \cdot & \cdot \\ \cdot & \cdot & \cdot & \cdot & \cdot & \cdot & \cdot \\ \cdot & \cdot & \cdot & \cdot & \cdot & \cdot & \cdot \\ 0 & 4 & 16x_{N+1}^2 & \cdots & & \cdot & (2N)^2 x_{N+1}^{2N-2} \end{bmatrix}\begin{bmatrix} \bar{d}_1 \\ \bar{d}_2 \\ \cdot \\ \cdot \\ \cdot \\ \bar{d}_{N+1} \end{bmatrix}$$

$$\equiv \bar{\mathbf{D}}^+\bar{\mathbf{d}} \equiv \bar{\mathbf{B}}^+\mathbf{y} \qquad \qquad \ldots(a)$$

$$\int_0^1 x^{a-1}W(x)P_i(x^2)P_j(x^2)dx = C_i\delta_{ij}; \quad i,j = 1,2,\ldots,N; \ a=2 \qquad \ldots(b)$$

$$\int_0^1 x^{a-1}\mathcal{F}(x,y)dx = \sum_{i=1}^{N+1}\bar{w}_i^+\mathcal{F}(x_i,y_i); \quad a=2 \qquad \ldots(c)$$

$$\bar{\mathbf{w}}^{+T} = \begin{bmatrix} \dfrac{1}{2} & \dfrac{1}{4} & \dfrac{1}{6} & \cdots & \dfrac{1}{2N+2} \end{bmatrix}\bar{\mathbf{Q}}^{-1} \qquad \ldots(d) \qquad \ldots(6.42)$$

Tables 6.2 ($a=2$, cylindrical geometry) and 6.3 ($a=2$, cylindrical geometry) give the roots of these orthogonal polynomials and the corresponding matrices (bars and + are omitted). Note that problems involving cartesian, cylindrical and spherical geometries can be treated as special cases of the general formulation, with $a=1$, 2 and 3, respectively.

Example 6.7: Rework example 6.6 using the above formulation. Use $N=2$ again.

The equation to be solved is

$$\nabla^2 y = \phi^2 f(y); \ (a=3)$$

$$y'(0)=0; \ y'(1) = -Bi_m\left[y(1)-1\right]$$

The OC equations are (* and bars on the matrix elements are being omitted, with $a=3$):

$$\sum_{j=1}^3 B_{kj}y_j = \phi^2 f(y_k); \ k=1,2$$

$$\sum_{j=1}^3 A_{3j}y_j = -Bi_m(y_3-1)$$

On substituting the values of the matrix elements we get

$$
\begin{bmatrix}
-15.67 & 20.03 & -4.365 \\
9.965 & -44.33 & 34.36 \\
1.697 & -10.70 & Bi_m + 9.00
\end{bmatrix}
\begin{bmatrix}
y_1 \\
y_2 \\
y_3
\end{bmatrix}
=
\begin{bmatrix}
\phi^2 f(y_1) \\
\phi^2 f(y_2) \\
Bi_m
\end{bmatrix}
\qquad ...(a)
$$

This can be contrasted with eq. (a) of example 6.6. It must be noted that the locations at which y_1 and y_2 are evaluated differ for these two cases—it is $x_1 = 0.2852$, $x_2 = 0.7651$ for example 6.6 (eq. a) and $x_1 = 0.4688$, $x_2 = 0.8302$ for the present example. Figure 6.3 (points ▣) show the results for this case too. The solutions are found to be $\mathbf{y}(P) = [-0.0044 \quad 0.1125 \quad 1]^T$, $\mathbf{y}(Q) = [0.7491 \quad 0.9320 \quad 1]^T$, and $\mathbf{y}(R) = [0.9482 \quad 0.9813 \quad 1]^T$. The effectiveness factors are $\eta\,(P) = 64.9661$, $\eta\,(Q) = 4.3976$, and $\eta\,(R) = 1.3373$. Figure 6.3 shows that the low order OC solutions for case (P) are particularly poor. This is because of the relatively sharp changes of $y\,(x)$ and $T\,(x)$ with respect to x for this case.

∎

We end our discussion of the orthogonal collocation method with a few comments. The technique can also be used in cases where the domain of x is other than [0, 1]. For example, we could have boundary value problems arising in fluid mechanics (as in penetration depth problems [18, 19]) where the domain of x extends from 0 to ∞. Integrals of the kind $\int_0^\infty e^{-x} y(x)\,dx$ may also be needed in some cases. Orthogonal collocation using Laguerre polynomials can then be used (see ref. 20). Similarly, OC techniques based on other orthogonal polynomials can be developed. In most (*but not all*) cases, the technique takes less computational effort than finite difference formulations for the same accuracy. Chapter 7 illustrates how this technique can be used to solve partial differential equations. The orthogonal collocation technique has also been applied [14] to staged operations [21, 22] (in chemical engineering), with the states in each stage being interpolated by polynomials (Hahn polynomials).

6.4 ORTHOGONAL COLLOCATION ON FINITE ELEMENTS (OCFE)

Figure 6.3a, Case (a), shows that the OC technique with $N = 2$ does not give us useful information on the y profile, since the values of y at the two internal collocation points are essentially zero. We need to use fairly large values of N before we can obtain the sharp profile as obtained by the high-N finite difference technique. For such N, the locations of several of the OC points will be in the 'inner region' where y is nearly zero, and is of little interest. The exercise is quite wasteful and expensive, particularly since the algebraic equations to be solved involve 'dense' matrices and not the simpler tridiagonal matrices, as in the finite difference technique. It is useful, then, to follow the procedure first suggested by Carey and Finlayson [23], referred to as orthogonal collocation on finite elements (OCFE). In this method, we first divide the domain of x into several subdomains, called finite elements (FEs). Figure 6.6 shows N_s finite elements, with the ith FE being of length, h_i. We place (usually) two internal OC points in each finite element, and number the boundary and internal OC points as shown. Thus, the ith FE extends from $x = x_j = \sum_{i=1}^{i-1} h_l$ to $x = x_{j+3} = \sum_{l=1}^{i} h_l$, with $j = 3(i-1) + 1$. We define a variable, $u^{(i)}$, on the ith FE, such that it is zero at its beginning, and unity at its end. Thus,

$$
u^{(i)} = \frac{x - x_j}{h_i}; \quad i = 1, 2, ..., N_s\,; \quad j = 3(i-1)+1 \qquad ...(6.43)
$$

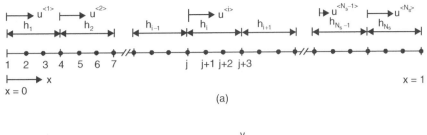

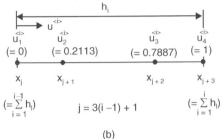

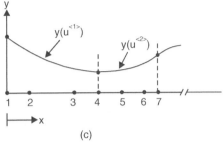

(b)

(c)

Fig. 6.6 (*a*) Finite elements with two internal OC points on each. (*b*) Details of the *i*th finite element and (*c*) splines on the first two FEs.

The locations of the two *internal OC* points in the *i*th FE can easily be written in terms of $u^{\langle i \rangle}$ using table 6.1 (note that the *y* cannot be symmetrical), as

$$u_2^{\langle i \rangle} = 0.2113 = \frac{x_{j+1} - x_j}{h_i}$$

$$u_3^{\langle i \rangle} = 0.7887 = \frac{x_{j+2} - x_j}{h_i}\ ;\quad j = 3(i-1) + 1\ ;\quad i = 1, 2, ..., N_s \qquad \qquad ...(6.44)$$

We now assume a (spline) solution, $y\,(u^{\langle i \rangle})$, of degree three in $u^{\langle i \rangle}$, on the *i*th FE as shown in fig. 6.6*c*. We then use the OC technique (residual zero at the two internal OC points, slopes continuous at the boundaries of the *i*th FE) to solve for *y* at points *j*, *j* + 1, *j* + 2 and *j* + 3 in this FE. This is quite simply done, and is illustrated for the isothermal TRAM below.

Example 6.8: Solve for *y* for the isothermal TRAM of example 6.1, with *Pe* = 6, *Da* = 2, using two finite elements of lengths $h_1 = 0.3$, $h_2 = 0.7$, and with two internal OC points in each.

The ODE-BVP is

$$\frac{1}{6}\frac{d^2 y}{dx^2} - \frac{dy}{dx} - 2y^2 = 0 \qquad \qquad ...(a)$$

$$x = 0 : \frac{dy}{dx} = 6(y - 1)$$

$$x = 1 : \frac{dy}{dx} = 0$$

We define $u^{\langle 1 \rangle}$ as

$$u^{\langle 1 \rangle} = \frac{x}{h_1} \qquad \qquad \dots (b)$$

We would like to make the residuals at points 2 and 3 (see fig. 6.6a) zero. We can use the **A** and **B** matrices for $N = 2$ in table 6.1 provided we work in terms of $u^{\langle 1 \rangle}$ (since $0 \le u^{\langle 1 \rangle} \le 1$). eq. ($a$) can be transformed in terms of $u^{\langle 1 \rangle}$ using eq. (b) to give

$$\frac{1}{6h_1^2} \frac{d^2 y}{du^{\langle 1 \rangle^2}} - \frac{1}{h_1} \frac{dy}{du^{\langle 1 \rangle}} - 2y^2 = 0 \qquad \qquad \dots (c)$$

We can now write the equations for making the residuals zero at points 2 and 3 [for the polynomial, $y(u^{\langle 1 \rangle})$, defined in $0 \le u^{\langle 1 \rangle} \le 1$]

at point 2:

$$\frac{1}{6h_1^2}\left[B_{21}y_1 + B_{22}y_2 + B_{23}y_3 + B_{24}y_4\right] - \frac{1}{h_1}\left[A_{21}y_1 + A_{22}y_2 + A_{23}y_3 + A_{24}y_4\right] - 2y_2^2 = 0$$

at point 3:

$$\frac{1}{6h_1^2}\left[B_{31}y_1 + B_{32}y_2 + B_{33}y_3 + B_{34}y_4\right] - \frac{1}{h_1}\left[A_{31}y_1 + A_{32}y_2 + A_{33}y_3 + A_{34}y_4\right] - 2y_3^2 = 0$$

Note that since $y(u^{\langle 1 \rangle})$ only extends from point 1 to point 4, we only use values y_1, y_2, y_3 and y_4 in these equations, alongwith matrices corresponding to $N + 2 = 4$. We can similarly write the original ODE in terms of $u^{\langle 2 \rangle}$ using

$$u^{\langle 2 \rangle} = \frac{x - x_4}{h_2}$$

as

$$\frac{1}{6h_2^2} \frac{d^2 y}{du^{\langle 2 \rangle^2}} - \frac{1}{h_2} \frac{dy}{du^{\langle 2 \rangle}} - 2y^2 = 0$$

For the polynomial, $y(u^{\langle 2 \rangle})$, defined in the domain $0 \le u^{\langle 2 \rangle} \le 1$, we can force the residuals to be zero at the internal OC points 5 and 6 giving

at point 5:

$$\frac{1}{6h_2^2}\left[B_{21}y_4 + B_{22}y_5 + B_{23}y_6 + B_{24}y_7\right] - \frac{1}{h_2}\left[A_{21}y_4 + A_{22}y_5 + A_{23}y_6 + A_{24}y_7\right] - 2y_5^2 = 0$$

at point 6:

$$\frac{1}{6h_2^2}\left[B_{31}y_4 + B_{32}y_5 + B_{33}y_6 + B_{34}y_7\right] - \frac{1}{h_2}\left[A_{31}y_4 + A_{32}y_5 + A_{33}y_6 + A_{34}y_7\right] - 2y_6^2 = 0$$

Note that point 5 is the second OC point in $0 \le u^{\langle 2 \rangle} \le 1$, and so elements of the second rows of **B** and **A** are used. Similarly, for expressing $\dfrac{d^2y}{du^{(2)^2}}$ at point 6, we use the third rows of **A** and **B** in table 6.1, alongwith values y_4, y_5, y_6 and y_7 at the four OC points in *this* FE.

The slope, $\dfrac{dy}{dx}$, of the spline, $y\,(u^{(1)})$, at the *internal* boundary point 4 in FE 1 is given by

$$\left.\frac{dy}{dx}\right|_{x_4^-} = \frac{1}{h_1}\left.\frac{dy}{du^{(1)}}\right|_{u^{(1)}=1} = \frac{1}{h_1}\left[A_{41}y_1 + A_{42}y_2 + A_{43}y_3 + A_{44}y_4\right]$$

The fourth row of **A** is used since x_4 is the fourth OC point in the domain $0 \le u^{(1)} \le 1$. Similarly, the slope, $\dfrac{dy}{dx}$, of the spline $y\,(u^{(2)})$, the internal boundary point, 4, in FE 2 is given by

$$\left.\frac{dy}{dx}\right|_{x_4^+} = \frac{1}{h_2}\left.\frac{dy}{du^{(2)}}\right|_{u^{(2)}=0} = \frac{1}{h_2}\left[A_{11}y_4 + A_{12}y_5 + A_{13}y_6 + A_{14}y_7\right]$$

These slopes must be equal so that the spline polynomials (cubic splines) in the two adjacent finite elements are smooth at the boundary point 4 (the *values* of the two polynomials are the same since the same y_4 is used in both the spline functions). Thus, we obtain

at point 4:

$$\frac{1}{h_1}\sum_{j=1}^{4}A_{4j}y_j - \frac{1}{h_2}\sum_{j=1}^{4}A_{1j}y_{j+3} = 0 \qquad\qquad …(d)$$

We now need to satisfy the boundary condition at the external boundary, $x = 0$. The spline, $y\,(u^{(1)})$, needs to be used. We have

at point 1:

$$\left.\frac{dy}{dx}\right|_{x=0} = \frac{1}{h_1}\left.\frac{dy}{du^{(1)}}\right|_{u^{(1)}=0} = \frac{1}{h_1}\left[A_{11}y_1 + A_{12}y_2 + A_{13}y_3 + A_{14}y_4\right]$$

$$= 6(y_1 - 1)$$

Similarly, at the other external boundary, $x = 1$, we use the spline, $y\,(u^{(2)})$, to give

at point 7:

$$\left.\frac{dy}{dx}\right|_{x=1} = \frac{1}{h_2}\left.\frac{dy}{du^{(2)}}\right|_{u^{(2)}=1} = \frac{1}{h_2}\left[A_{41}y_4 + A_{42}y_5 + A_{43}y_6 + A_{44}y_7\right] = 0$$

The equations for each of the seven OC points can be put in a matrix form as

$$
\begin{bmatrix}
\dfrac{A_{11}}{h_1}-6 & \dfrac{A_{12}}{h_1} & \dfrac{A_{13}}{h_1} & \dfrac{A_{14}}{h_1} & 0 & 0 & 0 \\[2ex]
\dfrac{B_{21}}{6h_1^2}-\dfrac{A_{21}}{h_1} & \dfrac{B_{22}}{6h_1^2}-\dfrac{A_{22}}{h_1} & \dfrac{B_{23}}{6h_1^2}-\dfrac{A_{23}}{h_1} & \dfrac{B_{24}}{6h_1^2}-\dfrac{A_{24}}{h_1} & 0 & 0 & 0 \\[2ex]
\dfrac{B_{31}}{6h_1^2}-\dfrac{A_{31}}{h_1} & \dfrac{B_{32}}{6h_1^2}-\dfrac{A_{32}}{h_1} & \dfrac{B_{33}}{6h_1^2}-\dfrac{A_{33}}{h_1} & \dfrac{B_{34}}{6h_1^2}-\dfrac{A_{34}}{h_1} & 0 & 0 & 0 \\[2ex]
\dfrac{A_{41}}{h_1} & \dfrac{A_{42}}{h_1} & \dfrac{A_{43}}{h_1} & \dfrac{A_{44}}{h_1}-\dfrac{A_{11}}{h_2} & -\dfrac{A_{12}}{h_2} & -\dfrac{A_{13}}{h_2} & -\dfrac{A_{14}}{h_2} \\[2ex]
0 & 0 & 0 & \dfrac{B_{21}}{6h_2^2}-\dfrac{A_{21}}{h_2} & \dfrac{B_{22}}{6h_2^2}-\dfrac{A_{22}}{h_2} & \dfrac{B_{23}}{6h_2^2}-\dfrac{A_{23}}{h_2} & \dfrac{B_{24}}{6h_2^2}-\dfrac{A_{24}}{h_2} \\[2ex]
0 & 0 & 0 & \dfrac{B_{31}}{6h_2^2}-\dfrac{A_{31}}{h_2} & \dfrac{B_{32}}{6h_2^2}-\dfrac{A_{32}}{h_2} & \dfrac{B_{33}}{6h_2^2}-\dfrac{A_{33}}{h_2} & \dfrac{B_{34}}{6h_2^2}-\dfrac{A_{34}}{h_2} \\[2ex]
0 & 0 & 0 & \dfrac{A_{41}}{h_2} & \dfrac{A_{42}}{h_2} & \dfrac{A_{43}}{h_2} & \dfrac{A_{44}}{h_2}
\end{bmatrix}
\times
$$

$$
\begin{bmatrix} y_1 \\ y_2 \\ y_3 \\ y_4 \\ y_5 \\ y_6 \\ y_7 \end{bmatrix}
=
\begin{bmatrix} -6 \\ 2y_2^2 \\ 2y_3^2 \\ 0 \\ 2y_5^2 \\ 2y_6^2 \\ 0 \end{bmatrix}
$$

or

$$\mathbf{Ay} = \mathbf{f}(\mathbf{y}) \qquad \qquad \ldots(e)$$

Generalization to higher number of FEs is quite simple (the ease with which we can apply the technique is to be noted). The block (of 4 × 4 size) diagonal structure of **A**, with intermeshing of corner elements, is to be noted. The successive substitutions technique can be used to obtain **y**, with the equations in each iteration being solved by fore and aft sweeps after a single LU decomposition of **A** (the block diagonal nature of **A** can be exploited to reduce computational effort as well as storage space—LU Decomp of only the blocks in necessary) [23]. The Newton-Raphson procedure can also be used to speed up the convergence, with similar exploitation of computer calculations and storage space [23]. The results for the TRAM are shown in fig. 6.7 (see prob. 6.34). The value of this technique is not so evident in this example, but can be easily demonstrated if we try to generate fig. 6.3a, case a, using only two FEs, of lengths 0.75 and 0.25.

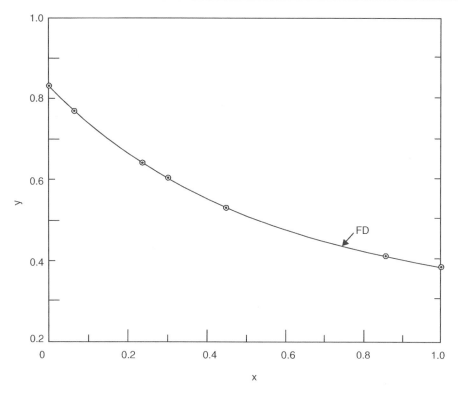

Fig. 6.7 Results for the isothermal TRAM using OCFE with two finite elements, as in example 6.8. Finite difference ($N = 7$) results of fig. 6.2 shown by the solid curve. FD results show $y(1) = 0.3827$ while OCFE results give $y(1) = 0.3873$. At other points, results are quite similar.

■

Integrals can also be evaluated quite easily, by summing up the contributions from each FE. Thus

$$\int_{x=0}^{1} y(x)\,dx = h_1 \int_{u^{\langle 1 \rangle}=0}^{u^{\langle 1 \rangle}=1} y\left(u^{\langle 1 \rangle}\right) du^{\langle 1 \rangle} + h_2 \int_{u^{\langle 2 \rangle}=0}^{u^{\langle 2 \rangle}=1} y\left(u^{\langle 2 \rangle}\right) du^{\langle 2 \rangle} + \ldots$$

$$= h_1 \left(w_1 y_1 + w_2 y_2 + w_3 y_3 + w_4 y_4\right) + h_2 \left(w_1 y_4 + w_2 y_5 + w_3 y_6 + w_4 y_7\right) + \ldots \qquad \ldots(6.45)$$

An obvious question is how to decide the values of h_i, without knowing the solution. Carey and Finlayson [23] suggest several schemes. In one, we assume the FEs arbitrarily and compute the values of y at the OC points. The residuals at the *internal* boundary point are evaluated (the residuals were *not* made zero at these points; instead, the fluxes or slopes were made continuous there) and new and smaller FEs introduced at those locations where they are large. A technique suggested by Pearson [24] can be used. In this, one evaluates the residual, $\left|\mathbb{R}_i\right|$ at all the $N_s + 1$ boundary points. The range, $\mathbb{R}$, of $\left|\mathbb{R}_i\right|$ is computed. If the change in the residual from one boundary to the other in any finite element is more than 1 percent of $\mathbb{R}$, we split up this FE into more FEs. Another scheme involving the integral

$$\int_{u^{\langle i \rangle}=0}^{1} \mathbb{R}^2\left(u^{\langle i \rangle}\right) du^{\langle i \rangle}$$ over the ith finite element, is also discussed by these workers. This is quite

cumbersome to use, since the coefficients, d_i (in eq. 6.23, using $\mathbf{d} = \mathbf{Q}^{-1}\mathbf{y}$) are required to evaluate $\mathbb{R}(x)$ or $\mathbb{R}\left(u^{\langle i \rangle}\right)$.

It may be mentioned that the OCFE technique can easily be used for composites by choosing the internal/external boundaries at the interfaces of the materials forming the composite. Continuity of the values of y at these interfaces is automatically ensured. However, eq. (d) in example 6.8 can be easily replaced by an approximate flux-continuity equation—for a heat transfer problem, for example, the thermal conductivities of the materials on the two sides of an interface will enter this equation.

Finlayson [3] has also developed the OCFE technique using a different set of trial functions than monomials (or shifted Legendre functions) for the piecewise continuous splines. A set of four Hermite polynomials is used. These enable one to automatically satisfy the continuity of the slopes of y (x) at the internal boundaries—thus reducing the size of the matrix **A** in eq. (e), example 6.8 by a factor of about 33%. Details can be obtained from ref. 3.

6.5 GALERKIN FINITE ELEMENT (GFE) TECHNIQUE

Another method for integrating ODE-BVPs is the Galerkin finite element technique. This method is quite accurate and is used extensively to integrate partial differential equations (see Chapter 7) encountered, for example, in fluid mechanics, structural analysis in civil engineering, etc. The technique is discussed here in some detail, since it helps establish the foundations for the development in next chapter, where it will be applied to partial differential equations.

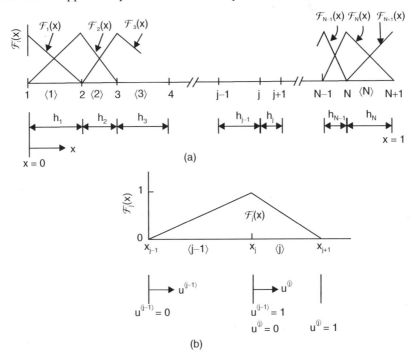

Fig. 6.8 Trial functions for Galerkin's FE technique.

The procedure is somewhat similar to OCFE. The domain $0 \le x \le 1$ is subdivided into N finite elements (FEs) of lengths, $h_1, h_2, \ldots, h_N$, as shown in fig. 6.8. The jth FE extends from $x_j \le x \le x_{j+1}$, where

$x_j = \sum_{i=1}^{j-1} h_i$. The solution, $y(x)$, is *assumed* to be given in terms of $N+1$ trial function, $\mathcal{F}_i(x)$, as

$$y(x) = y_1\mathcal{F}_1(x) + y_2\mathcal{F}_2(x) + ... + y_{N+1}\mathcal{F}_{N+1}(x) = \sum_{j=1}^{N+1} y_j\mathcal{F}_j(x) \qquad ...(6.46)$$

The trial functions, $\mathcal{F}_j(x)$, are not simple polynomials in x, in contrast to what was assumed in OCFE. The most commonly used function, $\mathcal{F}_j(x)$, is defined by

$$\mathcal{F}_j(x) = \frac{x - x_{j-1}}{h_{j-1}}; \quad x_{j-1} \le x \le x_j$$

$$= 1 - \frac{x - x_j}{h_j}; \quad x_j \le x \le x_{j+1}$$

$$= 0 \text{ elsewhere; } j = 2, 3, ..., N \qquad ...(6.47)$$

Thus, $\mathcal{F}_j(x)$ is a *continuous* function of x having discontinuous first derivatives at x_{j-1}, x_j and x_{j+1}. Its plot looks like a triangle, as shown in fig. 6.8b. This function increases linearly from 0 to unity when one goes from x_{j-1} to x_j, and then decreases linearly to a value of 0 at x_{j+1}. The two end functions are defined as 'half-triangles' or ramps (see fig. 6.8a):

$$\mathcal{F}_1(x) = 1 - \frac{x}{h_1} \quad ; \quad 0 \le x \le x_2$$

$$= 0 \quad ; \quad x_2 \le x \le x_{N+1}$$

$$\mathcal{F}_{N+1}(x) = 0 \quad ; \quad 0 \le x \le x_N$$

$$= \frac{x - x_N}{h_N} \quad ; \quad x_N \le x \le x_{N+1} \qquad ...(6.48)$$

It is observed from eq. 6.46 that y_j is the solution at location x_j. This is precisely why the coefficients were chosen as y_j in this equation.

Galerkin's technique forces the residual, $\mathbb{R}(x)$, to be orthogonal to the trial functions. Thus

$$\int_0^1 \mathbb{R}(x)\mathcal{F}_j(x)dx = 0 \qquad ...(6.49)$$

The motivation for doing this is based on a theorem which states that only a null function is orthogonal to a *complete* set of linearly independent functions [11].

The algebraic manipulations involved in this technique are slightly cumbersome due to the discontinuous nature of $\mathcal{F}_j(x)$, and are illustrated through the following example. It will be observed that this technique is not as simple to use as the OC or OCFE techniques, but it gives results which are extremely accurate.

Example 6.9: Solve for **y** for the isothermal TRAM of example 6.1, with $Pe = 6$ and $Da = 2$. Use different values of N and compare the results. The ODE is

$$\frac{1}{6}\frac{d^2 y}{dx^2} - \frac{dy}{dx} - 2y^2 = 0$$

The residual, $\mathbb{R}(x)$, can be obtained by substituting eq. 6.46 into the ODE, giving

$$\mathbb{R}(x) = \frac{1}{6}\sum_{i=1}^{N+1} y_i \frac{d^2 \mathcal{F}_i}{dx^2} - \sum_{i=1}^{N+1} y_i \frac{d\mathcal{F}_i}{dx} - 2\left[\sum_{i=1}^{N+1} y_i \mathcal{F}_i\right]^2$$

Equation 6.49, thus, gives

$$\int_{x=0}^{1} \frac{1}{6}\mathcal{F}_j \left[\sum_{i=1}^{N+1} y_i \frac{d^2 \mathcal{F}_i}{dx^2}\right] dx - \int_{x=0}^{1} \mathcal{F}_j \left[\sum_{i=1}^{N+1} y_i \frac{d\mathcal{F}_i}{dx}\right] dx = 2\int_{x=0}^{1} \mathcal{F}_j \left[\sum_{i=1}^{N+1} y_i \mathcal{F}_i\right]^2 dx \; ; \quad j = 1, 2, ..., N+1$$

Since $\mathcal{F}_i(x)$ are linear in x, $\dfrac{d^2 \mathcal{F}_i}{dx^2} = 0$ (except at the internal boundaries where $\dfrac{d\mathcal{F}_i}{dx}$ is discontinuous).

Thus, if we wish to retain the second order terms (and avoid solving a first order ODE), we need to integrate the first integral by parts, in the above equation. This gives

$$\underbrace{\frac{1}{6}\mathcal{F}_j\left[\sum_{i=1}^{N+1} y_i \frac{d\mathcal{F}_i}{dx}\right]_{x=0}^{x=1}}_{\text{I}} - \underbrace{\frac{1}{6}\int_{x=0}^{1}\frac{d\mathcal{F}_j}{dx}\left[\sum_{i=1}^{N+1} y_i \frac{d\mathcal{F}_i}{dx}\right] dx}_{\text{II}} - \underbrace{\sum_{i=1}^{N+1}\int_{0}^{1} y_i \mathcal{F}_j \frac{d\mathcal{F}_i}{dx} dx}_{\text{III}}$$

$$= 2\underbrace{\int_{x=0}^{1} \mathcal{F}_j\left[\sum_{i=1}^{N+1} y_i \mathcal{F}_i\right]^2 dx}_{\text{IV}} \; ; \quad j = 1, 2, ..., N+1 \qquad \qquad ...(a)$$

We consider the four terms in this equation, one by one.

The first term in eq. (a) is simplified using the boundary conditions at $x = 0$ and $x = 1$. At $x = 1$, the B.C. is $\dfrac{dy}{dx} = \sum_{i=1}^{N+1} y_i \dfrac{d\mathcal{F}_i}{dx} = 0$ and so term I does not contribute at $x = 1$. At $x = 0$, the boundary condition (see example 6.1) is

$$\left.\frac{dy}{dx}\right|_0 = \left[\sum_{i=1}^{N+1} y_i \frac{d\mathcal{F}_i}{dx}\right]_0 = 6\left[y(x=0)-1\right] = 6\left(y_1 - 1\right)$$

Term I thus becomes $-\mathcal{F}_j(x=0)\,(y_1 - 1)$. Since $\mathcal{F}_1(x=0) = 1$, and all other $\mathcal{F}_j$s are zero at $x = 0$, this term finally simplifies to $-(y_1 - 1)\,\delta_{j1}$ [$\delta_{ij} \equiv 1$ for $i = j$ and 0 for $i \neq j$]. It may be mentioned here that we are satisfying both the BCs at $x = 0$ and $x = 1$, as well as the orthogonality of the residual to $\mathcal{F}_1(x)$ and $\mathcal{F}_{N+1}(x)$. This is somewhat akin to the finite difference technique using central differences, in which we make both the residual zero at the boundary point, as well as satisfy the boundary condition (involving fluxes). In case the value of y is specified at an external boundary we can either use the above procedure, or equate y_1 (or y_{N+1}) to the appropriate values and do *not* force the residual to be orthogonal to $\mathcal{F}_1$ (or $\mathcal{F}_{N+1}$). Prob. 6.41 illustrates the use of these two procedures.

We now turn our attention to simplifying term II in eq. (a). Let us consider the case when $j = 1$. This term gives

$$\text{II}_{j=1} = -\frac{1}{6}\left[y_1 \int_{x=0}^{1} \frac{d\mathcal{F}_1}{dx}\frac{d\mathcal{F}_1}{dx}\,dx + y_2 \int_{x=0}^{1} \frac{d\mathcal{F}_1}{dx}\frac{d\mathcal{F}_2}{dx}\,dx + y_3 \int_{x=0}^{1} \frac{d\mathcal{F}_1}{dx}\frac{d\mathcal{F}_3}{dx}\,dx + \dots \right]$$

It may be noted that $\dfrac{d\mathcal{F}_1}{dx}$ is nonzero only in $x_1 \le x \le x_2$, while $\dfrac{d\mathcal{F}_3}{dx}$ is nonzero in $x_2 \le x \le x_4$. Thus, the product $\mathcal{F}_1'\,\mathcal{F}_3'$ is zero for all values of x (*i.e.*, functions $\mathcal{F}_1$ and $\mathcal{F}_3$ do not 'overlap'). The same holds for terms involving $\mathcal{F}_1'\,\mathcal{F}_4'$, ..., $\mathcal{F}_1'\,\mathcal{F}'_{N+1}$. The above equation simplifies to

$$\text{II}_{j=1} = -\frac{1}{6}\left[y_1 \int_{x=0}^{1} \mathcal{F}_1'\mathcal{F}_1'\,dx + y_2 \int_{x=0}^{1} \mathcal{F}_1'\mathcal{F}_2'\,dx \right]$$

Again, we note that $\mathcal{F}_1$ (and $\mathcal{F}_1'$) is nonzero only in $x_1 \le x \le x_2$. This leads to

$$\text{II}_{j=1} = -\frac{1}{6}\left[y_1 \int_{x=x_1}^{x_2} \mathcal{F}_1'\mathcal{F}_1'\,dx + y_2 \int_{x_1}^{x_2} \mathcal{F}_1'\mathcal{F}_2'\,dx \right]$$

From eqs. 6.47 and 6.48, we obtain

$$\frac{d\mathcal{F}_1}{dx} = -\frac{1}{h_1} \;\; ; \;\; \frac{d\mathcal{F}_2}{dx} = \frac{1}{h_1} \;\; ; \;\; x_1 \le x \le x_2.$$

Hence

$$\text{II}_{j=1} = -\frac{1}{6}\left[y_1 \int_{x=x_1=0}^{h_1} \left(-\frac{1}{h_1}\right)\left(-\frac{1}{h_1}\right)dx + y_2 \int_{0}^{h_1}\left(-\frac{1}{h_1}\right)\left(\frac{1}{h_1}\right)dx \right]$$

$$\equiv -\frac{1}{6}\left[y_1 B_{\downarrow\downarrow}^{\langle 1\rangle} + y_2 B_{\downarrow\uparrow}^{\langle 1\rangle} \right] = -\frac{1}{6}\left[y_1\left(\frac{1}{h_1}\right) + y_2\left(-\frac{1}{h_1}\right) \right]$$

The *superscript* $\langle 1\rangle$ on $B_{\downarrow\downarrow}^{\langle 1\rangle}$ indicates that the integral is to be evaluated over the first element. The first *subscript* on $B_{\downarrow\downarrow}^{\langle 1\rangle}$ (representing j) indicates that we are looking at the downgoing ramp (of $\mathcal{F}_j$), while the second subscript represents the downgoing ramp (of $\mathcal{F}_i$). Similarly, the two subscripts on $B_{\downarrow\uparrow}^{\langle 1\rangle}$ indicate that we are looking at the downgoing ramp of $\mathcal{F}_j$ and the upgoing ramp of $\mathcal{F}_i$ in $FE\,\langle 1\rangle$.

The above development can easily be generalized. For 'internal locations' of i and j, the second term in eq. (a) can be simplified (noting that $\mathcal{F}_j$ overlaps only with $\mathcal{F}_{j-1}$, $\mathcal{F}_j$ and $\mathcal{F}_{j+1}$) as

$$\text{II}_j = -\frac{1}{6}\int_{x=0}^{1} y_{j-1}\mathcal{F}_j'\mathcal{F}_{j-1}'\,dx - \frac{1}{6}\int_{x=0}^{1} y_j\mathcal{F}_j'\mathcal{F}_j'\,dx - \frac{1}{6}\int_{x=0}^{1} y_{j+1}\mathcal{F}_j'\mathcal{F}_{j+1}'\,dx$$

$$= -\frac{y_{j-1}}{6} \int_{x_{j-1}}^{x_j} \mathcal{F}_j' \mathcal{F}_{j-1}' \, dx - \frac{y_i}{6} \int_{x_{j-1}}^{x_j} \mathcal{F}_j' \mathcal{F}_j' dx - \frac{y_j}{6} \int_{x=j}^{x_{j+1}} \mathcal{F}_j' \mathcal{F}_j' dx - \frac{y_{j+1}}{6} \int_{x_j}^{x_{j+1}} \mathcal{F}_j' \mathcal{F}_{j+1}' \, dx$$

$$\equiv -\frac{1}{6} \left[y_{j-1} B_{\uparrow\downarrow}^{\langle j-1 \rangle} + y_j B_{\uparrow\uparrow}^{\langle j-1 \rangle} + y_j B_{\downarrow\downarrow}^{\langle j \rangle} + y_{j+1} B_{\downarrow\uparrow}^{\langle j \rangle} \right]$$

$$= -\frac{1}{6} \left[y_{j-1} \left(-\frac{1}{h_{j-1}} \right) + y_j \left(\frac{1}{h_{j-1}} \right) + y_j \left(\frac{1}{h_j} \right) + y_{j+1} \left(-\frac{1}{h_j} \right) \right] \qquad \ldots(b)$$

In the above integrals, the first of the $\mathcal{F}$s corresponds to $\mathcal{F}_j$ while the second one to $\mathcal{F}_i$. The second integral involving $\mathcal{F}_j' \mathcal{F}_j'$ is split up into two parts—one from x_{j-1} to x_j, and the other from x_j to x_{j+1}. This is done to account for the discontinuous nature of the $\mathcal{F}$ functions. It is quite easy to write the values of the four possible combinations of $B^{\langle j \rangle}$. The magnitude is $\dfrac{1}{h_j}$; the sign is positive if both ramps go in the same direction ($\uparrow\uparrow$ or $\downarrow\downarrow$) and negative if the two ramps associated with $\mathcal{F}_j$ and $\mathcal{F}_i$ in the $\langle j \rangle$th FE go in opposite directions ($\uparrow\downarrow$ or $\downarrow\uparrow$).

Thus, there are four terms in $\mathbf{B}^{\langle j \rangle}$

$$\mathbf{B}^{\langle j \rangle} \equiv \begin{bmatrix} B_{\downarrow\downarrow}^{\langle j \rangle} & B_{\downarrow\uparrow}^{\langle j \rangle} \\ B_{\uparrow\downarrow}^{\langle j \rangle} & B_{\uparrow\uparrow}^{\langle j \rangle} \end{bmatrix} = \begin{bmatrix} \dfrac{1}{h_j} & -\dfrac{1}{h_j} \\ -\dfrac{1}{h_j} & \dfrac{1}{h_j} \end{bmatrix} \qquad \ldots(c)$$

The second term in eq. (a) for $j = N + 1$ can be written as

$$\mathrm{II}_{j=N+1} = -\frac{1}{6} \left[y_N B_{\uparrow\downarrow}^{\langle N \rangle} + y_{N+1} B_{\uparrow\uparrow}^{\langle N \rangle} \right] \qquad \ldots(d)$$

A little thought leads to an easy generalization of the II_j terms. The triangular trial function, $\mathcal{F}_j$, is inspected. Only those FEs contribute where $\mathcal{F}_j$ is nonzero. Two terms are contributed by each of these FEs—one corresponding to an upgoing ramp of an appropriate $\mathcal{F}_i$ which overlaps with $\mathcal{F}_j$ in that FE, and one corresponding to a downgoing ramp of an overlapping $\mathcal{F}_i$ in that FE. The corresponding coefficient of the B term is y_i. With some practice on a few problems, one can write out these terms almost by inspection.

We now consider the third term in eq. (a).

$$\mathrm{III}_j = -y_1 \int_{x=0}^{1} \mathcal{F}_j \mathcal{F}_1' dx - y_2 \int_0^1 \mathcal{F}_j \mathcal{F}_2' dx - \ldots - y_{j-1} \int_0^1 \mathcal{F}_j \mathcal{F}_{j-1}' \, dx$$

$$-y_j \int_0^1 \mathcal{F}_j \mathcal{F}_j' dx - y_{j+1} \int_0^1 \mathcal{F}_j \mathcal{F}_{j+1}' \, dx - \ldots - y_{N+1} \int_0^1 \mathcal{F}_j \mathcal{F}_{N+1}' \, dx$$

$$= -y_{j-1} \int_{x_{j-1}}^{x_j} \mathcal{F}_j \mathcal{F}_{j-1}' \, dx - y_j \int_{x_{j-1}}^{x_j} \mathcal{F}_j \mathcal{F}_j' dx - y_j \int_{x_j}^{x_{j+1}} \mathcal{F}_j \mathcal{F}_j' dx - y_{j+1} \int_{x_j}^{x_{j+1}} \mathcal{F}_j \mathcal{F}_{j+1}' \, dx$$

$$\equiv -y_{j-1}C_{\uparrow\downarrow}^{\langle j-1\rangle} - y_j C_{\uparrow\uparrow}^{\langle j-1\rangle} - y_j C_{\downarrow\downarrow}^{\langle j\rangle} - y_{j+1}C_{\downarrow\uparrow}^{\langle j\rangle} \qquad \ldots(e)$$

Again, only those $\mathcal{F}_i$ contribute to the integrals which overlap with $\mathcal{F}_j$. The nomenclature of the C terms is similar to the B terms. The superscript indicates the finite element over which the integral is to be evaluated, the first subscript represents the direction of the $\mathcal{F}_j$ ramp function in the *FE*, and the second subscript, the direction of the *appropriate* $\mathcal{F}_i$ ramp which overlaps with $\mathcal{F}_j$ in that *FE*. The two special cases for $j = 1$ and $j = N + 1$ are given by

$$\text{III}_{j=1} = -y_1 C_{\downarrow\downarrow}^{\langle 1\rangle} - y_2 C_{\downarrow\uparrow}^{\langle 1\rangle}$$

$$\text{III}_{j=N+1} = -y_N C_{\uparrow\downarrow}^{\langle N\rangle} - y_{N+1}C_{\uparrow\uparrow}^{\langle N\rangle} \qquad \ldots(f)$$

Equation 6.47 can be used to give

$$\mathbf{C}^{\langle j\rangle} \equiv \begin{bmatrix} C_{\downarrow\downarrow}^{\langle j\rangle} & C_{\downarrow\uparrow}^{\langle j\rangle} \\ C_{\uparrow\downarrow}^{\langle j\rangle} & C_{\uparrow\uparrow}^{\langle j\rangle} \end{bmatrix} = \begin{bmatrix} -\dfrac{1}{2} & \dfrac{1}{2} \\ -\dfrac{1}{2} & \dfrac{1}{2} \end{bmatrix} \qquad \ldots(g)$$

The left hand side of eq. (*a*) corresponding to different values of j can now be combined into a matrix form [see eqs. (*b*)–(*g*)] as

$$\text{LHS} = \begin{bmatrix} -1-\dfrac{1}{6h_1}+\dfrac{1}{2} & \dfrac{1}{6h_1}-\dfrac{1}{2} & 0 & & 0 & 0 \\[2ex] \dfrac{1}{6h_1}+\dfrac{1}{2} & -\dfrac{1}{6h_1}-\dfrac{1}{6h_2}-\dfrac{1}{2}+\dfrac{1}{2} & \dfrac{1}{6h_2}-\dfrac{1}{2} & & 0 & 0 \\[2ex] 0 & \dfrac{1}{6h_2}+\dfrac{1}{2} & -\dfrac{1}{6h_2}-\dfrac{1}{6h_3}-\dfrac{1}{2}+\dfrac{1}{2} & \dfrac{1}{6h_3}-\dfrac{1}{2} & 0 \\[2ex] \cdot & \cdot & \cdot & \cdot & \cdot \\ 0 & 0 & 0 & 0 & 0.. \\ 0 & 0 & 0 & 0 & 0.. \end{bmatrix}$$

$$\begin{bmatrix} \cdot\;\cdots\;\cdot & 0 & 0 & 0 \\ \cdot\;\cdots\;\cdot & 0 & 0 & 0 \\ \cdot\;\cdots\;\cdot & 0 & 0 & 0 \\ \cdot\;\cdots\;\cdot & \cdot & \cdot & \cdot \\ \cdot\;\cdots\;\cdot & \cdot & \cdot & \cdot \\ \cdot\;\cdots\;\cdot & \dfrac{1}{6h_{N-1}}+\dfrac{1}{2} & -\dfrac{1}{6h_{N-1}}-\dfrac{1}{6h_N}-\dfrac{1}{2}+\dfrac{1}{2} & \dfrac{1}{6h_N}-\dfrac{1}{2} \\[2ex] \cdot\;\cdots\;\cdot & 0 & \dfrac{1}{6h_N}+\dfrac{1}{2} & -\dfrac{1}{6h_N}-\dfrac{1}{2} \end{bmatrix} \begin{bmatrix} y_1 \\ y_2 \\ y_3 \\ \cdot \\ \cdot \\ y_N \\ y_{N+1} \end{bmatrix} \equiv \mathbf{Ay} \qquad \ldots(h)$$

There is an extra constant, 1, in the $j = 1$ equation [from the 1st term in eq. (*a*)] which is missing from eq. (*h*), and will be taken to the right hand side later on. In the above equation, the $+\dfrac{1}{2}$ and $-\dfrac{1}{2}$ in the diagonal terms come from $C_{\uparrow\uparrow}^{\langle j-1 \rangle}$ and $C_{\downarrow\downarrow}^{\langle j \rangle}$, and are listed separately for ease of generalization.

We now consider term IV on the right hand side of eq. (*a*). We simplify this equation as follows, keeping in mind that the functions are nonzero only in small ranges of x:

$$\text{IV}_j \equiv 2 \int\limits_{x=0}^{1} \mathcal{F}_j \Big[y_1 \mathcal{F}_1 + y_2 \mathcal{F}_2 + ... + y_{j-1} \mathcal{F}_{j-1} + y_j \mathcal{F}_j + y_{j+1} \mathcal{F}_{j+1} + ... + y_{N+1} \mathcal{F}_{N+1} \Big]^2 dx$$

$$= \left[2 \int\limits_{x_{j-1}}^{x_j} \mathcal{F}_j \big[y_{j-1} \mathcal{F}_{j-1} + y_j \mathcal{F}_j \big]^2 dx \right] + \left[2 \int\limits_{x_j}^{x_{j+1}} \mathcal{F}_j \big[y_j \mathcal{F}_j + y_{j+1} \mathcal{F}_{j+1} \big]^2 dx \right]$$

$$\equiv D_\uparrow^{\langle j-1 \rangle} \big(y_{j-1}, y_j \big) + D_\uparrow^{\langle j \rangle} \big(y_j, y_{j+1} \big)$$

The special cases for $j = 1$ and $j = N + 1$ are

$$\text{IV}_{j=1} = 2 \int\limits_{x_1}^{x_2} \mathcal{F}_1 \big[y_1 \mathcal{F}_1 + y_2 \mathcal{F}_2 \big]^2 dx \equiv D_\downarrow^{\langle 1 \rangle} \big(y_1, y_2 \big)$$

$$\text{IV}_{j=N+1} = 2 \int\limits_{x_N}^{x_{N+1}} \mathcal{F}_{N+1} \big[y_N \mathcal{F}_N + y_{N+1} \mathcal{F}_{N+1} \big]^2 dx \equiv D_\uparrow^{\langle N \rangle} \big(y_N, y_{N+1} \big)$$

The values of the D integrals can be evaluated analytically for the present example, but for other problems analytical evaluation may pose difficulties. These integrals are normally evaluated using quadratures using two or three point formulae. Since the range of these integrals extend from x_{j-1} to x_j, etc., one needs to transform them using

$$u^{\langle j \rangle} = \frac{x - x_j}{h_j}; \quad j = 1, 2, ..., N \qquad\qquad ...(i)$$

as in the OCFE method. The integrals can be evaluated using eq. 6.29 with the **w** matrix from table 6.1. The evaluation of $D_\downarrow^{\langle j \rangle} \big(y_j, y_{j+1} \big)$ is illustrated here. We obtain

$$D_\downarrow^{\langle j \rangle} \big(y_j, y_{j+1} \big) \equiv 2 \int\limits_{x_j}^{x_{j+1}} \mathcal{F}_j(x) \big[y_j \mathcal{F}_j(x) + y_{j+1} \mathcal{F}_{j+1}(x) \big]^2 dx$$

$$= 2h_j \int\limits_{u^{\langle j \rangle}=0}^{1} \big[1 - u^{\langle j \rangle} \big] \big[y_j \big(1 - u^{\langle j \rangle} \big) + y_{j+1} u^{\langle j \rangle} \big]^2 du^{\langle j \rangle}$$

$$= 2h_j \sum\limits_{l=1}^{N_Q+2} w_l \big[1 - u_l^{\langle j \rangle} \big] \big[y_j \big(1 - u_l^{\langle j \rangle} \big) + y_{j+1} u_l^{\langle j \rangle} \big]^2$$

where N_Q is the number of internal quadrature points in the *j*th *FE*. If $N_Q = 2$, this becomes

$$D_\downarrow^{\langle j \rangle}\left(y_j, y_{j+1}\right) = 2h_j\left\{0.5[1-0.2113]\left[y_j\left(1-0.2113\right) + y_{j+1} \times 0.2113\right]^2\right.$$

$$\left. +0.5[1-0.7887]\left[y_j\left(1-0.7887\right) + y_{j+1} \times 0.7887\right]^2\right\}$$

The right hand side to be used with eq. (*h*) is then

$$\text{RHS} = \begin{bmatrix} D_\downarrow^{\langle 1 \rangle}\left(y_1, y_2\right) - 1 \\ D_\uparrow^{\langle 1 \rangle}\left(y_1, y_2\right) + D_\downarrow^{\langle 2 \rangle}\left(y_2, y_3\right) \\ D_\uparrow^{\langle 2 \rangle}\left(y_2, y_3\right) + D_\downarrow^{\langle 3 \rangle}\left(y_3, y_4\right) \\ \cdot \\ \cdot \\ \cdot \\ D_\uparrow^{\langle N \rangle}\left(y_N, y_{N+1}\right) \end{bmatrix} = \mathbf{f}\left(\mathbf{y}\right) \qquad \dots (j)$$

The final equation for *y* is given from eqs. (*h*) and (*j*) as

$$\mathbf{Ay} = \mathbf{f}\left(\mathbf{y}\right)$$

The successive substitutions technique can be used to evaluate the values of y_1, y_2, ..., y_{N+1}. Alternatively, the NR method followed by Thomas' algorithm can be used. Figure 6.9 shows some results on the isothermal TRAM using equi-sized FEs, and compares them with those obtained using the finite difference technique. Values of integrals involving *y*(*x*) can be obtained quite easily (see prob. 6.41) using eq. 6.46 and simplifying the integrals. If required, transformation of variables from *x* to $u^{(i)}$ may be made and quadratures used. In case the ODE incorporates a linear term involving *y* alone on the left-hand side, it can be simplified in a similar manner (this is left as an exercise, see prob. 6.43).

In problems involving spherical geometries, as in example 6.3, we may have equations of the following kind (see prob. 6.40)

$$\frac{d}{dx}\left(x^2\frac{dy}{dx}\right) = \phi^2 x^2 f\left(y\right)$$

Galerkin's finite element technique then gives

$$\int_{x=0}^{1} \mathcal{F}_j\left(x\right)\frac{d}{dx}\left(x^2\frac{dy}{dx}\right)dx = \phi^2 \int_{x=0}^{1} x^2\mathcal{F}_j\left(x\right)f\left(y\right)dx ; \qquad j = 1, 2, ..., N+1$$

The LHS can be integrated by parts and the expression for *y* from eq. 6.46 substituted to give

$$\left[\mathcal{F}_j\left(x\right)x^2\sum_{i=1}^{N+1}y_i\mathcal{F}_i'\right]_{x=0}^{1} - \sum_{i=1}^{N+1}y_i\int_{x=0}^{1}x^2\mathcal{F}_j'\mathcal{F}_i'dx$$

$$= \phi^2\int_{x=0}^{1}x^2\mathcal{F}_jf\left[\sum_{i=1}^{N+1}y_i\mathcal{F}_i\right]dx ; \qquad j = 1, 2, ..., N+1$$

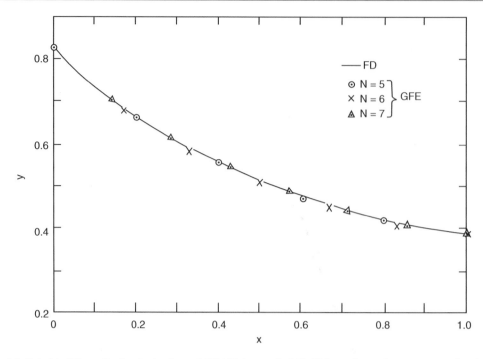

Fig. 6.9 Galerkin FE results for the isothermal TRAM (example 6.9). Values of y at the common end points are:

			GFE	
	$FD\ (N = 7)$	$N = 5$	$N = 6$	$N = 7$
$y\ (0)$	0.8304	0.82602	0.82758	0.82855
$y\ (1)$	0.3827	0.38653	0.40387	0.38689

The integrals, $\int_{x=0}^{1} x^2 \mathcal{F}_j' \mathcal{F}_i' dx$, can be simplified as the corresponding integral in example 6.9. The matrix $\mathbf{B}^{(j)}$ is slightly more difficult to obtain than given by eq. (c) in this example, since its elements involve x_j. Their evaluation is left as an exercise (see prob. 6.40 [3]). ∎

Several adaptations and extensions of the Galerkin finite element technique can be found in excellent texts (*e.g.*, refs. 25, 26) and reviews. This section attempts to give only a very elementary introduction to this important topic.

6.6 SHOOTING TECHNIQUES

In this technique, we reduce the second (or higher) order ODE-BVP into a set of first order ODEs, using the transformations described in sec. 5.1. However, the methods described in Chapter 5 cannot be used directly to solve these equations, since *all* the 'initial' conditions are not specified at the same value of x. The equation for the isothermal TRAM (example 6.1) can be transformed $\left(\text{using } y_1 \equiv y, y_2 = \dfrac{dy}{dx}\right)$ into the following set (see eq. 5.5):

$$\frac{dy_1}{dx} = y_2 \qquad \qquad \dots(a)$$

$$\frac{dy_2}{dx} = 6y_2 + 12y_1^2 \qquad \qquad \dots(b)$$

$$x = 0: \quad y_2 = 6(y_1 - 1) \qquad \qquad \dots(c)$$

$$x = 1: \quad y_2 = 0 \qquad \qquad \dots(d) \qquad \dots(6.50)$$

Such sets of N first-order nonlinear ODEs with some of the N conditions specified at $x = 0$, and the remaining at $x = 1$, also arise quite commonly when Pontryagin's minimum principle is used to obtain optimal trajectories (or histories, or profiles) [27]. A common technique of solving these equations is to *assume* the values of the missing variables at $x = 0$ (consistent with the specified conditions), integrate (shoot) the N equations from $x = 0$ to $x = 1$, and see if *all* the specified conditions at $x = 1$ are satisfied or not. This is referred to as the shooting method [3, 28–31]. A Newton-Raphson or successive substitutions technique can be used to correct for the assumed values at $x = 0$. The technique is illustrated below.

Example 6.10: Solve for the profile, $y(x)$, for the isothermal TRAM of example 6.1, using the shooting technique on eq. 6.50.

Since the condition $y_2(0)$ is specified, we shall assume a value for $y_1(0)$:

$$y_1(0) = s \qquad \qquad \dots(a)$$

which gives (consistency with given condition at $x = 0$):

$$y_2(0) = 6(s - 1) \qquad \qquad \dots(b)$$

Equations 6.50 (a, b), and eqs. (a and b) above can easily be integrated using a GEAR package (or a Runge-Kutta subroutine) to give $y_1(x)$ and $y_2(x)$. Both these profiles will depend on the value of s. The check to be used comes from the given boundary condition at $x = 1$ [eq. 6.50 (d)]:

$$\chi(s) \equiv y_2(1) = 0$$

We can change the value of s from iteration to iteration using the Newton-Raphson method. Since χ is a function of s alone, we use the 1-variable formula:

$$s^{(k+1)} = s^{(k)} - \frac{\chi(s^{(k)})}{\left.\dfrac{d\chi}{ds}\right|_{s^{(k)}}}$$

In order to obtain an expression for $\dfrac{d\chi}{ds}$, we define two new variables, ζ and η as [32]

$$\zeta(\chi, s) = \frac{\partial y_1(x, s)}{\partial s}$$

$$\eta(\chi, s) = \frac{\partial y_2(x, s)}{\partial s}$$

We can now write

$$\frac{d\zeta}{dx} = \frac{d}{dx}\left(\frac{\partial y_1}{\partial s}\right) = \frac{\partial}{\partial s}\left(\frac{dy_1}{dx}\right) = \frac{\partial}{\partial s}(y_2) = \eta$$

where eq. 6.50(a) has been used to replace $\dfrac{dy_1}{dx}$. Similarly

$$\frac{d\eta}{dx} = \frac{d}{dx}\left(\frac{\partial y_2}{\partial s}\right) = \frac{\partial}{\partial s}\left(\frac{dy_2}{dx}\right) = \frac{\partial}{\partial s}\left(6y_2 + 12y_1^2\right)$$

$$= \frac{6\partial y_2}{\partial s} + 24y_1\frac{\partial y_1}{\partial s} = 6\eta + 24y_1\zeta$$

The 'initial' conditions (at $x = 0$) for ζ and η can easily be deduced. Using eqs. (a) and (b) of this example, we obtain

$$\zeta(x=0) = \frac{\partial y_1(0)}{\partial s} = \frac{\partial s}{\partial s} = 1$$

$$\eta(x=0) = \frac{\partial}{\partial s}\left[y_2(0)\right] = \frac{\partial}{\partial s}\left[6(s-1)\right] = 6$$

In summary, we have to integrate the following ODEs simultaneously:

$$\frac{dy_1}{dx} = y_2$$

$$\frac{dy_2}{dx} = 6y_2 + 12y_1^2$$

$$\frac{d\zeta}{dx} = \eta$$

$$\frac{d\eta}{dx} = 6\eta + 24\zeta y_1$$

$$x = 0: \ y_1 = s$$

$$y_2 = 6(s-1)$$

$$\zeta = 1$$

$$\eta = 6 \qquad\qquad\qquad ...(c)$$

$\dfrac{d\chi}{ds}$ can be obtained using

$$\dot\chi = \frac{\partial}{\partial s}\left[y_2(1)\right] = \eta(1)$$

and the Newton-Raphson method can be written as

$$s^{(k+1)} = s^{(k)} - \left[\frac{y_2(1)}{\eta(1)} \right]^{(k)} \qquad \ldots(d)$$

The profiles, $y_1(x)$, $y_2(x)$, $\zeta(x)$ and $\eta(x)$, can be obtained by integration of eq. (c) using any value, $s^{(k)}$, and the computed values of $y_2^{(1)}$ and $\eta(1)$ can be used in eq. (d) to obtain an improved value, $s^{(k+1)}$. These iterations continue till the following convergence criterion is satisfied:

$$\left| \chi \right|^{(k)} = \left| y_2(1) \right|^{(k)} \le \varepsilon \qquad \ldots(e)$$

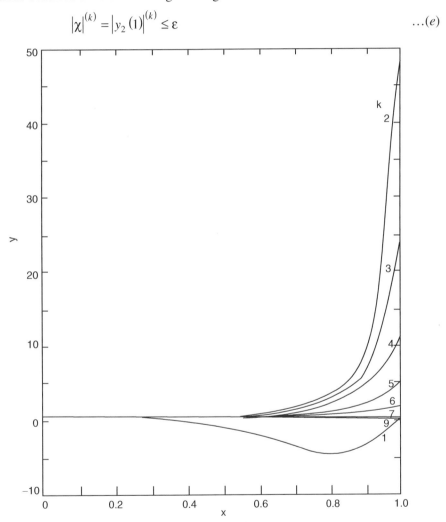

Fig. 6.10 $y(x)$ profiles for example 6.10 (isothermal TRAM) for different value of $s^{(k)}$ using eq. (c). Values of $s^{(k)}$ for different k are:

k	1	2	3	4	5	6	7	8	9
$s^{(k)}$	0.8000	0.8373	0.8359	0.8344	0.8331	0.8320	0.8315	0.8313	0.8313

Convergence was assumed to be reached when $|y_2(1)| \le 10^{-3}$.

Figure 6.10 shows how the profiles converge with $s^{(1)} = 0.8$, a value which is quite close to the value of $y(0)$ obtained using the finite difference technique (fig. 6.2). The significant changes near $x = 1$ as k increases are to be noted. A GEAR program was used to integrate the ODEs (TOL = 10^{-5}). Results with $s^{(1)} = 0.7$ do not converge to the correct profile, $y(x)$, while with $s^{(1)} = 0.84$, the converged results are obtained in only 7 iterations. The converged results compare well with the 7 point FD results (see prob. 6.45). ∎

At times, the integration of equations (c) (example 6.10) becomes unstable (see prob. 6.44) and it is more fruitful to assume conditions at $x = 1$ and integrate (or shoot) backwards from $x = 1$ and integrate (or shoot) backwards from $x = 1$ to $x = 0$ (reverse shooting). prob. 6.45 shows that the following algorithm is to be followed for the isothermal TRAM [28, 32]:

$$\frac{dy_1}{dx} = y_2$$

$$\frac{dy_2}{dx} = 12y_1^2 - 6y_2$$

$$\frac{d\zeta}{dx} = \eta$$

$$\frac{d\eta}{dx} = 24\zeta y_1 - 6\eta$$

$$x = 0 : \quad y_2 = 0$$

$$y_1 = s$$

$$\zeta = 1$$

$$\eta = 0$$

$$s^{(k+1)} = s^{(k)} - \left[\frac{y_2(1) + 6y_1(1) - 6}{\eta(1) + 6\zeta(1)}\right]^{(k)}$$

Check: $\left| y_2(1) + 6y_1(1) - 6 \right| \le \varepsilon$ ...(6.51)

where x in eq. 6.51 is $(1 - x)$ in eq. 6.50 (the star on x^* is being omitted). It is observed that convergence is easily attained even if the values of y at $x^* = 0$ in eq. 6.51 is taken to be 0.84—quite far from the finite difference value of 0.387. Figure 6.11 shows the $y(x)$ profile [x the same as in the original ODE, eq. 6.50] as a function of iteration number with $s^{(k)} = 0.8$. Comparison of figs. 6.10 and 6.11 shows the sensitivity of the results to small changes in the assumed value of $y(x = 0)$, as compared to the relative insensitivity to $y(x = 1)$ in the case of backward shooting. A more detailed discussion of this sensitivity (for a first-order reaction) is available in ref. 33.

The algorithm to be used can be easily developed for any ODE-BVP. Davis [30] gives the algorithm for multivariable cases, and the reader is referred to his excellent presentation. We end this section with the discussion that the shooting method *usually* requires less storage space than required by methods like OCFE, GFE, etc. Secondly, excellent and easily available computer codes for ODE-IVPs can be used to integrate the resulting equations. The NAG library has several programs (*e.g.*, DO2GAF, DO2RAF, etc.) which can be used to solve two point boundary value problems (first order ODEs). Similarly, the IMSL library has programs (*e.g.*, DTPTB) using the shooting technique.

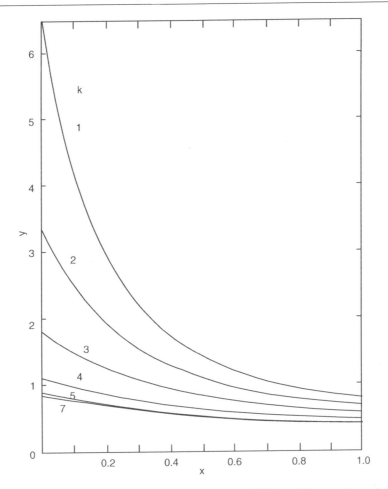

Fig. 6.11 y (x) for the isothermal TRAM using reverse shooting (eq. 6.51) for different values of k. x same as in the original ODE. y $(x = 1) = s^{(1)} = 0.8$.

6.7 CONCLUSIONS

In this chapter, we have described several techniques which are commonly used for solving ODE-BVPs. Many more adaptations, extensions, etc., are available, and the reader is referred to the current literature for these. prob. 6.47 describes yet another technique, referred to as quasilinearization [34, 35], in which the nonlinear terms in the ODE are linearized about any profile, y $[x^{(k)}]$, and then an improved profile, y $[x^{(k+1)}]$ is obtained using, for example, the finite difference method. The solution of the linearized ODE is faster, since linear algebraic equations are obtained with the FD technique, and Thomas' method can be used. Nonlinear ODE-BVPs can also be solved using invariant embedding [34–38]. This involves an adaptation of the shooting method—invariant embedding provides an estimate for the missing initial conditions for sets of first order, two point boundary value problems. The reader is referred to the excellent books for details.

In this chapter, we have solved the same problem (isothermal TRAM) using several different techniques, and have pointed out their relative advantages and disadvantages. The reader can make comparisons using appropriate problems in the set given at the end of this chapter. Comparison of results (using different techniques) of several other complex ODE-BVPs can also be found in the literature, and the reader is referred to these.

It may be mentioned that several adaptations have appeared in the current literature, which are quite 'problem specific', *i.e.*, they work very well for the problem(s) studied, but it is difficult to predict, *a-priori*, whether or not these would work on other problems. An example is the 'approximate collocation method' of Shah and Paraskos [39], in which basis functions which are analytical solutions of simpler problems (for first order reactions) are used. It is best to avoid using 'intelligent adaptations' [33], and stick to techniques having sounder mathematical basis.

Appendix 6A

REFORMULATION OF THE ORTHOGONAL COLLOCATION METHOD

An interesting and informative reformulation of the OC problem in sec. 6.3 is given below without derivation and without too many details (for which the reader can see ref. 12).

An alternate way (than eq. 6.18 or 6.23) of writing the solution, $y(x)$, of degree $N + 1$, for an ODE-BVP is in terms of the Lagrangian interpolation polynomials, $L_i^{(n+1)}(x)$ (see sec. 4.4) of degree $N + 1$, given slightly differently than in eq. 4.43 by

$$L_i^{(n+1)}(x) = \prod_{\substack{j=1 \\ j \neq i}}^{n+2} \left(\frac{x - x_j}{x_i - x_j} \right); \quad i = 1, 2, ..., N + 2 \qquad ...(A6.1)$$

The solution of the ODE-BVP can be assumed to be

$$y(x) = \sum_{i=1}^{N+2} L_i^{(n+1)}(x) y_i \qquad ...(A6.2)$$

An alternate way of writing $L_i^{(n+1)}(x)$ is in terms of a 'node polynomial', $\mathbb{P}_{N+2}(x)$, of degree $N + 2$:

$$L_i^{(n+1)}(x) = \frac{\mathbb{P}_{N+2}(x)}{(x - x_i)\mathbb{P}'_{N+2}(x_i)} \qquad ...(A6.3)$$

where

$$\mathbb{P}_{N+2}(x) \equiv (x - x_1)\left[(x - x_2)...(x - x_{N+1})\right](x - x_{N+2})$$

$$\equiv (x - x_1) P_N^{(\alpha,\beta)}(x)(x - x_{N+2}) \qquad ...(A6.4)$$

The node polynomial has zeros as $x_1 (= 0)$, x_2, x_3, ..., $x_{N+2} (= 1)$. $P_N^{(\alpha,\beta)}(x)$ is known as a Jacobi polynomial, and is defined by the orthogonality condition

$$\int_0^1 (1 - x)^\alpha x^\beta P_i^{(\alpha,\beta)}(x) P_j^{(\alpha,\beta)}(x) dx = C_i^{(\alpha,\beta)} \delta_{ij} ; \quad i, j = 1, 2, ..., N \qquad ...(A6.5)$$

Note that $P_i^{(0,0)}(x)$ are the shifted Legendre polynomials. Villadsen and Michelsen [12] give methods (and listings of computer codes) for obtaining the coefficients, γ_i, characterizing these polynomials:

$$P_i^{(\alpha,\beta)}(x) = (-1)^i \left[1 - \gamma_1 x + \gamma_2 x^2 - ... + (-1)^i \gamma_i x^i\right] \qquad ...(A6.6)$$

Eq. A6.4 indicates that x_2, x_3, ..., x_{N+1} are the roots of $P_N^{(\alpha,\beta)}(x)$.

The derivatives of $y(x)$ at x_j can easily be written from eq. A6.2 as

$$y'_j = \sum_{i=1}^{N+2} L_i^{(n+1)'}\left(x_j\right)y_i$$

$$y''_j = \sum_{i=1}^{N+2} L_i^{(n+1)''}\left(x_j\right)y_i \qquad\qquad ...(A6.7)$$

It is obvious that $L_i^{(n+1)'}(x_j)$ is A_{ji} and $L_i^{(n+1)''}(x_j)$ is B_{ji}. The derivatives of $L_i^{(n+1)}(x_j)$ can be obtained quite easily in terms of $\mathbb{P}_{N+2}(x)$ and its derivatives and are available in ref. 12, alongwith the computer listing for evaluating the matrices, **A** and **B**. Thus, we can easily obtain these matrices once we know the internal collocation points [roots of $P_N^{(\alpha,\beta)}(x)$].

The quadrature weightages, w_i, can also be evaluated for the following formula (Lobatto quadrature)

$$\int_0^1 y(x)(1-x)^\alpha x^\beta dx = \sum_{k=1}^{N+2} w_k y_k = \sum_{k=1}^{N+2} y_k \left[\int_0^1 L_k^{(n+1)}(x)(1-x)^\alpha x^\beta dx\right] \qquad ...(A6.8)$$

The simplified expressions for w_k are given in ref. 12, alongwith computer codes for their evaluation. It has been established [12] that the 'best' choice of the N interior *quadrature points* for evaluating the *integral* in eq. A6.8 are the roots of $P_N^{(\alpha+1,\,\beta+1)}(x)$. Then we obtain exact results using the $N+2$ values of y_i, even if $y_{\text{exact}}(x)$ is a polynomial of degree $2N+1$. Thus, if we are interested in obtaining accurate values $\int_0^1 y\,dx$ $\left(i.e.,\ \alpha=\beta=0\right)$, we should really use the roots of $P_N^{(1,1)}(x)$ as the internal OC points [instead of using the roots of the shifted Legendre polynomials, $P_N^{(0,0)}(x)$ as the quadrature points, as discussed in sec. 6.3. However, higher accuracies are obtained by increasing N rather than by changing values of α and β.

It only remains to show that the matrices **A** and **B**, and the quadrature weightages, **w**, for the case when $y(x)$ is written as in eq. A6.2, are the same as the matrices discussed in sec. 6.3. Since eqs. 6.23 and A6.2 both are polynomials of degree $N+1$ in x, and since both these polynomials pass through the points (x_1, y_1), (x_2, y_2), ..., (x_{N+2}, y_{N+2}), they are going to be identical, provided the OC points are the same. So, if we generate **A**, **B** and **W** using the Lagrangian interpolating polynomial formulation with the internal OC points as roots of $P_N^{(0,0)}(x)$, we will get the same results as in table 6.1.

PROBLEMS

6.1 The grid point locations in a finite difference reduction are not equi-spaced, but are defined by

$$\Delta x_i \equiv x_{i+1} - x_i;\ \ i=1, 2, ..., N$$

Obtain expressions for y_i' equivalent to eqs. 6.8(a–c).

6.2 Use eqs. 4.63 and 4.64 to derive eq. 6.9. Also, use eq. 4.65 to obtain

$$y_i' = \frac{\left[\dfrac{3}{2}y_i - 2y_{i-1} + \dfrac{1}{2}y_{i-2}\right]}{\Delta x} + \frac{y_i'''}{3}(\Delta x)^2$$

6.3 Obtain the following equations for y_i'':

(a) for non-equispaced grid points

$$y_i'' = \frac{2}{\Delta x_i + \Delta x_{i-1}} \left[\frac{y_{i+1} - y_i}{\Delta x_i} - \frac{y_i - y_{i-1}}{\Delta x_{i-1}} \right] - \frac{y_i'''}{3} \left(\Delta x_i - \Delta x_{i-1} \right)$$

(b) in terms of y at points ahead of i (for equispaced grid points)

$$y_i'' = \frac{-y_{i+3} + 4y_{i+2} - 5y_{i+1} + 2y_i}{(\Delta x)^2} + \frac{11}{12} y_i^{(4)} (\Delta x)^2$$

(**Hint:** use eq. 4.62b):

(c) in terms of y at points behind i, for equispaced grid points (**Hint:** use eq. 4.65):

$$y_i'' = \frac{2y_i - 5y_{i-1} + 4y_{i-2} - y_{i-3}}{(\Delta x)^2} + \frac{11}{12} y_i^{(4)} (\Delta x)^2$$

6.4 Obtain the final equations for the TRAM discussed in examples 6.1 and 6.2. Use the Newton-Raphson and Gauss-Seidel techniques to converge to the solution, using $N = 3$, 5 and 7. Use $y_i^{(1)} = 1 - x_i$ as the starting guess.

6.5 Obtain the algebraic equations for examples 6.1 and 6.2 using the finite difference technique, with the one-sided equations for y_1' and y_{N+1}', and the regular, two-sided equations (eqs. 6.8, 6.10) for y_i' and y_i'' at the intermediate points. Make sure $O[(\Delta x)^2]$ formulae are used in all cases. Compare with results from prob. 6.4.

6.6 Use the finite-difference technique with $N + 1$ grid points (with $N = 10$), to reduce the reaction-cum-diffusion problem in an isothermal, porous catalyst sphere (eq. 6.12) into a set of algebraic equations. Solve for the following values of the parameters:

$$Bi_m = 250$$

$$n = 2$$

Plot the concentration profiles for $\phi = 10^{-1}$, 10^0 and 10^1. Also compute the effectiveness factor, η, given for this case by

$$\eta = 3 \int_0^1 x^2 y^n dx$$

An appropriate quadrature may be used to evaluate the integral.

6.7 The diffusion-cum nth-order irreversible reaction in an isothermal, porous, catalyst *slab* is described by (see eq. 6.12)

$$\frac{d^2 y}{dx^2} = \phi^2 y^n$$

$$\left. \frac{dy}{dx} \right|_{x=0} = 0$$

$$y(x = 1) = 1$$

There is no mass transfer resistance in the film surrounding the slab. Use the finite-difference technique to reduce this into a set of algebraic equations of the form $\mathbf{Ay} = \mathbf{f}(\mathbf{y})$.

Check if you obtain the equations given in prob. 3.8 for $n = 2$. Use $\mathbf{A}\mathbf{y}^{(k+1)} = \mathbf{f}(\mathbf{y}^{(k)})$ with the Gauss-Seidel technique and obtain the profile, $y(x)$, numerically for $n = 1$ and $\phi = 10^{-1}$, 10° and 10^{1}, using $N = 10$. Compare with the analytical result [1]

$$y = \frac{\cosh(\phi x)}{\cosh(\phi)}$$

Also compare your results for $n = 2$ with those obtained in prob. 6.6 (for a sphere, with $Bi_m = 250$). Integrate the profile to evaluate the effectiveness factor and compare with the analytical result (for $n = 1$):

$$\eta = \frac{\tanh(\phi)}{\phi}$$

6.8 Simplify example 6.3 for the case when $Bi_m = \infty$, $\delta = 1$ ($y_{N+1} = 1$ then). Using different values for the number of finite-difference grid-points, obtain *three* sets of concentration and temperature profiles. Also evaluate the three effectiveness factors (eq. *f*, example 6.3). Use $\beta = 0.6$, $\gamma = 20$, $\phi = 0.5$. Compare your computed profiles with that shown in fig. 6.3. Use Thomas' algorithm and the NR techniques.

6.9 The problem of an isothermal Langmuir-Hinshelwood reaction (with one reactant in stoichiometric excess) occurring in a catalyst sphere can be modeled as [1, 3]

$$\frac{1}{x^2}\frac{d}{dx}\left(\frac{x^2 dy}{dx}\right) = \phi^2\left[\frac{y(E+y)}{(1+Ky)^2}\right] \equiv \phi^2 f(y)$$

$$x = 0 : \frac{dy}{dx} = 0$$

$$x = 1 : y = 1$$

where ϕ is the Thiele modulus, K is an adsorption constant, and E is the fraction excess of one of the reactants. Solve using the finite difference technique coupled with the Newton-Raphson method. Use $E = 1$, $K = 100$, $\phi = 110$ (multiple solutions are present [41]). Note that $f(1) \neq 1$ here, and we must use the following equation

$$\eta = \frac{\int_0^1 x^2 f(y) dx}{\int_0^1 x^2 f(1) dx}$$

for the effectiveness factor, instead of eq. (*f*) in example 6.3. Also obtain the $N = 2$ OC solution with $y(x^2)$, $a = 3$, and compare the results.

6.10 The following ODE-BVP describes heat transfer in a straight fin [40] of uniform cross section:

$$\frac{d^2\theta}{dx^2} - m^2\theta = 0$$

$$x = 0, \ \theta = 1$$

$$x = 1, \frac{d\theta}{dx} = -(Bi)\theta$$

where θ is the dimensionless temperature at any position in the fin, x is a dimensionless location, Bi is the dimensionless Biot number, and m^2 is the product of Bi and a dimensionless group involving fin dimensions (note that the m used here is slightly different than in most texts [40]). Obtain the set of algebraic equations to be solved using the finite difference technique. Obtain the temperature profile for $Bi = 0.04737$, $m = 2.1324$. Compare the profile obtained with the analytical solution

$$\theta = \frac{\cosh\left[m(1-x)\right] + \left(\dfrac{Bi}{m}\right)\sinh\left[m(1-x)\right]}{\cosh m + \left(\dfrac{Bi}{m}\right)\sinh m}$$

Use your temperature profile to obtain the effectiveness factor, η, as

$$\eta = \frac{1}{Bi + m^2} \frac{d\theta}{dx}\bigg|_{x=0}$$

and compare with the analytical value

$$\eta = \frac{m}{m^2 + Bi}\left[\frac{\sinh m + \dfrac{Bi}{m}\cosh m}{\cosh m + \dfrac{Bi}{m}\sinh m}\right]$$

Repeat using the OC technique with $N = 2$, and compare the results.

6.11 Use the finite difference technique on [34] (see examples 3.3 and 3.6)

$$\frac{d^2 y}{dx^2} - 2y^3 = 0$$

$$y(0) = 1$$

$$\left[\frac{dy}{dx} + y^2\right]_{x=1} = 0$$

to obtain a set of coupled, nonlinear algebraic equations in $\mathbf{y} = [y_1\ y_2\ \dots\ y_{N+1}]^T$. Use the Newton-Raphson technique and solve for $N = 2$, 4 and 10. Compare with the analytical solution, $y = 1/(x + 1)$. Use the composite Simpson's rule to evaluate

$$\int_{x=0}^{1} 3y^2 dx$$

Compare with the analytical value again.

6.12 The steady state one-dimensional heat transfer across an infinite slab (see fig. P. 6.12) of thickness, L, with no heat generation and with thermal conductivity being a *linear* function of temperature, $k = k_0 + k_0^*(T - T_0)$, is described by the following nonlinear ODE-BVP [3, 40]

$$(1+ay)\frac{d^2y}{dx^2}+a\left(\frac{dy}{dx}\right)^2=0$$

$$x=0: \ y=0 \ ; \ x=1 \ : \ y=1$$

In this equation, y is the dimensionless temperature $\left(\equiv\dfrac{T-T_0}{T_1-T_0}\right)$, x is the dimensionless position,

and $a\left[\equiv k_0^*\dfrac{(T_1-T_0)}{k_0}\right]$ is a dimensionless constant. Use the finite difference technique with $N+1$

equispaced grid points to obtain a set of algebraic equations. Check your results (for $N=3$) with the equations in prob. 3.5. Simplify using the Newton-Raphson technique. Solve for $N=10$, $a=1$, and compare your results with the analytical solution [40]:

$$y=-\frac{1}{a}+\frac{\left[1+(2a+a^2)x\right]^{\frac{1}{2}}}{a}$$

Also solve for $a=0$.
Evaluate the dimensionless heat flux given by

$$q\equiv\frac{(\text{flux})L}{k_0(T_1-T_0)}=-(1+ay)\frac{dy}{dx}$$

at $x=0$ and $x=1$, both from the computed $y(x)$ as well as analytically.

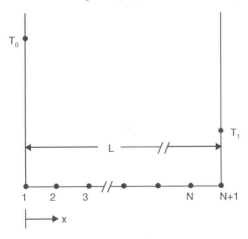

Fig. P. 6.12

A very interesting adaptation of prob. 6.12 has been suggested by Finlayson [3], when the thermal conductivity does not vary linearly with temperature, but is a known function, $k(T)$.

6.13 The following *coupled* ODE-BVPs characterize a system:

$$\frac{d^2y}{dx^2}+2y=f_1(x,y,z); \quad \frac{d^2z}{dx^2}+3z=f_2(x,y,z)$$

$$y(0) = 1, \quad y(1) = 3$$

$$z(0) = 2, \quad z(1) = 4$$

Obtain the set of algebraic equations for y_i and z_i, $i = 1, 2, \dots, N + 1$, for $N = 3$ using FD. Comment on how you could solve this set of equations using the method of successive substitutions. This is an example of how one solves problems with more than one dependent variable. Repeat with the OC technique with $N = 2$.

6.14 Apply the finite difference technique with the composite trapezoidal rule [eq. 4.76a], to obtain an algebraic equation for

$$\frac{d^2y}{dx^2} + 2yx = xy \int_0^1 \left[y(x)\right]^3 e^x dx$$

$$y(0) = 2; \quad y(1) = 4$$

Use $N = 2$. Solve to obtain $y(0.5)$. Note that the composite trapezoidal rule is of accuracy $O[(\Delta x)^3]$, while your expressions for y'', etc., are $O[(\Delta x)^2]$.

6.15 The flow on a suddenly accelerated plane wall (Stokes' first problem) can be described by [19, 42]

$$y'' + 50xy' = 0$$

$$x = 0 : \quad y = 1$$

$$x = 1 : \quad y = 0$$

where $y(x)$ is the dimensionless velocity and x is a dimensionless variable related to both the distance away from the plate, and time. Set up the algebraic equations and solve this problem using the finite difference technique. Use $N = 10$. Plot y vs. x (Schlichting [42] gives the plot of y vs. $5x$, using an analytical solution involving complementary error functions, with the domain of x extending to infinity). Compare with the $N = 2$ OC solution.

6.16 The flow of a viscous fluid around a flat disc rotating around an axis perpendicular to its plane, is described by [42]:

$$\frac{d^2F}{dx^2} = H\frac{dF}{dx} + \left(F^2 - G^2\right)$$

$$\frac{d^2G}{dx^2} = 2FG + H\frac{dG}{dx}$$

$$\frac{dH}{dx} = -2F$$

$$\frac{dP}{dx} = \frac{d^2H}{dx^2} - H\frac{dH}{dx}$$

$$x = 0 : H = 0 : G = 1$$

$$F = 0; \quad P = 0$$

$$x = 10 : \quad F = 0$$

$$G = 0$$

Here, F, G and H are the dimensionless velocities in the radial, tangential and axial directions respectively, and P is the dimensionless pressure (the condition at $x = 10$ should really be at $x = \infty$, but is used for convenience), and x is a dimensionless distance from the wall.

Obtain the finite difference form for the above equations. Simplify and solve using the NR technique for $N = 7$. Note that you can solve for F, G and H first and then use the fourth ODE above to evaluate P.

6.17 The boundary layer flow over a stationary flat plate can be described by [42]

$$2\frac{d^3y}{dx^3} + y\frac{d^2y}{dx^2} = 0$$

$$y(0) = 0$$

$$\frac{dy}{dx}(0) = 0$$

$$\frac{dy}{dx}(6) = 1$$

The asymptotic boundary condition $[y'(\infty) = 1]$ has been replaced by the condition on y' at $x = 6$ in the above equations [28]. The dimensionless velocity is given by $\frac{dy}{dx}$ (y is, thus, the dimensionless stream function), and x is a dimensionless coordinate involving the location of a point (both along the plate as well as perpendicular to it). The above ODE-BVP can be easily transformed into ($\alpha = y$, $\beta = y'$, $\gamma = y''$):

$$\frac{d\alpha}{dx} = \beta$$

$$\frac{d\beta}{dx} = \gamma$$

$$\frac{d\gamma}{dx} = -\frac{1}{2}\alpha\gamma$$

$$x = 0 \quad : \quad \alpha = \beta = 0$$

$$x = 7.5: \quad \beta = 1$$

Reduce these to the finite difference form. You need not re-nondimensionlize x, since the finite difference expressions for $\frac{d\alpha}{dx}$, etc., correct to $[O\,(\Delta x)^2]$, are still applicable. [**Hint:** Use the one-sided formula for y' given in prob. 6.2 at $x = 6$, and that given in eq. 6.9 for y' at $x = 0$]. Use the NR technique to obtain a set of linear algebraic equations. Then use an adapted Gauss-Seidel technique and solve using $N = 5$ and 9. Plot the dimensionless velocity, β, as a function of x.

6.18 In several fluid mechanics problems [as for example, in the creeping flow around a sphere, see p. 132 in Ref. 18] one needs to solve $\nabla^4 \psi = 0$, where ψ is the stream function. This involves fourth order and other derivatives. Obtain the following equations for some of the higher derivatives:

$$\frac{d^3y}{dx^3} = \frac{y_{i+2} - 2y_{i+1} + 2y_{i-1} - y_{i-2}}{2(\Delta x)^3} - \frac{(\Delta x)^2}{4} y_\xi^{(5)}$$

$$\frac{d^4y}{dx^4} = \frac{y_{i-2} - 4y_{i-1} + 6y_i - 4y_{i+1} + y_{i+2}}{(\Delta x)^4} - \frac{(\Delta x)^2}{6} y_\xi^{(6)}$$

These equations can be generalized (see Chapter 7) for partial derivatives. Refs. 43 and 44 give solutions of several such problems. Note that hypothetical points $0, -1, N + 2, N + 3$ appear in the fourth derivative, etc. These can be eliminated using *four* boundary conditions given for fourth order ODE-BVPs.

6.19 Use the transformation, $u = \dfrac{[x - (-1)]}{2}$ in the Legendre polynomials (eq. A4.2) and show that you obtain the shifted Legendre polynomials given in eq. 6.20. You can, thus, obtain the roots of the shifted Legendre polynomials from a table of the roots of Legendre polynomials.

6.20 Make a computer program which uses the roots of the appropriate polynomials (given in table 6.2) and generates matrices **Q, C** and **D**. Evaluate $\mathbf{Q}^{-1}$ and then obtain matrices **w, A** and **B** for N upto 6 (use the results of prob. 6.22 and 6.24 for obtaining **w**). Check your results against the matrices given in tables 6.1 and 6.3 for low N. Problem 6.19 can be used with roots of Legendre polynomials [17] to obtain roots of the shifted Legendre polynomials for even higher values of N, for the matrices in table 6.1.

6.21 Solve the algebraic equations obtained using the OC technique in example 6.4 for the isothermal TRAM. Check if you get the solutions given for $N = 2$. Also obtain results for $N = 1$ using this method.

6.22 Using eq. 6.23 for $y(x)$ in the integral in the following equation:

$$\int_0^1 y(x)\,dx = \sum_{i=1}^{N+2} w_i y(x_i)$$

show that

$$\begin{bmatrix} 1 & \frac{1}{2} & \frac{1}{3} & \cdots & \frac{1}{N+2} \end{bmatrix} \mathbf{d} = \begin{bmatrix} w_1 & w_2 & \cdots & w_{N+2} \end{bmatrix} \mathbf{y} \equiv \mathbf{w}^T \mathbf{y}$$

where **d** and **y** are as defined in eq. 6.25a. Thus, show that

$$\mathbf{w}^T = \begin{bmatrix} 1 & \frac{1}{2} & \frac{1}{3} & \cdots & \frac{1}{N+2} \end{bmatrix} \mathbf{Q}^{-1}$$

Assume that the collocation points are known. Check if this **w** can also be used if we need to evaluate the integral in eq. 6.29.

6.23 Substitute $x^* = 1 - x$ in the isothermal TRAM ODE-BVP (example 6.1) to obtain

$$\frac{1}{6}\frac{d^2y}{dx^{*2}} + \frac{dy}{dx^*} - 2y^2 = 0$$

$$\frac{dy}{dx^*} = 0 \quad \text{at} \quad x^* = 0$$

$$\frac{dy}{dx^*} = -6(y-1) \text{ at } x^* = 1$$

Assuming a series solution

$$y = d_1 + d_2 x^* + d_3 (x^*)^2 + d_4 (x^*)^3 + \dots$$

show that the coefficients are given by

$$d_2 = 0 \quad \left(\text{from BC at } x^* = 0\right)$$

$$d_3 = 6d_1^2$$

$$d_4 = -12d_1^2, \text{ etc.}$$

Thus, show that the solution does *not* contain only even powers of x^*. Observe how d_4 becomes

0 if the $\dfrac{dy}{dx^*}$ were not present in the ODE above (higher order coefficients like d_6, d_8, etc., will

also be zero then). Rework this using the ODE-BVP in eq. 6.30, and also, the equation in example 6.3.

6.24 Repeat the derivation of prob. 6.22 for the case when eq. 6.32 is used for $y(x)$. Obtain the relation between **w** and $\mathbf{Q}^{-1}$ for this case. Solve for $a = 1$, 2 and 3.

6.25 Obtain the OC solution for the nonisothermal reaction-diffusion problem (example 6.3). Use the $a = 1$ matrices with $y(x)$ given by eq. 6.32, as in example 6.6, with $N = 1$ and $N = 2$. Compare with finite difference results from prob. 6.8.

6.26 Consider the ODE-BVP in prob. 6.11. Apply the OC technique with $N = 1$ to obtain a set of three nonlinear algebraic equations for $y(x)$. Use the *BC* at $x = 0$ to get two coupled nonlinear algebraic equations and compare with the equations given in example 3.6. Compare with the exact results and the finite difference ($N = 2$) results from prob. 6.11. Also, compare the values of the integral,

$\displaystyle\int_0^1 3y^2 dx$, obtained by these methods. Repeat the OC calculations for $N = 2$.

6.27 Consider the ODE-BVP of prob. 6.12. Obtain a set of two coupled nonlinear algebraic equations using the $N = 2$ OC technique. Also obtain expressions for the flux. Solve for $a = 1$ (the parameter in the ODE) and compare with analytical values given in prob. 6.12.

6.28 Repeat prob. 6.6 (reaction-diffusion in an isothermal catalyst sphere, $n = 2$) using the OC technique with $N = 2$. Obtain results using the matrices from table 6.1, as well as using matrices for $a = 1$ and $a = 3$ from table 6.3. Notice how the use of $a = 3$ matrices leads to best results.

6.29 Repeat prob. 6.7 (reaction-diffusion in an isothermal catalyst slab, $n = 1$ and $n = 2$), using the OC technique with $N = 1$ and $N = 2$, using $y(x^2)$. Compare with finite difference results of prob. 6.7.

6.30 Consider the ODE-IVP

$$\frac{dy}{dx} = f(y, x)$$

We know the value y_n at $x = x_n$, and we wish to integrate the equation to obtain y_{n+1} at $x = x_{n+1}$, with $x_{n+1} - x_n \equiv h$. We wish to use the orthogonal collocation method to do so, with two internal OC points lying between x_n and x_{n+1}.

(a) Transform the ODE in terms of an independent variable, u, so that the domain of u is from 0 to 1 in this one step of size, h.

(b) Write down the appropriate algebraic equations to be solved, with all known values and nonlinear terms taken to the right [**Hint:** Express your results in terms of a 3 × 3 matrix of constants on the left hand side]. Substitute the values of the relevant matrices.

(c) Use the NR method to obtain an algorithm for solving the first of the 3 equations. Present detailed derivation.

(d) Generalize and give the equation to be solved finally to obtain y_{n+1}.

This is used in the program SOCOLL [*Comp. Chem. Eng.,* **8,** 243 (1984)] used for optimization.

6.31 Rework prob. 6.14 using the OC method with $N = 1$ and $N = 2$. Compare with the finite difference results obtained in prob. 6.14.

6.32 Solve, using the $N = 2$ OC procedure

$$\frac{d^2y}{dx^2} + \frac{dy}{dx} - y = e^y$$

$$y(0) = 0; \quad y(1) = 0$$

Solve using the NR procedure.

6.33 Consider the equation

$$y\frac{d^2y}{dx^2} - 2y^2xe^y = e^x$$

with

$$y(x = 0) = 1$$

and

$$\left[\frac{dy}{dx} + yx^2\right]_{x=1} = 0$$

Write the final equations for y_i (in matrix form) using an orthogonal collocation technique, with two internal collocation points. Also give the final expression for

$$I = \int_{x=0}^{x=1} x^2 e^{y^2} dx$$

in terms of the y_i.

Develop a Newton-Raphson cum Gauss-Seidel code and solve the set of final equations obtained.

6.34 Obtain the numerical results for the isothermal TRAM using OCFE, as described in example 6.8, and presented in fig. 6.7.

6.35 Formulate the equations for the nonisothermal reaction-diffusion problem of example 6.3 using the *general* OCFE technique with N_s finite elements [3]. Note that you will need to expand $\nabla^2 y$ into $\frac{d^2y}{dx^2}$ and $\frac{dy}{dx}$ terms. Use the matrices in table 6.1. How would you evaluate the integral $3\int_{x=0}^{1} x^2 f(x) dx$ in this case.

6.36 Consider the equation: $y'' = 2y^3$; $y(0) = 1$; $y'(1) + [y(1)]^2 = 0$ again. Divide the region $0 \le x \le 1$ into two finite elements: $0 \le x \le 0.6$, and $0.6 \le x \le 1.0$. In each of these, assume only *one* internal collocation point. Write down the simplified matrix equation (with numbers) assuming continuity of y and y' at the internal boundary. You should obtain the equations in prob. 3.9. Compare the results with those obtained from probs. 6.11 and 6.26.

6.37 Solve the following equation using OCFE (see prob. 6.9) [3]

$$\frac{1}{x^2}\frac{d}{dx}\left(x^2\frac{dy}{dx}\right) = \phi^2 f(y) \equiv \phi^2\left[\frac{y(1+y)}{(1+100y)^2}\right]$$

$$\frac{dy(0)}{dx} = 0,\; y(1) = 1$$

Take 2 FEs (equispaced) and 2 internal collocation points on each. Use the Newton-Raphson method to obtain linear algebraic equations, with different starting profiles to get three steady state profiles for $\phi = 110$.

6.38 Obtain the nonlinear algebraic equations for prob. 6.13 using the OCFE technique with 2 FEs, $0 \le x \le 0.3$, and $0.3 \le x \le 1.0$.

6.39 Consider the isothermal TRAM of example 6.9, using the Galerkin finite element method. Make a general purpose computer program to obtain the solution, **y,** for different values of N, the number of elements. Obtain results for equisize elements and see the influence of increasing N.

6.40 Formulate the equations for the isothermal reaction-diffusion problem of example 6.3 using the general Galerkin finite element technique with N finite elements.

6.41 Obtain algebraic equations for solving the isothermal reaction-diffusion problem in a slab, with an irreversible first order reaction taking place, and with no external film resistance (see prob. 6.7 with $n = 1$). Use Galerkin's FE technique with four equisize elements. Solve in two ways: one as in example 6.9 (with the BC and the ODE *both* being satisfied at $x = 0$), and the other, using

$$\left.\frac{dy}{dx}\right|_0 = 0 \; alone \; (i.e., -4a_1 + 4a_2 = 0).\text{ Compare the results with the analytical solutions given in}$$

problem 6.7. Also develop a formula for $\eta = \int_0^1 y\,dx$ for this technique. Evaluate η numerically from your solutions and compare with the analytical results.

6.42 Solve the following equation characterizing heat (or mass) transfer in an infinite slab with constant internal generation of heat (or mass) [3]:

$$\frac{d^2\theta}{dx^2} = -1;\; \theta(0) = \theta(1) = 0$$

using four equisize finite elements, using the Galerkin technique. How do your results change if you have 9 equisize elements.

6.43 A term incorporating y also appears in some ODE-BVPs. For example, one could have

$$\frac{d^2y}{dx^2} + \frac{dy}{dx} + y = f(y)$$

Derive the matrices that would arise from this new term, y, when Galerkin's FE technique is applied.

6.44 (*a*) Consider the isothermal TRAM of example 6.1, with $Pe = 6$, $Da = 2$. Convert the 2nd order ODE into two first order ODEs using $y_1 = y$, $y_2 = \dfrac{dy}{dx}$. Then make this into an IVP with $y_1 = c$;

$y_2 = 6 \, (c - 1)$ at $x = 0$, where c is some assumed constant. Obtain the eigenvalues of this ODE-IVP (use results of fig. 6.2 to estimate the range of the λs). Show that this ODE-IVP is unstable (integration of the equivalent ODE-IVP in the direction $x = 0$ to 1 and checking with the specified boundary condition at $x = 1$ for the BVP, called *shooting technique,* thus, is unstable). See ref. 33 for a more detailed discussion.

(*b*) Reconsider the same ODE. Transform it using $x^* = 1 - x$. Then, convert it into two first order ODEs using $y_1^* = y$, $y_2^* = \dfrac{dy}{dx^*}$. An initial condition $y_1 = c^*$ at $x^* = 0$ can again be assumed, and the two ODE-IVPs can be integrated from $x^* = 0$ to $x^* = 1$, with the given condition at $x^* = 1$ checked. Repeat part (*a*) to find the eigenvalues of *this* problem [*shooting* from $x = 1$ to $x = 0$ or ($x^* = 0$ or $x^* = 1$)] and show that this is much more stable than in part (*a*). Finlayson [p. 127 in Ref. 5] has an elaborate discussion on this.

6.45 Use the transformed ODE-BVP for the isothermal TRAM as obtained in prob. 6.44b and deduce eq. 6.51. Solve and obtain $y_1 \, (x)$ using a shooting method from $x = 1$ to $x = 0$. Also, integrate eq. (*c*) of example 6.10 (shooting from $x = 0$ to 1) and generate the results in fig. 6.10. Compare the results for the two cases.

6.46 Heat and mass transfer in a porous catalyst slab is described by [32]

$$\frac{d^2 y}{dx^2} = \phi^2 y \exp\left[\frac{\gamma\beta(1-y)}{1+\beta(1-y)}\right]$$

$$x = 0 \; : \; \frac{dy}{dx} = 0$$

$$x = 1 \; : \; y = 1$$

Cast these equations into a form suitable for shooting methods. Integrate to obtain the $y \, (x)$ profile for $\gamma = 20$, $\beta = 0.1$, $\phi = 1$.

6.47 **Quasilinearization** [34, 35]: In this technique, one starts with an *assumed* solution, $y_{(1)} \, (x)$, and then improves it using the solution of the *linearized* ODE. Consider the general, nonlinear ODE

$$\frac{d^2 y}{dx^2} \equiv y'' = f\left(x, \, y, \, y'\right)$$

Expand $f \, [x, \, y_{(k+1)}, \, y'_{(k+1)}]$ about $f \, [x, \, y_{(k)}, \, y'_{(k)}]$ using upto linear terms in a Taylor expansion [$y_{(k+1)}$ is the profile, $y(x)$, at the $(k + 1)$ th iteration] and obtain the following *linearized* ODE

$$\delta'' - \left[\frac{\partial f}{\partial y}\right]_{(k)} \delta - \left[\frac{\partial f}{\partial y'}\right]_{(k)} \delta' = -y''_{(k)} + f\left[x, \, y_{(k)}, \, y'_{(k)}\right]$$

where

$$\delta(x) \equiv y_{(k+1)} \, (x) - y_{(k)} \, (x)$$

Apply this technique to the ODE $y'' - 2y^3 = 0$ (prob. 6.11) to obtain

$$\delta'' - 6y_{(k)}^2 \delta = 2y_{(k)}^3 - y''_{(k)}$$

One can linearize the boundary conditions similarly. The BCs for prob. 6.11 are

$$y(0) = 1$$

$$y'(1) + y^2(1) = 0$$

Linearize these to obtain

$$\delta(0) = 1 - y_{(k)}(0)$$

$$\delta'(1) = -y'_{(k)}(1) - \left[y_{(k)}(1)\right]^2 - 2y_{(k)}(1)\delta(1)$$

Use the finite-difference technique [with an assumed $y_{(1)}(x)$] to obtain a set of *linear* algebraic equations for $\delta(x)$.

6.48 The dimensionless equations characterizing the steady state temperature distribution in a cladded cylindrical nuclear fuel element are given by [30]

$$a_f \frac{1}{r}\frac{d}{dr}\left(r\frac{d\theta}{dr}\right) = S(r) \qquad 0 \le r \le \lambda; \qquad \frac{d\theta}{dr} = 0 \text{ at } r = 0$$

$$a_c \frac{1}{r}\frac{d}{dr}\left(r\frac{d\theta}{dr}\right) = 0 \qquad \lambda \le r \le 1; \qquad \theta(r=1) = 1$$

with the flux continuity equation

$$k_f \frac{d\theta}{dr} = k_c \frac{d\theta}{dr} \text{ at } r = \lambda$$

In the above equation, k_f and k_c are the (constant) thermal conductivities of the fuel and cladding materials while a_f and a_c are constants. $S(r)$ is the rate of heat generation per unit volume, dependent upon the rate of thermal energy production by nuclear reaction in the fuel.

Assume two finite elements, $0 \le r \le \lambda$ and $\lambda \le r \le 1$, and a *single* internal collocation point in *each* element. Set up the final equations (with actual numbers where possible) in matrix form, for an OCFE analysis of the problem.

REFERENCES

1. G.F. Froment and K.B. Bischoff, *Chemical Reactor Analysis and Design,* 2nd ed., Wiley, New York, 1990.
2. E.W. Thiele, *Ind. Eng. Chem.,* **31**, 916 (1939).
   [a classic paper in chemical engineering]
3. B.A. Finlayson, *Nonlinear Analysis in Chemical Engineering,* McGraw-Hill, New York, 1980.
4. N.B. Ferguson, Ph.D. Dissertation, University of Washington, Seattle, WA, 1971.
5. B.A. Finlayson, *The Method of Weighted Residuals and Variational Principles*, Academic Press, New York, 1972.
6. P.P. Weisz and J.S. Hicks, *Chem. Eng. Sci.,* **17**, 265 (1962).
7. B.A. Finlayson, *Cat. Revs. Sci & Eng.,* **10**, 69 (1974).
   [several excellent examples discussed, e.g., SO_2 oxidation, ammonia, NO reduction reactors]
8. R. Aris, *The Mathematical Theory of Diffusion and Reaction in Permeable Catalysis,* Clarendon Press, Oxford, 1975.
   [a detailed discussion and review of this important problem]
9. C. Laczos, *J. Math. Phys.,* **17**, 123 (1938).
10. J.V. Villadsen and W.E. Stewart, *Chem. Eng. Sci.,* **22**, 1483 (1967).

11. F.B. Hildebrand, *Methods of Applied Mathematics*, 2nd ed., Prentice-Hall, Englewood Cliffs, NJ, 1965.

12. J. Villadsen and M.L. Michelsen, *Solution of Differential Equation Models by Polynomial Approximation*, Prentice-Hall, Englewood Cliffs, NJ, 1978.
[gives an excellent and *extensive* discussion of the OC and other techniques]

13. G. Szegö, *Orthogonal Polynomials*, Amer. Math. Soc. Colloq. Publ., **23** (1959).

14. W.E. Stewart, *Chem. Eng. Educ.*, **18**, 204 (1984).

15. B.A. Finlayson and L.E. Scriven, *Appl. Mech. Revs.*, **19**, 735 (1966).

16. A.K. Jana and S.K. Gupta. *J. Polym. Eng.*, **9**, 23 (1990).

17. A.H. Stroud and D. Secrest, *Gaussian Quadrature Formulas*, Prentice-Hall, Englewood Cliffs, NJ, 1966.

18. R.B. Bird, W.E. Stewart and E.N. Lightfoot, *Transport Phenomena*, 2nd ed., Wiley, New York, 2001.

19. S.K. Gupta and V. Gupta, *Fluid Mechanics and its Applications*, 2nd ed., Wiley Eastern, New Delhi, 2010.

20. V.M.G. Romero and B.E. Rodriguez, OC Solution for the Free Radical Polymerization with Diffusional Limitations, presented at the Annual Meeting of the AIChE, Miami, FL, Nov. 1986.

21. K.T. Wong and R. Luus, *Can. J. Chem. Eng.*, **58**, 382 (1980).

22. W.E. Stewart, K.L. Levien and M. Morari, *Proc. 2nd. Intl. Conf. Foundations of Computer Aided Process Design*, A.W. Westerberg and H.H. Chien, eds., CACHE Corp., New York, 1984, p. 535.

23. G.F. Carey and B.A. Finlayson, *Chem. Eng. Sci.*, **30**, 587 (1975).

24. C. Pearson, *J Math. Phys.*, **47**, 351 (1968).

25. J.N. Reddy, *An Introduction to the Finite Element Method*, McGraw Hill, New York, 1984.

26. O.C. Zienkiewicz, *The Finite Element Method*, 3rd ed., McGraw Hill, New York, 1977.
[this is an early classical text for this technique]

27. M.M. Denn. *Optimization by Variational Methods*, McGraw Hill, New York, 1969.

28. M. Kubicek and V. Hlavacek, *Numerical Solution of Nonlinear Boundary Value Problems with Applications*, Prentice Hall, Englewood Cliffs, NJ. 1983.
[an excellent text of several advanced techniques for solving ODE-BVPs numerically].

29. L. Fox, *The Numerical Solution of Two-Point Boundary Problems in Ordinary Differential Equations*, Oxford University Press, New York. 1957.

30. M.E. Davis, *Numerical Methods and Modeling for Chemical Engineers*, Wiley, New York, 1984.
[an excellent discussion of shooting techniques is given here]

31. H.B. Keller, *Numerical Methods for Two-point Boundary-Value Problems*, Blaisdell, Waltham, MA, 1968.

32. P.H. McGinnis, *Chem, Eng. Prog., Symp. Ser.* No. 55, **61**, 1 (1965).

33. A Varma, C. Georgakis, N.R. Amundson and R. Aris, *Comp. Meths. Appl. Mech. & Eng.*, **8**, 319 (1976).

34. R.E. Bellman and R.E. Kalaba, *Quasilinearization and Boundary Value Problems*, Elsevier, New York, 1965.

35. E.S. Lee, *Quasilinearization and Invariant Imbedding*, Academic Press, New York, 1968.

36. V.A. Ambarzumian, C.R. Acad. Sci. USSR, **38**, 229 (1943).

37. R. Bellman and G.M. Wing, *An Introduction to Invariant Imbedding*, Wiley, New York, 1975.

38. A.B.L. Agarwal and S.K. Saraf, *J. Math. Anal. & Appl.*, **72**, 524 (1979).

39. Y.T. Shah and J.A. Paraskos, *Chem. Eng. Sci.*, **30**, 465 (1975).

40. A.J. Chapman, *Heat Transfer*, 4th ed., Macmillan, New York, 1984.

41. C.N. Satterfield, C.W. Roberts and J. Hartman, *Ind. Eng. Chem. Fundam.*, **5**, 317 (1966) and **6,** 80 (1967).

42. H. Schlichting, *Boundary Layer Theory*, 7th ed., McGraw Hill, New York, 1987.

43. Y. Jaluria and K.E. Torrance, *Computational Heat Transfer*, Hemisphere, New York, 1986.

44. D.A. Anderson, J.C. Tannehill and R.H. Pletcher, *Computational Fluid Mechanics and Heat Transfer*, Hemisphere, New York, 1984.

Chapter 7

Partial Differential Equations

7.1 INTRODUCTION

Partial differential equations (PDEs) are encountered in engineering practice quite frequently. Several unsteady operations which are described by ODEs under steady state conditions, are described by PDEs when the operation is unsteady. For example (in chemical engineering) the unsteady reaction-diffusion problem in a spherical porous catalyst particle (eq. 6.1) is described by the following (parabolic[*]) PDE under isothermal conditions:

$$\frac{\partial c}{\partial t} = \frac{1}{r^2}\frac{\partial}{\partial r}\left(Dr^2\frac{\partial c}{\partial r}\right) - \mathcal{R}(c)$$

$$r = 0 \qquad : \qquad \frac{\partial c}{\partial r} = 0$$

$$r = R \qquad : \qquad -D\frac{\partial c}{\partial r} = k_g\left(c - c_0\right)$$

$$t = 0 \qquad\qquad c = 0 \qquad\qquad\qquad\qquad\qquad\qquad ...(7.1)$$

where t is the time, c is the concentration of a reactant, r is the radial position, and the other variables have the same meaning as in eq. 6.1. Note that we have used c and r as the symbols for concentration and position instead of y and x as in eq. 6.1. This is because x, y, z (or r, θ, z) will be used for position in this chapter. Another example (in chemical engineering) is a tabular reactor with the reaction mass flowing laminarly (parabolic velocity profile). This can be described fairly well under steady-state conditions, by the following set of coupled PDEs:

---

[*] A general *linear* second-order PDE:

$$a\frac{\partial^2 c}{\partial x^2} + b\frac{\partial^2 c}{\partial x \partial y} + d\frac{\partial^2 c}{\partial y^2} + e\frac{\partial c}{\partial x} + f\frac{\partial c}{\partial y} + gc = h$$

where a, b, d, e, f, g and h are functions of x and y, and not of c or its derivatives, is classified into one of three groups depending on the sign of the discriminant characterizing the second order terms [1]:

   $b^2 = 4ad$: parabolic; $b^2 < 4ad$: elliptic
   $b^2 > 4ad$: hyperbolic

A similar classification exists for quasi-linear PDEs [1] (see ref.1, chp. 8).

$$2\bar{v}\left(1 - \frac{r^2}{R^2}\right)\frac{\partial c}{\partial z} = \mathcal{R}(c, T) \qquad \text{...}(a)$$

$$2\bar{v}\left(1 - \frac{r^2}{R^2}\right)\rho C_p \frac{\partial T}{\partial z} = \frac{k}{r}\frac{\partial}{\partial r}\left(r\frac{\partial T}{\partial r}\right) + \rho(-\Delta H_r)\mathcal{R}(c, t) \qquad \text{...}(b)$$

$$r = 0 \; : \quad \frac{\partial T}{\partial r} = 0 \qquad \text{...}(c)$$

$$r = R \; : \quad -k\frac{\partial T}{\partial r} = U(T - T_J) \qquad \text{...}(d)$$

$$z = 0 \; : \; c = c_0, \; T = T_0 \qquad \text{...}(e) \qquad \text{...}(7.2)$$

where c and T are the concentration of the reactant and the temperature, $\bar{v}$ is the mean velocity of the reaction mass in the tubular reactor of radius R, r and z are the radial and axial locations, $\mathcal{R}(c, T)$ is the rate of depletion of the reactant $\left[= ck_0^* \exp\left(-\dfrac{E}{RT}\right)\right.$ for a first order irreversible reaction, $A \to$ products $\Big]$, which depends both on c and T, k is the thermal conductivity of the reaction mass, $(-\Delta H_r)$ is the heat of reaction, and ρ and C_p are the density and specific heat of the reaction mixture. Equation 7.2 (b) assumes that energy is transferred primarily by convection in the z-direction and primarily by conduction in the r-direction. Equation 7.2 (a) assumes no radial diffusion of the reactant even though radial gradients are present due to temperature variations in the r-direction. The boundary condition, eq. 7.2 (d), assumes that heat can be transferred (with overall heat transfer coefficient, U) to a jacket fluid at temperature, T_J. The isothermal TRAM (see example 6.1) operating under unsteady conditions, can be similarly described by

$$\frac{\partial c}{\partial t} = D\frac{\partial^2 c}{\partial z^2} - v\frac{\partial c}{\partial z} - \mathcal{R}(c) \qquad \text{...}(a)$$

$$z = 0 \; : \quad -D\frac{\partial c}{\partial z} = v(c_0 - c) \qquad \text{...}(b)$$

$$z = 1 \; : \quad -D\frac{\partial c}{\partial z} = 0 \qquad \text{...}(c)$$

$$t = 0 \; : \quad c = 0 \qquad \text{...}(d) \qquad \text{...}(7.3)$$

where v is the (plug-flow) velocity, c_0 is the feed concentration of the reactant, and the other variables have the same meaning as in eqs. 7.1 and 7.2.

Partial differential equations of a different kind (elliptic) arise in heat conduction problems in two or more directions. For example, the steady heat conduction in a 2-dimensional slab, $0 \le x \le L_x$, $0 \le y \le L_y$, can be described by

$$\frac{\partial^2 T}{\partial x^2} + \frac{\partial^2 T}{\partial y^2} = 0$$

$$x = 0 \; : \quad T = T_0 \; ; \quad y = 0 \; : \quad T = T_1$$

$$x = L_x \; : \quad T = T_2 \; ; \quad y = L_y \; : \quad T = T_3 \qquad \text{...}(7.4)$$

The wave-equation, on the other hand:

$$v^2 \frac{\partial^2 c}{\partial x^2} - \frac{\partial^2 c}{\partial t^2} = 0 \qquad \qquad ...(7.5)$$

is an example of a hyperbolic PDE. The techniques described in Chapter 6 can be easily extended to obtain solutions to these problems. We shall illustrate the use of these techniques in this chapter.

7.2 THE FINITE DIFFERENCE TECHNIQUE (METHOD OF LINES)

If one has a boundary-value type of problem in at least one of the independent variables [as, for example, in eqs. 7.1, 7.2(b), 7.3, etc.] then one can use the finite difference technique. This method is quite easy to apply, and its use is illustrated below for the solution of eq. 7.2.

Example 7.1: Integrate eq. 7.2.

One chooses $N + 1$ equispaced finite-difference grid 'lines', $r_1 (= 0)$, r_2, r_3, ..., $r_{N+1} (= R)$, (see fig. 7.1), with the spacing being $\Delta r = \dfrac{R}{N}$ (note that we are not working with dimensionless variables).

The values of c and T at the ith grid line are denoted by $c(r_i, z) = c_i(z)$ and $T(r_i, z) = T_i(z)$; $i = 1, 2, ..., N + 1$. Equations 6.8(c), 6.10, etc. can easily be adapted for partial derivatives to give

$$\left.\frac{\partial c}{\partial r}\right|_i = \frac{c_{i+1}(z) - c_{i-1}(z)}{2(\Delta r)} + O\left[(\Delta r)^2\right] \qquad \qquad ...(a)$$

$$\left.\frac{\partial^2 c}{\partial r^2}\right|_i = \frac{c_{i+1}(z) - 2c_i(z) + c_{i-1}(z)}{(\Delta r)^2} + O\left[(\Delta r)^2\right] \qquad \qquad ...(b)$$

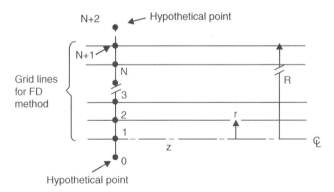

Fig. 7.1 Finite difference grid points (lines for example 7.1)

where it is implied that the value of z used for all the c_i's is the same. The residuals can now be equated to zero at the appropriate grid lines for eqs. 7.2(a) and (b). This leads to

$$2\bar{v}\left(1 - \frac{r_i^2}{R^2}\right)\frac{dc_i}{dz} = \mathcal{R}(c_i, T_i); \quad i = 1, 2, ..., N + 1$$

$$2\bar{v}\left(1-\frac{r_i^2}{R^2}\right)\rho C_p \frac{dT_i}{dz} = k\left[\frac{T_{i+1}-2T_i+T_{i-1}}{(\Delta r)^2} + \frac{1}{r_i}\frac{T_{i+1}-T_{i-1}}{2(\Delta r)}\right]$$

$$+\rho(-\Delta H_r)\mathcal{R}(c_i, T_i); \quad i = 2, 3, ..., N$$

where the dependence of c_i and T_i on z has not been explicitly written. At $r = r_1$, the boundary condition on T gives

$$\frac{T_2(z)-T_0(z)}{2(\Delta r)} = 0 \qquad \qquad ...(c)$$

where $r = r_0$ is a hypothetical grid line, at which the temperature is $T_0(z)$. $T_0(z)$ can be eliminated by making the residual of the PDE at $r = r_1$ equal to zero, as was done in chp. 6. This leads to

$$2\bar{v}\rho C_p \frac{dT_1}{dz} = k\left[\frac{d^2T}{dr^2} + \frac{1}{r}\frac{dT}{dr}\right]_{r=r_1} + \rho(-\Delta H_r)\mathcal{R}(c_1, T_1) \qquad ...(d)$$

The term $\frac{1}{r}\frac{\partial T}{\partial r}$ gives $\frac{0}{0}$ at $r = r_1 = 0$. L'Hospital's rule applied to this term reduces it to $\frac{\partial^2 T}{\partial r^2}$.

Thus, the term in brackets multiplying k in eq. (d) is $2\frac{\partial^2 T}{\partial r^2}$. Using the finite difference form, one has

$$2\bar{v}\rho C_p \frac{dT_1}{dz} = 2k\frac{T_2-2T_1+T_0}{(\Delta r)^2} + \rho(-\Delta H_r)\mathcal{R}(c_1, T_1)$$

which on using the FD form of the boundary condition, eq. (c), gives

$$2\bar{v}\rho C_p \frac{dT_1}{dz} = \frac{4k}{(\Delta r)^2}(T_2-T_1) + \rho(-\Delta H_r)\mathcal{R}(c_1, T_1)$$

One can, similarly, apply the finite difference technique at $r = r_{N+1}$. Making the residual zero at this line gives

$$2\bar{v}\left(1-\frac{r_{N+1}^2}{R^2}\right)\rho C_p \frac{dT_{N+1}}{dz} = k\left[\frac{T_{N+2}-2T_{N+1}+T_N}{(\Delta r)^2} + \frac{1}{R}\frac{T_{N+2}-T_N}{2(\Delta r)}\right]$$

$$+\rho(-\Delta H_r)\mathcal{R}(c_{N+1}, T_{N+1})$$

which, alongwith the finite difference form of the boundary condition,

$$-k\frac{T_{N+2}-T_N}{2(\Delta r)} = U(T_{N+1}-T_J)$$

gives (by eliminating the hypothetical T_{N+2})

$$2\bar{v}\left(1-\frac{r_{N+1}^2}{R^2}\right)\rho C_p \frac{dT_{N+1}}{dz} = k\left[\frac{2}{(\Delta r)^2}(T_N-T_{N+1}) - \frac{U}{k}(T_{N+1}-T_J)\left(\frac{1}{R}+\frac{2}{\Delta r}\right)\right]$$

$$+\rho(-\Delta H_r)\mathcal{R}(c_{N+1}, T_{N+1}) \qquad ...(e)$$

We have, thus, reduced the two PDEs into a coupled set of $N + 1$ nonlinear ODEs for $T_i(z)$; $i = 1$, 2, ..., $N + 1$; and $N + 1$ nonlinear ODEs for $c_i(z)$; $i = 1, 2, ..., N + 1$. It may be noted that the left hand side of eq. (e) becomes zero because of the no-slip condition ($r_{N+1} = R$) at the wall, and so this reduces to an algebraic equation. One could assume a small *numerical* slip at the wall, *i.e.*, use $\dfrac{v}{\bar{v}} \cong 10^{-4}$, or,

equivalently replace $2\left(1 - \dfrac{r_{N+1}^2}{R^2}\right)$ by 10^{-4}, and solve eq. (e) along with the other ODEs using a

computer program for integrating a set of coupled ODE-IVPs [note that values of $c_i (z = 0)$ and $T_i (z = 0)$, $i = 1, 2, ..., N + 1$, are specified by eq. 7.2(e)]. The effect of this numerical approximation on the results has been shown to be negligible [2]. The ODE-IVP computer package will give the values of $c_i (z)$ and $T_i (z)$ (*i.e.*, values along the 'lines', $r = r_i$, and hence the name of the technique) at different values of z. Alternatively, one can integrate the set of ODE-IVPs along with the algebraic equation [eq. (e) with left hand side zero], simultaneously using, say, the code DDASSL, to obtain the $2 (N + 1)$ variables, c_i, T_i; $i = 1, 2, ...,N + 1$, as a function of z. Numerical results for simple rate expressions can easily be obtained and are not presented here. ∎

We present here, however, numerical results for the slightly more complex and interesting case, namely, for the polymerization [2] of nylon 6 (see prob. 5.27). The system can be described by a set of five concentrations, $\mathbf{c} (r, T) \equiv [c_1(r, z) \ c_2(r, z) ... c_5(r, z)]^T$ and temperature, $T(r, z)$. The mass and energy balance equations are given by a generalization of eq. 7.2 as

$$2\bar{v}\left(1 - \frac{r^2}{R^2}\right)\frac{dc_j}{dz} = \mathcal{R}(\mathbf{c}, T); \quad j = 1, 2, ..., 5$$

$$2\bar{v}\left(1 - \frac{r^2}{R^2}\right)\rho C_p \frac{\partial T}{\partial z} = \frac{k}{r}\frac{\partial}{\partial r}\left(r\frac{\partial T}{\partial r}\right) + \rho \sum_{j=1}^{3} \frac{\left(-\Delta H_{r,j}\right)\mathcal{R}_j^*(\mathbf{c}, T)}{10^3}$$

$$r = 0 \quad : \quad \frac{\partial T}{\partial r} = 0$$

$$r = R \quad : \quad -k\frac{\partial T}{\partial r} = U\left(T - T_J\right)$$

$$z = 0 \quad : \quad \mathbf{c}(r, 0) = \begin{bmatrix} 8.8 & 0 & 0 & 0 & 0.16 \end{bmatrix}^T$$

$$T(r, 0) = 523 \text{ K} \qquad\qquad ...(7.6)$$

The rate terms, $\mathcal{R}_i (\mathbf{c}, T)$, are given in prob. 5.27 and are the terms on the right hand side of the mass balance equations ($\mathbf{c}$ replacing $\mathbf{y}$). The rates of reaction, $\mathcal{R}_j^*$, for the three chemical reactions among the five species [2] are given by

$$\mathcal{R}_1^* = k_1 c_1 c_5 - k_1' c_2$$

$$\mathcal{R}_2^* = k_2 c_3^2 - k_2' c_5 \left(c_4 - c_3\right)$$

$$\mathcal{R}_3^* = k_3 c_1 c_3 - k_3' \left(c_3 - c_2\right) \qquad\qquad ...(7.7)$$

The rate constants and ΔH_j are given in prob. 5.27. The other parameters used are (see ref. 2 for units and other details):

$$k = 0.21$$

$$\rho = \frac{1000}{\left\{1.0065 + 0.0123c_1 + (T - 495)\left(0.00035 + 7.0 \times 10^{-5} c_1\right)\right\}}$$

$$C_p = 0.6593\left(\frac{c_1}{8.8}\right) + \left(0.4861 + 3.37 \times 10^{-4} T\right)\left(1 - \frac{c_1}{8.8}\right)$$

$$U = 5.0$$

$$R = 0.6 \ m$$

$$T_J = 533 \ K \qquad \qquad \qquad \text{...(7.8)}$$

Figure 7.2 shows the temperature and c_1 (ε caprolactam) conversion profiles at different axial positions. These profiles were obtained using $N = 10$. Increasing N above this value did not affect the results perceptibly. More details on the numerical algorithm, variation of results with N, and some numerical tricks used (to overcome stiffness at $r = R$, $z = 0$, where the concentrations suddenly change from the feed values to equilibrium values due to the no-slip conditions at the wall), are discussed in ref. 2.

One could, in principle, study the stiffness of the set of ODE-IVPs obtained from the parabolic PDEs by application of the FD technique, using the methods discussed in Chapter 5 (see probs. 7.1 and 5.23 to obtain the maximum value of Δt to be used for integrating the resultant set of ODE-IVPs for the unsteady diffusion equation—another parabolic PDE). This would not be important if we use GEAR codes for integrating the resultant equations, since automatic adaptations of integration step size are made. The main problem encountered in this situation is that of having far too many ODE-IVPs. For example, in the nylon 6 reactor simulation discussed above, we have 6 ($N + 1$) ODE-IVPs to be integrated simultaneously. Special techniques have been developed to take care of such 'large' problems. One such technique is discussed in example 7.2 below, in which the ODE-IVPs are converted into algebraic equations using a simple integration algorithm.

Example 7.2: Apply the FD technique and the Crank-Nicholson method to the dimensionless diffusion equation (parabolic PDE):

$$\frac{\partial c}{\partial t} = \frac{\partial^2 c}{\partial x^2}$$

$$c(0, t) = c(1, t) = 0$$

$$c(x, 0) = 1$$

In this equation, t is the dimensionless time [actual time nondimensionalized by dividing by a characteristic diffusion time, $\frac{L^2}{D}$ (L is the slab thickness and D is the diffusivity)].

Problem 7.1 shows that the following set of ODE-IVPs are obtained on using the FD technique, with the grid-lines at x_1 (= 0), x_2(= Δx), ..., x_{N+1}(= 1):

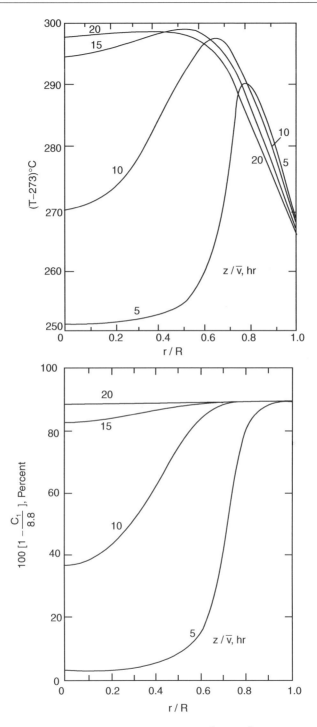

Fig. 7.2 Temperature and c_1 – conversion profiles [2] at four locations $\left[z/\overline{v}, \text{hr}\right]$ in a laminar flow reactor for conditions given in eq. 7.8. Note the equilibrium conversions near the wall (even near the entrance) due to the no-slip condition.

$$\begin{bmatrix} \dfrac{dc_2}{dt} \\[2mm] \dfrac{dc_3}{dt} \\[2mm] \cdot \\ \cdot \\ \cdot \\ \dfrac{dc_{N-1}}{dt} \\[2mm] \dfrac{dc_N}{dt} \end{bmatrix} = \dfrac{1}{(\Delta x)^2} \begin{bmatrix} -2 & 1 & 0 & 0 & \cdot & \cdot & 0 & 0 & 0 \\ 1 & -2 & 1 & 0 & \cdot & \cdot & 0 & 0 & 0 \\ \cdot & & & & \cdot & & & & \cdot \\ \cdot & & & & & \cdot & & & \cdot \\ \cdot & & & & & & \cdot & & \cdot \\ 0 & 0 & 0 & 0 & \cdot & \cdot & 1 & -2 & 1 \\ 0 & 0 & 0 & 0 & \cdot & \cdot & 0 & 1 & -2 \end{bmatrix} \begin{bmatrix} c_2 \\ c_3 \\ \cdot \\ \cdot \\ \cdot \\ c_{N-1} \\ c_N \end{bmatrix}$$

Note that we have a set of linear ODE-IVPs here.

Let us now define a double-index notation:

$$c_{i,\,j} \equiv c\left(x_i, t_j\right); \quad t_j \equiv (j-1)(\Delta t); \quad j = 1, 2, \ldots, \quad i = 1, 2, \ldots, N+1$$

Then the *implicit* Crank-Nicholson technique applied to the *i*th ODE above ($i = 3, 4, \ldots, N-1$) gives

$$\frac{dc_i}{dt} = \frac{c_{i,\,j+1} - c_{i,\,j}}{\Delta t} = \frac{1}{(\Delta x)^2}\left\{\frac{1}{2}\left[c_{i-1,\,j+1} - 2c_{i,\,j+1} + c_{i+1,\,j+1}\right] + \frac{1}{2}\left[c_{i-1,\,j} - 2c_{i,\,j} + c_{i+1,\,j}\right]\right\}$$

$$i = 3, 4, \ldots, N-1$$

or, on using $\alpha \equiv \dfrac{\Delta t}{(\Delta x)^2}$

$$-\frac{\alpha}{2}c_{i-1,\,j+1} + (1+\alpha)c_{i,\,j+1} - \frac{\alpha}{2}c_{i+1,\,j+1} = \frac{\alpha}{2}\left(c_{i-1,\,j} + c_{i+1,\,j}\right) + (1-\alpha)c_{i,\,j}; \qquad i = 3, 4, \ldots, N-1$$

Using the special versions for $i = 2$ and N, we can write these equations in the following matrix form:

$$\begin{bmatrix} (1+\alpha) & -\dfrac{\alpha}{2} & 0 & \cdots & 0 & & & & & \\[2mm] -\dfrac{\alpha}{2} & (1+\alpha) & -\dfrac{\alpha}{2} & \cdots & 0 & & & & & \\[2mm] \cdot & & \cdot & \cdot & & & & & & \\ \cdot & & \cdot & \cdot & & & & & & \\ \cdot & & & \cdot & & & & & & \\ 0 & 0 & 0 & \cdots & -\dfrac{\alpha}{2} & (1+\alpha) & -\dfrac{\alpha}{2} & 0 & 0..0 & 0 & 0 \\[2mm] 0 & 0 & 0 & \cdots & 0 & -\dfrac{\alpha}{2} & (1+\alpha) & -\dfrac{\alpha}{2} & 0..0 & 0 & 0 \\[2mm] 0 & 0 & 0 & \cdots & 0 & 0 & -\dfrac{\alpha}{2} & (1+\alpha) & -\dfrac{\alpha}{2}..0 & 0 & 0 \\[2mm] \cdot & & & & & & & & & \\ 0 & 0 & 0 & \cdots & 0 & 0 & 0 & 0 & 0..0 & -\dfrac{\alpha}{2} & (1+\alpha) \end{bmatrix} \begin{bmatrix} c_{2,\,j+1} \\[2mm] c_{3,\,j+1} \\ \cdot \\ \cdot \\ \cdot \\ c_{i-1,\,j+1} \\[2mm] c_{i,\,j+1} \\[2mm] c_{i+1,\,j+1} \\ \cdot \\ c_{N,\,j+1} \end{bmatrix}$$

$$
= \begin{bmatrix} \dfrac{\alpha}{2} c_{3,j} + (1-\alpha)c_{2,j} \\ \cdot \\ \cdot \\ \dfrac{\alpha}{2}\left(c_{i-1,j} + c_{i+1,j}\right) + (1-\alpha)c_{i,j} \\ \cdot \\ \cdot \\ \dfrac{\alpha}{2} c_{N-1,j} + (1-\alpha)c_{N,j} \end{bmatrix} \qquad \begin{array}{l} \longleftarrow \text{1st row} \\ \\ \\ \longleftarrow i\text{th eqn.} \end{array}
$$

or

$$
\mathbf{A}\mathbf{c}_{j+1} = \mathbf{f}\left(\mathbf{c}_j\right)
$$

The matrix, $\mathbf{A}$, is a tridiagonal matrix comprising of constants. A single LU Decomp (exploiting the tridiagonal nature of $\mathbf{A}$) and multiple fore and aft sweeps starting with the IC: $\mathbf{c}\ (t=0)=1$, gives, sequentially, the profiles $\mathbf{c}(\Delta t)$, $\mathbf{c}(2\ \Delta t)$, $\mathbf{c}[3\ (\Delta t)]$, etc. Note the marching forward in the t direction, after a set of $N-2$ equations are solved simultaneously. Since the Crank-Nicholson technique has been shown to be A-stable, we can use any Δt and still get stable (though not necessarily accurate) results. Note that for certain ranges of Δt (or α), this technique gives oscillatory results. It may be pointed out that we obtain *linear* algebraic equations since we start with linear PDEs.

Nonlinear PDEs will lead to nonlinear algebraic equations, and techniques discussed in Chapter 3 will have to be used to linearize them. Once again, if the matrices characterizing the algebraic equations are not too dense, we can use adaptations of the techniques of Chapter 3 to reduce computer times.

■

Example 7.3 shows how we obtain *extremely* large sets of coupled algebraic equations from even simple elliptic PDEs.

Example 7.3: Obtain the algebraic equations by applying the finite difference technique followed by appropriate methods of integrating ODE-IVPs, to the unsteady, 2-dimensional heat-transfer problem:

$$
\frac{\partial T}{\partial t} = \alpha\left(\frac{\partial^2 T}{\partial x^2} + \frac{\partial^2 T}{\partial y^2}\right)
$$

$$
t = 0 \quad : \quad T = F(x,y)
$$

$$
x = 0 \quad : \quad T = T_1 \ ; \quad x = L_x \quad : \quad T = T_3
$$

$$
y = 0 \quad : \quad T = T_2 \ ; \quad y = L_y \quad : \quad T = T_4
$$

where $T(x,y,t)$ is the temperature at location x, y at time t, and α is the thermal diffusivity.

We draw a 2-dimensional (rectangular) grid, as shown in fig. 7.3. There are $N_x + 1$ equispaced grid lines numbered 1 (at $x=0$), 2, ..., $N_x + 1$ (at $x = L_x$), in the x-direction, and $N_y + 1$ grid lines numbered 1, 2, ..., $N_y + 1$, in the y-direction. The temperature, T, at point (i,j) is given by

$$
T_{i,j}(t) = T(x_i, y_i, t)
$$

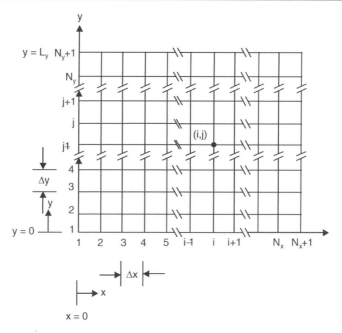

Fig. 7.3 FD grid lines for the 2–D unsteady heat transfer problem of example 7.3.

We can force the residual to be zero at each of the *internal* grid points to give a set of coupled ODE-IVPs:

$$\frac{dT_{i,j}}{dt} = \frac{\alpha}{(\Delta x)^2}\left[T_{i+1,\,j} - 2T_{i,j} + T_{i-1,\,j}\right] + \frac{\alpha}{(\Delta y)^2}\left[T_{i,\,j+1} - 2T_{i,j} + T_{i,\,j-1}\right]$$

$$i = 2, 3, ..., N_x \; ; \quad j = 2, 3, ..., N_y \qquad\qquad ...(a)$$

The values of $T_{i,j}$ at the boundary points are easily written using the boundary conditions (use mean values at the corners).

We can easily write the stability requirement using results of chp. 5 (eq. 5.72)

$$(\Delta t)|\lambda|_{max} \le |p|$$

where $|p|$ is the intercept of the stability envelope for the technique used for integrating the ODE-IVPs, and λ are the eigenvalues of the Jacobian matrix, **A.** Using

$$|\lambda|_{max} \le \underset{r}{Max} \sum_{s}|A_{rs}|$$

we obtain for the present example

$$|\lambda|_{max} \le \frac{\alpha}{(\Delta x)^2}\left[1 + |-2| + 1\right] + \frac{\alpha}{(\Delta y)^2}\left[1 + |-2| + 1\right]$$

$$= 4\alpha\left(\frac{1}{(\Delta x)^2} + \frac{1}{(\Delta y)^2}\right)$$

Hence, for stability, we must ensure

$$\frac{4\alpha \left[\left(\frac{1}{\Delta x} \right)^2 + \left(\frac{1}{\Delta y} \right)^2 \right] \Delta t}{|p|} \leq 1$$

It is easy to see from prob. 7.1 and this result that we must use is smaller values of Δt for the 2-dimensional problem, than for the 1-dimensional problem. The computer time required is observed to increase not only because we have a larger number of ODE-IVPs (corresponding to the larger number, approximately $N_x N_y$, of grid points), but also because of the smaller value of Δt that we are forced to choose due to stability requirements (this is compensated to some extent, by the fact that we need to integrate the ODE-IVPs for only about half the value of t as compared to the 1-D problem, to reach near-steady state values).

We could obtain a set of algebraic equations by using, say, the implicit Crank-Nicholson technique (this permits choice of larger Δt values since it is *A*-stable). We define

$$T_{i,j}^k \equiv T\left(x_i, y_i, t_k \right)$$

where $t_k = (k-1)\, \Delta t;\ k = 1, 2, \ldots$ This gives

$$\frac{T_{i,j}^{k+1} - T_{i,j}^k}{\Delta t} = \frac{\alpha}{(\Delta x)^2} \left[\frac{1}{2}\left(T_{i+1,j}^{k+1} - 2T_{i,j}^{k+1} + T_{i-1,j}^{k+1} \right) + \frac{1}{2}\left(T_{i+1,j}^k - 2T_{i,j}^k + T_{i-1,j}^k \right) \right]$$

$$+ \frac{\alpha}{(\Delta y)^2} \left[\frac{1}{2}\left(T_{i,j+1}^{k+1} - 2T_{i,j}^{k+1} + T_{i,j-1}^{k+1} \right) + \frac{1}{2}\left(T_{i,j+1}^k - 2T_{i,j}^k + T_{i,j-1}^k \right) \right]$$

or, for the special case, $\Delta x = \Delta y$ and with $\beta \equiv \dfrac{\alpha(\Delta t)}{(\Delta x)^2}$, we obtain

$$\left[-\frac{\beta}{2}T_{i-1,j} - \frac{\beta}{2}T_{i,j-1} + \left(1 + \frac{4\beta}{2} \right)T_{i,j} - \frac{\beta}{2}T_{i,j+1} - \frac{\beta}{2}T_{i+1,j} \right]^{k+1}$$

$$= \left[\frac{\beta}{2}T_{i-1,j} + \frac{\beta}{2}T_{i,j-1} + \left(1 - 2\beta \right)T_{i,j} + \frac{\beta}{2}T_{i,j+1} + \frac{\beta}{2}T_{i+1,j} \right]^k$$

$$\equiv f_{ij}\left(\mathbf{T}^k \right) \qquad\qquad \ldots(b)$$

where f_{ij} does *not* indicate that this is the i, j element of a matrix, but indicates that it is the term corresponding to the equation for location (i, j) in the grid. We can put these equations together (with substitution of the boundary values) into a matrix form to get a set of equations [3] having the following structure (see prob. 7.5)

$$\mathbf{A}\mathbf{T}^{k+1} \equiv \left[..0, 0, -\frac{\beta}{2}, 0, ..0, 0, \underbrace{-\frac{\beta}{2}}_{\substack{N_y-2 \\ \text{zeroes}}}, \underbrace{1+\frac{4\beta}{2}}_{\substack{\text{dia-} \\ \text{gonal} \\ \text{term}}}, -\frac{\beta}{2}, 0, 0, ..0, \underbrace{-\frac{\beta}{2}}_{\substack{N_y-2 \\ \text{zeroes}}}, 0, 0, .. \right] \begin{bmatrix} T_{2,2} \\ T_{2,3} \\ \cdot \\ \cdot \\ T_{2,N_y} \\ \cdot \\ \cdot \\ T_{i-1,j-1} \\ T_{i-1,j} \\ T_{i-1,j+1} \\ \cdot \\ \cdot \\ T_{i-1,N_y} \\ T_{i,2} \\ \cdot \\ \cdot \\ T_{i,j-1} \\ T_{i,j} \\ T_{i,j+1} \\ \cdot \\ \cdot \\ T_{i,N_y} \\ T_{i+1,2} \\ \cdot \\ \cdot \\ T_{i+1,j-1} \\ T_{i+1,j} \\ T_{i+1,j+1} \\ \cdot \\ \cdot \\ T_{N_x,N_y} \end{bmatrix}^{k+1} = \mathbf{f}(\mathbf{T})^k \ ...(c)$$

A large and sparse 'pentadiagonal' matrix, **A**, characterizes this problem. Even for 10 *internal* finite difference grid points in each direction we have a 100×100 **A** matrix associated with 100 variables or equations. Even the Gauss-Seidel technique described in chapter 1 becomes too slow for solving such equations and special methods have been developed. ∎

One popular technique to solve such sets of algebraic equations is the *line-iterative* technique. In this, subsets of variables are solved simultaneously. For example, we first select the equations for $T_{2,j}^{k+1}$, $T_{3,j}^{k+1}$, ..., $T_{N_x,j}^{k+1}$ from eq. (*c*). These variables correspond to a horizontal 'line' in fig. 7.3 (hence the name). We write, then,

$$\begin{bmatrix} & & & & & \\ & & & & & \\ 0 \, .. 0 & -\dfrac{\beta}{2} & 1+2\beta & -\dfrac{\beta}{2} & 0 \,...0 & \\ & & & & & \end{bmatrix} \begin{bmatrix} T_{2,j} \\ T_{3,j} \\ \cdot \\ \cdot \\ \cdot \\ T_{i-1,j} \\ T_{i,j} \\ T_{i+1,j} \\ \cdot \\ \cdot \\ \cdot \\ T_{N_x,j} \end{bmatrix}^{k+1} = \begin{bmatrix} \dfrac{\beta}{2} T_{i,j-1}^{k+1} + \dfrac{\beta}{2} T_{i,j+1}^{k+1} + f_{ij}\left(\mathbf{T}^k\right) \end{bmatrix} \qquad ...(7.9)$$

Note that unknown temperatures [$T_{i,j-1}^{k+1}$ and $T_{i,j+1}^{k+1}$ for the *i*, *j* equation, etc.] occur on the right hand side too. We can *assume* values for these unknowns [e.g., values $T_{i,j-1}^{k+1,\,s=1}$ and $T_{i,j+1}^{k+1,s=1}$ in the, *i*, *j* equation, etc.; *s* being the iteration number] and solve for the variables on the left-hand side of eq. 7.9 to give improved values, $T_{2,j}^{k+1,\,s=2}$, $T_{3,j}^{k+1,\,s=2}$, ..., $T_{N_x,j}^{k+1,s=2}$. Thomas' algorithm can be used to solve for these $N_x - 1$ variables *simultaneously* [or Jacobi, Gauss-Seidel or relaxation techniques used to solve *this* smaller set of $N_x - 1$ equations]. We repeat this procedure 'line-by-line', starting from $j = 2$ and ending at $j = N_y$. Really speaking, we have partitioned the larger pentadiagonal matrix into a smaller number, $N_y - 1$, of sets, each comprising of $N_x - 1$ equations. The entire procedure is again repeated to obtain *still* better values, $T_{2,j}^{k+1,\,s=3}$, $T_{3,j}^{k+1,\,s=3}$, ..., $T_{N_x,j}^{k+1,\,s=3}$; $j = 2, 3, ..., N_y$. This continues till convergence is attained. This line-iterative procedure is found to be *about* twice as rapid as compared to solving the entire set of $(N_x - 1)(N_y - 1)$ equations in eq. (*c*), example 7.3, simultaneously. prob. 7.6 gives the flow-chart for the line-Jacobi iterative technique.

An extremely popular technique for solving ODEs of the type given in eq. (*a*), example 7.3, is the alternating direction implicit (ADI) method of Peaceman and Rachford [5, 6]. In this, the time-step, Δt, is divided into two half-steps. In the first half-step, an implicit expression (backward-Euler in *t*) is used for the *x*-terms and an explicit expression (Euler) is used for the *y*-terms. Thus, eq. (*a*), example 7.3, gives:

$$\frac{T_{i,j}^{k+\frac{1}{2}} - T_{i,j}^{k}}{\dfrac{(\Delta t)}{2}} = \frac{\alpha}{(\Delta x)^2}\left[T_{i+1,j}^{k+\frac{1}{2}} - 2T_{i,j}^{k+\frac{1}{2}} + T_{i-1,j}^{k+\frac{1}{2}}\right] + \frac{\alpha}{(\Delta y)^2}\left[T_{i,j+1}^{k} - 2T_{i,j}^{k} + T_{i,j-1}^{k}\right] \qquad ...(7.10)$$

or

$$-\frac{\beta}{2}T_{i-1,\,j}^{k+\frac{1}{2}} + (1+\beta)T_{i,\,j}^{k+\frac{1}{2}} - \frac{\beta}{2}T_{i+1,\,j}^{k+\frac{1}{2}} = \frac{\alpha(\Delta t)}{2(\Delta y)^2}T_{i,\,j-1}^{k} + \left[1 - \frac{\alpha(\Delta t)}{(\Delta y)^2}\right]T_{i,\,j}^{k} + \frac{\alpha(\Delta t)}{2(\Delta y)^2}T_{i,\,j+1}^{k} \quad ...(7.11)$$

where $\beta = \dfrac{\alpha(\Delta t)}{(\Delta x)^2}$, as earlier. If the values of T at all the internal grid points are known at $t = (k-1)\,\Delta t$,

eq. 7.11 gives a tridiagonal matrix relating the unknowns, $T_{i,\,j}^{k+\frac{1}{2}}$, for any j to the known quantities, and Thomas' algorithm (or Gauss-Seidel or relaxation techniques modified for such systems—see prob. 1.20) can be used to solve for them easily. This can be repeated for all values of j. Then, in the second half-step, the y-terms are treated implicitly while the x-terms explicitly, to give

$$\frac{T_{i,\,j}^{k+1} - T_{i,\,j}^{k+\frac{1}{2}}}{\dfrac{(\Delta t)}{2}} = \frac{\alpha}{(\Delta x)^2}\left[T_{i+1,\,j}^{k+\frac{1}{2}} - 2T_{i,\,j}^{k+\frac{1}{2}} + T_{i-1,\,j}^{k+\frac{1}{2}}\right] + \frac{\alpha}{(\Delta y)^2}\left[T_{i,\,j+1}^{k+1} - 2T_{i,\,j}^{k+1} + T_{i,\,j-1}^{k+1}\right] \quad ...(7.12)$$

or

$$-\left[\frac{1}{2}\frac{\alpha(\Delta t)}{(\Delta y)^2}\right]T_{i,\,j-1}^{k+1} + \left[1 + \frac{\alpha(\Delta t)}{(\Delta y)^2}\right]T_{i,\,j}^{k+1} - \left[\frac{1}{2}\frac{\alpha(\Delta t)}{(\Delta y)^2}\right]T_{i,\,j+1}^{k+1}$$

$$= \frac{\beta}{2}T_{i-1,\,j}^{k+\frac{1}{2}} + (1-\beta)T_{i,\,j}^{k+\frac{1}{2}} - \frac{\beta}{2}T_{i+1,\,j}^{k+\frac{1}{2}} \quad ...(7.13)$$

Again, a tridiagonal matrix relates the unknowns, $T_{i,\,j}^{k+1}$, to the knowns, $T_{i,\,j}^{k+\frac{1}{2}}$ for any i and can be solved for. This can be repeated for different values of i. Thus, instead of solving equations having a pentadiagonal matrix. [eq. (c), example 7.3], we need to solve two sets of equations characterized by tridiagonal matrices. This has been found to be quite effective *usually* (the rates of convergence generally depend on the problem solved). It has been shown that this technique is unconditionally stable [4]. Several other computationally efficient schemes have been described by Jain et al. [4], Finlayson [3] and Davis [7] (also see prob. 7.9), and the reader is referred to these.

Bank and Rose [8] have developed adaptations of the Newton-Raphson method to speed up the convergence of *nonlinear* algebraic equations (resulting from application of the FD technique to nonlinear PDEs) involving large and sparse matrices. Alternatively, we can apply the NR technique to the nonlinear algebraic equations obtained after using the FD method with an integration algorithm, and then use the efficient iterative techniques to solve the resulting algebraic equations. Schemes with nested iterations will result again.

We end this section with a final example.

Example 7.4: Obtain the FD form of the first order PDE

$$\frac{\partial T}{\partial t} + \frac{\partial T}{\partial x} = 0 ; \quad -\infty < x < \infty$$

$$T(0, x) = T^*(x)$$

An ingeneous technique is used to solve this equation. We can write a Taylor expansion as

$$T_i^{k+1} = T_i^k + (\Delta t)\left(\frac{\partial T}{\partial t}\right)_i^k + \frac{(\Delta t)^2}{2}\left(\frac{\partial^2 T}{\partial t^2}\right)_i^k + \dots$$

$$= T_i^k - (\Delta t)\left(\frac{\partial T}{\partial x}\right)_i^k + \frac{(\Delta t)^2}{2}\left(\frac{\partial^2 T}{\partial x^2}\right)_i^k + \dots$$

where we have used the PDE to replace $\frac{\partial T}{\partial t}$ and $\frac{\partial^2 T}{\partial t^2}$ (for the latter, we have used $\frac{\partial^2 T}{\partial t\,\partial x} = \frac{\partial^2 T}{\partial x\,\partial t}$ and the PDE twice).

Expanding the differentials we obtain

$$T_i^{k+1} = T_i^k - \frac{(\Delta t)}{2(\Delta x)}\left(T_{i+1}^k - T_{i-1}^k\right) + \frac{(\Delta t)^2}{2(\Delta x)^2}\left(T_{i+1}^k - 2T_i^k + T_{i-1}^k\right) \qquad \dots(a)$$

Using $r \equiv \dfrac{(\Delta t)}{(\Delta x)}$, we can rewrite this equation as

$$T_i^{k+1} = T_i^k - \frac{r}{2}\left(T_{i+1}^k - T_{i-1}^k\right) + \frac{r^2}{2}\left(T_{i+1}^k - 2T_i^k - T_{i-1}^k\right)$$

$$= \frac{r}{2}(r+1)T_{i-1}^k + \left(1 - r^2\right)T_i^k + \frac{r}{2}(r-1)T_{i+1}^k \qquad \dots(b)$$

eq. (*b*) is referred to as the Lax-Wendroff [9] formula and is quite popular [4] [it is stable for $0 \le r \le 1$, and is of order $(\Delta t)^2$ and $(\Delta x)^2$]. Other algorithms for integrating this PDE can also be developed (see ref. 4). Note that if the domain of x was $0 < x < \infty$, we would require a condition $T(t, 0)$ too (see prob. 7.13).

eq. (*b*) can be compared with the following FD form of the PDE

$$\frac{T_i^{k+1} - T_i^k}{\Delta t} = -\frac{T_{i+1}^k - T_{i-1}^k}{2(\Delta x)} \qquad \dots(c)$$

which is explicit in t and uses the central difference form for $\frac{\partial T}{\partial x}$. It appears that we have added a 'numerical dispersion'[3] term $\left[\left(\frac{\Delta t}{2}\right)\frac{\partial^2 T}{\partial x^2}\right]$ to eq. (*c*) to obtain eq. (*b*). This leads to errors in the solution obtained, as discussed below. ∎

Figure 7.4 presents the solution [3] of the PDE

$$\frac{\partial T}{\partial t} + \frac{\partial T}{\partial x} = 0 \; ; \;\; 0 \le x \le \infty$$

$$T(x, 0) = 0 \; ; \;\; T(0, t) = 1 \qquad \dots(7.14)$$

[the exact solution is a *sharp* front (at *all* values of t) decreasing from $T = 1$ to 0 at a location x, the front moving forward at unit velocity]. These results were obtained using OCFE (see later) instead of FD, since the latter would require an exorbitant amount of computer time, but similar qualitative behaviour would be observed with the FD technique, using eq. (*c*) of example 7.4.

Oscillations are observed at small values of t (unless Δx and Δt are extremely small), but these die out as t increases, and the steep front is smoothened out simultaneously. Use of the Lax-Wendroff formula removes the oscillations (the effect of numerical dispersion), but also smoothens the front. One has to choose between computational costs and numerical accuracy. Such behaviour is characteristic of PDEs whose solutions exhibit sharp changes. Figure 7.4 indicates that we could reduce the computational effort substantially if we used *moving finite elements* [10, 12], such that a large number of finite elements are located where the front is, at any t. This technique is described later in the chapter.

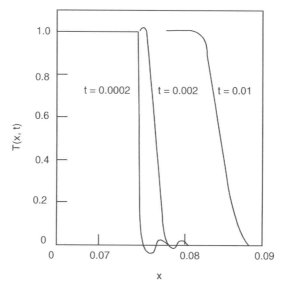

Fig. 7.4 Solution [3] of eq. 7.14 using OCFE in the x-direction. 200 FEs used. t redefined so that sharp front is at $x = 0.075$ at $t = 0$. $\Delta t = 2 \times 10^{-4}$. [Reprinted from ref. 3, copyright 1980 with permission from McGraw Hill Inc., New York, USA]

Several computer codes are available which may be used to integrate parabolic and elliptic PDEs. Both the NAG and IMSL libraries have codes based on the finite difference technique which can integrate nonlinear parabolic PDEs having several dependent variables *but having only a single space dimension* [*e.g.*, D03PBF, D03PGF, etc., in the NAG library and DPDES in the IMSL library, use a GEAR package to integrate the ODE-IVPs which the code generates]. The IMSL also distributes separately, PDETWO (ACM software No. 565), for integrating systems of parabolic PDEs involving two space variables. This uses the FD technique with Gear's method. The NAG library contains programs for integrating *linear* elliptic PDEs, but these are not too robust [7]. The programs, FPS2H or FPS3H in IMSL, solve the 2–D or 3–D Poisson's (or Helmholtz's) equation in a rectangular/3–D box domain using the FD technique with fast-Fourier transform methods to solve the resulting *linear* algebraic equations. The library ELLPACK [available from Prof. John R. Rice, Math Science 428, Purdue University, West Lafayette, IN 47907, USA, TF: (317)–494–6007] contains over 30 programs using various techniques (FD, OCFE and GFE) to integrate PDEs. The reader is advised to explore the options and programs available at his/her organization to see if an appropriate code is available.

7.3 ORTHOGONAL COLLOCATION

The Orthogonal collocation (OC) technique can be used to simplify PDEs in a manner quite like the FD method. The only difference here, as compared to chp. 6 is that we assume series solutions which incorporate all the independent variables in a convenient manner. The technique is best illustrated through examples.

Example 7.5: Obtain the ODE-IVPs for the PDEs in example 7.1, using the OC technique.

We must first nondimensionalize the radial coordinate so that its domain is from 0 to 1 (this is not necessary for the FD technique, but is required for the OC method). This gives

$$2\overline{v}\left(1-r^2\right)\frac{\partial c}{\partial z} = \mathcal{R}(c, T)$$

$$2\overline{v}\rho C_p\left(1-r^2\right)\frac{\partial T}{\partial z} = \left(\frac{k}{R^2}\right)\frac{1}{r}\frac{\partial}{\partial r}\left(r\frac{\partial T}{\partial r}\right) + \rho\left(-\Delta H_r\right)\mathcal{R}(c, T)$$

$$r = 0 \quad : \quad \frac{\partial T}{\partial r} = 0$$

$$r = 1 \quad : \quad -\frac{\partial T}{\partial r} = \left(\frac{UR}{k}\right)\left(T - T_J\right)$$

$$z = 0 \quad : \quad c = c_0, T = T_0$$

where r now is the dimensionless radial position (r here is $\dfrac{r}{R}$ of example 7.1). We need not make z dimensionless. Since we have symmetry at $r = 0$, and since we have a term $\dfrac{1}{r}\dfrac{\partial}{\partial r}\left(r\dfrac{\partial T}{\partial r}\right)$ entering, we shall use the OC formulation corresponding to cylindrical geometries [eq. 6.32 for y; eq. 6.42(b), adapted for PDEs, in the r-direction]. We can assume the solution as

$$T(r, z) = \overline{d}_1(z) + \overline{d}_2(z)r^2 + \overline{d}_3(z)r^4 + ... + \overline{d}_{N+1}(z)r^{2N}$$

with a similar expression for $c\ (r, z)$ being written. eq. 6.35(a) can be replaced by

$$\mathbf{T}(z) \equiv \begin{bmatrix} T_1(z) \\ T_2(z) \\ \cdot \\ \cdot \\ \cdot \\ T_{N+1}(z) \end{bmatrix} = \begin{bmatrix} 1 & r_1^2 & r_1^4 & \cdots & r_1^{2N} \\ 1 & r_2^2 & r_2^4 & \cdots & r_2^{2N} \\ \cdot & & & & \\ \cdot & & & & \\ \cdot & & & & \\ 1 & r_{N+1}^2 & r_{N+1}^4 & \cdots & r_{N+1}^{2N} \end{bmatrix} \begin{bmatrix} \overline{d}_1(z) \\ \overline{d}_2(z) \\ \cdot \\ \cdot \\ \cdot \\ \overline{d}_{N+1}(z) \end{bmatrix} \equiv \overline{\mathbf{Q}}^+\overline{\mathbf{d}}(z) \quad ...(a)$$

where

$$T_i(z) \equiv T(r_i, z); \qquad i = 1, 2, ..., N+1$$

and r_i are the OC points (see fig. 7.5) given in table 6.3 for various values of N. Note that the matrix, $\overline{Q}^+$, is the same as in chp. 6. eq. 6.35(b) can be replaced by

$$
\mathbf{T}'(z) \equiv
\begin{bmatrix}
\dfrac{\partial T_1(z)}{\partial r} \\[2mm]
\dfrac{\partial T_2(z)}{\partial r} \\[2mm]
\cdot \\
\cdot \\
\cdot \\
\dfrac{\partial T_{N+1}(z)}{\partial r}
\end{bmatrix}
=
\begin{bmatrix}
0 & 2r_1 & 4r_1^3 & \cdots & 2Nr_1^{2N-1} \\
0 & 2r_2 & 4r_2^3 & \cdots & 2Nr_2^{2N-1} \\
\cdot \\
\cdot \\
\cdot \\
0 & 2r_{N+1} & 4r_{N+1}^3 & \cdots & 2Nr_{N+1}^{2N-1}
\end{bmatrix}
\begin{bmatrix}
\overline{d}_1(z) \\[2mm]
\overline{d}_2(z) \\[2mm]
\cdot \\
\cdot \\
\cdot \\
\overline{d}_{N+1}(z)
\end{bmatrix}
$$

$$
= \overline{C}^+ \overline{d}(z) = \left(\overline{C}^+ \overline{Q}^{+-1}\right)\mathbf{T}(z) \equiv \overline{A}^+ \mathbf{T}(z) \qquad\qquad \ldots(b)
$$

where $\dfrac{\partial T_i(z)}{\partial r} \equiv \dfrac{\partial T}{\partial r}\Big|_{r=r_i}$. Similarly, eq. 6.42($a$) can be replaced by

$$
\nabla^2 \mathbf{T}(z) \equiv
\begin{bmatrix}
\nabla^2 T_1(z) \\[2mm]
\nabla^2 T_2(z) \\[2mm]
\cdot \\
\cdot \\
\cdot \\
\nabla^2 T_{N+1}(z)
\end{bmatrix}
=
\begin{bmatrix}
0 & 4 & 16r_1^2 & \cdots & (2N)^2 r_1^{2N-2} \\
0 & 4 & 16r_2^2 & \cdots & (2N)^2 r_2^{2N-2} \\
\cdot \\
\cdot \\
\cdot \\
0 & 4 & 16r_{N+1}^2 & \cdots & (2N)^2 r_{N+1}^{2N-2}
\end{bmatrix}
\begin{bmatrix}
\overline{d}_1(z) \\[2mm]
\overline{d}_2(z) \\[2mm]
\cdot \\
\cdot \\
\cdot \\
\overline{d}_{N+1}(z)
\end{bmatrix}
$$

$$
= \overline{D}^+ \overline{d}(z) = \overline{B}^+ \mathbf{T}(z) \qquad\qquad \ldots(c)
$$

where $\nabla^2 T_i(z)$ indicates $\dfrac{1}{r}\dfrac{\partial}{\partial r}\left(r\dfrac{\partial T}{\partial r}\right)\Big|_{r_i}$ as before. We can now force the residual to be zero at any *internal* OC line, $r = r_i$. This gives.

$$
2\overline{v}\rho C_p \left(1 - r_i^2\right)\frac{dT_i(z)}{dz} = \left(\frac{k}{R^2}\right)\sum_{j=1}^{N+1} \overline{B}_{ij}^+ T_j(z) + \rho\left(-\Delta H_r\right)\mathcal{R}\left[c_i(z), T_i(z)\right]
$$

$$
2\overline{v}\left(1 - r_i^2\right)\frac{dc_i(z)}{dz} = \mathcal{R}\left[c_i(z), T_i(z)\right]
$$

$$
ICs: \; c_i(0) = c_0 \; ; \; T_i(0) = T_0 \; ; \quad i = 1, 2, \ldots, N
$$

Again, the BCs at $r = 0$ are automatically satisfied. The BC at $r = 1$ can be written as

$$-\frac{\partial T_{N+1}(z)}{\partial r} = -\sum_{j=1}^{N+1} \bar{A}_{N+1,\,j}^{+} T_j(z) = \left(\frac{UR}{k}\right)\left(T_{N+1}(z) - T_J\right)$$

Thus, the procedure to write the OC equations is seen to be quite simple, and parallels that discussed in Chapter 6 for ODE-IVPs. A GEAR package can be used to integrate these equations. Note that use of the Crank-Nicholson technique to reduce the ODEs into algebraic equations will not lead to sparse matrices as when the FD technique was used.   ■

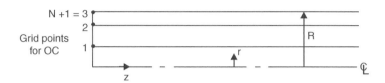

Fig. 7.5 OC grid lines for example 7.5. The placement of the grid lines correspond to the cylindrical geometry, with $N = 2$.

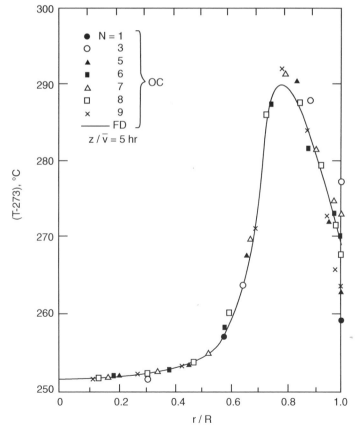

Fig. 7.6 Temperature profiles [13] at location $z/\bar{v} = 5$ hr in a laminar-flow reactor using orthogonal collocation in the r-direction, with different values of N. FD results of fig. 7.2 shown by solid curve.

Once again we present OC results for the more complex and interesting case, namely, the polymerization of nylon 6 in tubular reactors [13] (see fig. 7.2 for FD results on the same problem). Figure 7.6 shows the temperature profiles at $\frac{z}{v} = 5$ hr for different choices of N. The oscillations of the profile about the "correct" profile as N increases, is to be observed. In fact, it can be seen that the $N = 8$ results are better than the $N = 9$ results. It is obvious that the OC technique does not offer much advantage over the FD technique in *this* case, since the small N results are quite poor. One should use OCFE instead, for this problem; possibly with one of the FEs extending from $0 < r < 0.65$, where the gradients of T are small.

Example 7.6: Reduce the following elliptic PDE into algebraic equations, using OC in both the x and y directions:

$$\frac{\partial^2 T}{\partial x^2} + \frac{\partial^2 T}{\partial y^2} = f(x, y); \quad 0 \le x, \ y \le 1$$

$$x = 0 \quad : \quad T = T_1^*$$

$$x = 1 \quad : \quad T = T_2^*$$

$$y = 0 \quad : \quad T = T_3^*$$

$$y = 1 \quad : \quad \frac{\partial T}{\partial y} = 0$$

Equations having the above form describe a whole variety of physical situations, e.g., steady state heat transfer in a 2–D slab with internal heat generation, flow of an incompressible Newtonian fluid in a 2–D duct [3], etc.

We number the grid lines for the OC formulation as shown in fig. 7.7(a), with $i = 1, 2, ..., N_x + 2$ and $j = 1, 2, ..., N_y + 2$. The values of x_i and y_i are as given in table 6.2. Note that N_x and N_y could be different. We define $T_{ij} = T(x_i, y_j)$.

We can easily show (see prob. 7.28) that

$$\left[\frac{\partial^2 T}{\partial x^2}\right]_{i, j} = \sum_{k=1}^{N_x+2} B_{ik} T_{kj}$$

$$\left[\frac{\partial^2 T}{\partial y^2}\right]_{i, j} = \sum_{k=1}^{N_y+2} B_{jk} T_{ik}, \text{ etc.} \qquad \qquad ...(a)$$

The similarity of eq. (a) with the expressions used in chp. 6 is to be noted. While evaluating $\left[\frac{\partial^2 T}{\partial y^2}\right]_{i, j}$, we fix the x-coordinate at $x = x_i$ and multiply the elements of the jth row of **B** to the values of T along *this* line [crossed locations in fig. 7.7(a)]. Similarly, while evaluating $\left[\frac{\partial^2 T}{\partial x^2}\right]_{i, j}$, we multiply the *i*th row of **B** with the *T* values at positions along the line $y = y_j$ (squares in fig. 7.7a). The residual at any *internal* OC point (i, j), should be made zero. This gives

$$\sum_{k=1}^{N_x+2} B_{ik} T_{kj} + \sum_{k=1}^{N_y+2} B_{jk} T_{ik} = f\left(x_i, y_j\right)$$

$$i = 2, 3, ..., N_x + 1$$

$$j = 2, 3, ..., N_y + 1$$

The boundary condition at $y = 1$ can also be written quite easily. It leads to

$$\sum_{k=1}^{N_y+2} A_{N_y+2,k} T_{i,k} = 0; \quad i = 2, 3, ..., N_x + 1$$

It may be noted that we have not used the flux = 0 condition at the locations $(0, 1)$ and $(1, 1)$.

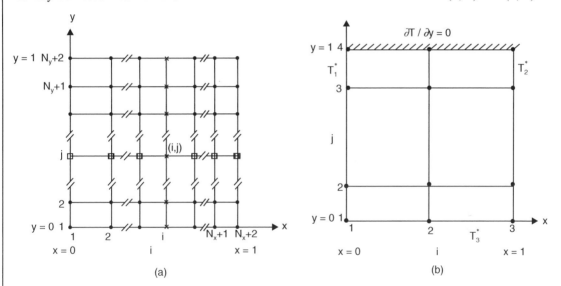

Fig. 7.7 OC grids for example 7.6 (*a*) general (*b*) $N_x = 1$, $N_y = 2$, with locations according to table 6.1.

Some amount of arbitrariness exists in this, as mentioned earlier in this chapter.

The above equations can be simplified by substituting the values of the given temperature at the three boundaries.

If we assume $N_x = 1$, $N_y = 2$, we can write the appropriate equations as [see fig. 7.7(*b*), table 6.1]

$$T_{1,1} = \frac{\left(T_1^* + T_3^*\right)}{2}; \qquad\qquad T_{2,1} = T_3^*; \quad T_{3,1} = \frac{\left(T_2^* + T_3^*\right)}{2}$$

$$T_{1,2} = T_1^*; \qquad\qquad T_{3,2} = T_2^*$$

$$T_{1,3} = T_1^*; \qquad\qquad T_{3,3} = T_2^*$$

$$T_{1,4} = T_1^*; \qquad\qquad T_{3,4} = T_2^*$$

$i = 2, j = 2$:

$$4T_{1,2} - 8T_{2,2} + 4T_{3,2} + 16.39T_{2,1} - 24T_{2,2} + 12T_{2,3} - 4.392T_{2,4} = f_{2,2}$$

$i = 2, j = 3$:

$$4T_{1,3} - 8T_{2,3} + 4T_{3,3} - 4.392T_{2,1} + 12T_{2,2} - 24T_{2,3} + 16.39T_{2,4} = f_{2,3}$$

$i = 2, j = 4$ (BC)

$$-T_{2,1} + 2.196T_{2,2} - 8.196T_{2,3} + 7T_{2,4} = 0$$

The linear algebraic equations can be solved using any iterative technique. Note that nonlinear algebraic equations would be obtained if f is a nonlinear function of T. Methods discussed in Chapter 3 would then have to be used to obtain solutions. ∎

It must be emphasized that we can use different values of N_x and N_y, as in the above example. We can also use the OC points and the matrices for the symmetrical case in one direction, and for the unsymmetrical case in another direction, etc. (e.g., in prob. 7.20, if we do not redefine z). A little practice will enable one to write down the OC form of PDEs almost effortlessly. Integrals can also be evaluated quite easily to obtain mean values of the dependent variable, using the **w** matrices in Chapter 6. Thus, in example 7.6, we could use (see prob. 7.29)

$$\bar{T} \equiv \int\limits_{x=0}^{1} \int\limits_{y=0}^{1} T\, dx\, dy = \frac{\sum\limits_{k=1}^{N_x+2} \sum\limits_{l=1}^{N_y+2} (wx)_k (wy)_l T_{kl}}{\sum\limits_{k=1}^{N_x+2} \sum\limits_{l=1}^{N_y+2} (wx)_k (wy)_l} \qquad ...(7.15)$$

where (**wx**) is the **w** matrix for the collocation points selected in the x-direction and (**wy**) that for the y-direction.

7.4 ORTHOGONAL COLLOCATION ON FINITE ELEMENTS (OCFE)

It was observed in fig. 7.6 that the OC technique does not offer any advantage over the FD method for simulating the polymerization of nylon 6 in a tubular reactor. In fact, this method does not work too well whenever sharp gradients are encountered. The OCFE technique is then preferred. Again, the procedure is similar to that used in the solution of ODE-BVPs, and we illustrate its use below. It may be mentioned that the OCFE technique is not usually applied to elliptical PDEs, and more powerful codes are available which are based on the Galerkin method, for solving such equations. These are discussed in the next section.

Example 7.7: Apply the OCFE technique (in the r direction) to the PDEs in example 7.5:

$$2\bar{v}(1 - r^2)\frac{\partial c}{\partial z} = \mathcal{R}(c, T)$$

$$2\bar{v}\rho C_p (1 - r^2)\frac{\partial T}{\partial z} = \left(\frac{k}{R^2}\right)\left[\frac{\partial^2 T}{\partial r^2} + \frac{1}{r}\frac{\partial T}{\partial r}\right] + \rho(-\Delta H_r)\mathcal{R}(c, T)$$

$$r = 0 \quad : \quad \frac{\partial T}{\partial r} = 0$$

$$r = 1 \quad : \quad -\frac{\partial T}{\partial r} = \left(\frac{UR}{k}\right)(T - T_J)$$

$$z = 0 \quad : \quad T = T_0, \; c = c_0$$

and obtain appropriate ODE-IVPs/algebraic equations. Assume ($N_s = 2$) finite elements of lengths h_1 and h_2 and 2 internal OC points on each (see fig. 6.6, with x replaced by r). We have $u_2^{\langle i \rangle} = 0.2113$ and $u_3^{\langle i \rangle} = 0.7887$, $i = 1, 2$.

We force the residuals to be zero at the two internal OC points in the first FE. This gives (for constant ρ, $\bar{v}$, C_p, k, $-\Delta H_r$, and U).

$$2\bar{v}\rho C_P\left(1 - r_2^2\right)\frac{dT_2}{dz} = \frac{k}{R^2}\left[\frac{1}{h_1^2}\left\{16.39T_1 - 24T_2 + 12T_3 - 4.392T_4\right\}\right.$$

$$\left. + \frac{1}{r_2 h_1}\left\{-2.732T_1 + 1.732T_2 + 1.732T_3 - 0.732T_4\right\}\right] + \rho\left(-\Delta H_r\right)\mathcal{R}\left(c_2, T_2\right)$$

$$2\bar{v}\rho C_P\left(1 - r_3^2\right)\frac{dT_3}{dz} = \frac{k}{R^2}\left[\frac{1}{h_1^2}\left\{-4.392T_1 + 12T_2 - 24T_3 + 16.39T_4\right\}\right.$$

$$\left. + \frac{1}{r_3 h_1}\left\{0.732T_1 - 1.732T_2 - 1.732T_3 + 2.732T_4\right\}\right] + \rho\left(-\Delta H_r\right)\mathcal{R}\left(c_3, T_3\right)$$

$$2\bar{v}\left(1 - r_2^2\right)\frac{dc_2}{dz} = \mathcal{R}\left(c_2, T_2\right)$$

$$2\bar{v}\left(1 - r_3^2\right)\frac{dc_3}{dz} = \mathcal{R}\left(c_3, T_3\right)$$

with

$$r_2 = h_1 u_2^{\langle 1 \rangle} = 0.2113 h_1$$

$$r_3 = h_1 u_3^{\langle 1 \rangle} = 0.7887 h_1$$

Similar equations forcing the residual to be zero at internal OC points 5 and 6 (see fig. 6.6) can be written as

$$2\rho C_P \bar{v}\left(1 - r_5^2\right)\frac{dT_5}{dz} = \frac{k}{R^2}\left[\frac{1}{h_2^2}\left\{16.39T_4 - 24T_5 + 12T_6 - 4.392T_7\right\}\right.$$

$$\left. + \frac{1}{r_5 h_2}\left\{-2.732T_4 + 1.732T_5 + 1.732T_6 - 0.732T_7\right\}\right]$$

$$+ \rho\left(-\Delta H_r\right)\mathcal{R}\left(c_5, T_5\right)$$

$$2\rho C_P \bar{v}\left(1-r_6^2\right)\frac{dT_6}{dz} = \frac{k}{R^2}\left[\frac{1}{h_2^2}\left\{-4.392T_4 + 12T_5 - 24T_6 + 16.39T_7\right\}\right.$$

$$\left. + \frac{1}{r_6 h_2}\left\{0.732T_4 - 1.732T_5 - 1.732T_6 + 2.732T_7\right\}\right] + \rho\left(-\Delta H_r\right)\mathcal{R}\left(c_6, T_6\right)$$

$$2\bar{v}\left(1-r_5^2\right)\frac{dc_5}{dz} = \mathcal{R}\left(c_5, T_5\right)$$

$$2\bar{v}\left(1-r_6^2\right)\frac{dc_6}{dz} = \mathcal{R}\left(c_6, T_6\right)$$

$$r_5 = h_1 + 0.2113h_2$$

$$r_6 = h_1 + 0.7887h_2$$

The slope-continuity condition at point 4 (internal boundary point) is written as (from $\frac{\partial T}{\partial r}$ and $\frac{\partial c}{\partial r}$ continuous)

$$\frac{1}{h_1}\left[-T_1 + 2.196T_2 - 8.196T_3 + 7T_4\right] = \frac{1}{h_2}\left[-7T_4 + 8.196T_5 - 2.196T_6 + T_7\right]$$

$$\frac{1}{h_1}\left[-c_1 + 2.196c_2 - 8.196c_3 + 7c_4\right] = \frac{1}{h_2}\left[-7c_4 + 8.196c_5 - 2.196c_6 + c_7\right]$$

The external boundary conditions can be written as

$$\frac{1}{h_1}\left[-7T_1 + 8.196T_2 - 2.196T_3 + T_4\right] = 0$$

$$\frac{1}{h_2}\left[-T_4 + 2.196T_5 - 8.196T_6 + 7T_7\right] = \left(\frac{UR}{k}\right)\left(T_7 - T_J\right)$$

The equations for c_i can be written in matrix form as

$$2\bar{v}\begin{bmatrix} 1 & 0 & 0 & 0 & 0 & 0 & 0 \\ 0 & \left(1-r_2^2\right) & 0 & 0 & 0 & 0 & 0 \\ 0 & 0 & \left(1-r_3^2\right) & 0 & 0 & 0 & 0 \\ 0 & 0 & 0 & 0 & 0 & 0 & 0 \\ 0 & 0 & 0 & 0 & \left(1-r_5^2\right) & 0 & 0 \\ 0 & 0 & 0 & 0 & 0 & \left(1-r_6^2\right) & 0 \\ 0 & 0 & 0 & 0 & 0 & 0 & 10^{-4} \end{bmatrix}\begin{bmatrix} \dfrac{dc_1}{dz} \\[2mm] \dfrac{dc_2}{dz} \\[2mm] \dfrac{dc_3}{dz} \\[2mm] \dfrac{dc_4}{dz} \\[2mm] \dfrac{dc_5}{dz} \\[2mm] \dfrac{dc_6}{dz} \\[2mm] \dfrac{dc_7}{dz} \end{bmatrix}$$

$$
=\begin{bmatrix}
\mathcal{R}(c_1, T_1) \\
\mathcal{R}(c_2, T_2) \\
\mathcal{R}(c_3, T_3) \\
-\dfrac{c_1}{h_1} + \dfrac{2.196c_2}{h_1} - \dfrac{8.196c_3}{h_1} + \left(\dfrac{7}{h_1} + \dfrac{7}{h_2}\right)c_4 - \dfrac{8.196c_5}{h_2} + \dfrac{2.196c_6}{h_2} - \dfrac{c_7}{h_2} \\
\mathcal{R}(c_5, T_5) \\
\mathcal{R}(c_6, T_6) \\
\mathcal{R}(c_7, T_7)
\end{bmatrix}
$$

where the residual has been made zero at points 1 (no boundary conditions on c at $r = 0$) and 7 too (with a small slip introduced at the wall, $r = 1$, to avoid problems of computing equilibrium values at the wall, due to the no-slip conditions, corresponding to T_7).

Similarly, the equations for T_i can be assembled to give

$$
(2\bar{v}\rho C_P)
\begin{bmatrix}
0 & 0 & 0 & 0 & 0 & 0 & 0 \\
0 & (1-r_2^2) & 0 & 0 & 0 & 0 & 0 \\
0 & 0 & (1-r_3^2) & 0 & 0 & 0 & 0 \\
0 & 0 & 0 & 0 & 0 & 0 & 0 \\
0 & 0 & 0 & 0 & (1-r_5^2) & 0 & 0 \\
0 & 0 & 0 & 0 & 0 & (1-r_6^2) & 0 \\
0 & 0 & 0 & 0 & 0 & 0 & 0
\end{bmatrix}
\begin{bmatrix}
\dfrac{dT_1}{dz} \\
\dfrac{dT_2}{dz} \\
\dfrac{dT_3}{dz} \\
\dfrac{dT_4}{dz} \\
\dfrac{dT_5}{dz} \\
\dfrac{dT_6}{dz} \\
\dfrac{dT_7}{dz}
\end{bmatrix}
=
$$

$$
\frac{k}{R^2}
\begin{bmatrix}
-\dfrac{7}{h_1} & \dfrac{8.196}{h_1} & \dfrac{-2.196}{h_1} & \dfrac{1}{h_1} & 0 & 0 & 0 \\[2ex]
\dfrac{16.39}{h_1^2}-\dfrac{2.732}{r_2 h_1} & \dfrac{-24}{h_1^2}+\dfrac{1.732}{r_2 h_1} & \dfrac{12}{h_1^2}+\dfrac{1.732}{r_2 h_1} & \dfrac{-4.392}{h_1^2}+\dfrac{0.732}{r_2 h_1} & 0 & 0 & 0 \\[2ex]
\dfrac{-4.392}{h_1^2}+\dfrac{0.732}{r_3 h_1} & \dfrac{12}{h_1^2}-\dfrac{1.732}{r_3 h_1} & \dfrac{-24}{h_1^2}-\dfrac{1.732}{r_3 h_1} & \dfrac{16.39}{h_1^2}+\dfrac{2.732}{r_3 h_1} & 0 & 0 & 0 \\[2ex]
-\dfrac{1}{h_1} & \dfrac{2.196}{h_1} & \dfrac{-8.196}{h_1} & \dfrac{7}{h_1}+\dfrac{7}{h_2} & \dfrac{-8.196}{h_2} & \dfrac{2.196}{h_2} & \dfrac{-1}{h_2} \\[2ex]
0 & 0 & 0 & \dfrac{16.39}{h_2^2}-\dfrac{2.732}{r_5 h_2} & \dfrac{-24}{h_2^2}+\dfrac{1.732}{r_5 h_2} & \dfrac{12}{h_2^2}+\dfrac{1.732}{r_5 h_2} & \dfrac{-4.392}{h_2^2}-\dfrac{0.732}{r_2 h_2} \\[2ex]
0 & 0 & 0 & \dfrac{-4.392}{h_2^2}+\dfrac{0.732}{r_6 h_2} & \dfrac{12}{h_2^2}-\dfrac{1.732}{r_6 h_2} & \dfrac{-24}{h_2^2}-\dfrac{1.732}{r_6 h_2} & \dfrac{16.39}{h_2^2}+\dfrac{2.732}{r_6 h_2} \\[2ex]
0 & 0 & 0 & -\dfrac{1}{h_2} & \dfrac{2.196}{h_2} & \dfrac{-8.196}{h_2} & \dfrac{7}{h_2}-\dfrac{U}{R}
\end{bmatrix}
$$

$$
\times
\begin{bmatrix}
T_1 \\ T_2 \\ T_3 \\ T_4 \\ T_5 \\ T_6 \\ T_7
\end{bmatrix}
+
\begin{bmatrix}
0 \\
\rho(-\Delta H_r)\mathcal{R}(c_2,T_2) \\
\rho(-\Delta H_r)\mathcal{R}(c_3,T_3) \\
0 \\
\rho(-\Delta H_r)\mathcal{R}(c_5,T_5) \\
\rho(-\Delta H_r)\mathcal{R}(c_6,T_6) \\
-\dfrac{U}{R}T_J
\end{bmatrix}
\qquad \ldots(a)
$$

or

$$
\mathbf{C}_1\frac{d\mathbf{c}}{dz} = \mathbf{f}_1\left(\mathbf{c},\mathbf{T}\right)
$$

$$
\mathbf{C}_2\frac{d\mathbf{T}}{dz} = \mathbf{A}\mathbf{T} + \mathbf{f}_2\left(\mathbf{c},\mathbf{T}\right)
$$

These equations can easily be generalized for a larger number of finite elements. It is to be noted that these equations involve coupled differential-algebraic systems, and DDASSL can be used to integrate them. Alternatively, we can use the Crank-Nicholson technique to express $c_{i,j+1}$ and $T_{i,j+1}$ [where $c(r,z)$ and $T(r,z)$ are being used] in terms of $c_{i,j}$ and $T_{i,j}$ as was done in example 7.2 [the Newton-Raphson technique also needs to be applied to obtain linear algebraic equations]. One more technique [3] is described in prob. 7.33. Since these techniques and their adaptations have been so extensively discussed earlier, they are not being repeated. ∎

We close this section with the comment that we can adapt the OCFE technique for problems whose solutions show sharp *moving* fronts. We can use some of the techniques discussed in Chapter 6 to decide on the placement of the FEs, and *move them* as required so that there are several FEs at the location of the moving front. The unsteady isothermal TRAM described by eq. 7.3 (non dimensional equations given in prob. 7.4) can be solved best using such moving FE schemes [10–12] (also see prob. 7.34). fig. 7.8 [14] shows the c-profiles obtained at different values of *t* using one such moving finite element (MFE) code (this code is based on the Galerkin technique, however, and not the OC technique). Details of MFE methods fall outside the scope of the text, and the reader is referred to the literature.

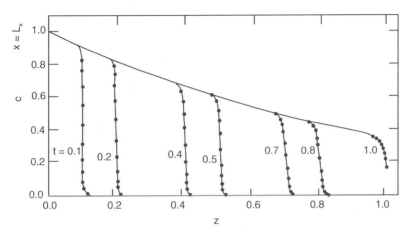

Fig. 7.8 Moving FE technique results for the unsteady, isothermal TRAM with a first-order irreversible reaction taking place [14]. $Pe = 10^4$, $Da = 1$. Dark dots represent boundaries of the FEs. Dots indicate the finite element locations at any *t* (the number of internal points within each FE is different). [Reprinted from ref. 14, copyright 1991, with permission from Pergamon Press Ltd. Headington Hill Hall, Oxford OX3 OBW, UK]

A few computer codes are available commercially which use the OC and OCFE techniques to integrate PDEs. The IMSL library has MOLCH, which integrates parabolic PDEs in one space dimension using the OCFE techniques with cubic Hermite polynomials (as basis functions—see discussion at the end of sec. 6.4). Gear's method is used to integrate the resulting (nonlinear) ODE-IVPs. Similarly, IMSL distributes the program, PDECOL (ACM Algorithm 540) which integrates parabolic PDEs in one space dimension, using basis functions which are polynomials of degree 3 to 20. This is coupled to a GEAR package for integrating the ODE-IVPs. The ELLPACK library (see end of sec. 7.2) has programs using the OCFE technique for elliptic PDEs as well.

7.5 THE GALERKIN FINITE ELEMENT (GFE) TECHNIQUE

It is easy to extend the Galerkin finite element method to solve parabolic PDEs involving one space variable. The developments in secs. 6.5 and 7.4 can be used and this is left as an exercise (prob. 7.35). It is more interesting to develop this technique for elliptic problems in two space variables, since the algebraic operations are a bit more cumbersome. Moreover, it is for these PDEs that the GFE method has been most extensively used in the recent past and these codes are part of CAE (computer-aided engineering) packages. We shall give only an elementary description of this technique, sufficient to solve *simple* problems. The interested reader is referred to several excellent texts on this topic (refs. 15 to 17 are only three of the several available texts), which give detailed proofs and descriptions of the technique as well as of computer codes available for integrating this class of PDEs. The first *formal* presentation of this technique is attributed [15] to Turner et al. [18], even though similar concepts have been used as early as in 1941 [19].

The procedure and the notation we follow are similar to those used in sec. 6.5 (with *x* and *y* being the independent variables here, and *c* being the dependent variable). We assume that the domain of the independent variables extends over an area $\mathcal{A}$ in the x–y space, and this area is enclosed by a curve (boundary), C. The domain, $\mathcal{A}$, is assumed to be subdivided into N_E triangular finite elements of different sizes, numbered from 1 to N_E, as shown in fig. 7.9. The FEs are constructed such that the (usually) irregular boundary is fairly well approximated by them. We shall discuss the GFE technique only for triangular finite elements, each associated with three nodes (the vertices), even though rectangular FEs, as well as triangular FEs with more than three nodes (e.g., a node at the centroid in addition to the vertices, or nodes at the mid-points of the three sides, etc.) can be used [15]. The jth triangular FE has its nodes say, at (x_l, y_l), (x_m, y_m) and (x_n, y_n). We assume that there are a total of N_N independent nodes corresponding to the N_E triangular finite elements. The subdivision of any 2-dimensional domain having complex geometry into several smaller domains of simpler geometry, is an important feature of the finite element techniques.

We now *assume* a solution, $c\,(x, y)$, in terms of N_N trial or basis functions, $\mathcal{F}_i(x, y)$, as follows:

$$c\left(x, y\right) = c_1 \mathcal{F}_1\left(x, y\right) + c_2 \mathcal{F}_2\left(x, y\right) + \ldots + c_{N_N} \mathcal{F}_{N_N}\left(x, y\right) \qquad \ldots(7.16)$$

We extend the equations for the basis functions used in sec. 6.5 to two space variables. We choose the function, $\mathcal{F}_i(x, y)$, such that it has a value of unity at the ith node, and decreases to zero at all *nearest neighbouring* nodes [c_i is, therefore, the value of $c\,(x, y)$ at the ith node]. In addition, $\mathcal{F}_i(x, y)$ varies linearly with x or y in the subdomain enclosed by the nearest neighbours of node i. As an example, $\mathcal{F}_5(x, y)$ in fig. 7.9(a) has a value of 1.0 at point 5, and decreases to zero at points 1, 4, 7 and 9. $\mathcal{F}_5(x, y)$ is zero outside of the subdomain (quadrilateral) enclosed by 1-4-7-9. Thus, this function looks like a 'tent' [see fig. 7.9(c)] with a central support of height unity at point 5, and the roof consisting of

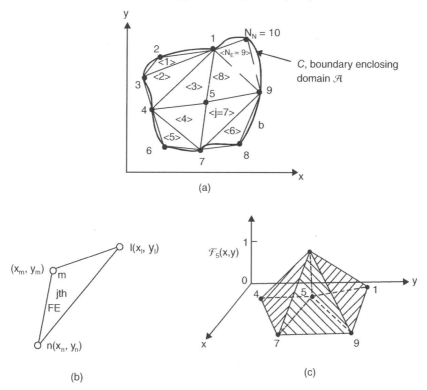

(a)

(b)

(c)

Fig. 7.9 (*a*) Triangular finite elements spanning the domain of a problem; (*b*) the *j*th FE and (*c*) part of the 'tent' function, $\mathcal{F}_5(x, y)$, shown.

four triangular pieces, stitched together, and nailed to the ground at points, 1, 4, 7 and 9. Part of this tent function (with three of the four triangular roof-pieces) are shown in fig. 7.9(c). These functions are discontinuous, and satisfy certain fundamental requirements as discussed in more advanced texts [15]. It can now be deduced that the function, $\mathcal{F}_i(x, y)$, can be described *in the jth element* by the equation (see fig. 7.9(b))*

$$\mathcal{F}_i^{\langle j \rangle}(x, y) \equiv \frac{1}{2\mathcal{A}^{\langle j \rangle}}(\alpha_i + \beta_i x + \gamma_i y); \quad i = l, m, n \qquad \ldots(a)$$

$$\left.\begin{array}{l} \alpha_j = x_m y_n - x_n y_m \\ \beta_l = y_m - y_n \\ \gamma_l = x_n - x_m \end{array}\right\} \begin{array}{l} l \neq m \neq n; \\ l, m, n \text{ permute in a} \\ natural \text{ order*} \end{array} \qquad \ldots(b)$$

$$\mathcal{A}^{\langle j \rangle} = \frac{1}{2}\begin{vmatrix} 1 & x_l & y_l \\ 1 & x_m & y_m \\ 1 & x_n & y_n \end{vmatrix} = \text{area of jth element} \qquad \ldots(c) \qquad \ldots(7.17)$$

An example will clarify the use of eq. 7.17(b), and its generalization to give $\alpha_m, \beta_m, \gamma_m$ and $\alpha_n, \beta_n, \gamma_n$.

Example 7.8 The coordinates of the 4th triangular finite element in fig. 7.9(a) are given by ($x_5 = 1$, $y_5 = 1$), ($x_4 = 0.5$, $y_4 = 1$) and ($x_7 = 1$, $y_7 = 0.5$), with $l = 5$, $m = 4$ and $n = 7$ (taken counter-clockwise). Obtain $\mathcal{F}_5^{\langle 4 \rangle}(x, y)$ (having value 1 at node 5). Also obtain $\mathcal{F}_4^{\langle 4 \rangle}(x, y)$ (having value 1 at node 4).

Equation 7.17 leads to

$$\mathcal{F}_5^{\langle 4 \rangle}(x, y) = \frac{1}{2\mathcal{A}^{\langle 4 \rangle}}\left[\alpha_l + \beta_l x + \gamma_l y\right]$$

$$\alpha_l = x_4 y_7 - x_7 y_4 = (0.5)(0.5) - (1.0)(1.0) = -0.75$$

$$\beta_l = y_4 - y_7 \quad = 1 - 0.5 = 0.5$$

$$\gamma_l = x_7 - x_4 \quad = 1 - 0.5 = 0.5$$

$$\mathcal{A}^{\langle 4 \rangle} = \frac{1}{2}\begin{vmatrix} 1 & 1 & 1 \\ 1 & 0.5 & 1 \\ 1 & 1 & 0.5 \end{vmatrix} = \frac{1}{8}$$

Hence

$$\mathcal{F}_5^{\langle 4 \rangle}(x, y) = 4\left[0.5x + 0.5y - 0.75\right]$$

$$= 2x + 2y - 3$$

It can easily be confirmed that $\mathcal{F}_5^{\langle 4 \rangle}(x, y) = 1$ at $x = 1$, $y = 1$; and is zero at (0.5, 1) and (1, 0.5).

Note that this is only *part* of the complete tent function, $\mathcal{F}_5(x, y)$—that part which lies in the 4th FE.

---

* l, m, n permuting in *natural* order means sequences of the kind (l, m, n), (n, l, m), (m, n, l) and excludes sequences like (m, l, n), etc.

We need to obtain expressions for $\mathcal{F}_5^{\langle 3 \rangle}(x, y)$, $\mathcal{F}_5^{\langle 8 \rangle}(x, y)$ and $\mathcal{F}_5^{\langle 7 \rangle}(x, y)$ to complete the description of the tent function, $\mathcal{F}_5(x, y)$. Outside of the quadrilateral 1-4-7-9, $\mathcal{F}_5(x, y)$ is zero.

We now obtain a part of *another* tent function, $\mathcal{F}_4(x, y)$:

We have from eq. 7.17

$$\mathcal{F}_4^{\langle 4 \rangle}(x, y) = \frac{1}{2\mathcal{A}^{\langle 4 \rangle}}[\alpha_m + \beta_m x + \gamma_m y]$$

with (note the positioning of the subscripts in the first term in the equation for α_m, and of the subscripts in the equation for β_m):

$$\alpha_m = x_n y_l - x_l y_n = 1 \times 1 - 1 \times 0.5 = 0.5$$

$$\beta_m = y_n - y_l = 0.5 - 1 = -0.5$$

$$\gamma_m = x_l - x_n = 1 - 1 = 0$$

Hence

$$\mathcal{F}_4^{\langle 4 \rangle}(x, y) = 4[0.5 - 0.5x + 0y] = 2 - 2x$$

It can be confirmed that this function has a value of 1.0 at node 4; and values 0 at nodes 5 and 7. The formulae for α_n, β_n and γ_n are similarly, given by

$$\alpha_n = x_l y_m - x_m y_l$$

$$\beta_n = y_l - y_m$$

$$\gamma_n = x_m - x_l$$ ∎

As in the simpler case discussed in sec. 6.5, the functions $\mathcal{F}_i(x, y)$ for which node i lies on the boundary, C, are 'chopped' or truncated tents which are zero everywhere outside C *as well*. Thus, for example, in fig. 7.9, the function, $\mathcal{F}_3(x, y)$ is defined by $\mathcal{F}_3^{\langle 1 \rangle}(x, y)$ over element 1, and by $\mathcal{F}_3^{\langle 2 \rangle}(x, y)$ over element 2, both of which can easily be obtained using eq. 7.17. At all other values of x and y, $\mathcal{F}_3(x, y)$ is zero. Likewise, $\mathcal{F}_4(x, y)$ comprises of nonzero functions, $\mathcal{F}_4^{\langle 2 \rangle}(x, y)$, $\mathcal{F}_4^{\langle 3 \rangle}(x, y)$, $\mathcal{F}_4^{\langle 4 \rangle}(x, y)$ and $\mathcal{F}_4^{\langle 5 \rangle}(x, y)$ only.

Having developed expressions for the linear, discontinuous, basis functions, we now substitute the assumed solution, $c(x, y)$, as given in eq. 7.16, in the PDE, and obtain the residual, $\mathbb{R}(x, y)$. We make this residual orthogonal to each of the N_N basis functions (over the domain, $\mathcal{A}$), and simplify the resulting N_N equations. We illustrate the procedure for simplification, as well as the technique for incorporating the boundary conditions, through a relatively simple example.

Example 7.9 Consider the steady heat conduction with generation in a 2-dimensional slab shown in fig. 7.10. The triangular FEs to be used are also shown in this figure. Simplify the GFE equations corresponding to the PDE (Poisson equation)

$$\frac{\partial^2 T}{\partial x^2} + \frac{\partial^2 T}{\partial y^2} = Q(x, y)$$

on C_1: $T = 0$;   on C_2: $\dfrac{\partial T}{\partial y} = 0$

on $\quad C_3: \quad \dfrac{\partial T}{\partial x} = 4$

$Q(x, y) :\ 0$ on elements $\langle 1 \rangle$, $\langle 2 \rangle$, $\langle 3 \rangle$ and $\langle 5 \rangle$

$Q(x, y) : -1.5$ on $\langle 4 \rangle$ $\hfill ...(a)$

In this equation, Q is the ratio of the rate of heat generated per unit volume, and the thermal conductivity.

We have to satisfy the following equation in the Galerkin method:

$$\iint_{\mathcal{A}} v \left[\nabla^2 T - Q \right] dx\, dy = 0 \qquad ...(b)$$

where $v\,(x, y)$ is a test function $[\mathcal{F}_j;$ to be substituted later]. We integrate this equation by parts (as in example 6.9) so that only first order partial derivatives are present, and use of linear trial functions does not lead to a dropping of the second order terms. To do this, we use the following identity [1] in eq. (b)

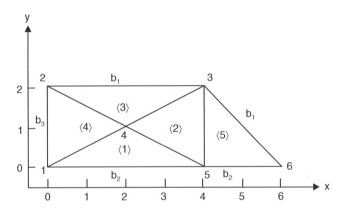

Fig. 7.10 FEs for example 7.9.

$$\underline{\nabla} \cdot \left(f\, \mathbf{u} \right) = f \underline{\nabla} \cdot \mathbf{u} + \mathbf{u} \cdot \underline{\nabla} f$$

and obtain (using $f = v$ and $\mathbf{u} = \underline{\nabla} T$)

$$\iint_{\mathcal{A}} \underline{\nabla} \cdot \left(v \underline{\nabla} T \right) dx\, dy - \iint_{\mathcal{A}} \underline{\nabla} T \cdot \underline{\nabla} v \, dx\, dy - \iint_{\mathcal{A}} v Q \, dx\, dy = 0$$

We now use the divergence theorem [1]

$$\iint_{\mathcal{A}} \underline{\nabla} \cdot \mathbf{u} \, dx\, dy = \oint_{C} \mathbf{u} \cdot \hat{\mathbf{n}}\, ds; \ C \quad \text{counterclockwise}$$

where $\hat{\mathbf{n}}$ is the unit outward normal to the boundary, C, and ds is an infinitesimal element of length on the boundary. Use of this equation leads to

$$\oint_{C} v \underline{\nabla} T \cdot \hat{\mathbf{n}}\, ds - \iint_{\mathcal{A}} \underline{\nabla} T \cdot \underline{\nabla} v \, dx\, dy = \iint_{\mathcal{A}} v Q \, dx\, dy \qquad ...(c)$$

Equation (c) is known as the variational or weak form [15] of the PDE [eq. (a)]. This form has the advantage that it has weaker continuity requirements on T than does the original PDE. Also whenever a classical solution (*i.e.*, one which satisfies the original PDE) exists, it coincides with the solution of the variational form of the PDE [15]. These details as well as the variational forms of more general second as well as fourth order PDEs are available in ref. 15.

We can break up the line integral in eq. (*c*) over the three sectors, C_1, C_2 and C_3, to account for the boundary conditions. We shall consider this later. At present, we assume a solution

$$T(x, y) = \sum_{i=1}^{N_N=6} T_i \mathcal{F}_i(x, y)$$

with $\mathcal{F}_i(x, y)$ as defined earlier. Substitution in eq. (*c*) and use of $v = \mathcal{F}_j$, leads to

$$\underbrace{-\sum_{i=1}^{6} T_i \iint_{\mathcal{A}} \underline{\nabla} \mathcal{F}_i \cdot \underline{\nabla} \mathcal{F}_j \, dx \, dy}_{\mathrm{I}} + \underbrace{\oint_c \mathcal{F}_j (\hat{\mathbf{n}} \cdot \underline{\nabla} T) \, ds}_{\mathrm{II}} = \underbrace{\iint_{\mathcal{A}} \mathcal{F}_j Q \, dx \, dy}_{\mathrm{III}} \quad ; \quad j = 1, 2, ..., 6 \quad ...(d)$$

We now simplify the terms one by one. We consider a general term in I

$$\mathrm{I}_{ij} = -T_i \iint_{\mathcal{A}} \underline{\nabla} \mathcal{F}_i \cdot \underline{\nabla} \mathcal{F}_j \, dx \, dy \quad ; \quad i, j = 1, 2, ..., 6$$

$$= -T_i \iint_{\mathcal{A}} \left[\frac{\partial \mathcal{F}_i}{\partial x} \frac{\partial \mathcal{F}_j}{\partial x} + \frac{\partial \mathcal{F}_i}{\partial y} \frac{\partial \mathcal{F}_j}{\partial y} \right] dx \, dy$$

The integral can be broken up into a sum of several terms, each integrated over individual FEs:

$$\mathrm{I}_{ij} = -T_i \iint_{\langle 1 \rangle} \left(\underline{\nabla} \mathcal{F}_i \cdot \underline{\nabla} \mathcal{F}_j \right) dx \, dy - T_i \iint_{\langle 2 \rangle} \left(\underline{\nabla} \mathcal{F}_i \cdot \underline{\nabla} \mathcal{F}_j \right) dx \, dy - ...$$

$$-T_i \iint_{\langle N_N \rangle} \underline{\nabla} \mathcal{F}_i \cdot \underline{\nabla} \mathcal{F}_j \, dx \, dy$$

Only those terms are non-zero where $\mathcal{F}_i$ and $\mathcal{F}_j$ (and so $\underline{\nabla} \mathcal{F}_i$ and $\underline{\nabla} \mathcal{F}_j$) overlap (as in the 1–D example 6.9). It is easy to see that terms like $T_4 \iint_{\langle 2 \rangle} \underline{\nabla} \mathcal{F}_4 \cdot \underline{\nabla} \mathcal{F}_6 \, dx \, dy$ in fig. 7.10, are zero. We define

$$\mathbb{B}_{ji}^{\langle k \rangle} \equiv -\iint_{\langle k \rangle} \underline{\nabla} \mathcal{F}_i \cdot \underline{\nabla} \mathcal{F}_j \, dx \, dy$$

with the evaluation of $\mathbb{B}$ (in terms of the coordinates of the vertices of the *k*th FE), discussed later. We write term I in eq. (*d*) for two values of *j* to illustrate the methodology used:

$$j = 1$$

$$\mathrm{I} = -T_1 \iint_{\mathcal{A}} (1, 1) - T_2 \iint_{\mathcal{A}} (2, 1) - T_4 \iint_{\mathcal{A}} (4, 1) - T_5 \iint_{\mathcal{A}} (5, 1)$$

$$= T_1 \left[\mathbb{B}_{1,1}^{\langle 1 \rangle} + \mathbb{B}_{1,1}^{\langle 4 \rangle} \right] + T_2 \left[\mathbb{B}_{1,2}^{\langle 4 \rangle} \right] + T_4 \left[\mathbb{B}_{1,4}^{\langle 1 \rangle} + \mathbb{B}_{1,4}^{\langle 4 \rangle} \right] + T_5 \left[\mathbb{B}_{1,5}^{\langle 1 \rangle} \right]$$

$j = 4$

$$I = -T_1 \iint_{\mathcal{A}} (1, 4) - T_2 \iint_{\mathcal{A}} (2, 4) - T_3 \iint_{\mathcal{A}} (3, 4) - T_4 \iint_{\mathcal{A}} (4, 4) - T_5 \iint_{\mathcal{A}} (5, 4) - T_6 \iint_{\mathcal{A}} (6, 4)$$

$$= T_1 \left[\mathbb{B}_{4,1}^{\langle 1 \rangle} + \mathbb{B}_{4,1}^{\langle 4 \rangle} \right] + T_2 \left[\mathbb{B}_{4,2}^{\langle 3 \rangle} + \mathbb{B}_{4,2}^{\langle 4 \rangle} \right] + T_3 \left[\mathbb{B}_{4,3}^{\langle 2 \rangle} + \mathbb{B}_{4,3}^{\langle 3 \rangle} \right]$$

$$+ T_4 \left[\mathbb{B}_{4,4}^{\langle 1 \rangle} + \mathbb{B}_{4,4}^{\langle 2 \rangle} + \mathbb{B}_{4,4}^{\langle 3 \rangle} + \mathbb{B}_{4,4}^{\langle 4 \rangle} \right] + T_5 \left[\mathbb{B}_{4,5}^{\langle 1 \rangle} + \mathbb{B}_{4,5}^{\langle 2 \rangle} \right] + T_6 [0]$$

The integrals used here are schematic representations of the more detailed forms used earlier. We consider term III in eq. (d) next. Since Q is nonzero only on the fourth element, we have

$$III = -1.5 \iint_{\langle 4 \rangle} \mathcal{F}_j \, dx \, dy = 0; \quad \text{for } j = 3, 5, 6$$

$$\equiv 1.5 \mathbb{D}_j^{\langle 4 \rangle}; \quad \text{for } j = 1, 2, 4$$

We again, postpone evaluation of the constants, $\mathbb{D}_j^{\langle 4 \rangle}$. Evaluation of this term for more complex cases is easy. The integral can be written in terms of a sum of integrals over such individual element, and nonzero contributions will come only when *both* Q and $\mathcal{F}_i$ are nonzero in an element.

We now turn our attention to the boundary conditions, and on term II in eq. (d). From the assumed solution for $T(x, y)$ in terms of the basis functions, it can be seen that the boundary condition, $T = 0$, on C_1 leads to $T_2 = T_3 = T_6 = 0$ (this may be substituted in the expressions for term I derived above, to further simplify them). This simplification gives three of the six unknowns ($T_1 - T_6$), and so we need only three more conditions. Thus, we need to make the residual in eq. (d) zero only for $j = 1, 4$ and 5. It is for these values of j that we simplify term II in eq. (d).

We first write term II in terms of a sum of three integrals over different parts of the closed curve C (counterclockwise)

$$II = \underbrace{\int_{C_1} \mathcal{F}_j \left(\hat{\mathbf{n}} \cdot \underline{\nabla} T \right) ds}_{a} + \underbrace{\int_{C_2} \mathcal{F}_j \left(\hat{\mathbf{n}} \cdot \underline{\nabla} T \right) ds}_{b} + \underbrace{\int_{C_3} \mathcal{F}_j \left(\hat{\mathbf{n}} \cdot \underline{\nabla} T \right) ds}_{c} ; \quad j = 1, 4, 5 \qquad \dots(e)$$

Term a in eq. (e) is zero for $j = 1$ since $\mathcal{F}_1 = 0$ on C_1. Similarly, $\mathcal{F}_4 = 0$ and $\mathcal{F}_5 = 0$ on lines 2–3 and 3–6 on which we integrate term a. Hence, this term does not contribute (note that it would have been non-zero if j was 2 or 3, but we do not need these conditions). In term b, eq. (e), $\hat{\mathbf{n}} \cdot \underline{\nabla} T$ on curve C_2 is $-\dfrac{\partial T}{\partial y}$ which is zero from the boundary condition. Hence, term b also drops out. In term c, $\hat{\mathbf{n}} \cdot \underline{\nabla} T$ is $-\dfrac{\partial T}{\partial x}$ on C_3 and we have

$$\int_{C_3} \mathcal{F}_j \left(\hat{\mathbf{n}} \cdot \underline{\nabla} T \right) ds = -\int_{C_3} \mathcal{F}_j \frac{\partial T}{\partial x} ds = 4 \int_{y=0}^{2} \mathcal{F}_j^{\langle 4 \rangle} dy \equiv 4 \mathbb{E}_{j, 1-2}^{\langle 4 \rangle}; \quad j = 1, 4, 5$$

Note that $\mathbb{E}_{4, 1-2}^{\langle 4 \rangle} = \mathbb{E}_{5, 1-2}^{\langle 4 \rangle} = 0$, since $\mathcal{F}_4$ and $\mathcal{F}_5$ are zero along C_3. The extension to cases where C_3 involves more *FE*s is easily written.

We summarize the various equations obtained above as

$$T_2 = T_3 = T_6 = 0$$

$$
\begin{bmatrix}
\mathbb{B}_{11}^{\langle 1 \rangle}+\mathbb{B}_{11}^{\langle 4 \rangle} & \mathbb{B}_{14}^{\langle 1 \rangle}+\mathbb{B}_{14}^{\langle 4 \rangle} & \mathbb{B}_{15}^{\langle 1 \rangle} \\
\mathbb{B}_{41}^{\langle 1 \rangle}+\mathbb{B}_{41}^{\langle 4 \rangle} & \mathbb{B}_{44}^{\langle 1 \rangle}+\mathbb{B}_{44}^{\langle 2 \rangle}+\mathbb{B}_{44}^{\langle 3 \rangle}+\mathbb{B}_{44}^{\langle 4 \rangle} & \mathbb{B}_{45}^{\langle 1 \rangle}+\mathbb{B}_{45}^{\langle 2 \rangle} \\
\mathbb{B}_{51}^{\langle 1 \rangle} & \mathbb{B}_{54}^{\langle 1 \rangle}+\mathbb{B}_{54}^{\langle 2 \rangle} & \mathbb{B}_{55}^{\langle 1 \rangle}+\mathbb{B}_{55}^{\langle 2 \rangle}+\mathbb{B}_{55}^{\langle 5 \rangle}
\end{bmatrix}
\begin{bmatrix}
T_1 \\ T_4 \\ T_5
\end{bmatrix}
= 33
\begin{bmatrix}
-4\mathbb{E}_{1,\,1-2}^{\langle 4 \rangle}+1.5\mathbb{D}_1^{\langle 4 \rangle} \\
1.5\mathbb{D}_4^{\langle 4 \rangle} \\
0
\end{bmatrix}
$$

Obtaining the final form of this equation may appear quite complicated, but with some practice, one can write down the equations without too much effort. Generalized methods of generating this equation are discussed in more advanced texts [15–17], and these are useful in writing computer codes. Our aim here is only to develop an elementary understanding of the technique, and so these details are omitted. ∎

We now give expressions for the terms $\mathbb{B}_{ji}^{\langle k \rangle}$, $\mathbb{D}_j^{\langle k \rangle}$ and $\mathbb{E}_{j,\,C_3}^{\langle k \rangle}$. These integrals arise in other problems too, and so the expressions given below are quite useful. These are being given for the FE shown in fig. 7.9(b):

$$\mathbb{B}_{l,\,m}^{\langle j \rangle} = -\frac{1}{4\mathcal{A}^{\langle j \rangle}}\left[\beta_l \beta_m + \gamma_l \gamma_m \right] \qquad \ldots(a)$$

$$\mathbb{D}_l^{\langle j \rangle} = \frac{\mathcal{A}^{\langle j \rangle}}{3} \qquad \ldots(b)$$

$$\mathbb{E}_{l,\,l-n}^{\langle j \rangle} = \frac{+\sqrt{\left(x_n - x_l\right)^2 + \left(y_n - y_l\right)^2}}{2}$$

$$\mathbb{E}_{l,\,l-m}^{\langle j \rangle} = \frac{+\sqrt{\left(x_m - x_l\right)^2 + \left(y_m - y_l\right)^2}}{2}$$

$$\mathbb{E}_{l,\,n-m}^{\langle j \rangle} = 0 \qquad \ldots(c) \qquad \ldots(7.18)$$

where $\mathcal{A}^{\langle j \rangle}$, β and γ are as defined in eq. 7.17. As an illustration, we have (with $l = 5$, $m = 3$, $n = 4$ in element $\langle 2 \rangle$ of example 7.9) from eq. 7.17 and 7.18

$$\beta_5 = y_3 - y_4 = 1; \quad \gamma_5 = x_4 - x_3 = -2$$

$$\mathbb{B}_{5,5}^{\langle 2 \rangle} = -\frac{1}{4\times\left(\dfrac{1}{2}\times 2 \times 2\right)}\left[\beta_5^2 + \gamma_5^2\right]$$

$$= -\frac{1}{8}(1+4) = -\frac{5}{8}$$

$$\mathbb{D}^{\langle 4 \rangle} = \frac{\mathcal{A}^{\langle 4 \rangle}}{3} = \frac{1}{3}\left[\frac{1}{2} \times 2 \times 2\right] = \frac{2}{3}$$

$$\mathbb{E}_{1,\,1-2}^{\langle 4 \rangle} = \frac{2}{2} = 1 \qquad\qquad\qquad ...(7.19)$$

The set of algebraic equations obtained using the GFE technique can be solved using methods discussed earlier in this chapter as well as in previous chapters.

The variational form for more general 2-dimensional PDEs is given in appendix 7A. Details on rectangular FEs as well as triangular FEs with more than three nodes per finite element and corresponding basis functions, $\mathcal{F}_i^{\langle j \rangle}(x, y)$, are available in advanced texts [15–17]. Note that we can use nonlinear basis functions if we have more nodes than three in the triangular FEs. Also, we may keep in mind that point sources (Q in the PDE of example 7.9 being described by a delta function) can easily be taken care of in the GFE technique (term III will be related to the value of $\mathcal{F}_j$ at the location of the point source).

Having discussed the GFE technique for integrating PDEs, we now present one example (without too many details), almost purely to illustrate how powerful this method really is. We present the finite element solution for 'fountain-flow' [20] which occurs near the advancing liquid-air interface while filling mold-cavities. Such studies are of considerable interest in injection molding operations. The flow pattern in a rectangular channel [see fig. 7.11a] can be made steady by using a moving frame of reference, *i.e.*, the channel walls ($y = \pm H$) are moving to the left with velocity, V_{av}, the average velocity with which liquid is pumped through the mold cavity as observed by a stationary observer. The Navier-Stokes and continuity equations [21, 22] simplify (under creeping-flow conditions) to

$$\frac{\partial V_x}{\partial x} + \frac{\partial V_y}{\partial y} = 0$$

$$0 = -\frac{\partial p}{\partial x} + \frac{\partial \tau_{xx}}{\partial x} + \frac{\partial \tau_{yx}}{\partial y}$$

$$0 = -\frac{\partial p}{\partial y} + \frac{\partial \tau_{xy}}{\partial x} + \frac{\partial \tau_{yy}}{\partial y}$$

on AD	:	$V_x = f(y)$	;	$V_y = 0$
on AB	:	$\tau_{xy} = 0$	;	$V_y = 0$
on DC	:	$V_x = -V_{av}$	;	$V_y = 0$
on BC	:	$\mathbf{V} \cdot \hat{\mathbf{n}} = \mathbf{0}$		...(7.20)

These equations are solved for a Newtonian fluid with

$$f(y) = -V_{av} + \frac{3V_{av}}{2}\left[1 - \left(\frac{y}{H}\right)^2\right] \qquad \text{(fully developed, pressure driven)}$$

$$\tau_{xx} = 2\eta\frac{\partial V_x}{\partial x}: \quad \tau_{yx} = \tau_{xy} = \eta\left[\frac{\partial V_y}{\partial x} + \frac{\partial V_x}{\partial y}\right]$$

$$\tau_{yy} = 2\eta \frac{\partial V_y}{\partial y} \qquad \qquad ...(7.21)$$

[the equations are also solved for power-law constitutive equations as well as for fluids following the Carreau model [20, 21], in rectangular as well as cylindrical cavities] [20]. The FE grid chosen is shown in fig. 7.11(*b*), and a computer code [23], MACVIP, is used. The concentration of the FEs near the free surface is to be observed.

An interesting complication arises in this problem. This is the determination of the location of the free surface (fortunately, the location of AD with respect to the free surface is unimportant, as long as it is taken beyond a distance of about 2H from the later). The location of the free surface is taken as an additional unknown. This location is assumed (through iteration), the Navier-Stokes and continuity equations are solved for V_x, V_y and p using all except one of the boundary conditions (namely **V**. $\hat{\mathbf{n}}$ = 0 at the free surface), and the residual in this boundary condition is used to modify the free surface location (see ref. 20 for more details—this is an adaptive grid FE technique).

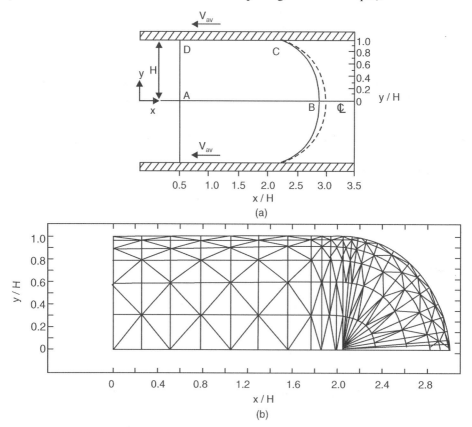

Fig. 7.11 (*a*) Schematic diagram for the flow domain in a channel of rectangular cross section, (*b*) the FE grid used [20] (298 elements, 647 nodes). The computed front for flow of Newtonian fluid is also shown in (*a*) and is found to differ from a semi circular shape. [Reprinted from ref. 20, copyright 1986, with permission from Society of Plastics Engineers Inc., Brookfield Center, CT 06804, USA]

Figure 7.12 shows the instantaneous velocity vectors with respect to a *stationary* observer (*i.e.*, the solution obtained is transformed by adding | V_{av} | **i**). The fluid particles near the center decelerate and are diverted outwards as they approach the *moving* free surface, and eventually reach the channel walls. The shape of the free surface differs slightly from a semicircle as shown in fig. 7.11(*b*) (see ref. 20 for detailed results on this as well as for flow of non-Newtonian fluids). These workers have also extended [24] this study to find how *an* element of liquid moves and distorts (an element moves forward and outward towards the free surface, then slowly makes a half turn as it goes outwards towards the wall. Still later, it forms a "*V*" shape near the wall before finally becoming parallel to the wall—consistent with experimental observations of Schmidt [25]).

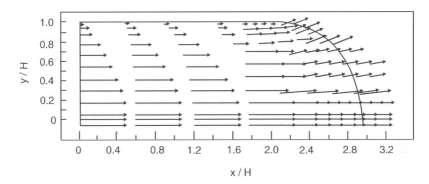

Fig. 7.12 Velocity vectors as observed by a stationary observer for one set of conditions [20]. Length of vector at $x/H = 0$, $y/H = 0$, represents $1.5\, V_{av}$. [Reprinted from ref. 20, copyright 1986, with permission from Society of Plastics Engineers Inc., Brookfield Center, CT 06804, USA]

The current literature abounds in examples of the use of the GFE technique and its various adaptations, to solve complicated, real-life problems. Table 7.1 lists *a few* more examples which one can read at this level (these, obviously, reflect the authors' personal preferences or prejudices!). Computer codes using this technique have also become available in the recent years. For example, the ELLPACK library [27] (see end of sec. 7.2) has some programs for integrating elliptic PDEs using the GFE technique but is limited to rectangular domains. IMSL distributes a program, 2DEPEP which uses the Crank-Nicholson technique and the GFE method to integrate parabolic PDEs in two space dimensions. It uses quadratic basis functions and triangular FEs [28]. This code can also be used to integrate elliptic PDEs. Another code available is DISPL [29], which uses cubic basis functions with the GFE technique, and can solve parabolic (in two space dimensions) or elliptic PDEs on rectangular domains. Davis [7] has presented results obtained from DISPL on two problems. Listings and descriptions of GFE programs are also available in texts. For example, Reddy [15] presents details of two programs, FEM1D (for an ODE-BVP) and FEM2D for parabolic PDEs involving two space dimensions, *i.e.*, with an extra $\dfrac{\partial u}{\partial t}$ term added in eq. A7.5). Computer codes using the GFE technique for specialized applications are also available, as for example, for structural-analysis problems [30], fluid-mechanics [31], design and analysis of cured-rubber parts [32], etc.

We close our discussion of the GFE technique by a mention of the more general Galerkin-Petrov method. In this, the function, v, to which the residual is made orthogonal are not the basis functions [see eq. (*b*) of example 7.9], but are from *another* set of linearly independent functions (thus, this is a more general weighted-residual method). This could, at times, give more accurate results (see p. 49 in Ref. 15 for an example) than the Galerkin technique.

Table 7.1 A Few examples where the GFE Technique has been Used

Reference	Problem Description
Finlayson [3] (Chapter 6)	Die-swell of a Newtonian fluid flowing through a channel or pipe.
Finlayson [3] (Chapter 6)	Heat conduction in a long 'box' in which a heated cylinder maintained at constant temperature, is embedded.
Reddy [15] (Chapter 4)	Groundwater flow in a homogeneous aquifer with two pumps (point sinks) and a river (line source) passing through.
Reddy [15] (Chapter 4)	Potential flow of a fluid around a rigid, stationary cylinder confined (symmetrically) between two flat plates.
Coyle et al. [26]	High conversion radical polymerization (in the presence of the gel effect), with time and chain-length of polymer as the independent variables (the chain length is treated as a continuous variable). Nonlinear ODEs are obtained (see prob. 7.35), which are solved using the backward Euler technique, followed by Newton-Raphson iteration.
Sereno et al. [14]	Unsteady TRAM (see probs. 7.4, 7.24) with first order irreversible reaction. Linear ODEs are obtained (see prob. 7.35). Moving FE technique is used since there is a relatively sharp front which is moving forward with time. Also, in some FEs, nonlinear basis functions are used having extra internal nodes.

7.6 CONCLUSIONS

As in chapter 6, it is found that the finite difference and OC techniques are quite easy to use in the solution of PDEs. However, when sharp gradients are present the computational effort required becomes prohibitive. It is here that finite element techniques (OCFE, GFE) prove useful. An adaptive-mesh strategy similar to that discussed in Chapter 6, can be used to change the FE locations and sizes so that more FEs are placed in regions where sharp gradients exist. This is also the basis of moving finite element techniques, where the region of sharp gradients moves with time, and the finite element locations also do so. These FE packages with FE placement and adaptation codes are usually coupled with excellent computer graphics codes in CAD or CAE (computer aided design or engineering) packages for special applications, which are quite popular these days.

APPENDIX 7 A 15

Variational Forms of PDEs

We consider the following general PDE in two dimensions:

$$\frac{\partial F}{\partial u} - \frac{\partial}{\partial x}\left(\frac{\partial F}{\partial u_x}\right) - \frac{\partial}{\partial y}\left(\frac{\partial F}{\partial u_y}\right) = 0 \quad \text{in } \mathcal{A} \qquad \ldots(A7.1)$$

where $u_x \equiv \dfrac{\partial u}{\partial x}$, $u_y \equiv \dfrac{\partial u}{\partial y}$ and $F = F(x, y, u, u_x, u_y)$. We would like to satisfy

$$\iint_{\mathcal{A}} v\left[\frac{\partial F}{\partial u} - \frac{\partial}{\partial x}\left(\frac{\partial F}{\partial u_x}\right) - \frac{\partial}{\partial y}\left(\frac{\partial F}{\partial u_y}\right)\right] dx\, dy = 0 \qquad \ldots(A7.2)$$

where v is a test function. We transfer the partial differentiation with respect to x and y to the test function, v, so that the resulting expression contains only derivatives of first order in u and v. Using the gradient and divergence theorems [1], we can obtain [15]

$$\iint_{\mathcal{A}} \left[\frac{v\partial F}{\partial u} + \frac{\partial v}{\partial x}\frac{\partial F}{\partial u_x} + \frac{\partial v}{\partial y}\frac{\partial F}{\partial u_y}\right] dx\, dy - \oint_C v\left(\frac{\partial F}{\partial u_x}n_x + \frac{\partial F}{\partial u_y}n_y\right) ds \qquad \ldots(A7.3)$$

where n_x, n_y are the direction cosines of the outward normal, $\vec{\mathbf{n}}$, at any location of the boundary, C, and ds is the length of an infinitesimal segment of the boundary. This is the variational form of eq. A7.1. If we take

$$F = \frac{1}{2}\left[k_1\left(\frac{\partial u}{\partial x}\right)^2 + k_2\left(\frac{\partial u}{\partial y}\right)^2\right] + fu \qquad \ldots(A7.4)$$

then the PDE (eq. 7.1) becomes

$$-\frac{\partial}{\partial x}\left(k_1\frac{\partial u}{\partial x}\right) - \frac{\partial}{\partial y}\left(k_2\frac{\partial u}{\partial y}\right) + f = 0 \qquad \ldots(A7.5)$$

Equation A7.3 then becomes

$$\iint_{\mathcal{A}} \left[vf - k_1\frac{\partial v}{\partial x}\frac{\partial u}{\partial x} - k_2\frac{\partial v}{\partial y}\frac{\partial u}{\partial y}\right] dx\, dy - \oint_C v\left[k_1\frac{\partial u}{\partial x}n_x + k_2\frac{\partial u}{\partial y}n_y\right] ds \qquad \ldots(A7.6)$$

Equation A7.6 is the variational form of the PDE in eq. A7.5.

PROBLEMS

7.1 Use the FD technique on the *dimensionless* diffusion equation $\dfrac{\partial c}{\partial t} = \dfrac{\partial^2 c}{\partial x^2}$; $c(0, t) = c(1, t) = 0$;

$c(x, 0) = 1$, to obtain a set of ODE-IVPs. Compare your equations with those given in prob. 5.23. Problem 5.23 computes the maximum value of Δt to be used for integrating the ODEs if the

Nystrom form of the explicit Runge-Kutta technique is used. Note how we can eliminate the algebraic equations and get a set of ODE-IVPs alone, which can be used in a GEAR program.

7.2 Obtain numerical concentration profiles for the unsteady (dimensionless) diffusion problem described in prob. 7.1. Use a GEAR package to integrate your equations. Evaluate the average (over x) value of c as a function of t.

7.3 A packed-bed nonisothermal reactor with radial dispersion can be described by the following set of dimensionless equations [3, 33, 34]:

$$\frac{\partial c}{\partial z} = \alpha \frac{1}{r} \frac{\partial}{\partial r}\left(r \frac{\partial c}{\partial r} \right) + \beta \mathcal{R}(c, T)$$

$$\frac{\partial T}{\partial z} = \alpha' \frac{1}{r} \frac{\partial}{\partial r}\left(r \frac{\partial T}{\partial r} \right) + \beta' \mathcal{R}(c, T)$$

$$r = 0 \quad : \quad \frac{\partial c}{\partial r} = 0 ; \quad \frac{\partial T}{\partial r} = 0$$

$$r = 1 \quad : \quad \frac{\partial c}{\partial r} = 0$$

$$\frac{\partial T}{\partial r} = -Bi\left(T - T_J \right)$$

$$z = 0 \quad : \quad c = 0 ; \quad T = 1$$

where the dimensionless groups are defined in ref. 3. The rate of reaction term for an irreversible nth order reaction is $\mathcal{R}(c, T) = (1 - c)^n \exp\left[\gamma - \dfrac{\gamma}{T} \right]$.

Apply the FD technique with grid lines at $r = r_i$; $i = 1, 2, ..., N + 1$ [$r_1 = 0$; $r_{N+1} = 1$] and solve the equations *numerically* using a GEAR program, for $\alpha = 1$, $\alpha' = 1$, $\beta = 0.3$, $\beta' = 0.2$, $\gamma = 20$, $Bi = 1$, $T_j = 0.92$, $n = 1$. These values lead to severe hot-spots in the reactor. Finlayson [34] gives results with $N = 6$ and $\Delta z = 0.002$ (using a Crank-Nicholson scheme).

7.4 The unsteady isothermal TRAM equation with an irreversible first order reaction taking place (eq. 7.3) can be non dimensionalized to

$$\frac{\partial c}{\partial t} = \frac{1}{Pe} \frac{\partial^2 c}{\partial z^2} - \frac{\partial c}{\partial z} - (Da)c$$

$$z = 0 \quad : \quad \frac{\partial c}{\partial z} = Pe(c - 1)$$

$$z = 1 \quad : \quad \frac{\partial c}{\partial z} = 0$$

$$t = 0 \quad : \quad c = 0$$

where c, z and t are *now* nondimensionalized variables [$\dfrac{c}{c_0}$, $\dfrac{z}{L}$ and $\dfrac{t}{\left(\dfrac{L}{v}\right)}$ in terms of actual

variables]. Use the $N + 1$ grid-line FD technique to obtain a set of ODE-IVPs. Attempt to solve these using a GEAR package with $Pe = 10^4$, $Da = 1$, $N = 10$ and 100. Very sharp changes in the c profile will be observed [14], and you may have to use very large values of N to get good results [moving finite-element techniques [10–12, 14] are better suited to handle such problems].

7.5 Complete eq. (*b*) in example 7.3 using the given boundary conditions for T. Use $N_x = N_y = 3$, and simplify to obtain only four equations corresponding to the internal grid points.

7.6 *Line Jacobi Method* [3, 4]: Assuming values for $T_{i,\,j-1}^{k+1,s=1}$ and $T_{i,\,j+1}^{k+1,\,s=1}$, etc., develop the algorithm for solving the set of $N_x - 1$ equations in eq. 7.9 using the Jacobi technique. Thus, develop the following flow-chart:

Know all $T_{i,\,j}^{k}$; $i = 2, 3, ..., N_x$; $j = 2, 3, ..., N_y$

Assume all $T_{i,\,j}^{k+1,\,*}$; $i = 2, 3, ..., N_x$; $j = 2, 3, ..., N_y$

> Do $\quad j = 2, 3, ..., N_y$
>
> > Assume $T_{i,\,j}^{k+1,\,s=1} = T_{i,\,j}^{k+1,\,*}$; $i = 2, 3, ..., N_x$
>
> > Do $\quad s = 1, 2, 3, ...,$ till convergence
> >
> > > Do $\quad i = 2, ..., N_x$
> > >
> > > > $T_{i,\,j}^{k+1,\,s+1} = \dfrac{1}{1+2\beta}\left[\dfrac{\beta}{2}\left(T_{i,\,j-1}^{k+1,\,*} + T_{i,\,j+1}^{k+1,\,*}\right) + f_{ij}\left(\mathbf{T}^k\right) + \dfrac{\beta}{2}\left(T_{i-1,\,j}^{k+1,\,s} + T_{i+1,\,j}^{k+1,\,s}\right)\right]$

After this *full set* of computations, we update the values of all the $T_{i,\,j}^{k+1,\,*}$, using the results obtained, and repeat this set of computations.

The line Gauss-Seidel technique is also easily written, and converges (usually) even faster. In this technique, *updated* values of $T_{i,\,j-1}^{k+1}$ and $T_{i-1,\,j}^{k+1}$ are to be used.

7.7 Consider example 7.3 for the 2–D steady state case, *i.e.*, for

$$\frac{\partial^2 T}{\partial x^2} + \frac{\partial^2 T}{\partial y^2} = 0$$

$$x = 0 \;:\; T = T_1 \;;\quad x = L_x \;:\; T = T_3$$

$$y = 0 \;:\; T = T_2 \;;\quad y = L_y \;:\; T = T_4$$

Obtain the set of algebraic equations to be solved and write the algorithm for solving these using
(*a*) the line Gauss-Seidel technique
(*b*) the ADI method

7.8 Use the Crank-Nicholson scheme to obtain algebraic equations for the FD equations in example 7.1 (for a single species). Then write the algorithm involving a line Gauss-Seidel technique to solve these equations. You may consider only the equations for the internal grid points.

7.9 *Alternating Direction Explicit Scheme* [3]: Consider the following scheme to convert eq. (*a*), example 7.3, to a set of algebraic equations:

$$T_{i,j}^{k+1} = T_{i,j}^{k} + \frac{\alpha(\Delta t)}{(\Delta x)^2}\left[T_{i+1,j}^{k} - 2T_{i,j}^{k+1} + T_{i-1,j}^{k+1}\right] + \frac{\alpha(\Delta t)}{(\Delta y)^2}\left[T_{i,j+1}^{k+1} - 2T_{i,j}^{k} + T_{i,j-1}^{k}\right]$$

Show that (with all $T_{i,j}^{k}$ known, and with boundary values also specified) if we solve the above equations in the sequence: increasing i; decreasing j

$$\left(i.e., \quad\begin{array}{l} \text{Do} \quad i = 2, 3, ..., N_x \\ \quad \text{Do} \quad j = N_y, N_y - 1, ..., 2 \\ \quad\quad T_{i,j}^{k+1} = \cdots \end{array}\right)$$

we get an explicit set of computations. Confirm the explicit nature of the computations using a grid with $N_x = N_y = 6$.

7.10 Consider the PDE

$$\frac{\partial^2 T}{\partial x^2} + \frac{\partial^2 T}{\partial y^2} = f(x, y)$$

Use the FD technique *with unevenly-spaced grid points* and obtain an algebraic equation for $T_{i,j}$ [see prob. 6.3(*a*)]. This technique can also be used for treating Dirichlet boundary conditions (*T* specified) with irregular boundaries.

7.11 Obtain the FD form of the 1–D wave equation (hyperbolic PDE):

$$\frac{\partial^2 T}{\partial t^2} = \frac{\partial^2 T}{\partial x^2} ; \quad 0 \le x \le 1$$

$$T(x, 0) = \sin(\pi x)$$

$$\frac{\partial T}{\partial t}(x, 0) = 0$$

$$T(0, t) = 0$$

$$T(1, t) = 0$$

Use the explicit formulae for both t and x. Obtain numerical results using $\Delta x = \frac{1}{4}$, $\Delta t = \frac{3}{16}$ and obtain results till $t = \frac{15}{16}$. Compare your results with the analytical solution:

$$T(x, t) = \sin(\pi x)\cos(\pi t)$$

Jain et. al. [4] discuss the use of implicit and ADI schemes for solving this equation, as well as the 2–D wave equation.

7.12 Use the explicit Euler formula on eq. (*a*), example 7.3. to obtain a set of algebraic equations.

7.13 For the first-order PDE

$$\frac{\partial T}{\partial t} + \frac{\partial T}{\partial x} = 0 \quad ; \quad 0 \le x \le \infty$$

$$T(0, x) = f(x) \; ; \quad T(t, 0) = g(t)$$

deduce (using the implicit Euler technique in the x direction, and a first order formula for $\dfrac{\partial T}{\partial t}$)

$$T_i^{k+1} = \frac{1}{1+r}\left[T_i^k + rT_{i-1}^{k+1}\right]$$

Show that this can be solved such that no trial and error is required. Similarly, deduce the *leap-frog* scheme:

$$T_i^{k+1} = T_i^{k-1} - r\left(T_{i+1}^k - T_{i-1}^k\right)$$

This is stable for $0 < r \le 1$ and is of order $(\Delta t)^2$ and $(\Delta x)^2$. $r \equiv \Delta t/\Delta x$.

7.14 Ravetkar [35] derived the following partial differential equation (in spherical coordinates) to describe the diffusion of ligands to active patches on a single, spherical, enzyme molecule:

$$\frac{\partial \psi}{\partial t} = r^4 \frac{\partial^2 \psi}{\partial r^2} + r^2 \cot\theta \frac{\partial \psi}{\partial \theta} + r^2 \frac{\partial^2 \psi}{\partial \theta^2} + \frac{r^2}{\sin^2\theta}\frac{\partial^2 \psi}{\partial \phi^2}$$

$$0 \le r \le 1, \; 0 \le \theta \le \pi, \; 0 \le \phi \le 2\pi$$

$$\text{I.C:} \quad \psi(r \le 1, \theta, \phi, t=0) = 1$$

$$\text{B.C.:} \quad \psi(r=1, 0 \le \theta \le \theta_0, \phi, t) = 0$$

$$\frac{\partial \psi}{\partial r}(r=1, \theta > \theta_0, \phi, t) = 0$$

$$\psi(r=0, \theta, \phi, t) = 1$$

(Note that r is the dimensionless reciprocal of the radial position from the center of the sphere, so that $r = 1$ is at the sphere and $r = 0$ is far away). Use the finite difference scheme and develop a set of algebraic equations to be solved. Use an implicit scheme for the $\dfrac{\partial^2 \psi}{\partial r^2}$ term, and an explicit scheme for the other terms (with respect to t). Also, study the boundary conditions, as well as any special problems that may arise at $r = 0$ and $r = 1$. Note also that we do not have 'boundary' conditions for θ and ϕ in this problem, but these are not required.

7.15 The convective diffusion equation for an isothermal, first-order reaction occurring in a laminar flow reactor is described by (p. 180 in Ref. 36)

$$2(1-r^2)\frac{\partial c}{\partial z} = \left(\frac{D\bar{t}}{R^2}\right)\left(\frac{1}{r}\frac{\partial c}{\partial r} + \frac{\partial^2 c}{\partial r^2}\right) - (k\bar{t})c$$

$$c(r, 0) = c_{in}$$

$$\frac{\partial c}{\partial r} = 0 \text{ at } r = 0 \text{ and at } r = 1$$

Obtain *FD* results for $(k\bar{t}) = 1$ and $\dfrac{D\bar{t}}{R^2} = 0.1$

7.16 The 1–D flow a fluid between two flat plates spaced a distance, h, apart, with one plate at rest, and the other starting to move impulsively at $t = 0$, with velocity u_0, is described by (p. 83 in Ref. 37)

$$\frac{\partial u}{\partial t} = \left(\frac{\nu}{h^2}\right)\frac{\partial^2 u}{\partial x^2}$$

$$u(x, 0) = 0$$

$$u(0, t) = 1$$

$$u(1, t) = 0$$

where u is the dimensionless velocity, and x is the dimensionless position. Set up the FD equations and solve for $\dfrac{\nu}{h^2} = 5$ (also see prob. 7.1).

7.17 The unsteady 1–D heat transfer in an infinite slab (see prob. 6.12) of thickness L, with thermal conductivity being a linear function of temperature, is described by the following dimensionless equation:

$$\frac{\partial T}{\partial t} = (1 + aT)\frac{\partial^2 T}{\partial x^2} + a\left(\frac{\partial T}{\partial x}\right)^2$$

$$T(x, 0) = 0$$

$$T(0, t) = 1$$

$$T(1, t) = 0$$

where the non-dimensionalization is slightly different than in prob. 6.12. Apply the FD technique and obtain a set of ODE-IVPs to be solved.

7.18 The unsteady reaction-diffusion in a spherical catalyst particle is described by [3, 38]

$$M_2 \frac{\partial c}{\partial t} = \frac{1}{x^2}\frac{\partial}{\partial x}\left[x^2\left(\frac{\partial c}{\partial x}\right)\right] - \phi^2 \mathcal{R}(c, T)$$

$$M_1 \frac{\partial T}{\partial t} = \frac{1}{x^2}\frac{\partial}{\partial x}\left[x^2\left(\frac{\partial T}{\partial x}\right)\right] + \phi^2 \beta \mathcal{R}(c, T)$$

$$x = 0 \quad : \quad \frac{\partial c}{\partial x} = \frac{\partial T}{\partial x} = 0$$

$$x = 1 \quad : \quad -\frac{\partial c}{\partial x} = Bi_m\left[c(1, t) - g_2(t)\right]$$

$$-\frac{\partial T}{\partial x} = Bi\left[T(1, t) - g_1(t)\right]$$

$$t = 0 \quad : \quad c(x, 0) = c_0(x)$$

$$T(x, 0) = T_0(x)$$

Set up the ODEs to be integrated using the OC method. ref. 38 gives the results obtained using

a Gear integration package, for $\mathcal{R} = c\exp\left[\gamma - \dfrac{\gamma}{T}\right]$, $\gamma = 20$, $\beta = 0.6$, $\phi^2 = 0.25$, $M_1 = 176$, $M_2 = 199$,

$Bi = Bi_m = \infty$, $T_0 = 1.05$, $c_0 = 1.0$, $T(1, t) = g_1(t) = 1.0$, $c(1, t) = g_2(t) = 1.0$

7.19 The desorption of a gas from a liquid stream in a wetted-wall column can be described by [7] the following PDE:

$$\left(1 - \eta^2\right)\frac{\partial f}{\partial \zeta} = \frac{\partial^2 f}{\partial \eta^2}$$

$$\frac{\partial f}{\partial \eta} = 0 \quad \text{at} \quad \eta = 1$$

$$f = 0 \quad \text{at} \quad \eta = 0$$

$$f = 1 \quad \text{at} \quad \zeta = 0$$

Note that the problem, *as defined above*, is NOT symmetric about $\eta = 0$ (do NOT redefine variables to make them symmetric).

Carry out an orthogonal collocation solution *in the η direction*, using $N = 2$ (*i.e.*, two internal OC points), and simplify to obtain a set of *two* ODE-IVPs. Do not solve these.

7.20 An axially dispersed isothermal chemical reactor can be described by the following dimensionless equations:

$$\frac{\partial f}{\partial z} - \frac{1}{Pe_a}\frac{\partial^2 f}{\partial z^2} = \frac{1}{Pe_r}\left[\frac{1}{r}\frac{\partial}{\partial r}\left(r\frac{\partial f}{\partial r}\right)\right] + (Da)f$$

$$1 - f = \frac{1}{Pe_a}\frac{\partial f}{\partial z} \quad \text{at } z = 0$$

$$\frac{\partial f}{\partial z} = 0 \quad \text{at} \quad z = 1$$

$$\frac{\partial f}{\partial r} = 0 \quad \text{at} \quad r = 0 \ \left(\text{symmetry}\right)$$

$$\frac{\partial f}{\partial r} = 0 \quad \text{at} \quad r = 1 \ \left(\text{no flux}\right)$$

Note symmetry in the r-direction, and lack of symmetry in the z-direction. Use 1 (internal) collocation point in the r-direction and 2 internal collocation points in the z-direction, and set up *all* the algebraic equations necessary to solve the problem. Define $F_{I, J} = f(r_I, z_J)$. Use actual numbers for the matrix elements. Collect all your equations into a neat matrix form: $(\mathbf{AA})_{8 \times 8}\mathbf{F}_{8 \times 1} = \mathbf{B}_{8 \times 1}$ with $\mathbf{F}^T = [F_{11}, F_{12}, F_{13}, F_{14}, F_{21}, F_{22}, F_{23}, F_{24}]$, so that one could use LU Decomp easily. Do not solve your final set of algebraic (matrix) equations.

7.21 The *dimensionless* equation describing steady-state heat transfer to a fluid under fully developed laminar flow inside a cylindrical pipe (with walls heated electrically) is given by (pp. 295–296 in Ref. 21; also see example 4.10):

$$\nabla_r^2\theta \equiv \frac{\partial^2\theta}{\partial r^2}+\frac{1}{r}\frac{\partial\theta}{\partial r}=\left(1-r^2\right)\frac{\partial\theta}{\partial z}$$

$$z=0,\qquad \theta=0$$

$$r=1,\qquad \frac{\partial\theta}{\partial r}=-1$$

$$r=0,\qquad \frac{\partial\theta}{\partial r}=0$$

Note the symmetry in the r-direction.

(a) Apply orthogonal collocation with *one internal* collocation point and *solve* to get $\theta(z)$ at the collocation points. *Solve* the ODE obtained *analytically*.

(b) Compare your numerical values from your OC result with the following solution given in p. 296 in Ref. 21:

$$\theta=-4z-r^2+\frac{r^4}{4}+\frac{7}{24}$$

at appropriate values of r and for $z=0.5$.

(c) For the physical situation described here, the dimensionless bulk temperature is given by

$$\theta_b \equiv \frac{\int_{r=0}^{1}\theta\left(1-r^2\right)r\,dr}{\int_0^1\left(1-r^2\right)r\,dr}=4\int_{r=0}^{1}\theta\left(1-r^2\right)r\,dr$$

Obtain a general equation to get $\theta_b(z)$ using $\theta_1(z)$ and $\theta_2(z)$ of part a.

7.22 Consider

$$\frac{\partial^2 T}{\partial x^2}=\frac{\partial^2 T}{\partial y^2}$$

with BCs:

$$x=0\ ;\quad T=f_0(y)$$
$$x=1\ ;\quad T=f_1(y)$$
$$y=1\ ;\quad T=g_0(x)$$
$$y=0\ ;\quad \frac{\partial T}{\partial y}=0$$

Apply OC exploiting symmetry in the y direction about $y=0$. Use one *internal* collocation point in the y direction, and one *internal* collocation point in the x direction. *Set up* the 2–D OC algebraic equations. Substitute the values of the matrix elements as appropriate. Solve to get the *numerical* value of the T at the collocation points if

$$f_0(y) = 0.1y \qquad\qquad g_0(x) = 0.1 + 0.1x$$

$$f_1(y) = 0.2y$$

7.23 Consider the following PDE [3] (see probs. 7.17):

$$\frac{\partial c}{\partial t} = \frac{\partial}{\partial x}\left[(1 + \alpha c)\frac{\partial c}{\partial x}\right] = (1 + \alpha c)\frac{\partial^2 c}{\partial x^2} + \alpha\left(\frac{\partial c}{\partial x}\right)^2$$

$$c(0, t) = 1$$

$$c(x, 0) = 0$$

$$\frac{\partial c}{\partial x} = 0 \quad \text{at} \quad x = 1$$

Using two internal grid points, obtain the ODEs using the OC technique. Do *not* solve the ODEs on the computer.

(**Hint:** Redefine the x-axis so that symmetry at $x_{new} = 0$ is attained)

7.24 Obtain the ODE-IVPs with two internal OC points (in the z-direction) in the case of the unsteady, isothermal TRAM (prob. 7.4). The profile is so sharp that integration of these ODEs will give poor results; however, these equations will prove handy when we apply the OCFE technique.

7.25 Formulate prob. 7.3 (packed bed reactor with radial dispersion) using the OC technique. Deduce the one internal collocation point equations by hand. Solve for the parameter values given in prob. 7.3. Finlayson [3, 34] gives numerical solutions of the ODEs so obtained. He finds that the $N = 2$ results are almost indistinguishable from higher-N results. However, when parameter values are such that sharp profiles are present, we need to use $N = 6$. Interestingly, the stiffness of the ODEs is found to increase as N increases.

7.26 Gupta et al. [39] present the equations characterizing the third-stage wiped-film reactor used for polyester production. In this there is a 'bulk' phase which moves downstream from the feed-end to the product end (ζ direction). In between, rotating blades take up the reaction mass, coat it in a thin layer (reaction and diffusion take place), collect the material and mix it back into the bulk phase. The equations can be summarized as (see ref. 39 for details of model):

Bulk-Phase

$$\frac{-dc_{w,b}}{d\zeta} + a_1\left[c_b^2 - \frac{c_{w,b}(1 - c_b)}{K}\right] - a_2 N_w = 0$$

$$\frac{-dc_b}{d\zeta} + a_1\left[-c_b^2 + \frac{c_{w,b}(1 - c_b)}{K}\right] = 0$$

$$\zeta = 0 \quad : \quad c_b = \frac{1}{\mu_{n0}}$$

$$c_{w,b} = \frac{K}{\mu_{n0}(\mu_{n0} - 1)}$$

Film

$$\frac{\partial c_{w,f}}{\partial \tau} = a_3 \frac{\partial^2 c_{w,f}}{\partial \xi^2} + a_4 \left[c_f^2 - \frac{c_{w,f}\left(1-c_f\right)}{K} \right]$$

$$\frac{\partial c_f}{\partial \tau} = a_4 \left[-c_f^2 + \frac{c_{w,f}\left(1-c_f\right)}{K} \right]; \quad \begin{array}{c} 0 \le \xi \le 1 \\ 0 \le \tau \le 1 \end{array}$$

$$\tau = 0 \;;\; c_{w,f} = c_{w,b}\left(\zeta\right)$$

$$c_f = c_{f,b}\left(\zeta\right)$$

$$\xi = 0 \;;\; \frac{\partial c_{w,f}}{\partial \xi} = 0 \text{ for all } \tau$$

$$\xi = 1 \;;\; c_{w,f} = 0$$

Interconnection between bulk and film

$$N_w = \int_{\xi=0}^{1} \left[\left(c_{\omega,b} - c_b\right)_\zeta - \left(c_{w,f} - c_f\right)_{\tau=1} \right] d\xi$$

Write the OC equations for the wiped-film and obtain a set of ODE-IVPs to be solved. Attempt to make a computer code (or read up ref. 39) which solves the bulk-phase equations for a small distance, $\Delta\zeta$, then solves the film phase equations (using the computed bulk phase values) from $\tau = 0$ to $\tau = 1$, computes N_w and uses this in the next stage of the bulk-phase computations. Use

$$\mu_{n0} = 50 \qquad K = 0.5 \qquad a_1 = 2000 \qquad a_2 = 1000$$

$$a_3 = 10^{-4} \qquad a_4 = 2$$

7.27 You can write the OC expression of $\left.\dfrac{\partial^2 T}{\partial x^2}\right|_j$ in two ways:

$$\left.\frac{\partial^2 T}{\partial x^2}\right|_j = \sum_{k=1}^{N+2} B_{jk} T_k$$

or

$$\left.\frac{\partial^2 T}{\partial x^2}\right|_j = \left.\frac{\partial}{\partial x}\left(\frac{\partial T}{\partial x}\right)\right|_j = \sum_{i=1}^{N+2} A_{ji}\left(\frac{\partial T}{\partial x}\right)_i = \sum_{i=1}^{N+2} A_{ji} \sum_{k=1}^{N+2} A_{ik} T_k$$

Confirm for $N = 2$ (non symmetrical case) if

$$B_{jk} = \sum_{i=1}^{N+2} A_{ji} A_{ik}$$

Use this to simplify the PDE (see prob. 7.23)

$$\frac{\partial c}{\partial t} = \frac{\partial}{\partial x}\left[D(c)\frac{\partial c}{\partial x}\right]$$

$$c(0, t) = 1; \quad c(1, t) = 0; \quad c(x, 0) = 0.$$

Use $N = 1$

7.28 Deduce eq. (a) of example 7.6. Hint: Assume

$$T(x, y) = \sum_{k=1}^{N_x+2} \sum_{l=1}^{N_y+2} d_k d_l^* x^{k-1} y^{l-1}$$

with d_k and d_l^* as constants. Write matrix equations for the subsets, $\begin{bmatrix} T_{1,j} & T_{2,j} & \cdots & T_{N_x+2,j} \end{bmatrix}^T$ and $\begin{bmatrix} T_{i,1} & T_{i,2} & \cdots & T_{i,N_y+2} \end{bmatrix}^T$ separately in terms of $\mathbf{d}$ and $\mathbf{d}^*$ respectively.

7.29 Deduce eq. 7.15, and then write the expression for $\overline{T}$ for the problem discussed in example 7.6, with $N_x = 1$, $N_y = 2$.

7.30 Reduce the PDE of example 7.3 into a set of ODE-IVPs, using the 2-dimensional OC technique. In this case, the coefficients, d_k and d_l^* in prob. 7.28, become functions of time.

7.31 Write the OCFE (2FEs, 2 internal OC points in each) equation for the PDE in prob. 7.19. Solve using a DDASSL package if available; else use the Crank-Nicholson scheme.

7.32 Obtain the OCFE equations (2FEs, 2 internal OC points in each) for the system of equations given in prob. 7.18 (unsteady reaction-diffusion in a porous catalyst sphere [3, 38]).

7.33 One explicit technique [3] of solving the DAEs obtained on applying the OCFE method to PDEs is described here for eq. (a) of example 7.7. We first take only the ODEs, using values at $z = z_n$ on the right and use any explicit scheme to obtain values of T at OC points 2, 3, 5 and 6 at $z = z_n + \Delta z$. We then write the algebraic equations and express T_1^{n+1}, T_4^{n+1} and T_7^{n+1} in terms of all other variables at $n + 1$: $(T_2^{n+1}, T_3^{n+1}, T_5^{n+1}, T_6^{n+1})$. These algebraic equations can be solved using Thomas' algorithm (called smoothing). Illustrate this for eq. (a) of example 7.7 for T only (you can solve these equations only after performing a similar decoupling of the equations for c_i).

7.34 Apply the OCFE techniques (N_s FEs, 2 internal OC points in each FE) to the PDE in prob. 7.4 (unsteady, isothermal TRAM), in the z-direction.

7.35 Consider the isothermal TRAM with an irreversible second order reaction taking place, operating under unsteady conditions. The PDE is given by (for $Pe = 6$, $Da = 2$)

$$\frac{\partial c}{\partial t} = \frac{1}{6}\frac{\partial^2 c}{\partial z^2} - \frac{\partial c}{\partial z} - 2c^2$$

$$z = 0 \quad : \quad \frac{\partial c}{\partial z} = 6(c - 1)$$

$$z = 1 \quad : \quad \frac{\partial c}{\partial z} = 0$$

$$t = 0 \quad : \quad c = 0$$

(see prob. 7.4 and example 6.9). Use the GFE technique and obtain a set of ODE-IVPs for a general N. Use the 'triangular' basis-functions [Hint: the results of example 6.9 can easily be extended].

7.36 Derive eq. 7.18(c).

7.37 Set up and solve the GFE equations for the heat conduction problem [3]

$$\frac{\partial^2 T}{\partial x^2} + \frac{\partial^2 T}{\partial y^2} = -1$$

$T = 0$ all around C.

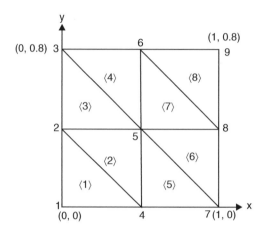

Fig. P7.37

Use the FEs shown in fig. P7.37. Note that there is only one unknown variable, T_5.

7.38 Consider the steady, 2–D heat conduction problem with internal 'generation':

$$\frac{\partial^2 T}{\partial x^2} + \frac{\partial^2 T}{\partial y^2} = 6$$

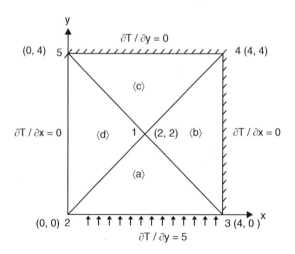

Fig. P7.38

with the boundary conditions shown in fig. 7.38. Obtain the GFE for $j = 1$ using the FEs shown.

Obtain your results in the form

$$\sum_{i=1}^{5} a_i T_i = a_6$$

with actual values for the coefficients a_1, a_2, a_5 and a_6.

7.39 Consider the steady, 2–D heat conduction in the I-beam shown in fig. P7.39:

$$\frac{\partial^2 T}{\partial x^2} + \frac{\partial^2 T}{\partial y^2} = Q$$

The face 4-8-7-11-12-16 is insulated while $T = 0$ on the other three faces (1-2-3-4, 1-5-6-10-9-13, and 13-14-15-16). $Q = -2$ on elements $\langle 7 \rangle$ and $\langle 8 \rangle$ and $Q = 0$ elsewhere. Set up the GFE equations in terms of $\mathbb{B}$, $\mathbb{D}$ and $\mathbb{E}$. Do not evaluate these coefficients. Assume the $T = 0$ condition to be valid for nodes 4 and 16.

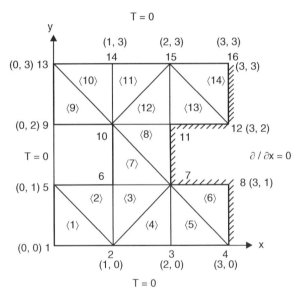

Fig. P7.39

7.40 The first order irreversible reaction-cum-diffusion in the *finite*, cylindrical, porous catalyst pellet under non-isothermal conditions can be described by the following dimensionless PDE [40]:

$$\frac{\partial^2 c}{\partial r^2} + \frac{1}{r} \frac{\partial c}{\partial r} + a^2 \frac{\partial^2 c}{\partial z^2} = \phi^2 c \exp\left[\gamma - \frac{\gamma}{1 + \beta(1-c)} \right] \equiv \phi^2 f(c)$$

$$r = 0 \ : \ \frac{\partial c}{\partial r} = 0$$

$$r = 1 \ : \ c = 1$$

$$z = 0 \ : \ \frac{\partial c}{\partial z} = 0$$

$$z = 1 \ : \ c = 1$$

where a is the diameter/length ratio, z is the dimensionless axial location, and the other terms have the same meaning as in example 6.3. Use the GFE technique and obtain the set of algebraic equations. Davis [7] presents results for this problem using code, DISPL, for $\beta = 0.1$, $\gamma = 30$, $\phi = 2$, $a = 1$.

7.41 Expressions for $\dfrac{\partial^2 T}{\partial x^2}$ and $\dfrac{\partial^2 T}{\partial y^2}$ have been obtained for the OC formulation. Obtain an expression for the mixed derivative, $\dfrac{\partial^2 T}{\partial x \partial y}\bigg|_{i,j}$ at location x_i, y_i in terms of the appropriate OC matrices. If $N_x = 1$ and $N_y = 2$ $(a = 1)$ write, with matrix elements substituted, a series expression for $\dfrac{\partial^2 T}{\partial x \partial y}\bigg|_{2,3}$.

REFERENCES

1. F.B. Hildebrand, *Advanced Calculus for Applications*, Prentice Hall, Englewood Cliffs, NJ, 1962.
2. D. Pal and S.K. Gupta, *Polymer*, **30**, 1918 (1989).
3. B.A. Finlayson, *Nonlinear Analysis in Chemical Engineering*, McGraw Hill, New York, 1980.
4. M.K. Jain, S.R.K. Iyenger and R.K. Jain, *Numerical Methods for Scientific and Engineering Computation*, Wiley Eastern, New Delhi, 1985.

   [a very crisply-written book. Discusses several techniques]
5. D.W. Peaceman and H.H. Rachford, *JSIAM*, **3**, 28 (1955).
6. D.W. Peaceman, *Fundamentals of Numerical Reservoir Simulation,* Elsevier, New York, 1977.
7. M.E. Davis, *Numerical Methods and Modeling for Chemical Engineers*, Wiley, New York, 1984.
8. R.E. Bank and D.J. Rose, *SIAM J. Numer. Anal.*, **17**, 806 (1980).
9. B. Wendroff, *Theoretical Numerical Analysis*, Academic, New York, 1966.
10. R. Alexander, P. Manselli and K. Miller, *Moving Finite Elements for the Stefan Problem in two Dimensions, Rend. Accad. Naz. Lincei (Rome)*, Serie VIII, Vol. LXVII, fasc, 1–2, pp. 57–61(1979).
11. K. Miller and R.N. Miller, *SIAM J. Numer. Anal.*, **18**, 1019, 1033 (1981).
12. B.A. Finlayson, *Numerical Methods for Problems with Moving Fronts*, Ravenna Park Pub. Inc., 6315, 22nd Ave. NE, Seattle, WA 98115-6919(1991).

    [refs. 10–12 discuss moving finite elements for the solution of PDEs].
13. A.K. Jana and S.K. Gupta, *J. Polym. Eng.*, **9**, 23 (1990).
14. C. Sereno, A. Rodriguez and J. Villadsen, *Comp. Chem. Eng.*, **15**, 25 (1991).

    [a good discussion of the moving finite element method]
15. J.N. Reddy. *An Introduction to the Finite Element Method*, McGraw Hill, New York, 1984.
16. O.C. Zienkiewicz and R.L. Taylor, *The Finite Element Method*, 4th ed., Mc Graw Hill, London, 1989.
17. S.S. Rao, *The Finite Element Method in Engineering*, Pergamon, Oxford, UK, 1982.

    [refs. 15–17 are some classic texts on FE methods].
18. M. Turner, R. Chough, H. Martin and L. Topp, *J. Aero. Sci.*, **23**, 805 (1956).
19. A. Hrenikoff, *J. Appl. Mech., Trans. ASME*, **8**, 169 (1941).
20. H. Mavridis, A.N. Hrymak and J. Vlachopoulos, *Polym. Eng. Sci.*, **26**, 449 (1986).
21. R.B. Bird, W.E. Stewart and E.N. Lightfoot, *Transport Phenomena*, Wiley, New York, 1960.
22. V. Gupta and S.K. Gupta, *Fluid Mechanics and its Applications*, 2nd Ed., New Age International (P) Ltd., New Delhi, 2010.

23. E. Mitsoulis, Ph. D. Thesis, Dept. of Chemical Engineering, McMaster University, Hamilton, ON, Canada, 1984.

24. H. Mavridis, A.N. Hrymak and J. Vlachopoulos, *J. Rheol.*, **30**, 555 (1986).

25. L.R. Schmidt, *Polym. Eng. Sci.*, **14**, 797 (1974) .

26. D.J. Coyle, T.J. Tuling and M. Tirrell, *Ind. Eng. Chem. Fundam.*, **24**, 343 (1985).

27. J.R. Rice and R.F. Boisvert, *Elliptic Problem Solving with ELLPACK*, Springer Verlag, New York, 1983.

28. G. Sewell, in *Adv. Computer Methods for PDEs–III*, (eds., R. Vishnevetsky and R.S. Stepleman), IMACS (AICA), Rutgers University, New Brunswick, NJ, 1979. [Details of code 2DEPEP]

29. G.K. Leaf, M. Minkoff, G.D. Byrne, D. Sorensen, T. Bleakney and J. Saltzman, Rept. ANL-77-12, Argonne National Lab., Argonne, IL, 1977.
[Details of code DISPL]

30. R.J. Melosh, *Structural Engineering Analysis by Finite Elements*, Prentice Hall, Englewood Cliffs, NJ, 1990.

31. C. Taylor and T.G. Hughes, *Finite Element Programming of the Navier-Stokes Equations*, Pineridge, Swansea, UK (1981).

32. D.W. Nicholson and N.W. Nelson, *Rubber Chem. Tech.*, **63**, 368 (1990).

33. J.J. Carberry, *Chemical and Catalytic Reaction Engineering*, McGraw Hill, New York, 1976.

34. B.A. Finlayson, *Chem. Eng. Sci.*, **26**, 1081 (1971).

35. D.D. Ravetkar, Ph. D. Dissertation, Univ. of Bombay, Mumbai, 1989.

36. E.B. Nauman, *Chemical Reactor Design*, Wiley, New York, 1987.

37. H. Schlichting, *Boundary Layer Theory*, 6th ed., McGraw Hill, New York, 1968.

38. N.B. Ferguson and B.A. Finlayson, *Chem. Eng. J.*, **1**, 327 (1970).

39. S.K. Gupta, A.K. Ghosh, S.K. Gupta and A. Kumar, *J. Appl. Polym. Sci.*, **29**, 3217 (1984).

40. J. Villadsen and M.L. Michelsen, *Solution of Differential Equation Models by Polynomial Approximation*, Prentice Hall, Englewood Cliffs, NJ, 1978.

Index

336